# CHEMICAL
# CRYSTALLOGRAPHY

# CHEMICAL
# CRYSTALLOGRAPHY

## AN INTRODUCTION TO
## OPTICAL AND X-RAY METHODS

BY

C. W. BUNN

SECOND EDITION

OXFORD
AT THE CLARENDON PRESS

*Oxford University Press, Amen House, London E.C.4*

GLASGOW NEW YORK TORONTO MELBOURNE WELLINGTON
BOMBAY CALCUTTA MADRAS KARACHI LAHORE DACCA
CAPE TOWN SALISBURY NAIROBI IBADAN ACCRA
KUALA LUMPUR HONG KONG

FIRST EDITION 1945
SECOND EDITION 1961
REPRINTED LITHOGRAPHICALLY
AT THE UNIVERSITY PRESS, OXFORD
FROM SHEETS OF THE SECOND EDITION

1963

# PREFACE TO THE SECOND EDITION

Since the publication of the first edition in 1945, there have been considerable developments in the power and scope of methods of deducing the arrangements of atoms in crystals from X-ray diffraction phenomena; and to cover these developments, even in bare outline, it has been necessary to enlarge certain chapters. The general plan of the book remains unchanged, and in the earlier chapters only minor alterations and additions have been made; but in the latter half of the book substantial additions have been made, and the titles of the last two chapters have been changed to cover the enlarged scope. The subjects covered by new sections include X-ray intensity statistics in relation to space-group symmetry, molecular transforms and optical analogue methods of representing them, anomalous scattering and its application to the determination of the absolute configuration of enantiomorphic molecules, the determination of phase angles in non-centrosymmetric crystals, the relations between the phases and amplitudes of different reflections of centrosymmetric crystals, and small-angle scattering. In crystal optics, the calculation of refractive indices from bond polarizability data is included. There is an additional appendix on the transformation of indices when changing crystallographic axes.

My aim throughout has been to explain the principles involved in as simple a manner as I can contrive, without sacrificing precision of statement.

I wish to thank the respective authors and publishers for permission to use the following diagrams and plates from other publications. Fig. 32 *b* from F. C. Phillips, *An Introduction to Crystallography* (Longmans Green, 1946). Figs. 62 and 63 from Peiser, Rooksby, and Wilson, *X-Ray Diffraction by Polycrystalline Materials* (The Institute of Physics, 1955). Fig. 69 from A. J. C. Wilson, *Rev. Sci. Inst.* 1949, **20**, 831. Figs. 147 and 166 from Lipson and Cochran, *The Determination of Crystal Structures* (Bell, 1953). Fig. 214 from *The Chemistry of Penicillin* (Princeton Univ. Press, 1949). Fig. 215 from Cox, Cruickshank, and Smith, *Proc. Roy. Soc.* 1958, **A247**, 1. Fig. 231 from Hanson, Lipson, and Taylor, *Proc. Roy. Soc.* 1953, **A218**, 371. Fig. 232 from *J. Chem. Soc.* 1947, p. 297. Plate II (*a*) from Wyckoff, *Acta Cryst.* 1948, **1**, 292, (*b*) from Dawson and Vand, *Proc. Roy. Soc.* 1951, **A206**, 555. · Plate XV from Hanson and Lipson, *Acta Cryst.* 1952, **5**, 145. Plate XVI from Lipson and Cochran, *The Determination of Crystal Structures* (Bell, 1953),

and from C. A. Taylor, *Acta Cryst.* 1952, **5**, 141.  I am especially in-
debted to the authors mentioned for good prints for Plates  II, XV,
and XVI.

C. W. B.

# FROM THE
# PREFACE TO THE FIRST EDITION

CRYSTALLOGRAPHIC methods are used in chemistry for two main purposes—the identification of solid substances, and the determination of atomic configurations; there are also other applications, most of which, as far as technique is concerned, may be said to lie between the two main subjects. This book is intended to be a guide to these methods. I have tried to explain the elementary principles involved, and to give as much practical information as will enable the reader to start using the methods described. I have not attempted to give a rigorous treatment of the physical principles: the approach is consistently from the chemist's point of view, and physical theory is included only in so far as it is necessary for the general comprehension of the principles and methods described. Nor have I attempted to give an exhaustive account of any subject; the aim throughout has been to lay the foundations, and to give sufficient references (either to larger works or to original papers) to enable the reader to follow up any subject in greater detail if he so desires.

The treatment of certain subjects is perhaps somewhat unorthodox. Crystal morphology, for instance, is described in terms of the concept of the unit cell (rather than in terms of the axial ratios of the earlier morphologists), and is approached by way of the phenomena of crystal growth. The optical properties of crystals are described solely in terms of the phenomena observed in the polarizing microscope. X-ray diffraction is considered first in connexion with powder photographs; it is more usual to start with the interpretation of the diffraction effects of single crystals. These methods of treatment are dictated by the form and scope of the book; they also reflect the course of the writer's own experience in applying crystallographic methods to chemical problems. It is therefore hoped that they may at any rate seem natural to those to whom the book is addressed—students of chemistry who wish to acquire some knowledge of crystallographic methods, and research workers who wish to make practical use of such methods. If the book should come to the notice of a more philosophical reader, I can only hope that any qualms such a reader may feel about its avoidance of formal physical or mathematical treatment may be somewhat offset by the interest of a novel, if rather severely practical, viewpoint.

The difficulties of three-dimensional thinking have, I hope, been lightened as much as possible by the provision of a large number of diagrams (most of them original); but crystallography is emphatically not a subject which can be learnt solely from books: solid models should be used freely—models of crystal shapes, of atomic and molecular configurations, of reciprocal lattices and of vectorial representations of optical and other physical properties.

C. W. B.

# CONTENTS

## PART II. STRUCTURE DETERMINATION

CONTENTS

# NOTE ON POSITION OF
# THE PLATES

Plates I–XVI face pages 18, 19, 68, 114, 132, 139,
149, 174, 180, 189, 210, 235, 260, 296, 297 and 429
respectively

# I

## INTRODUCTORY SURVEY

MOST solid substances are crystalline, that is to say, the atoms or molecules of which they are composed are packed together in a regular manner, forming a three-dimensional pattern. In some solids—many minerals, for instance—the fact that they are crystalline is obvious to the unaided eye; the plane faces and the more or less symmetrical shape of the particles are evidence of an orderly internal structure. In other solids all we see is a powder or some irregular lumps; but with the aid of the microscope and the still more delicate X-ray methods we have come to realize that most of the solids with which we are familiar, from rocks to sand and soil, from the chemical reagents on our laboratory shelves to paint pigments and cleaning powders, from steel and concrete to bones and teeth, really consist of small crystals. Even such apparently unlikely materials as wood, silk, and hair are at any rate partly crystalline; the molecules composing them are to some extent packed together in an orderly way, though the regularity of arrangement is not maintained throughout the whole of the material.

The crystalline condition is, in fact, the natural condition in the solid state; at low temperatures atoms and molecules always try to arrange themselves in a regular manner. When they do not succeed in doing so there is good reason for their failure. Some glasses, for instance, are super-cooled liquids in which crystals have not been able to grow owing to very rapid cooling and the very high viscosity of the liquid; low-temperature decomposition products such as 'amorphous' carbon are formed at such temperatures that atomic movements are too sluggish to permit crystal growth; some polymers (such as 'bakelite') are composed of molecules which are large and irregular in structure and cannot pack together neatly.

Even in these 'amorphous' substances order is not entirely lacking: just because atoms behave as spheres with definite radii, their centres cannot be randomly distributed because they hold each other off at definite distances. Locally there are in non-crystalline solids, and even in liquids, arrangements of atoms which are somewhat similar to those found in crystals; the orderliness is, however, very local, and is not maintained with exact repetition over long distances, as it is in crystals. The difference between non-crystalline and crystalline substances is a

B

difference of range of orderliness: in non-crystalline substances orderliness extends over few atoms or molecules, while in crystalline substances it extends over very large numbers.

The fact that in most solid substances the atoms or molecules are arranged in an orderly manner is of great significance for the chemist, whether he is a philosopher in a university or an analyst in an industrial laboratory. The chemist is interested in such things as the structure of molecules, the nature of the bonds between atoms, and the arrangement of ions; and he uses every property of a substance which can give him any information on these matters. He is also inevitably concerned with methods for the identification and analysis of the substances he encounters. Crystals, in virtue of the orderly arrangement of the atoms or molecules composing them, have very special properties, which not only make possible the most precise determinations of molecular structures, but also provide powerful and certain methods of identification and analysis.

**Anisotropy.** To begin with, the properties of a crystal are, in general, not the same in all directions. A crystal grows, not as a sphere, but as a polyhedron; it dissolves more quickly in some directions than in others; its refractive index (except in certain special cases) varies with the direction of vibration of the light waves; its magnetic susceptibility, its cohesion, its thermal expansion, its electrical conductivity, all vary with direction in the crystal. This variation of properties with crystal direction, or 'anisotropy', is a consequence of the

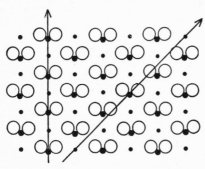

FIG. 1. Crystal properties vary with direction.

regular packing of atoms or molecules in a crystal. In a normal liquid or a gas the atoms or molecules are oriented at random, and consequently the properties are the same in all directions; individual molecules may be strongly anisotropic, but owing to the random orientation of the large numbers of molecules present, even in microscopic samples, the properties are averaged out in all directions. In a crystal the atoms are drawn up in ranks; pass through it in imagination, first in one direction and then in another, and (unless you have chosen two special directions) you will encounter the constituent atoms or molecules at different intervals and perhaps (if there are different kinds of atoms) in a different order in the two directions. (See Fig. 1, a two-dimensional analogy.) Since the arrangement of the atoms or molecules in a crystal varies with direction, certain properties of the crystal must also vary with direction.

Crystals thus have a greater wealth and variety of measurable characteristics than liquids or gases. This circumstance can be turned to good account; we can use these varied directional properties for the identification of crystalline substances. Since there are more characteristic magnitudes to determine, identification by physical methods is often much more certain for crystals than it is for liquids or gases.

**Identification of crystals under the microscope.** Of the characteristics which are most useful for identification purposes the most readily determined are shape and refractive indices. The determinative method which has proved most valuable for microscopic crystals (such as those in the average experimental or industrial product) is to measure the principal refractive indices (up to three in number, depending on the symmetry of the crystal) and, if possible, to find the orientation of the principal optical directions with respect to the geometrical form of the crystal. This information, which can all be obtained by simple and rapid microscopic methods, is usually sufficient to identify any crystalline substances whose properties have previously been recorded. Mixtures of two or more crystalline substances can be identified by the same method; in phase equilibrium studies and in industrial research it is not uncommon to encounter mixtures of three or four constituents, all of which can be identified in this way.

This method of identification sometimes has certain advantages over chemical analysis. A single substance can often be identified in a few minutes where a chemical analysis might take hours, and only very small quantities of material are required. But in general the method must not be regarded as a rival to chemical analysis but as a valuable complement. It gives essential information in cases where chemical analysis does not tell the whole story or does not even touch the most important part of the story. Where substances capable of crystallizing in two or more different forms are concerned (for instance, the three forms of calcium carbonate—calcite, aragonite, and vaterite), chemical analysis cannot distinguish between them, and a crystallographic method is essential. The greatest advantages, however, are shown in the analysis of mixtures of several solid phases. Chemical analysis tells us which atoms or ions are present, as well as the proportion of each, but it does not usually tell us which of these are linked together. For instance, a solid obtained in a phase equilibrium study of the reciprocal salt pair $NaNO_3$—$KCl$—$(H_2O)$ is shown by chemical analysis to contain all four ions, Na, K, $NO_3$, Cl, in certain proportions. But which substances are present? NaCl, $NaNO_3$, and $KNO_3$, or NaCl, $NaNO_3$, and KCl, or perhaps all four possible salts, NaCl, $NaNO_3$, KCl, $KNO_3$? This question can be most readily settled by a crystallographic method of identification. As another example, consider a refractory material whose composition can be represented as so much alumina and so much silica; are those present as separate constituents or are they combined as an aluminium silicate? If they are combined, which of the several known aluminium silicates is present? And is the material all aluminium silicate, or is there some excess silica as well as an aluminium silicate? If there is excess silica, which of the several forms of silica is present? These questions can be settled by crystallographic identification. If the crystals are large enough to be seen as individuals under the microscope, they can usually be identified by refractive index measurements; the crystals need not have a regular geometrical shape, for refractive index measurements can be made quite as well on completely irregular crystal fragments as on well formed crystals.

This method was first developed by mineralogists, but it is now being used to an increasing extent in such problems of inorganic chemistry as those just mentioned. In the organic field it has so far made slower progress, because other rapid and convenient physical methods (the measurement of melting-points, and the use of infra-red absorption spectra) are available; but the microscopic crystallographic method could find a wide field of usefulness, especially in circumstances in which these other methods are inadequate—for instance, when a sample contains a mixture of solid phases.

**Origin of anisotropic properties of crystals.** If we inquire a little more deeply into the origin of the anisotropic properties of crystals, we can distinguish two factors. Consider first crystals composed of un-ionized molecules. The molecules themselves may be anisotropic; a long molecule, for instance, has a greater refractivity for light vibrating along it† than for light vibrating across it, while a flat molecule has a greater refractivity for light vibrating in the plane of the molecule than for light vibrating perpendicular to this plane. The same is true for polyatomic ions. This is the first factor. The second is the way in which the molecules or polyatomic ions are packed. In some crystals all the

---

† The vibration direction is defined as the direction of the electric vector of the waves. (See Chapters III and VIII.)

molecules are packed parallel to each other, and these crystals have properties which correspond with those of individual molecules. A crystal composed of long molecules all packed parallel as in Fig. 2 a (a crystal of a long-chain hydrocarbon, for instance) is likely to have a high refractive index for light vibrating along the molecules, and low refractive indices for light vibrating in all directions perpendicular to the molecules. In other crystals the molecules are not all parallel to each other; sometimes half the molecules have one orientation and half another orientation, as in Fig. 2 b; sometimes the arrangement is still

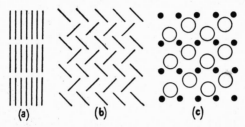

FIG. 2. a. Long molecules packed parallel. b. Long molecules arranged so that there are two different orientations. c. In some crystals composed of monatomic ions, anisotropy results from the mode of packing of the ions.

more complex (it depends on the shape of the molecules and the inter-molecular forces). The properties of these crystals correspond, not with those of a single molecule, but with those of a small group of two or more differently oriented molecules.

To turn now to crystals composed of 'unattached' atoms or monatomic ions, which are individually isotropic. Here it is only the second factor —the effect of arrangement—which can be responsible for anisotropy in the crystal. It is the orderliness of arrangement itself which, because it gives rise to different atomic distributions in different directions (Fig. 2 c), confers properties varying with crystal direction. The degree of anisotropy is usually far less in these crystals than in crystals containing molecules or polyatomic ions which are themselves anisotropic.

**Molecular type and arrangement deduced from anisotropic properties of crystals.** It is evident that, in dealing with crystals of unknown structure, the anisotropic properties may often be used to give direct information about the general shape of the molecules or polyatomic ions in the crystals and the way in which the molecules or ions are packed. A strongly anisotropic crystal must contain strongly anisotropic molecules or polyatomic ions packed in such a way that the anisotropies of the different molecules or ions do not neutralize each other, and a consideration of the properties of the crystal in all directions may lead to a fair idea of the general shape of the molecules or ions and the way they are packed. This use of optical and other properties to give information about molecular or ionic shape and arrangement is a striking example of the advantages conferred by the ordered structure of crystals. A molecule is too small to study individually by methods available at the present time; but a crystal, in which a large number of molecules are packed in a regular manner, is in a sense a vastly enlarged model of a molecule or a small group of molecules, and when we observe the optical properties of such a crystal under the microscope, we are observing in effect the optical properties of a molecule or a small group of molecules, and this may tell us something about the shape of the molecules and the way they are packed in the crystal.

**The use of X-rays.** All the information mentioned hitherto is obtained by old and well established methods, of which by far the most important and generally useful is the determination of optical properties under the microscope. Visible light, however, give us only a rough idea of the internal structure of a crystal; its waves, being much longer than the distances between atoms, are much too coarse to show the details. If we want a more detailed picture of the structure of molecules and the arrangement of atoms and ions, as well as a yet more powerful method of identification, we must use much shorter waves, of about the same length as the distances between atoms. The X-rays, produced when high-speed electrons hit atoms, happen to be about the right length. The discovery of this fact, due to Laue in 1912, was, of course, one of the most important discoveries in the present century; it opened the way, not only to an understanding of the nature of X-rays, but also to the determination of the exact arrangement of the atoms in crystals. True, we cannot get a direct image of the atomic pattern in a crystal; X-rays cannot be focused in the convenient ways used for visible light. What we have to do is to study the diffraction effects produced when X-rays pass through a crystal, and build up an image of the structure by calculation. The diffraction of X-rays by crystals is not essentially different from that of visible light by a diffraction grating; but to synthesize the image from the diffracted waves we must use, not lenses, but equations.

(It is possible, starting with the data provided by the X-ray diffraction pattern, to form an image experimentally by a method employing visible light: the interference of light waves take the place of calculations (W. L. Bragg, 1939, 1942 a). But it is not possible to produce an image in one experimental operation, using X-rays alone.)

**Electron density maps.** Since it is the electrons in the atoms which are responsible for the diffraction of X-rays, the image we build up by calculation is a sort of contour map of electron densities in the crystal. Two or three such maps or projections, giving views of the structure from two or three different directions, are sufficient to enable us to build a complete space model of the crystal structure, showing the exact position of every atom ; or, better still, it is possible, by a more ambitious programme of calculations, to produce a three-dimensional distribution of electron density which is itself a model of the crystal structure. The different sorts of atoms can be identified by their different electron densities. The value of such a model is obviously enormous. The exact arrangement of ions and their distances apart (giving the coordination numbers and 'sizes' of the ions) ; the exact spatial configuration and interatomic distances in polyatomic ions and organic molecules (with all that this tells us about the specific properties of these bodies and the nature of the bonds between the atoms) ; the mode of packing of molecules (which depends on the shape and the intermolecular forces)— these are some of the fundamentals revealed at once by such a model. In the words of Bernal and Crowfoot (1933 c), the intensive analysis of X-ray diffraction patterns 'is one of the chief means of transformation from the classical qualitative, topological chemistry of the nineteenth century to the quantum-mechanical, metrical chemistry of the present day'.

**Limitations of X-ray methods.** If it were possible to find the structure of every crystalline substance in this way, chemists would no longer have to spend their time in deducing the structures of new substances by more or less indirect methods; they could turn all their energies to preparation and synthesis. In the future it may well be possible to determine the structure of any crystal by X-ray methods without chemical evidence of any sort, but at the present time there are certain difficulties which restrict the scope of such methods.

As may be imagined, the building by calculation of an image of the pattern of atoms in a crystal is a complex and lengthy task. Moreover, it is not (except in special cases) straightforward; that is to say, we cannot proceed straight from the experimental data (the positions and intensities of the diffracted X-ray beams) to the calculation of the image ; at one stage it is nearly always necessary to use the procedure of trial and error, that is, to think of an atomic arrangement, calculate the diffraction effects it would give, and compare these with the actual diffraction effects observed; if they do not agree, another arrangement must be tried, and so on. Only when the approximate atomic positions have been found in this way is it possible to calculate the final image in all its details from the experimental data. For the simpler structures this does not present any great difficulties, but for the more complex structures much depends on the extent of knowledge available at the time for the building of trial structures. In the early days of X-ray crystallography, only the structures of elements and simple salts could be tackled with any hope of success, but with the accumulation of knowledge, structures of ever-increasing complexity have been successfully worked out. Up to the present time (1959) many inorganic structures of considerable complexity (such as the silicate minerals, the alums, and the hetero-polyacids like phosphotungstic acid) have been worked out completely. Among organic compounds progress was at first slower, but as soon as the structures of the principal fundamental types of molecules (normal paraffin chain, benzene ring, naphthalene nucleus) were well established, the pace accelerated, and recently, the structures of such complex substances as dyestuffs, carbohydrates, sterols, antibiotics, vitamins, and high polymers have been solved, and even substances of extreme complexity (proteins) are being actively studied by this method. X-ray analysis at first merely confirmed the conclusions of organic chemistry, but now it plays a useful part in research on chemical constitution.

**Use of X-ray diffraction patterns for identification.** Even when complete structure determination is not possible, however, much valuable information of a less detailed character may be obtained by X-ray methods. In the first place, the diffracted beams produced when X-rays pass through crystals may be recorded on photographic films or plates, and the patterns thus formed may be used quite empirically, without any attempt at interpretation, to identify crystalline substances, in much the same way as we use optical emission spectra to identify elements, or infra-red absorption spectra to identify molecules. Each crystalline substance gives its own characteristic pattern, which is different from the patterns of all other substances; and the pattern is of such complexity (that is, it presents so many measurable quantities) that in most cases it constitutes by far the most certain physical criterion for identification. The X-ray method of identification is of greatest value in cases where microscopic methods are inadequate; for instance, when the crystals are opaque or are too small to be seen as individuals under the microscope. The X-ray diffraction patterns of different substances generally differ so much from each other that visual comparison is usually sufficient for identification, if patterns taken with the same camera are available; for comparison with published patterns, measurement of the positions of recorded diffractions and conversion into standard units are necessary. Mixtures of two or more different substances which are present as separate crystals give X-ray diffraction patterns consisting of the superimposed patterns of the constituents.

**Information obtainable by partial interpretation of X-ray diffraction patterns.** Between the recording of an X-ray diffraction pattern and the elucidation of the complete atomic arrangement there are several well defined stages. Arrival at each stage gives more and more intimate information about the substance in question. It may be possible to form conclusions about the degree of purity of a substance, to determine its molecular weight more accurately than by any other method, to discover something about the symmetry of the molecules or ions in the crystal, or to determine the overall dimensions of the molecules. Individual circumstances, the nature of the substance, and the size and form of the crystals determine in each case how far it is possible or desirable to go.

**Value of using more than one method.** It must be emphasized that the combination of different lines of evidence is often of much greater value than any single method of approach. In any laboratory using crystallographic methods, it would be a mistake to rely on X-ray methods alone; the combination of evidence given by X-ray diffraction patterns with that given by optical properties, habit, cleavage, and so on may lead to valuable conclusions in circumstances where each of these lines of evidence taken by itself would leave unresolved ambiguities.

**Plan of this book.** It will be evident from the foregoing survey of the principal applications of crystallographic methods to chemical problems that these applications fall into two classes; firstly, the use of crystal properties for the purpose of identifying substances; secondly, the elucidation of the internal structure of crystals by interpretation of their properties. This natural division determines the plan of this book, which is in two main parts, on identification and internal structure respectively.

Part I (on identification) comprises four chapters. Chapter II is an introduction to the shapes of crystals and the relation between shape and structure, and Chapter III is an elementary account of crystal optics; some knowledge of both subjects is essential, not only for the identification of crystals by microscopic methods, but also for the understanding of the problems of structure determination dealt with in Part **II**. Chapter IV deals with procedure in microscopic methods of identification.

Chapter V, on identification by X-ray methods, is concerned with the practical details of taking X-ray powder photographs, and also includes elementary diffraction theory, taken as far as is necessary for most identification problems.

Part II deals, in six chapters, with the principles underlying the progressive stages in the elucidation of internal structure. Chapters VI and VII deal with the principles of structure determination by trial; Chapter VIII with the use of physical properties (such as habit, cleavage, and optical, magnetic, pyro- and piezo-electric properties) as auxiliary evidence in structure determination. In Chapter IX are to be found several examples of the derivation of complete structures. Chapter X gives an introductory account of the use of direct and semi-direct methods based on the calculation of electron density distributions and vector distributions from X-ray diffraction data.

Certain crystals give diffuse X-ray reflections; there are various possible causes for this—small crystal size, structural irregularities, or thermal movements. The consideration of these phenomena in Chapter XI leads on to a brief introduction to the interpretation of the very diffuse diffraction patterns given by non-crystalline substances.

# PART I.  IDENTIFICATION

## II

## THE SHAPES OF CRYSTALS

ANYONE who has seen the well-formed crystals of minerals in our museums must have been impressed by the great variety of shapes exhibited: cubes and octahedra, prisms of various kinds, pyramids and double pyramids, flat plates of various shapes, rhombohedra and other less symmetrical parallelepipeda, and many other shapes less easy to describe in a word or two. These crystal shapes are extremely fascinating in themselves; artists (notably Dürer) have used crystal shapes for formal or symbolic purposes, while many a natural philosopher has been drawn to the attempt to understand first of all the geometry of crystal shapes considered simply as solid figures, and then the manner in which these shapes are formed by the anisotropic growth of atomic and molecular space-patterns.

But this book has a practical object, as its title proclaims. Our purpose in this chapter is to inquire to what extent crystal shapes can be criteria for identification, and how much they tell us about the atomic and molecular space-patterns within them.

In view of the great variety of crystal shapes and the rich face-development on many crystals, it is natural to expect that, on the basis of accurate methods of measurement and a sound system of classification, it would be possible to identify crystals by their shapes alone; and, indeed, attempts have been made, first by Fedorov and later by Barker and his school, to develop such a method resting on the measurement of the angles between face-normals. There is no doubt that when well formed crystals, large enough to be handled individually so that they can be mounted on a goniometer, are available, this morphological method of identification is a practicable one; Barker (1930) demonstrated this, and others, following in his footsteps, have compiled an index of crystals arranged according to interfacial angles on the principles worked out by Barker (Porter and Spiller, 1951, 1956). But as a standard method of identification in a chemical laboratory it has very serious limitations. One of them is that the crystals formed in laboratory experiments or in industrial processes are often too small to be handled individually; they can only be examined under the microscope, and under these conditions angular measurements either cannot be made at all, or, if they can be made, are only approximate. Another is that the shapes of such crystals are often not sufficiently characteristic; sometimes there are too few faces on each crystal; or perhaps the substance grows in the form of skeletal crystals without definite faces; or, worse still, the crystals may be broken into irregular pieces. To identify such materials we need a method which does not depend on shape, but on some characteristics of the crystal material itself—properties of the atomic space-pattern. The properties most conveniently measured under the microscope are the optical constants, particularly the refractive indices; and in practice the measurement of refractive indices has proved by far the most useful single method of identifying crystalline substances under the microscope. The technique is described in the next chapter.

There is no need, however, to ignore crystal shape in identification work. On the contrary, whenever crystals do show good face-development their shapes, even if they cannot be measured precisely but only observed in a qualitative way, reinforce and implement the evidence provided by optical properties, especially if the relations between the principal optical and geometrical directions can be discovered.

This is one reason for studying crystal shapes. Another and more weighty reason is that crystal shapes tell us a great deal about the relative dimensions and the symmetries of the atomic and molecular space-patterns constituting the crystalline material.

In this chapter, therefore, we make some inquiry into the origins of crystal shapes and their classification on the basis of symmetry characteristics.

**Shape varies with conditions of growth.** The shape of a crystal, taken as it stands, is not a fixed characteristic of the substance in question. In the first place, the shape is controlled to some extent by the supply of material round the crystal during growth. In uniform surroundings, as in a stirred solution, crystals of sodium chloride grow as cubes, but if they grow, well separated, on the bottom of a dish of stagnant solution, they grow as square tablets whose thickness is not more than half their other dimensions; the reason is that growth can occur only upwards and sideways, not downwards. If the crystals on the bottom of the dish are crowded, the tablets formed are not all square; many have unequal edges owing to local variations in the supply of solute. As another example, sodium chlorate, $NaClO_3$, when grown rapidly in a stirred solution, forms cubes, but when grown very slowly in a still solution grows in the form of a modified cube showing additional facets on the edges and corners (Fig. 3). Crystals which grow in rod-like forms—such as gypsum, $CaSO_4.2H_2O$, which is also illustrated in Fig. 3—usually tend to grow longer and thinner when formed rapidly than when growth is slow.

These are, comparatively speaking, minor variations of shape; but the crystal shapes of some substances may be completely altered by the presence of certain other substances in the mother liquor. Sodium chloride grows from a pure solution in the form of cubes, but if the mother liquor contains 10 per cent. of urea, the crystals which grow (Fig. 3) are octahedra (Gille and Spangenberg, 1927). Yet the internal structure—the pattern of atoms —of this substance is not changed by such differing external conditions; it is only the form of the bounding surface of the crystalline material which is changed. It is evident that if we want to use crystal shapes for identification we must, so to speak, get behind the shape as it stands, and try to deduce from the actual shape something about

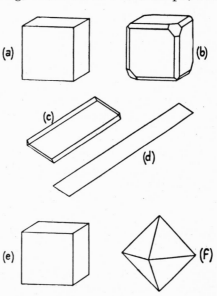

FIG. 3. Variation of crystal shape with conditions of growth. Sodium chlorate, $NaClO_3$, grown (a) rapidly and (b) slowly; gypsum, $CaSO_4.2H_2O$, grown (c) slowly and (d) rapidly; sodium chloride, NaCl, grown. (e) from pure solution and (f) from solution containing 10 per cent. of urea.

the internal structure. The possibility of doing this is indicated by the fact that the angles between the faces of the long thin gypsum crystals in the sketch are exactly the same as those of the shorter crystals. Likewise, all octahedra of sodium chloride, however much they differ in size, and however unequal the areas of the different faces of any one crystal may be, have exactly the same interfacial angles. The slopes of the various faces are in fact controlled by the rigid, precise internal structure. The relation between totally different shapes of any one substance—such as the cubes and octahedra of sodium chloride—is less obvious; but it can be shown that the faces of cubes and octahedra are oriented in precise but different ways with respect to the internal atomic pattern.

Two pieces of information about the fundamental atomic pattern may be deduced from the actual shape of a crystal, provided this crystal shows a sufficient variety of faces and is large enough to permit measurements of the angles between the faces. One is a knowledge of the shape and relative dimensions of the unit of pattern. The other is a partial knowledge of the symmetries of the atomic arrangement.

**The unit of pattern ('unit cell').** A crystal consists of a large number of repetitions of a basic pattern of atoms. Just as in many textile

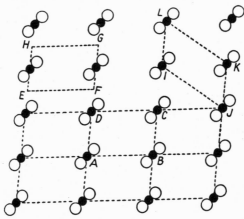

FIG. 4. A plane pattern. Lower part divided into identical unit cells such as *ABCD*. Alternative unit cells *EFGH* and *IJKL* are also outlined.

materials and wallpapers a pattern is repeated over and over again on a surface, so in a crystal a particular grouping of atoms is repeated many times in space. The reason for the formation of regular patterns is that atoms, ions, or molecules tend to settle down in positions of minimum energy; for each atom, ion, or molecule a particular environment of neighbours has a lower energy content than any other, and there is therefore a tendency for this arrangement to be taken up everywhere.

The only patterns of exactly repeated environments capable of indefinite extension are those in which successions of pattern-units lie on straight lines. Consider the shape of the unit of pattern, first of all in the simpler case of a plane pattern, such as that shown in Fig. 4. Mark any point such as *A*, and then mark other points whose surroundings are exactly the same (in orientation as well as geometrical character) as those of $A$; these points fall on straight lines which divide the pattern into a number of exactly similar parallelogram-shaped areas. Each area, such as $ABCD$, represents one unit of pattern; the whole pattern can be built up by parallel contiguous repetitions of $ABCD$. Of course, we might have started by choosing a differently situated point $E$, but we should have arrived at the same shape $EFGH$ for the unit of pattern; the position of the origin does not matter. Note that $IJKL$ may equally claim to be the unit of pattern, inasmuch as it contains one unit of pattern and has exactly the same area as $ABCD$ or $EFGH$; and many other still more elongated areas, each containing one unit of pattern, could be drawn; in practice, however, it is usually most convenient to accept as the unit of pattern the area with the shortest sides, that is to say, the area most nearly approaching rectangular shape.

All patterns on surfaces can be divided into similar areas in this way, and the unit of pattern is always a parallelogram. The shape and dimensions of the parallelogram vary in different ways; it is possible to have square units, rectangular units with unequal sides, and non-rectangular units with either equal or unequal sides.

In a crystal we can do the same thing in three dimensions. Again the choice of origin does not matter, and again we can divide the whole structure into units (of volume this time) by joining similarly situated points by straight lines. Fig. 5 shows the arrangement of the ions in a crystal of caesium bromide. Any caesium ion has exactly the same surroundings as any other, and if the centre of each is joined to the centres of its nearest neighbours, the whole structure is found to be divided into cubes, each of which has caesium ions at its corners and a bromine ion at its centre. The centre of a bromine ion might equally well have been selected as the origin, and then the cubic units of pattern would have bromine ions at their corners and caesium ions at their centres. (Note that no bromine ion 'belongs' specifically to any one caesium ion; its relations to the eight caesium ions surrounding it are equal. There are thus no 'molecules' of CsBr in the crystal; the structure is simply a stack of positively-charged caesium ions and negatively-charged bromine ions.)

Fig. 5 also shows an example of a molecular structure—that of hexamethylbenzene, $C_6(CH_3)_6$. The molecules, which can be represented as disks, are all stacked parallel to each other, and if the centre of each molecule is joined to those of its nearest neighbours, the structure is divided into a number of identical units of pattern, each of which is a non-rectangular 'box' with all three sets of edges unequal in length.

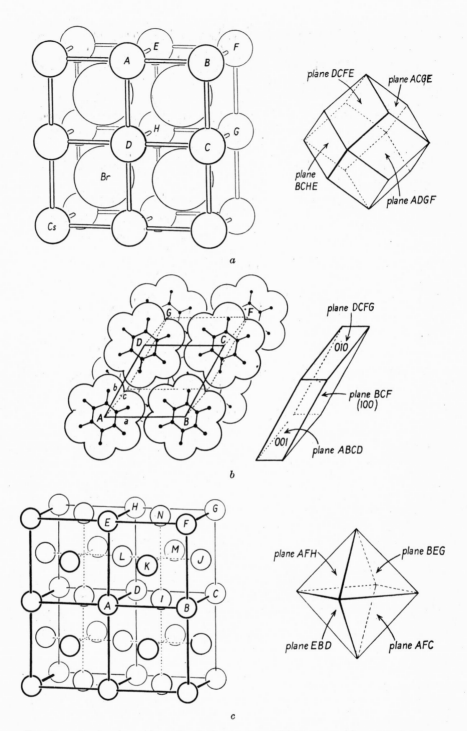

FIG. 5. *a*. Caesium bromide, CsBr. Left, structure. Right, shape of crystal. *b*. Hexamethylbenzene, C₆(CH₃)₆. Left, structure. Right, shape of crystal. *c*. Copper. Left, structure. Right, shape of crystal.

The unit of pattern in a crystal is always a 'box' bounded by three pairs of parallel sides. The shape and dimensions of the box, that is, the lengths of its three different sorts of edges ('axes') and the angles between them, are characteristic for each different crystal species; in some crystals the box is a cube, in others it is rectangular with unequal edges, in others the angles are not right angles, and so on. We shall not at this point catalogue the various types of shape; we merely observe that various shapes of pattern-unit are possible; the crystal structure of caesium bromide represents the most highly symmetrical and that of hexamethylbenzene the least symmetrical of the possible shapes.

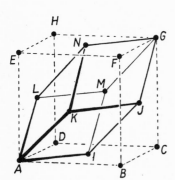 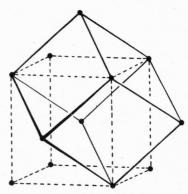

Fig. 6. Face-centred cubic unit cell of copper (left), and body-centred cubic unit cell of α iron (both shown by broken lines). In each case a unit containing one pattern-unit (one atom) is heavily outlined.

It is sometimes more appropriate to use for purposes of reference a box containing more than one unit of pattern. For instance, in crystals of metallic copper the atoms are arranged in the manner shown in Figs. 5 c and 6. All the atoms have precisely the same surroundings, and the true unit of pattern, formed by joining similarly situated points so as to divide the structure into 'boxes' with atoms at the corners only, is the heavily outlined rhombohedron in Fig. 6; there is one atom, one pattern-unit, to each 'box'. (One at each corner of the box makes eight in all; but each one is shared between the eight boxes which meet at the corner; therefore each box has the volume of one pattern-unit.) But it is found that atoms $A, B, C, D, E, F, G$, and $H$ fall at the corners of a cube, and atoms $I, J, K, L, M$, and $N$ in the centres of the faces of the same cube. This cube is accepted as the unit cell, in spite of the fact that it contains four pattern-units comprising one copper atom each. (The corner atoms count as one to each cube; the six atoms in the face centres are each shared between two cubes; thus the number of atoms per unit cube is $1+3 = 4$.) There are two reasons for this. The first and more important reason is that the symmetries of the complete arrangement are the same as those of crystals in which the shape of the true pattern-unit is cubic; crystal symmetry will not be discussed here—an introductory account of it is given later in this chapter. The second reason for accepting the four-atom cube as the unit cell is that a cube is a more convenient frame of reference than a rhombohedron. This particular 'compound' unit cell is described as 'face-centred'. Other types of 'compound' unit cell are the body-centred, with identical pattern-units in the centres of the cells as well as at the corners (see the structure of $\alpha$ iron in Fig. 6), and the side-centred, with identical pattern-units at the centres of one pair of opposite faces in addition to those at the corners. The arrangement of the pattern-units, the assemblage of points each of which represents one pattern-unit, is called the space-lattice. The points of the space-lattice—the 'lattice points'—are thus corners of the true unit of pattern; the conventionally accepted unit cell may be simple or compound; if compound, it may contain two or more space-lattice points.

We now have to consider the faces of crystals and their relation to the geometry of the precisely patterned assemblage of atoms which constitutes the solid material. This subject is best approached by thinking about the manner in which crystals grow. Crystals usually have plane faces, firstly because they do not grow at the same rate in all directions, and secondly as a result of the specific manner in which solid material is deposited.

**Crystal growth.** Suppose we had the task of packing a large number of atoms or ions or molecules together to form a predetermined arrangement. We should find that the most convenient way of building up the structure was to arrange one layer of building units, then put a second layer on top of the first, and so on. But we should have to choose which layer to put down first, and there are many different layers which might be selected; there are very many ways in which a crystal structure could be divided into layers by planes passing through it. A few possible ways are shown in Fig. 7. In practice we should choose the 'simplest' possible plane, that is to say, a plane which is as layer-like as possible, a plane in which the building-units—atoms in some crystals, ions or molecules in others—are packed closely together. Thus, to build the crystal of hexamethylbenzene (Fig. 5 $b$), it would obviously be more convenient to choose planes such as $ABCD$ and $DCFG$, which are parallel to the

PLATE I

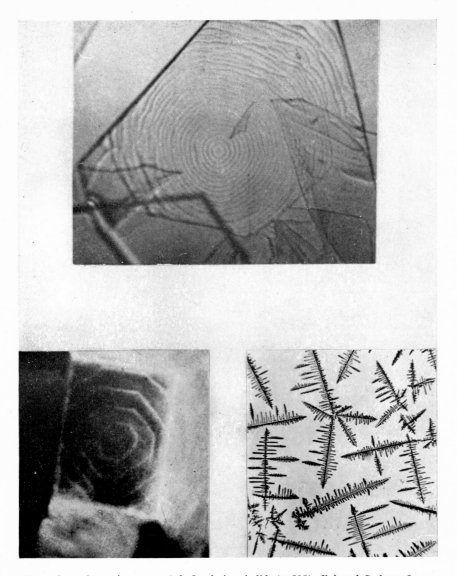

Above: layer formation on crystal of cadmium iodide (× 600). Below, left: layer formation on crystal of sodium chloride (× 1400). Below, right: skeletal growths of ammonium chloride (× 20).

PLATE II

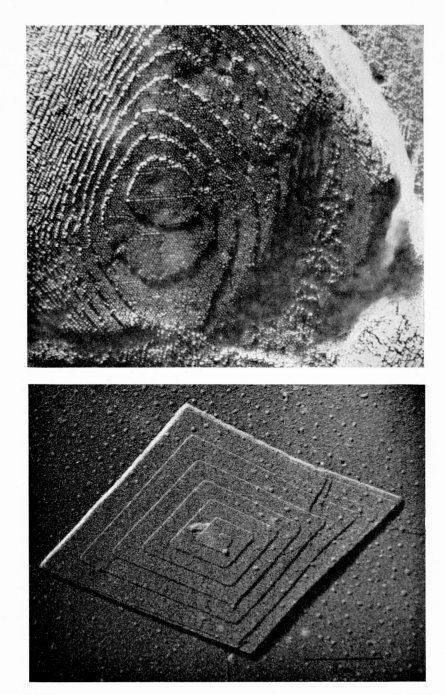

Above: Concentric monomolecular layers on Rothamsted necrosis protein. Magnification 50,000 (Wyckoff, 1948). Below: spiral monomolecular layer structure on crystal of $n$-hexatriacontane, $C_{36}H_{74}$. Magnification 20,000. (Dawson and Vand, 1951)

side of the unit cell, rather than a plane such as *BDF*, which is inclined to all the edges of the unit cell, as the basis for our building operation.

This is apparently what happens in nature when a crystal grows from a solution or melt. When growing crystals are watched under the microscope, using a high magnification and dark ground illumination, layers

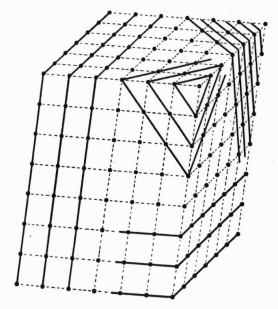

FIG. 7. Dividing a crystal into layers. A few of the simpler ways.
(Each dot is a lattice point.)

can often be seen (Plate I) spreading over the faces one after another (Marcelin, 1918; Volmer, 1923; Kowarski, 1935), usually starting in the centres of the faces (Bunn and Emmett, 1949); sometimes it can be seen that relatively thick layers which spread at a moderate speed are built up from thinner, much more rapidly spreading layers, some of which overtake others to form the thicker layers. This suggests that the same thing occurs down to the molecular or ionic scale; and photographs in the electron microscope of the surfaces of crystals whose growth has been arrested (for they cannot be photographed by this method in the act of growth) do show steps, often one molecule in height (Dawson and Vand, 1951); indeed, on crystals composed of molecules large enough to show up individually, the molecules, drawn up in a regular array, are seen to form concentric unimolecular layers (Wyckoff, 1948) corresponding to the much thicker ones which are seen in the optical microscope in the

act of spreading (see Plate II). This process occurs only on certain
planes; most crystals are bounded by only a few faces, sometimes all
of the same type (for instance, in cubic crystals), though more frequently
of a few different types; and in structurally simple crystals these types
are always densely packed planes.

In the hexamethylbenzene crystal the most densely packed planes are
those parallel to the unit cell edges, and we find that crystals of hexamethylbenzene grown from a pure solution in benzene are parallelepipeda with the three pairs of faces parallel to the faces of the unit cell
(Lonsdale, 1929). In caesium bromide (Fig. 5) the most densely packed
planes are those such as $ACGE$ which cut two edges of the unit cell at
equal angles and are parallel to the third, and caesium bromide crystals
(grown from pure aqueous solution) are rhombic dodecahedra which are
bounded entirely by such planes (Groth, 1906–19). In crystalline copper
(Fig. 5 c) the most densely packed planes are those such as $BEG$ which
cut the three edges of the unit cell symmetrically (note that atoms $K, J$,
and $N$ fall on plane $BEG$); copper crystals grow from the vapour as
octahedra, the faces of which are just these most densely packed planes
(Groth, 1906–19).

For some of the more complex crystals it is not easy to define plane
density of packing of atoms or molecules: a plane parallel to a crystal
face, taken at any level, passes through many atoms, but it cannot pass
through the centres of more than a small proportion of them. For
instance, the particular plane of the lead chloride crystal illustrated in
Fig. 38, if it passes through the centres of the atoms at the corners of the
marked unit area, does not pass exactly through the centres of any of
the other atoms, which lie at various distances above or below the plane
of the paper. It would be difficult to say which of these should 'count'
in the reckoning of plane density of packing of atoms. (See Niggli, 1920.)
But plane density of lattice points is a precisely defined magnitude;
and it is on this that we must focus our attention—for it is found that
the faces of crystals are always densely packed with lattice points. In
other words, if we regard the group of atoms associated with a lattice
point as the building unit, we may say that the faces of crystals are
planes of high reticular density of building units.

It will be evident that, since the faces are parallel to definite planes
of lattice points, the interfacial angles are constant in different crystals
of the same substance. Variations in local conditions during growth
may cause some crystals of hexamethylbenzene, for instance, to be
longer or thinner than others in the same batch; and the eight faces of

a copper crystal, which in uniform growth conditions would grow to the same size, may in practice be found to have very different sizes; but whatever the variation in the actual dimensions of crystals of any particular substance, the interfacial angles are constant, provided that the same type of face is present.

Sparsely packed planes usually do not appear as faces on growing crystals, but if we deliberately create such surfaces we can study their growth. Fig. 8 illustrates what happens when a cubic crystal of sodium chlorate ($NaClO_3$) is partly dissolved to a rounded shape so as to present all possible surfaces, and then put into a supersaturated solution. The diagram is two-dimensional for the sake of simplicity—it is a section through the middle of the crystal. At first, small faces appear on the corners of the square section; but it is found that the rate of growth of these small faces—the thickness of solid deposited in a unit of time—is greater than that of the cube faces, and as a result of this, the small faces ultimately disappear and the final crystal is entirely bounded by the most slowly growing faces, the ordinary cube faces. (See also Artemeev, 1910; Spangenberg, 1928.) This experiment brings out the fact that the faces which appear on growing crystals are those with the smallest rate of thickening. A small rate of thickening, with perhaps a great rate of spreading, are the growth characteristics one expects of the planes with highest reticular density and widest interplanar spacing.

When crystals grow rapidly in stirred, strongly supersaturated solutions (as they often do under the usual conditions of crystallization in the laboratory or in industrial plant) there is a plentiful supply of solute round each growing crystal; external conditions are fairly uniform, and the controlling factor is the architecture of the crystal. Under these conditions the picture of crystal growth given in the previous paragraphs adequately represents what happens;† the crystals are bounded by very few faces—the minimum number of the most slowly growing 'simple' planes necessary to enclose a solid figure. On the other hand, crystals of many minerals, for instance, have grown very slowly in very slightly supersaturated solutions in which the supply of solute is very limited and may vary locally owing to stagnant conditions, convection currents, the proximity of other crystals, and so on. The external conditions thus play a large part in determining the shape; faces which, given equal chances, would grow at different rates may actually grow at the same

† Except in extreme conditions (very high supersaturation), when skeletal crystals are formed; and a few substances grow in skeletal form under ordinary conditions. See later.

rate, and vice versa. These crystals therefore often show a variety of facets which do not appear on crystals grown rapidly. Subsidiary facets may also appear if the temperature of a crystallizing solution fluctuates; partial dissolution rounds off the crystals, and when growth is resumed, small facets appear on the rounded corners, and these may not have time or opportunity to eliminate themselves by rapid growth as in Fig. 8. The production of beautiful, richly faceted crystals by the simple method of leaving a dish of solution for several days on a laboratory bench without temperature control is undoubtedly often due to such temperature fluctuations. It is still true, however, that all the faces on such richly faceted crystals are fairly simple planes, in the sense that they have a fairly high reticular density of lattice points. It is also true that the principal faces are in general simpler than the subsidiary facets.

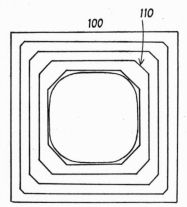

The shape of a crystal may be modified, or even completely changed, by the presence of certain impurities in the solution (see Fig. 3). The reason is that the impurities are strongly adsorbed only on certain faces of the crystal, thereby retarding the growth of these faces (Gaubert, 1906; Bunn, 1933; Royer, 1934). The impurity may be adsorbed on faces which normally grow rapidly (that is, planes which are not the simplest and do not normally appear), and in these circumstances the rate of growth of these faces may be so much reduced that they become the predominant faces on the crystal. The presence of modifying impurities may often be unsuspected; hence we sometimes find crystals exhibiting for no apparent reason faces not of the simplest type.

FIG. 8. A rounded crystal of sodium chlorate, on being put into supersaturated solution, develops 110 and 100 faces. The more rapidly growing 110 faces are subsequently eliminated.

Abnormal external conditions may thus be responsible for an apparent breakdown in the principle of simplicity of faces. However, apparent exceptions to the principle cannot always be attributed to abnormal external conditions. It is not justifiable to regard the principle of simplicity as more than a broad generalization; that is to say, even when external conditions are normal, the faces on crystals, though always simple, are not necessarily the simplest possible. (See also Niggli, 1920.) The rates of growth of crystal faces are of course determined by the distribution of the forces between the atoms, ions, or molecules, and it is not to be expected that a purely geometrical generalization (as the principle of simplicity is) would adequately cover such complexities. In particular, it is to be noted that in ionic crystals the distribution of electric charges in the various planes plays an important part (Kossel, 1927; Stransky, 1928; Brandes and Volmer, 1931).

Nevertheless, the broad generalization is of the greatest value; for we can measure the angles between the faces of a crystal, and, assuming that these faces are simple—that is, they are densely packed with lattice points and are either parallel to the unit cell faces or are related in some simple way to the unit cell—we can usually deduce the type of unit cell, and very often calculate its relative dimensions and angles.

Not all crystals are solid polyhedra. We may approach the subject of irregularities in crystals by remarking that when a crystal is growing from a solution, it sometimes happens that growth in the centres of the faces stops, while growth in the outer regions of the faces (near the edges and corners) continues. A hollow is thus formed in the centre of each face. If, as often happens, the hollow is subsequently closed over, mother liquor is included in the crystal. This may be repeated more than once, and is a common cause of opacity in crystals, and also of the subsequent caking of crystalline products when stored. (Mother liquor diffuses out, and deposits solute at the points of contact of crystals, cementing them together.)

If such cavities are not closed over, the final crystals have hollow faces; often there is a step-formation down each hollow. In extreme cases growth is maintained only towards the corners of crystals, leading to skeletal forms, in which successive branching occurs, as in ammonium chloride, illustrated in Plate I; the directions of growth here are the axial directions of the cubic unit cell. When crystals grow in thin films or droplets of liquid, distortion may occur; a familiar example is ice, which forms irregular tree-like patterns when it crystallizes from liquid on window panes.

Such tendencies may be reduced by growing crystals very slowly, for instance, by extremely slow cooling or evaporation. In fact, when it is desired to obtain perfect crystals for goniometric or X-ray work, the golden rule is to grow them as slowly as possible. Excessive nucleus formation in solutions can often be avoided by removing dust particles in the following way. A solution saturated at, say, 30° C is made up and allowed to cool without disturbance to room temperature; it is then suddenly disturbed, so that a shower of small crystals is formed; these carry down with them any nucleus-forming particles which were in the solution. The solution is then filtered, warmed slightly to destroy any new nuclei formed during filtration, and then left undisturbed to evaporate slowly.

Another method, often useful for organic substances, is to make a solution in one solvent and to cover this with a less dense liquid in which the substance is much less soluble; crystals grow at the interface. The two solvents must be at least partially miscible.

Sparingly soluble salts which are conveniently formed by precipitation reactions may sometimes be induced to form good crystals by a diffusion method. Solutions of the reagents in the same solvent are put in two separate beakers, both completely filled and standing in a larger vessel; solvent is carefully poured in to cover both beakers, and the arrangement is then left undisturbed (L. M. Clark: private communication).

The amount of structural information obtainable by the morphological study of skeletal crystals is naturally very limited, especially when they are distorted. In order to be able to deduce the shape of the unit cell it is necessary to have well-formed polyhedral crystals. The faces of such crystals are, as we have already seen, related in some simple way to the unit cells. We must now define more closely what is meant by the last phrase—'related in some simple way to the unit cells'—and to do this it is necessary to give some account of the accepted nomenclature of crystal planes.

**Nomenclature of crystal planes.** Attention has already been drawn to the many ways of dividing a crystal into layers by sets of planes passing through lattice points (Fig. 7). Each of these sets of parallel planes is described by three numbers such as 210 or 132, the meaning of which is best shown by a few examples. For simplicity, think first of all in only two dimensions, that is, look at the crystal along one axis—say the c axis—as in Fig. 9. In this diagram the points, each of which represents a row of lattice points one behind the other, are seen to lie on sets of straight lines (planes seen edgewise). Every point lies on one of these planes. Now along the axial directions count the number of planes crossed between one lattice point and the next; these numbers are the index numbers. Thus, for the set of planes in the bottom right-hand corner, three planes are crossed in going along a from one lattice point to the next, and two planes in going along b from one lattice point to the next; the first two index numbers are therefore 32. The third index number is 0, because this set of planes is parallel to the c axis, and therefore no planes are crossed in going along $c$; this set of planes is thus the 320 set. Other sets of planes, with indices 110, 100, 010, and 120 (all parallel to the $c$ axis), are also illustrated in this diagram. If one has to travel in a negative axial direction, the corresponding index is given a negative sign; thus, for the set of planes in the centre of the

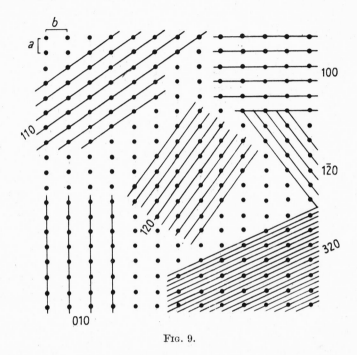

FIG. 9.

right-hand side of Fig. 9, one plane per lattice point is crossed when travelling in the positive $a$ direction, and the same planes are encountered, two per lattice point, when travelling in the negative $b$ direction; this set of planes is therefore called $1\bar{2}0$. It could equally well be called $\bar{1}20$, if only the orientation of the set of planes is under consideration; however, for many purposes, the direction from a particular standpoint is important, and so from any one particular lattice point the set of planes in one direction (involving positive $a$ and negative $b$) would be called $1\bar{2}0$, while the set in the opposite direction (negative $a$ and positive $b$) would be called $\bar{1}20$. Similarly, the set of planes labelled as 120 for the direction of positive $a$ and positive $b$ would be called $\bar{1}\bar{2}0$ when travelling in the opposite direction.

A set of planes inclined to all three axes is shown in Fig. 10. Along $a$, three planes are crossed between one lattice point and the next; along *b*, one plane is crossed at each lattice point, and along *c*, two planes per lattice point; the indices are 312.

Alternatively, one could say that these planes cut the *a* axis at intervals of *a*/3 (*a* being the repeat distance in this direction), the *b* axis at intervals of *b*/1, and the *c* axis at intervals of *c*/2, the indices being defined as the reciprocals of these intercepts. This comes to the same

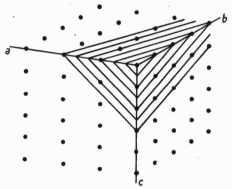

Fig. 10. This set of parallel planes has indices 312.

thing as the definition already given, and corresponds to that found in most textbooks of crystal morphology; but it is really simpler to think of numbers of planes rather than reciprocals of intercepts; and, moreover, the present definition links up with the method of indexing X-ray reflections (see Chapter VI).

Each type of plane is a possible crystal face, although in actual fact only a few simple types of plane usually appear as crystal faces. The next sketch, Fig. 11, shows an actual crystal (ammonium sulphate) with the indices of its front faces marked. This sketch will also serve to illustrate the conventions about crystal set-up and positive and negative directions. In order to show as many faces as possible, crystals are drawn as seen from a viewpoint inclined to all three axes and defined in the following way. Imagine first of all the crystal with its *c* axis vertical and its 010 plane seen edgewise; now shift the eye a little to the right and upwards. The *c* axis still appears vertical, the *b* axis lies left and right but not quite in the plane of the paper, and the *a* axis points a little to the left and downwards as it appears to come out above the paper. Usually perspective drawing is not attempted; most crystal drawings are orthogonal projections. Positive directions are upwards along *c*, to the right along *b*, and forwards (above the paper) along *a*. Intercepts in the negative directions are represented by minus signs above the index numbers, thus: $1\bar{2}0$, $\bar{1}\,\bar{1}\,\bar{1}$. Naturally it is sometimes necessary to depart from the conventional viewpoint to illustrate particular features of crystals more clearly.

An extension of this sytem of nomenclature is sometimes encountered in descriptions of crystals of hexagonal type (Fig. 12). The unit

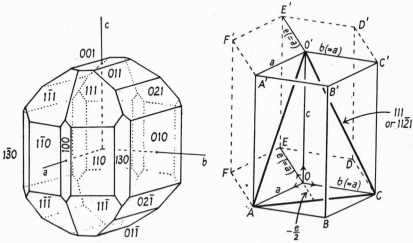

FIG. 11. A crystal of ammonium sulphate (class *mmm*). (After Tutton.)

FIG. 12. Indices of planes of hexagonal crystals. *ABCDEFA'B'C'D'E'F'*, hexagonal prism; *ABCOA'B'C'O'*, unit cell. *ACO'*, plane which, in conformity with indices of crystals of other systems, is called 111. For the sake of treating the three equivalent directions *OA*, *OC*, and *OE* equally, this plane is sometimes known as $11\bar{2}1$.

cell of these crystals has a diamond-shaped base, the $a$ and $b$ axes being equal in length and inclined to each other at an angle of 120°. The $c$ axis is perpendicular to the other two. Although only two horizontal axes are strictly necessary for purposes of description, nevertheless there are three horizontal directions, all exactly equivalent, at 120° to each other; any two of them could be taken as the $a$ and $b$ axes. In order to bring out this feature, index numbers referring to all three horizontal axes, as well as the vertical ($c$) axis, are given, thus: $11\bar{2}1$. The last number refers to the $c$ axis, the first three to the horizontal axes. The third index, which is always necessarily numerically equal to the sum of the first two but of opposite sign, is really redundant. This nomenclature will be found in descriptions of the shapes of hexagonal crystals, but for internal crystal planes it is customary to omit the third index.

The indices of single crystal faces are sometimes enclosed in brackets, thus: (100); this distinguishes a face from the corresponding set of internal planes 100. Curly brackets signify a set of equivalent faces: for a cubic crystal {100} would mean the set 100, $\overline{1}$00, 010, 0$\overline{1}$0, 001, and 00$\overline{1}$.

**The law of rational indices.** We have seen that the faces of structurally simple crystals, the planes on which deposition of solid occurs layer by layer, are in general those planes which have a high reticular density of lattice points in each plane and wide interplanar spacing. Sometimes the faces are the planes with the densest packing and the widest interplanar spacing, but there are many exceptions to this, for various reasons which have already been mentioned. It remains true, however, that in all cases the actual faces of a crystal are planes of high (though not necessarily the highest) reticular density. We may call these the 'simple' planes.

It is evident from Figs. 9 and 10 that these planes have small indices; we may therefore state that the actual faces on crystals are planes with small indices. In this form the generalization is what is known as the 'law of rational indices', which says simply that all the faces on a crystal may be described, with reference to the three axes, by three small whole numbers. It is frequently found that all the faces of even richly faceted crystals can be described by index numbers not greater than 3; numbers greater than 5 are very rare.

It is the recognition of the law of rational indices which makes it possible to deduce probable unit cell shapes from crystal shapes. (It is, of course, not possible to discover the absolute dimensions; X-ray or electron diffraction photographs are necessary for this purpose (Chapter VI).) The general principle is to find that unit cell (its angles and relative dimensions) which will enable us to describe all the faces of the crystal by the smallest whole numbers, and, in particular, the largest faces by the smallest numbers. There is a further condition: all faces which appear to be equivalent (for instance, all the eight faces of a regular octahedron) are given similar indices, that is, are assumed to be related in the same way to the most appropriate unit cell; in other words, the directions of unit cell edges are chosen in conformity with the symmetry of the crystal. We shall return to this subject later in this chapter. Meanwhile, the first step in the attempt to deduce the angles and relative dimensions of the unit cell of a crystal from its actual shape is the accurate measurement of the angles between all the faces of the crystal.

**Measurement of interfacial angles, and graphical representation.** The most accurate method of measuring the angles between crystal faces is an optical one, which makes use of the reflection of light by the plane faces. The crystal is mounted on the stem of a goniometer head (Fig. 13) by means of wax, shellac, or plasticine; a beam of parallel

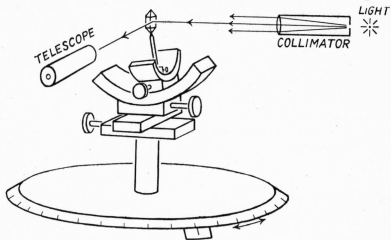

FIG. 13. Principle of the reflecting goniometer. The adjusting head comprises two mutually perpendicular arc movements and two cross movements.

light from the collimator strikes the crystal, which is rotated until one of its faces reflects the beam into the telescope, which is at any convenient angle to the collimator. A suitable sharply defined aperture is provided in the collimator, so that its image can be adjusted accurately to the cross-wires of the telescope. The crystal is then rotated until the light is reflected by the next face; the angle through which the goniometer head has been turned is the angle between the normals of the two faces. It is evident that, in order to get reflections from both faces into the telescope, the crystal must be adjusted very carefully by means of the arc movements of the goniometer head. This is simplest when the crystal is mounted on the goniometer head so that one of the face-normals is approximately parallel to one of the arc movements; this arc is adjusted until the reflection from this face appears accurately on the cross-wires. The crystal is now rotated so that the reflection from another face (preferably one which is roughly at right angles to the first) enters the telescope; by a movement of the second arc this reflection is brought to the cross-wires.

It is found that, when the reflections from two faces are registered accurately on the cross-wires of the telescope, other faces automatically give their reflections when the crystal is rotated further; for instance, all the vertical faces of the ammonium sulphate crystal in Fig. 11 give their reflections one after the other as the crystal is rotated round the c axis. Such a set of faces is called a 'zone', and the axis of rotation parallel to all the faces is called the 'zone axis'. All the faces of any crystal fall on one or other of a few zones, and therefore in order to measure all the interfacial angles each of these zone axes in turn must be set parallel to the axis of rotation of the goniometer head. On a single-circle goniometer, this must be done by remounting the crystal for each zone, but two-circle goniometers which obviate the necessity of such resetting are also obtainable.

It is often useful to be able to represent precisely on a flat surface the three-dimensional relations between the interfacial angles. The most convenient projection for most purposes is the stereographic projection, which is derived in the following way. From a point within the crystal imagine lines drawn outwards normal to all the faces (Fig. 14). Round the crystal describe a sphere having the point at its centre. The positions at which the face-normals meet the surface of the sphere are known as the poles of the faces. The crystal is thus replaced by a set of points on the surface of the sphere, each point representing the orientation of a crystal face. In this way we have left behind the actual shape of the crystal, with the irregularities arising from the conditions of growth, and are now dealing simply with the orientations of faces—that is, with the orientations of lattice planes, which are related in a simple way to the unit cell. The sphere is now projected on to a selected plane—the equatorial plane in Fig. 14 b—by joining all points on its upper half to the 'south pole' and all points on its lower half to the 'north pole'. The great advantage of this projection (Fig. 14 c) is that all zones of faces fall either on arcs of circles or else on straight lines, a circumstance which much facilitates graphical construction. (Each such arc or straight line passes through opposite points on the equatorial circle.) Poles in the northern hemisphere are denoted by dots, those in the southern hemisphere by little rings.

For further information on stereographic projections and the spherical trigonometry necessary for handling goniometric data, books by Miers (1929), Tutton (1922), and Barker (1922) may be consulted.

**Deduction of possible unit cell shape from crystal shape. Preliminary.** In this book we are concerned chiefly with optical and X-ray methods, and we shall consider crystal morphology only so far as is necessary for the full use of such methods for identification or for structure determination. But although it is not intended to deal with morphological methods in a quantitative way, it is very necessary to consider in rather more detail the relation between the external shape of a crystal and that of its unit cell; and this subject is perhaps best developed in the guise of a consideration of the problem of deducing the probable unit cell shape from the external shape of a crystal. We have already seen that the principle on which the attempt is based is the principle of simplicity of indices, coupled with the conformity of the indices with the symmetry of the crystal. We now see how this principle can be applied in practice. First of all, we shall see the principle of simplicity in action by itself; and we shall then find it necessary to consider crystal symmetry in some detail.

The planes with the simplest indices—100, 010, and 001—are those which are parallel to the sides of the unit cell, and we find that on many crystals these form the principal faces, and on some crystals (especially those grown rapidly in strongly supersaturated solutions) the only faces. One example, hexamethylbenzene, has already been given; it forms non-rectangular parallelepipeda with the

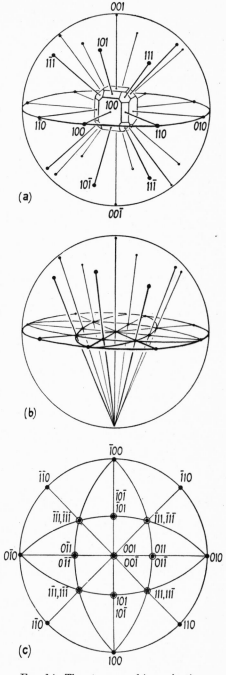

Fig. 14. The stereographic projection.

three pairs of faces parallel to the unit cell faces. Another example is anhydrite, $CaSO_4$; the unit cell of this crystal is a rectangular box with unequal edges, and it grows as a rectangular brick with unequal edges, though it must be emphasized that the relative dimensions of the crystal itself have no direct connexion with the dimensions of the unit cell. (The rates of growth of the various faces of any crystal depend, in the first place, on the forces between the atoms, ions, or molecules in different directions, and these forces have no direct connexion with the unit cell dimensions; moreover, these rates of growth are affected by external conditions.) Such crystals tell us the angles of the unit cell, but they do not tell us anything about the relative dimensions of the unit cell edges.

If we are to be able to calculate the relative dimensions of the unit cell of any crystalline substance, some of the faces on the crystals must be inclined to the faces of the unit cell. Suppose we have a crystal of the shape shown in Fig. 15 $a$—a rectangular brick with the (unequal) edges bevelled (an orthorhombic crystal). We naturally assume that the faces which are perpendicular to each other are parallel to the faces of the unit cell, which is evidently a rectangular box. The indices of the principal faces are thus assumed provisionally to be 100, 010, and 001. The simplest indices for the faces which bevel the edges are 110, 011, and 101. If we assume that a face is 011, we are assuming that successive identical planes of lattice points parallel to this face are parallel to the $a$ axis, and that in passing along either $b$ or $c$, only one plane is crossed in the interval between one lattice point and the next (see Fig. 15 $b$). It is evident that $c/b = \cot \theta$. In the same way, by assuming that another face is 110, we can obtain $a/b$; and this settles the shape of the unit cell and the indices of the remaining faces; thus, the third different bevelling face might turn out to be, not 101 as first suggested, but 201 or 102. If our crystals also have faces cutting off the corners (Fig. 15 $c$), the indices of these faces can be found (by slightly more complex trigonometry) from the angles between these 'corner' faces and the principal faces.

Alternatively, it might have been assumed initially that these 'corner' faces are 111, 11$\bar{1}$, and so on; this assumption would have given us a set of axial ratios, from which the indices of the bevelling faces could be deduced.

It is always possible to find alternative sets of indices, corresponding to different axial ratios, for any crystal. Thus, consider the ammonium sulphate crystal (Fig. 11), which, like the example just given, has a rectangular unit cell. Let us call the faces 110, 011, 130, 021, and 111 $p, q, p', q'$, and $o$ respectively. If it had been assumed that $q'$ is 011 and $p$ 110, then this group of faces would be 110, 012, 130, 011, and 112. Or it might have been assumed that $p'$ is 110 and $q$ 011, in which case the group of faces would be, 310, 011, 110, 021, 311. But the sets of indices given by the second and third schemes are less simple than those

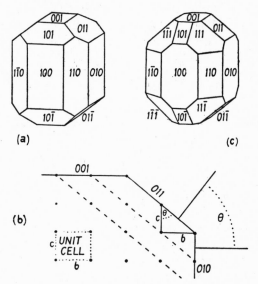

FIG. 15. Determination of the probable shape of the unit cell from interfacial angles.

resulting from the first assumptions, and therefore the axial ratios derived in the first scheme are accepted as the probable relative dimensions of the unit cell edges. This turns out to be correct.

Here we have the key to morphological crystallography. The principle followed throughout is to find that unit cell shape which, subject to the condition that similar faces shall have similar indices, will allow all the faces of a crystal to be indexed by the smallest possible whole numbers, the principal faces being given, as a general rule, the simplest indices. This method was developed during the last century, long before X-rays were discovered, though the term 'unit cell' was not used. The set of axes deduced in this way was regarded primarily as the most convenient frame of reference for the accurate description and classification of any crystal. Nevertheless, it is clearly more than a convenient frame of reference; it corresponds to some fundamental feature of the ultimate structure of the crystal. We know now, as the result of the study of the atomic structure of crystals by X-ray methods, that the relative axial dimensions deduced by morphological methods are in fact very often the exact relative dimensions of the unit cell. Even when they are not correct, there is always a very simple relation between the 'morphological' unit and the true unit; one of the morphological axes is perhaps twice as long or half as long (in relation to the other axes) as it should be. This obviously means that the principle of simplest indices is not strictly true for these crystals; some of the faces on these crystals are, so to speak, not the simplest but the next in order of simplicity. There is no doubt about the general soundness of the principle of simplest indices, but it is not a rigid law.

The examples given hitherto have been particularly simple ones, because some of the faces have been at right angles to each other, and this has given the clue to the type of unit cell. But many crystals do not possess faces parallel to the unit cell faces, and for such crystals the type of unit cell, and possible indices for the principal faces, are very often not by any means obvious. To approach such problems it is necessary to introduce the all-important subject of crystal symmetry. The type of unit cell is entirely bound up with the symmetry of the atomic arrangement; it is, in fact, the symmetry of the atomic arrangement which decides which (if any) of the unit cell angles shall be right angles, and how many of its edges shall be equal. Therefore if we can recognize the symmetries of any particular crystal, this leads us at once to the unit cell type and to the probable directions of unit cell edges.

And this is not all. Each type of unit cell may arise from a number of different types of atomic arrangement, and some of the symmetry characteristics of these different types of atomic arrangements are revealed by shape-symmetries. In classifying crystals we can first of all divide them into several *systems* according to unit cell types, and then each system can be divided into several *classes* according to those symmetry characteristics which are revealed by shape. The consideration of crystal symmetry may thus take us farther than the mere derivation of unit cell type.

**Internal symmetry and crystal shape.** Consider first one of the simplest and most highly symmetrical of atomic arrangements, that which is found in crystals of sodium chloride and in many other simple binary compounds. The atomic arrangement is shown in Fig. 16 a. The unit cell is a cube; if we take the corner of the unit cell to be the centre of a sodium ion, there are also sodium ions at the centre of each face, the lattice being a face-centred one; the chlorine ions are half-way

along the edges and also in the centre of the unit cell. Note first that
the reason why the three mutually perpendicular axes are equal in
length is that the arrangement of atoms is precisely the same along one
axis as it is along the other two; the 100 plane has exactly the same
arrangement of atoms as the 010 and 001 planes; secondly, that when
a sodium chloride crystal grows in a pure solution, it is inevitable that,
provided the three types of faces have the same chance (in a stirred
solution, for instance), they grow at the same rate, and the crystal
becomes a perfect cube.

If sodium chloride crystals are grown in a solution containing 10 per
cent. of urea, they grow as regular octahedra, but although the external
shape is different from that of crystals grown from a pure solution, the
internal structure is exactly the same; the same internal lattice is
bounded by surfaces of a different type in the two sorts of crystals.
The octahedral faces (111, 11$\bar{1}$, 1$\bar{1}$1, $\bar{1}$11, 1$\bar{1}$$\bar{1}$, $\bar{1}$1$\bar{1}$, $\bar{1}$$\bar{1}$1, and $\bar{1}$$\bar{1}$$\bar{1}$) are
perpendicular to the cube diagonals; the atomic arrangement on all
octahedral faces is the same, and if we proceed from any point in the
crystal along any of the eight diagonal directions, we shall come across
the same atomic distribution (alternate layers of sodium and chlorine
ions); consequently, in uniform growth conditions all the octahedral
faces grow at the same rate, and the crystals grow as perfectly regular
octahedra.

Now although the cube and the regular octahedron are quite different
solid shapes, yet their symmetries are exactly the same; and it can be
seen (in Figs. 16–19) that the symmetries of these solid figures are those
of the arrangement of atoms in a sodium chloride crystal. Rotate a cube
about an axis perpendicular to one of its faces and passing through its
centre (Fig. 16 b); after a quarter of a turn it presents exactly the same
appearance as it did at first; after half a turn, again the same appearance, and likewise after three-quarters of a turn; in fact, it presents the
same appearance four times during a complete revolution; the axis is
an axis of fourfold symmetry. There are three such fourfold axes, all
at right angles to each other, and parallel to the cube edges. A regular
octahedron likewise has three fourfold axes, passing through its corners
(Fig. 16 c). These fourfold axes correspond with those of the atomic
arrangement; every line which passes through a row of atoms parallel
to a unit cell edge is an axis of fourfold symmetry, since the atomic
arrangement (regarded as extending indefinitely in space) presents the
same appearance four times during a complete revolution round this
line. Similarly, there are, passing through the edges of both cube and

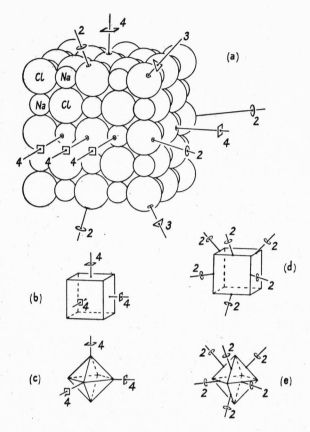

Fig. 16. *a*. The atomic arrangement in sodium chloride, and some of its axes of symmetry. *b* and *c*. Fourfold axes of cube and octahedron. *d* and *e*. Twofold axes of cube and octahedron.

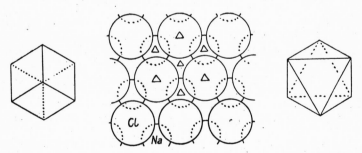

Fig. 17. Centre: atomic arrangement in sodium chloride, seen along a threefold axis of symmetry. Left: cube seen along a body diagonal. Right: octahedron seen along a face-normal.

octahedron, six axes of twofold symmetry, involving identity of appearance twice during a complete revolution (Fig. 16 *d* and *e*); and finally, passing through the cube corners and perpendicular to the octahedron faces, four axes of threefold symmetry, involving identity of appearance three times during a complete revolution (Fig. 17). All these axes are symmetry elements of the atomic arrangement.

Sodium chloride crystals also possess another type of symmetry; imagine a plane parallel to one pair of cube faces, passing through the centre of the crystal (Fig. 18); this plane divides the crystal into two halves, each the mirror image of the other, and is therefore called a plane of symmetry. There are two sets of such planes of symmetry: a set of three mutually perpendicular planes parallel to the three pairs of cube faces, and a set of six bisecting the angles between the first set. These planes of symmetry, which are also possessed by the regular octahedron, correspond with the planes of symmetry

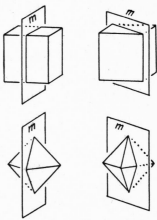

FIG. 18. Planes of symmetry in cube and octahedron.

of the atomic arrangement—planes passing through sheets of atoms.

There is one other element of symmetry possessed by sodium chloride crystals. For each face, edge, or corner of the cube or octahedron there is an exactly similar face, edge, or corner diametrically opposite; the centre of the cube or octahedron (Fig. 19) is therefore called a centre of symmetry. The centre of symmetry possessed by these shapes corresponds with the centre of symmetry in the atomic arrangement; the centre of any sodium or chlorine ion is a centre of symmetry, since along any direction from the selected ion the arrangement encountered is exactly repeated in the diametrically opposite direction. A centre of symmetry is often called a centre

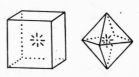

FIG. 19. Both cube and octahedron possess a centre of symmetry, which corresponds to the centre of symmetry in each atom of the crystal.

of inversion because a particular grouping on one side of it is an inverted or mirror-image copy of the grouping on the other side, just as a pin-hole camera produces an inverted image of the original object.

We turn now to sodium chlorate, $NaClO_3$. This crystal also has a cubic unit cell, and rapidly grown crystals are simple cubes; but slowly grown crystals (Fig. 20, left) show subsidiary faces on the edges and corners, and if these crystals are examined it will be found that their symmetries are different from those of sodium chloride. For instance, there are only four 'corner' faces (111 type), not eight; and the axes passing through the centres of the cube faces are in this case not fourfold

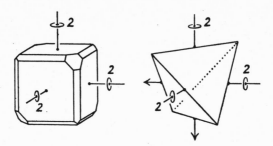

FIG. 20. Sodium chlorate crystals with tetrahedron faces.

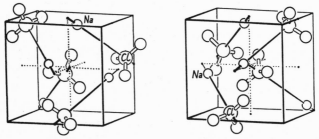

FIG. 21. Structures of left- and right-handed sodium chlorate crystals. The crystal on the left rotates the plane of polarization of light (see p. 90) to the left (anticlockwise for a light beam approaching the eye).

but only twofold. Similarly, when we encourage the growth of 111 faces by the presence of sodium thiosulphate in the solution, we obtain tetrahedra, not octahedra (Buckley, 1930); a regular tetrahedron (Fig. 20, right) has three mutually perpendicular twofold axes but no fourfold axes. Evidently the rate of growth of four of the faces of type 111 is much less than that of the other four. The known atomic arrangement (Fig. 21) shows clearly the reason why there is a difference. The chlorate ion ($ClO_3$) has the form of a low triangular pyramid with the chlorine atom as apex and the oxygen atoms forming an equilateral triangular base. The arrangement of these pyramidal ions on faces of type 111 is rather complex, for there are four different orientations; but for the present purpose we need not consider this in detail; we need only note that on four of the planes of type 111 there are pyramidal ions with

their bases facing outwards (and none with an exactly reversed orientation), while on the other four it is the apexes which face outwards;
hence the surface forces on four of the planes are quite different from
those of the other four, and the rates of growth are therefore different—
so much so that one set never appears on crystals at all. The tetrahedron

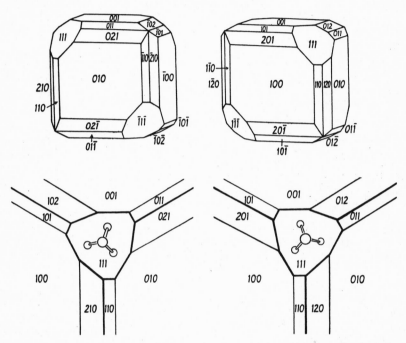

FIG. 22. Shapes of left- and right-handed sodium chlorate crystals, and orientation
of ClO₃ groups on 111 faces. (Point-group symmetry of sodium chlorate—23.) The
crystal on the left is laevo-rotatory (rotates the plane of polarization of light to
the left).

has no centre of symmetry, and each threefold axis is called a polar axis
since its two ends are not equivalent.

If sodium chlorate grew always in the form of regular tetrahedra we
might think the atomic arrangement has planes of symmetry, for the
regular tetrahedron is a solid figure which has such planes. But crystals
of this substance grown very slowly in pure solution (Fig. 22) present
evidence of an internal symmetry even lower than that of a simple
tetrahedron. Truncating the cube edges there are not only {110} faces
but also faces of type {210}; but only twelve out of a possible twenty-
four of this type are present, one to each cube edge; thus, on a particular
crystal, 210 is present but not 120. The threefold axes (cube diagonals)

are maintained, as they are in all crystals belonging to the cubic system; and so are the twofold axes characteristic of a tetrahedron; but in consequence of the presence of this half-set of {210} faces, the crystal has no planes of symmetry. If we look down a threefold axis towards the 111 (tetrahedral) face of the crystal shown in Fig. 22, left, we see a 210 type of face always in advance (clockwise) of a 110 type of face. The reason can again be seen quite directly from the known atomic structure of the crystal; the $ClO_3$ ions are placed so that their chlorine-oxygen bonds do not point to the corners of the tetrahedral faces; the ions are rotated to a 'skew' position. It should be noted that in addition to the crystal illustrated on the left of Fig. 22, there is an equivalent but not identical type (Fig. 22, right) in which the faces of type 210 are on the other side of the 110 faces; in these crystals, evidently, the $ClO_3$ ions are twtsted round in the opposite direction to those in the first-mentioned crystals. The two types of crystal are mirror-images of each other, both as regards their external shape and their atomic arrangements; they are, like left- and right-handed gloves, equivalent but not identical.

The external form of a crystal may thus reveal, not only the shape of the unit cell, but to some extent the symmetries of the internal atomic arrangement. For each different type of unit cell (each different crystal system) there are several types of internal symmetry which may be revealed by crystal shape; in the cubic system, for instance, there are five different classes recognizable by external shape-symmetry, that of sodium chloride having the highest and that of sodium chlorate the lowest symmetry. Such information is not always obtainable, however; very often, especially when crystals grow rapidly, they have too few faces, and the apparent symmetry of the crystals is higher than the real internal symmetry; but when this information *can* be obtained, it is of value for identification purposes and for structure determination. The possibilities of identity for a crystal observed to have the form of a regular tetrahedron are in some degree limited by the obvious fact that it cannot belong to the most highly symmetrical class of the cubic system; its internal symmetry is not higher than tetrahedral (though it might be lower). And in setting out to determine the atomic arrangement of a crystal having a tetrahedral habit all arrangements having fourfold axes of symmetry are ruled out from the start.

The above remarks on symmetry of shape apply only to crystals grown in uniform external conditions. When external conditions are not uniform, crystallographically equivalent faces are often found to be very unequal in size, but, however unequal they are in size, the angles between them are constant, and the symmetries of the internal atomic arrangement, though not shown by the shape as a whole, are exhibited by the interfacial angles. The best way of thinking of such cases is to imagine lines drawn outwards from a point within the crystal, each line being perpendicular to a crystal face; this assemblage of perpendiculars or 'poles' (which is best represented on paper by the stereographic projection) exhibits the symmetries of the atomic arrangement. There is an important possible source of confusion here; certain faces may be missing owing to accidental local variations of growth conditions. However, it will usually be obvious that such absences are accidental, as opposed to the systematic absences like those shown by sodium chlorate crystals. For instance, when only one of a set of eight faces is missing the absence is obviously accidental. It is only when a set of faces is halved or quartered, for instance, that the circumstance has any significance with regard to internal symmetry. The examination of a number of crystals from the same batch will usually resolve such difficulties; not all the crystals will have the same accidental absences or accidental variations of shape, and examination of a number of crystals will usually give a sound idea of shape-symmetry.

Crystal shapes idealized in this way may be regarded as the result of the co-operation of selected elements of symmetry. In crystals belonging to the cubic system we find the planes and axes of symmetry occurring in sets of three or four or six, in consequence of the identity of atomic arrangement along three mutually perpendicular directions; but in crystals belonging to some of the other systems we may find them in smaller sets or in isolation. Crystals of cassiterite, $SnO_2$, for instance, which belong to the tetragonal system, exhibit a single fourfold axis, perpendicular to two sets of two twofold axes; there are also planes of symmetry in sets of one or two (Fig. 23). Crystals of sodium meta-periodate trihydrate, $NaIO_4 . 3H_2O$, have one threefold axis (of polar character) as their only element of symmetry (Fig. 24). Meta-bromo-nitrobenzene (orthorhombic system) has one twofold (polar) axis and two planes of symmetry parallel to this axis (Fig. 25). Para-quinone (monoclinic system) has one twofold axis and a plane of symmetry perpendicular to this axis (Fig. 26).

The number of different types of symmetry elements is very small. In addition to the symmetry axes already mentioned, the only other straightforward rotation axis is the sixfold axis, involving identity of appearance six times in the course of one complete revolution. Crystals of potassium dithionate, $K_2S_2O_6$, exhibit this type of symmetry (Fig. 27).

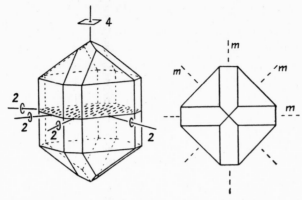

FIG. 23. Cassiterite, $SnO_2$. Left: general view, showing axes of symmetry and equatorial plane of symmetry. Right: view down fourfold axis, showing vertical planes of symmetry. Class $4/mmm$.

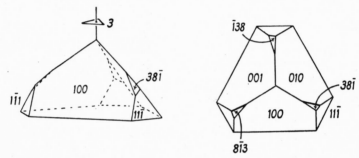

FIG. 24. $NaIO_4.3H_2O$ (class 3). Left: general view. Right: view along threefold axis.

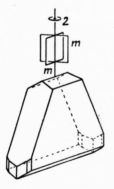

FIG. 25. Symmetries of meta-bromonitrobenzene (class $mm$).

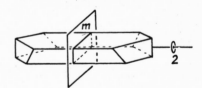

FIG. 26. Symmetries of para-quinone (class $2/m$).

Axes of fivefold or greater-than-sixfold symmetry do not occur in crystals, though it is possible to construct solid figures showing such symmetries. The reason is that space-patterns—regular repetitions of structural units in space—cannot have such symmetries. Nor, for that matter, can plane-patterns; it is easy to confirm this by drawing patterns of dots on paper.

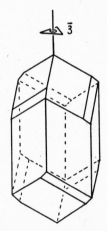

FIG. 27. Potassium dithionate, $K_2S_2O_6$ (class $6/mmm$). Left: general view. Right: view down sixfold axis. (*Note.* Atomic arrangement has lower symmetry.)

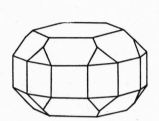

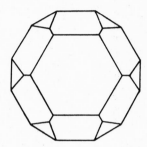

FIG. 28. The fourfold inversion axis. Urea, $O:C(NH_2)_2$. Class $\bar{4}2m$.

FIG. 29. The threefold inversion axis Dioptase, $CuH_2SiO_4$. Class $\bar{3}$.

Finally, there is another type of symmetry axis which involves, not simple rotation, but combined rotation and inversion through a point. Crystals of urea, $O:C(NH_2)_2$, are prisms of square cross-section, terminated at each end by a pair of sloping faces (Fig. 28); all four sloping faces make the same angles with the prism faces, but if we wish to imagine a bottom face—say $\bar{1}1\bar{1}$—moved into the position of a top face, we must rotate through 90° and invert through a point at the centre of the crystal, thus arriving at 111 or $\bar{1}\,\bar{1}1$. All four sloping faces can be accounted for by repetitions of this compound operation. The prism axis of such a crystal is known as a fourfold axis of rotatory inversion, or fourfold inversion axis. There are also three- and sixfold inversion axes. The threefold inversion axis, which is equivalent to an ordinary threefold axis plus a centre of symmetry, is exemplified in crystals of dioptase, $CuH_2SiO_4$ (Fig. 29). The sixfold inversion axis is equivalent to a straightforward threefold axis with a plane of symmetry normal to it. A twofold inversion axis is equivalent to a plane of symmetry, and is usually known by the latter name.

All idealized crystal shapes bounded by plane faces exhibit either no symmetry at all or else a combination of some of the elements of symmetry in this very short list. Crystals having no symmetry are very rare.

It has been said at the beginning of this section that the symmetries displayed by the shapes of crystals grown in uniform surroundings are those of the atomic space-pattern (or at any rate are not lower than those of the atomic space-pattern). This statement needs amplification. In some atomic space-patterns—parallel contiguous repetitions of units of pattern—there can be discerned types of symmetry elements involving translation: screw axes involving combined rotation and translation, and glide planes involving combined reflection and translation. (Examples will be found in Chapter VII.) Such symmetry elements involving translation naturally cannot be displayed by crystal shapes, which are, to speak formally, assemblies of face-types round a point, having no element of translation. Crystal shapes therefore display symmetry elements which may be regarded as screw axes and glide planes deprived of their elements of translation; that is to say, an atomic space-pattern having screw axes gives rise to a crystal shape displaying the corresponding simple rotation axes, and a space-pattern having glide planes gives rise to a crystal shape displaying straightforward reflection planes. Thus, several different types of atomic space-patterns (space-group symmetries) give rise to the same crystal shape-symmetry (point-group symmetry). The space-group symmetries are considered more fully in Chapter VII; here we are concerned only with point-group symmetry.

**Nomenclature of symmetry elements and crystal classes.** It is convenient to have short, self-explanatory symbols with which to refer to the various crystal classes. Some of the names used formerly for the crystal classes are rather cumbrous (e.g. monoclinic hemimorphic hemihedry), and others (e.g. tetragonal hemihedry of the second type) are not self-explanatory. Moreover, different authorities have quite

different name-systems. The point-group nomenclature adopted inter-
nationally and given in *International Tables for X-ray Crystallography*
(1952) provides symbols which are not only extremely concise, but also
self-explanatory in that they present the essential symmetries of the
point-groups.

Two-, three-, four-, or sixfold rotation axes of symmetry are represented by the numbers 2, 3, 4, and 6, while three-, four-, and sixfold
inversion axes have the symbols
$\bar{3}$, $\bar{4}$, and $\bar{6}$. In conformity with
this scheme, asymmetry is repre-
sented by the figure 1 (only one
repetition in a complete rotation),
and a centre of symmetry, or inversion through a point, by $\bar{1}$. A
plane of symmetry is represented
by the letter *m* ('mirror').

In putting together the symbols
to denote the symmetries of any
crystal class the convention is to
give the symmetry of the principal
axis first—for instance, 4 or $\bar{4}$ for tetragonal classes. If there is a plane
of symmetry perpendicular to the
principal axis, the two symbols are

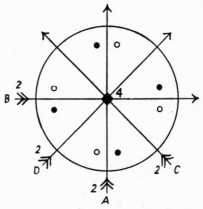

Fig. 30. Stereographic projection of point-
group 42. The association of a fourfold
axis and a twofold axis (*A*) at right angles
to each other gives rise inevitably to three
more twofold axes (*B, C,* and *D*).

associated thus: $\dfrac{4}{m}$ ('four over *m*'), or, more conveniently for printing,

4/*m*. Then follow the symbols for the secondary axes, if any, and then

any other symmetry planes. (Note that 4/*mmm* means $\dfrac{4}{m}$ *mm*, that is,

the second and third *m*'s refer to planes of symmetry parallel to the
fourfold axis.)

Secondary axes may be in sets, but there is no need to mention more
than one. Thus if, to a principal fourfold axis, we add a secondary
twofold axis (perpendicular to the principal axis), the action of the
fourfold axis inevitably creates another twofold axis at right angles to
the first; and further, we find that there are inevitably two more twofold
axes bisecting the angles between the first two. This is illustrated in
Fig. 30, a stereographic projection in which a point represents the pole
of a general plane; if *A* is the secondary twofold axis which is first
introduced, the direct action of the fourfold axis is to create another

twofold axis at $B$, together with the other face-poles shown; and it is then found that there are also twofold axes at $C$ and $D$. The class symbol is, however, given simply as 42.

Further abbreviations are sometimes made, the principle being to give only those elements which are necessary to describe the class symmetry uniquely. Thus, crystals of hexabromoethane (Fig. 34 $f$) have three non-equivalent, mutually perpendicular twofold axes, with a plane of symmetry perpendicular to each; the full class symbol would be $2/m \ 2/m \ 2/m$, but it is sufficient to leave out the axial symbols and write simply $mmm$; the three planes of symmetry automatically call into being the twofold axes. Similarly, one of the cubic classes has the full symbol $2/m \ 3$, but $m3$ is adequate to describe uniquely the class symmetry. (Note that $3m$ is quite a different class—a trigonal class with planes of symmetry parallel to the threefold axis.)

**The thirty-two point-group symmetries or crystal classes.** All the possible point-group symmetries—the combinations of symmetry elements exhibited by idealized crystal shapes—are different combinations of the symmetry elements already described, that is,

the centre of symmetry $(\bar{1})$,
the plane of symmetry $(m)$,
the axes of symmetry (2, 3, 4, and 6), and
the inversion axes $(\bar{3}, \bar{4}, \text{ and } \bar{6})$.

The derivation of the point-group symmetries will not be described in detail, but the relations between them are brought out in the series of miniature stereographic projections shown in Fig. 31. The principle followed is to represent the position of a general plane $hkl$ by its pole, first of all for the asymmetric class 1, the other classes being developed by systematic additions of symmetry elements. Thus, in the first row are classes having only the principal rotation axes (normal to the plane of the paper); in the second row are those having the corresponding inversion axes. A plane of symmetry is added, perpendicular to a principal rotation axis in the third row and parallel to it in the fourth row. The fifth row shows the result of adding a plane of symmetry parallel to a principal inversion axis. In the sixth row a secondary two-fold axis is added to a principal rotation axis, giving the holoaxial class in each system, while the last row shows the holohedral class in each system, obtained by adding planes of symmetry both parallel and per-pendicular to the principal rotation axis. The enantiomorphous classes are those in the first and sixth rows—those possessing rotation axes only.

Note how, very often, the association of two elements of symmetry

inevitably creates further elements. We have already seen an example
of this in class 42 (Fig. 30). The class symbols given in Fig. 31 are, first,

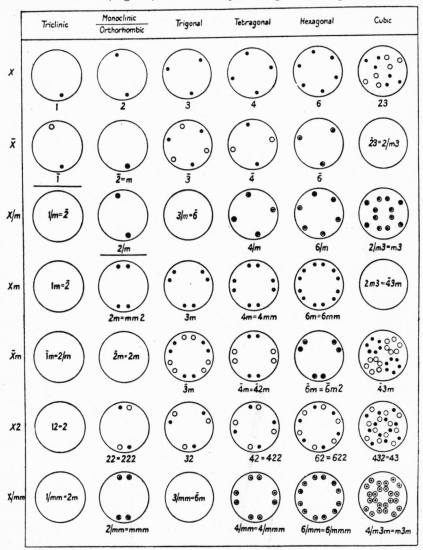

FIG. 31. The thirty-two crystal classes.

those which conform to the scheme of derivation in this diagram (these
are sufficient—sometimes more than sufficient—to characterize the
classes uniquely), and following these the conventional symbols given
in *International Tables*, which in some cases are longer ($4mm$, $\overline{4}2m$), and
in others shorter ($m3m$), than the first-mentioned symbols.

The cubic classes stand somewhat apart from the rest. They have as their distinctive feature four threefold axes lying along cube diagonals; these are secondary axes. The primary axes may be either twofold or fourfold.

Examples of crystals are shown in Figs. 32–37 and in various other drawings in this book. Familiarity with crystal symmetry is, however, best attained by handling and contemplating idealized models of crystals.

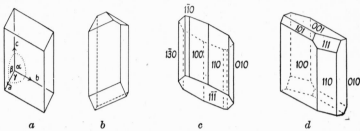

a            b            c            d

FIG. 32. Triclinic system. *a*. Unit cell type. *b*. Strontium hydrogen tartrate hydrate $SrH_2(C_4H_4O_6)_2.4H_2O$. Class 1. *c*. $CuSO_4.5H_2O$. Class $\bar{1}$. *d*. 1,4 dinitro 2,5 dibromo-benzene. Class $\bar{1}$.

## The unit cell types or crystal systems

*Triclinic* (*sometimes called anorthic*). Crystals lacking symmetry of any kind naturally have the most 'general' type of unit cell, the three axes of which are all inclined to each other at different angles and unequal in length. The addition of a centre of symmetry does not alter the situation, for this most general type of unit cell has a centre of symmetry and is appropriate for this class also. These two classes, 1 and $\bar{1}$, constitute the triclinic system (Fig. 32).

The lattice points of a triclinic crystal may be joined in various ways to form differently shaped unit cells (see p. 151). It is usually most convenient to use the cell with the shortest edges, unless there is some special feature which recommends some other direction as a unit cell edge. Donnay (1943) recommends that the shortest axis shall be called *c* and the longest *b*; and that the angles $\alpha$ and $\beta$ shall be obtuse.

When axes are chosen on morphological grounds there is a convention, not always followed, that the principal zone axis is called *c*, and that, of the other two, the longer is called *b*; and the obtuse angles between the axes are usually specified, rather than the acute angles.

*Monoclinic*. The single twofold axis of class 2 is an obvious direction for a unit cell edge, and this edge has usually been called *b*. The existence of the twofold axis means that neighbouring lattice points lie on a plane normal to the twofold axis; therefore all the lattice points lie in planes normal to this axis; thus the *a* and *c* edges of the unit cell are both normal to $b$, but since there is no other element of symmetry, they are inclined to each other; and the three axes are unequal in length. The shorter of the two inclined axes is called $c$, and the obtuse angle $\beta$ between $a$ and $c$ is usually specified, rather than the acute angle.

The same type of unit cell is appropriate for class $m$, the $a$ and $c$ axes lying in the plane of symmetry, with the $b$ axis normal to this plane. It is equally appropriate for class $2/m$. The three classes 2, $m$, and $2/m$ constitute the monoclinic system (Fig. 33).

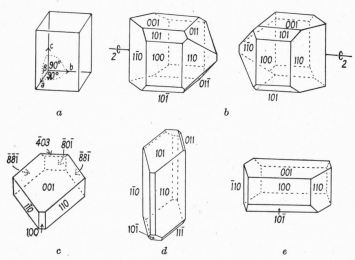

FIG. 33. Monoclinic system. (See also Fig. 26.) $a$. Unit cell type. $b$. Left- and right-handed tartaric acid. Class 2. $c$. 2,4,6 Tribromobenzonitrile. Class $m$. $d$. $p$-Dinitrobenzene. Class $2/m$. $e$. $(CH_3COO)_2Pb.3H_2O$. Class $2/m$.

It would have been better if the unique axis were called $c$, to bring the nomenclature into line with that of tetragonal, hexagonal, and the polar orthorhombic crystals, which all have their unique axes labelled $c$; but the $b$ convention for monoclinic crystals became firmly established in the nineteenth century. However, the International Union of Crystallography decided in 1951 to approve the alternative setting with the unique axis labelled $c$, and in *International Tables for X-ray Crystallography* (1952) both settings are recognized; the $c$ convention is called the 'first setting', and the $b$ convention the 'second setting'. It was agreed that the second setting should be accepted as standard for morphological and structural crystallographic studies, but that the first setting can be used where there is a special reason for this alternative.

*Orthorhombic (sometimes called rhombic)*. In class $mm$ ($= 2mm$) the lattice points lie in planes normal to the twofold axis; they also lie in the mutually perpendicular planes of symmetry $m$ which are parallel to the twofold axis. The lattice is thus entirely rectangular, and the unit cell is a rectangular box with unequal edges. The twofold axis is usually called $c$; of the other two, the longer is called $b$.

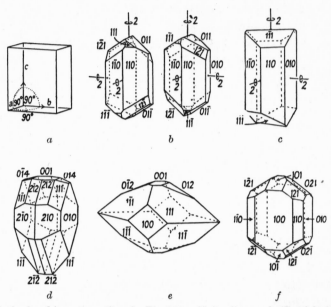

FIG. 34. Orthorhombic system. (See also Fig. 25.) $a$. Unit cell type. $b$. $(H.COO)_2Sr.2H_2O$. Class 222. Left- and right-handed crystals. $c$. 1-Brom, 2-hydroxy-naphthalene. Class 222. $d$. Picric acid. Class $mm$. $e$. Oxalic acid. Class $mmm$. $f$. $C_2Br_6$. Class $mmm$.

The same type of unit cell is appropriate for classes 222 and $mmm$ ($= 2/m\ 2/m\ 2/m$); the cell edges lie along the twofold axes. Donnay (1943) recommends that the longest shall be called $b$ and the shortest $c$. When axes are chosen on morphological grounds the axis of the principal prism zone is labelled $c$, while $b$ is the longer of the other two. The three classes $mm$, 222, and $mmm$ constitute the orthorhombic system (Fig. 34).

*Hexagonal and trigonal.* In many crystals having a single three- or sixfold rotation axis or inversion axis the unique axis is taken as one of the unit cell edges, and this axis is called $c$. In all these crystals there are, in a plane normal to the principal axis, three equivalent directions which are at 120° to each other (see p. 27). Any two of these may be called $a$ and $b$. The unit cell thus has a diamond-shaped base, with $a$ and $b$ edges at 120° to each other and equal in length; $c$ is perpendicular to $a$ and $b$ and different in length.

The twelve classes which may be referred to such a unit cell are : 3, 3$m$, 32 ; $\bar{3}$, $\bar{3}m$ ; $\bar{6}$, $\bar{6}m2$ ; 6, 6/$m$, 6$mm$, 62, 6/$mmm$. For examples, see Fig. 35.

It is often more convenient to refer some trigonal crystals to a rhombohedral cell which has three equal axes making equal angles not 90° with each other. The three equal rhombohedral axes are equally inclined to the $c$ axis of the hexagonal-type cell.

*Tetragonal.* In all crystals having a single fourfold rotation axis or inversion axis there are, normal to this unique direction, two equivalent

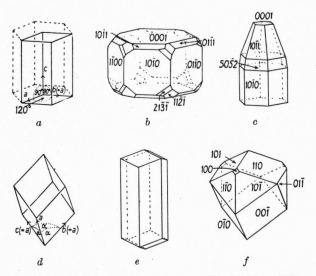

FIG. 35. Hexagonal and trigonal systems. (See also Figs. 24, 27, and 29.) *a*. Hexagonal-type unit cell. *b*. Apatite, $3Ca_3(PO_4)_2.CaF_2$. Class 6/$m$. *c*. Hydrocinchonine sulphate hydrate, $(C_{19}H_{24}ON_2)_2.H_2SO_4.11H_2O$. Class 6$m$. *d*. Rhombohedral-type unit cell. *e*. A habit of calcite, $CaCO_3$. Class $\bar{3}m$. *f*. $KBrO_3$. Class 3$m$.

directions perpendicular to each other. The unit cell is thus entirely rectangular, with two edges ($a$ and $b$) equal in length, and the remaining edge (the fourfold axis) different in length. The seven classes of the tetragonal system are : $\bar{4}$, $\bar{4}2m$ ; 4, 4/$m$, 4$mm$, 42, and 4/$mmm$ (Fig. 36).

*Cubic* (*sometimes called isometric, or tesseral*). All crystals having four secondary threefold axes have three mutually perpendicular directions all equivalent to each other. The unit cell is thus a cube, the secondary threefold axes being the cube diagonals. The five classes of the cubic system are : 23, $m3$ (= 2/$m3$), $\bar{4}3m$, 43 (= 432), and $m3m$ (= 4/$m$ 3 2/$m$). Examples are shown in Fig. 37.

The various names used formerly for the crystal classes are to be

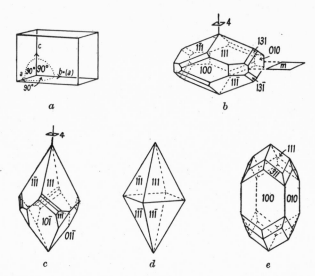

FIG. 36. Tetragonal system. (See also Fig. 28.) *a*. Unit cell type. *b*. Phloroglucinol diethyl ether. Class 4/*m*. *c*. Wulfenite, PbMoO$_4$. Class 4. *d*. Anatase, TiO$_2$. Class 4/*mmm*. *e*. Zircon, ZrSiO$_4$. Class 4/*mmm*.

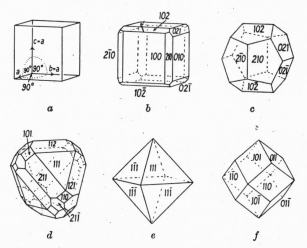

FIG. 37. Cubic system. (See also Figs. 16–22.) *a*. Unit cell type. *b* and *c*. Two habits of pyrites, FeS$_2$. Class *m*3. *d*. Tetrahedrite, Cu$_3$SbS$_3$. Class $\bar{4}3m$. *e*. Spinel, MgAl$_2$O$_4$. Class *m*3*m*. *f*. Almandine (Garnet), Fe$_3$Al$_2$(SiO$_4$)$_3$. Class *m*3*m*.

found, collected in a table of concordances, in *International Tables for X-ray Crystallography* (1952).

The essential symmetries and unit cell types for the different crystal systems are summarized in Table I.

## TABLE I

| System | Essential symmetry | Unit cell |
|---|---|---|
| Triclinic. | No planes, no axes. | Angles $\alpha$, $\beta$, and $\gamma$ unequal and not 90°. Edges $a$, $b$, and $c$ unequal. |
| Monoclinic. | One twofold axis, or one plane. | $\alpha = \gamma = 90°$. $\beta$ not 90°. $a$, $b$, and $c$ unequal. |
| Orthorhombic. | Three mutually perpendicular twofold axes, or two planes intersecting in a twofold axis. | $\alpha = \beta = \gamma = 90°$. $a$, $b$, and $c$ unequal. |
| Trigonal and Hexagonal. | One threefold axis, or one sixfold axis. | (1) $\alpha = \beta = 90°$. $\gamma = 120°$. $a = b$. $c$ different from $a$ and $b$. (2) $\alpha = \beta = \gamma$, not 90°. $a = b = c$. |
| Tetragonal. | One fourfold axis or fourfold inversion axis. | $\alpha = \beta = \gamma = 90°$. $a = b$. $c$ different from $a$ and $b$. |
| Cubic. | Four threefold axes. | $\alpha = \beta = \gamma = 90°$. $a = b = c$. |

**Deduction of a possible unit cell shape and point-group symmetry from interfacial angles.** When all the interfacial angles of a crystal have been measured on the goniometer, and the symmetries deduced by the contemplation of stereographic projections, the procedure in deducing the relative lengths of the unit cell edges and the angles between them follows from the contents of the foregoing notes. In most classes the directions of the edges are prescribed by the symmetry elements; when they are not, the principle of simplest indices is called in to indicate the probable directions. In some of the tetragonal and hexagonal classes there are two sets of secondary axes or symmetry planes, providing alternative positions for the secondary ($a$ and $b$) edges of the unit cell; the principle of simplest indices is again called in, but its verdict will not necessarily be correct; X-ray diffraction photographs are necessary to settle such questions. In certain other tetragonal and hexagonal classes there is a single set of secondary twofold axes which are naturally chosen as probable unit cell edges. But this again is not necessarily correct: in some crystals the unit cell edges are parallel to twofold axes, while in others they bisect the twofold axes. The morphological axes are, however, entirely adequate for morphological purposes; and the morphological axial ratio $c/a$ is related in a simple way to the axial ratio of the unit cell—usually by a factor of $\sqrt{2}$ in the tetragonal system and $\sqrt{3}$ in the hexagonal system.

Attention has already been drawn to the fact that the idealized shape of a crystal may exhibit a symmetry higher than that of the arrangement of atoms. Sodium chlorate crystals when grown rapidly in pure solution are cubes, the symmetry of which is holohedral ($m3m$); when sodium thiosulphate is present in the solution the crystals grow as tetrahedra (symmetry $\bar{4}3m$); only when grown slowly in pure solution do the crystals exhibit the symmetry of the atomic arrangement—that of the enantiomorphous class 23. In this case, and in many others, the true point-group symmetry was known before the atomic arrangement was discovered by X-ray methods; but in the case of sodium nitrite, $NaNO_2$, which is orthorhombic, the habit of the crystals gives no evidence that the symmetry is other than holohedral ($mmm$), yet the X-ray diffraction

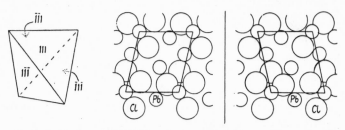

Fig. 38. Left, bisphenoid of $PbCl_2$. Centre and right, arrangements of atoms on 111 and $\bar{1}$11. The atoms depicted are those which lie on, or not far below, the plane of the corner atoms.

pattern leaves no doubt that the atomic arrangement has the point-group symmetry $mm$—the polar class of the orthorhombic system. (See Chapter IX.)

The opposite may occur if crystal growth takes place in a solution containing particular impurities. Miles (1931) showed that when lead chloride crystals, whose internal structure has the orthorhombic holo-hedral symmetry $mmm$, grow in a solution containing dextrine, they form bisphenoids, the symmetry of which is 222. It seems curious that a holohedral crystal should in any circumstances assume a hemihedral (holoaxial) shape. The reason is that the substance in solution which modifies the shape of the lead chloride crystals is itself asymmetric, and only left-handed molecules are present. Consider the arrangement of atoms at a particular level on the 111 plane of the lead chloride crystal (Fig. 38). This plane-pattern has no symmetry, and if we call the arrangement on 111 left-handed, the arrangement on $\bar{1}$11 is right-handed. Now, modification of crystal habit by dissolved impurities is due to adsorption of the impurity molecules on specific crystal faces, this adsorption reducing the rate of growth of these faces. If asymmetric left-handed molecules are present in the solution, and these are adsorbed on the 111 face, they are not likely to fit well on the $\bar{1}$11 face; conse-quently the rate of growth of 111 (as well as that of the equivalent faces

$\bar{1}\bar{1}1$, $\bar{1}1\bar{1}$, and $1\bar{1}\,\bar{1}$) is reduced, while that of $\bar{1}11$ (and $\bar{1}\,\bar{1}\,\bar{1}$, $11\bar{1}$, and $1\bar{1}1$) is not, and the resulting crystal is entirely bounded by the first-mentioned set of planes and thus has a hemihedral form. To produce an effect of this sort, molecules of the dissolved impurity need not be entirely without symmetry, but they must lack planes of symmetry, inversion axes, and a centre of symmetry.

Such effects are probably rare, and when crystals are grown from solutions of high purity there is little danger of the occurrence of shapes which are misleading in this way. Nevertheless, the knowledge that such phenomena can occur prompts caution in accepting morphological evidence on internal symmetry when the conditions of growth are incompletely known (see p. 269). For further examples of discrepancies between morphological and structural symmetry, see Kleber (1955/6).

The shapes and orientations of the etching pits formed in crystal faces by appropriate solvents are also used as clues to internal symmetry (Miers, 1929). Here again, solvent molecules having only axial symmetry must be avoided, as they may produce misleading effects, for reasons similar to those given in the case of crystal shape (Herzfeld and Hettich, 1926, 1927).

The use of shape-symmetry and other morphological features in the study of the internal structure of crystals will be considered further in Part 2 of this book (Chapters VII and VIII). Here we are concerned with crystal shapes in so far as they afford evidence for the purpose of identification.

**Identification by shape.** When a substance which it is desired to identify consists of well-formed single (that is, not aggregated) crystals of sufficient size to be handled, the interfacial angles may be measured on the goniometer; it is then possible to look up the morphological information on likely substances either in Groth's *Chemische Krystallographie* or in papers scattered through the literature (chiefly chemical and mineralogical journals). An indirect method of this sort is, however, not always entirely satisfactory: possible substances may be overlooked. The desire for a direct method has led to attempts to devise a system in which morphological characteristics are measured and the results referred to a classified index. Barker (1930) devised a system in which certain 'key' angles of the measured unknown crystal are looked up in an index in which substances are arranged in order of the magnitudes of these key angles. The selection of the key angles for an unknown crystal involves the indexing of all the faces on the crystal, and thus implies the deduction of a possible unit cell shape. Barker does not use the term 'unit cell', and does not claim for his system anything more than that it is a consistent scheme for the morphological description and identification of crystals; but the term 'unit cell' will be retained here, since the treatment in this book is entirely based on this conception.

For the purpose of identification the fact that the 'morphological unit cell' does not always coincide with the true unit cell does not matter, provided that all crystals of the same species give the same morphological cell in the hands of different investigators. The problem is to devise rules which ensure this, even in the triclinic system, where none of the axial directions are fixed by symmetry. The rules devised by Barker, together with some additions by Porter and Spiller (1939), constitute a sound system. The rules will not be described here in detail; but we may observe that the system is based on a thorough-going acceptance of the principle of simplicity of indices, and that a definition of simplicity is given—all indices composed only of 0's and 1's being regarded as equally simple, and all others complex. Another point is that class-symmetry within a particular system is ignored; this is necessary in view of the frequency with which crystals display in their shapes too high a point-group symmetry (this being in some cases variable with growth conditions). An index of crystals based on the Barker system has been published (Porter and Spiller, 1951, 1956).

One limitation of morphological methods has already been mentioned: some crystals, especially those grown rapidly, are entirely bounded by faces parallel to the unit cell sides, and measurements of the interfacial angles of such crystals can only give the angles between the axes, not their relative lengths (except where symmetry indicates that two or more axes are equal in length, as in the cubic, tetragonal, hexagonal, and trigonal systems). Another limitation arises from the fact that all crystals belonging to the cubic system have the same shape of unit cell, and therefore cannot be identified by purely morphological methods. It is true that different crystals belonging to the cubic system often have different bounding faces, some growing normally as octahedra, others as tetrahedra, and so on; but there are many different crystals of octahedral habit, and many others of tetrahedral habit. In addition, it must be remembered that the shape may be completely changed by the presence of certain impurities in the solution. Thus, shape is of very little use for identification in the case of crystals belonging to the cubic system.

It is not intended to describe purely morphological methods of identification in any more detail in this book, for we are concerned with the crystals found in the average experimental or industrial product, and for these crystals the practical limitations imposed by small size or irregular shape are often sufficient to rule out goniometric methods. With regard to size, it should be realized that crystals as small as one- or two-tenths of a millimetre in each direction can be handled and measured on the goniometer. Generally speaking, however, crystals suitable for goniometric measurements are either specially selected mineral specimens or crystals specially grown for the purpose. Not all crystals can be grown under laboratory conditions to a size suitable for handling; very spar- ingly soluble substances, for in- stance, might require a geological age for growth to such a size. Moreover, it may be desired to identify the products of chemical reactions in which it is not possible to prescribe suitable crystalliza- tion conditions.

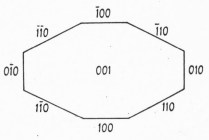

FIG. 39. Orthorhombic crystal lying on (001) on microscope slide.

For well-formed microscopic crystals the scope of purely morpholo- gical methods is usually limited to qualitative observations which may enable us to deduce the type of unit cell. Sometimes it may be possible to measure interfacial angles approximately, but only when the crystals lie in such a way that the two faces in question are both parallel to the line of vision; for instance, if an orthogonal crystal is lying on the slide on its (001) face (Fig. 39), the angle between (110) and (010) faces could be measured by bringing them successively parallel to the eyepiece cross-wire, and reading off the angle through which the slide or the eyepiece has been turned. This would give us an approximate value for the axial ratio. For very many crystals, however, interfacial angles cannot be measured; we may be able to conclude that a crystal probably has a tetragonal or a monoclinic unit cell, but we cannot deduce the relative dimensions of the cell.

Further, it may often be desired to identify poorly formed crystals such as needle-like crystals without definite faces, or skeletal growths, or even completely irregular fragments. This can only be achieved by measuring some properties of the crystal material itself, properties which are independent of the shape of the crystals. Of such properties, by far the most important and the most convenient for measurement are the optical properties, especially the refractive indices. An elementary account of the optical properties of crystals will be found in Chapter III.

Before leaving the subject of crystal shape, there are a few other morphological features which are sometimes encountered and must be mentioned briefly.

**Spiral growth layers.** It has been mentioned earlier that close examination of the faces of some crystals discloses a step formation, and

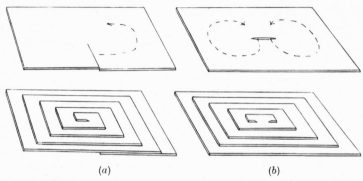

(a)                              (b)

FIG. 40.   Growth of thin crystals from (a) a single screw disclocation, (b) two screw dislocations of opposite sign.

very often a series of concentric layers. On certain crystals, however, the layer system is seen to be, not concentric, but spiral; in fact, it should be described not as a series of layers but as one continuous layer in spiral form. This feature, although it has been seen on a few crystals (notably cadmium iodide, $CdI_2$) under the optical microscope, has been revealed more clearly and on a much smaller scale under the electron microscope. Crystals of the straight-chain paraffin hydrocarbons often show it particularly clearly, and a good example is given in Plate II. Most of the crystals on which spiral layers have been seen are those which grow in the form of very thin plates, and it appears that at an early stage an extremely thin crystal suffers what is called a screw dislocation by, so to speak, being half-torn; the crystal is perhaps too thin to support its own weight, or perhaps the molecules settle down in incorrect positions and get progressively out of line; the upper part then grows over the lower, and a continuation of this leads to the spiral step structure (Fig. 40 a). The chief interest of this type of surface structure is that it throws some light on the process of growth, at any rate in certain types of crystal. The chance of formation of a nucleus of an entirely new layer on an atomically perfect surface is small, unless the supersaturation of the solution is high, and if crystals like those of the paraffin hydrocarbons had to wait on the formation of new layers they would remain exceedingly thin; the occurrence of screw dislocations makes it possible for growth to continue even if new layers are not started, and so the crystals, though still thin plates, are thicker than they would otherwise be. Even concentric layers, such as those seen on most crystals, can originate in two opposite screw dislocations, as in Fig. 40 $b$; but not all concentric layers are formed in this way: on some

$a$ $b$ $c$

FIG. 41. Twinning. $a$. Gypsum, $CaSO_4.2H_2O$. Two individuals joined at a well-marked plane (100). $b$. 'Interpenetration' twin of fluorspar, $CaF_2$. One individual is rotated 60° with respect to the other. The junction surface in such twins is often very irregular. $c$. 'Mimetic' twin of ammonium sulphate, $(NH_4)_2SO_4$. Six individuals, with three different orientations (numbered).

crystals, such as the protein crystal in Plate II, monomolecular layers without screw dislocations can be seen; they probably grew in conditions of high supersaturation.

**Twinning.** Two or more crystals of the same species are sometimes found joined together at a definite mutual orientation, this orientation of the individual crystals being constant in different examples of any one species. Such crystals are said to be twinned. Certain species show this phenomenon frequently, and some species invariably. The most frequent type of twinning is that of calcium sulphate dihydrate (gypsum), which is often found in the form shown in Fig. 41 $a$. The two crystals appear to be joined at the 100 plane. At the junction there is presumably a sheet of atoms common to the two individuals; when the crystal nucleus was formed, two lattices were probably built by deposition on opposite sides of this common sheet of atoms.

Sometimes twinned crystals appear to be interpenetrating, as in the calcium fluoride twin illustrated in Fig. 41 $b$. Here we may imagine (in the crystal nucleus) a common 111 sheet of atoms, the symmetry of which is trigonal; the crystal on one side of it is rotated 60° with respect to the one on the other side. The twin plane is not always respected during subsequent growth; one individual may encroach on the domain of the other, so that the junction surface in the final crystal is irregular.

There are many other types of composite shape which arise as the result of twinning; for further examples, see the textbooks of Miers and Dana.

Twinning always involves the addition of a plane or an axis of symmetry, and the symmetry of the composite shape may thus be higher than that of an individual crystal of the same species. When the composite shape has no re-entrant angles it may appear deceptively like that of a single crystal of higher symmetry; thus, ammonium sulphate crystals grown in solutions containing ferric ions form hexagonal prisms (Fig. 41 c). The atomic arrangement in ammonium sulphate crystals has orthorhombic symmetry, but the conjunction of six sectors with three different orientations (opposite sectors having the same lattice orientation) gives rise to apparent hexagonal symmetry. The same thing occurs in aragonite, the orthorhombic form of calcium carbonate. (For the atomic structure on the twin plane see Bragg, 1924 a.) The occurrence of such mimetic twinning may cause confusion if its existence is not realized. The study of such phenomena is greatly assisted by the use of the polarizing microscope; this is dealt with in the next chapter.

In some crystals the energy of addition of material to a crystal face in such a way as to start a new twinned individual may be almost the same as that of carrying on a single-crystal structure; frequent changes may thus occur, giving rise to a fine lamellar 'repeated-twinning' structure. Here again the polarizing microscope may reveal at once the composite character of the structure.

**Cleavage.** The cohesion of crystals is not the same in all directions. It may be very strong in some directions and very weak in others; so much so that many crystals, on crushing or grinding, break almost exclusively along certain planes. The most striking of familiar examples is mica, a potassium aluminium silicate mineral which readily cleaves into thin sheets. Similarly crystals of calcite, the rhombohedral variety of calcium carbonate, break into small rhombohedra; sodium chloride crystals tend to break along planes parallel to the cube faces; calcium fluoride (fluorspar) crystals cleave along the octahedral planes. Minerals like chrysotile ('asbestos') have more than one cleavage parallel to the same crystal direction and very readily split into fibres.

Cleavage planes are always planes of high reticular density of atomic or molecular packing and large interplanar spacing, the cohesion being strong in the plane and weak at right angles to the plane. Cleavage planes thus have simple indices, and in fact are often parallel to the principal faces of the crystal; thus calcite, when precipitated in the laboratory, often grows in the form of simple rhombohedra whose faces are parallel to the cleavage planes. But this statement, like the principle of simplest indices for the faces of growing crystals, is only a broad generalization, not a rigid rule. An exception, for instance, is shown by calcium fluoride, which usually grows as cubes but cleaves along octahedral faces (Wooster, N., 1932). Another is penta-erythritol, $C(CH_2OH)_4$, which grows as tetragonal bipyramids but has basal cleavage (001).

**Polymorphism.** Some substances form, under different conditions, crystals of quite different internal structure; they are then said to be polymorphic. The different structures are different packings of the same building units. Sometimes one particular structure can only exist within a definite temperature range, and if the temperature goes outside this range there is a rapid reorganization of the building units (atoms, molecules, or ions) to form a different arrangement. Sulphur, for instance, forms an orthorhombic arrangement at room temperature and a monoclinic arrangement above 95° C. An extreme example is ammonium nitrate, which exists in five different crystalline forms, each of which changes to another at a definite temperature. Other substances exist in two or more forms which are apparently equally stable at the same temperature. Calcium carbonate, for instance, occurs in a rhombohedral form, calcite, and an orthorhombic form, aragonite, both of which have existed in the earth's crust for geological ages. Actually calcite is probably slightly more stable than aragonite at all temperatures, but the atomic motions in aragonite crystals at ordinary temperatures are so small that no reorganization is possible. There is also a much less stable form, $\mu$-$CaCO_3$ or vaterite, which is apparently hexagonal.

**Isomorphism and mixed crystal formation.** The atomic arrangement in crystals of ammonium sulphate, $(NH_4)_2SO_4$, is entirely analogous to that found in potassium sulphate ($K_2SO_4$) crystals, the ammonium ion playing the same role in the structure as the potassium ion. The unit cell dimensions of the two crystals are very nearly the same, and the shapes of crystals grown under similar conditions are almost the same. Accurate goniometric measurements would be necessary to distinguish between the two crystals by morphological methods. Such crystals are said to be isomorphous. The reason for this close resemblance is that ammonium and potassium ions are very similar in size and chemical character; they can therefore fit into the same arrangement with sulphate ions. When the ionic sizes are closely similar, they can replace each other indiscriminately in the lattice; a mixed solution of ammonium and potassium sulphates deposits crystals which may

contain any proportions of the two substances, and which have unit
cell dimensions intermediate between those of the pure components.
Such crystals are called 'mixed crystals' or 'crystalline solid solutions'.

Not all isomorphous substances form mixed crystals. Calcite ($CaCO_3$)
and sodium nitrate ($NaNO_3$) form similar atomic arrangements, their
unit cells are both rhombohedra of very similar dimensions, and also the
corresponding ions are closely similar in size; but they do not form

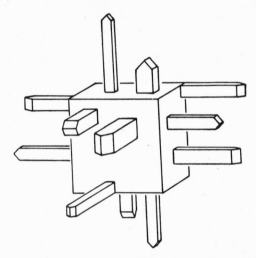

FIG. 42. Oriented overgrowths of urea on ammonium chloride.

mixed crystals: the reason presumably is that their solubilities in water
are extremely different.

**Oriented overgrowth.** Isomorphous substances which do not form
mixed crystals may do the next best thing; one crystal may grow on
the other in parallel orientation. Sodium nitrate grows on calcite in this
way. Isomorphism is not, however, a necessary condition for oriented
overgrowth; it is sufficient if the arrangement of atoms on a particular
plane of one crystal is similar, in type and dimensions, to the arrangement on one of the planes of the other crystal; the two structures may
be in other respects completely different from each other (Royer, 1926,
1933). Thus, tetragonal urea, $O=C{<}_{NH_2}^{NH_2}$, grows with its 001 plane
precisely oriented in contact with the cube faces of ammonium chloride,
$NH_4Cl$, Fig. 42; the two structures are completely different except for
a formal and dimensional similarity on the planes in question (Bunn,
1933).

**Spherulitic growth.** Some substances, under certain conditions, crystallize not as single crystals or twinned combinations, but as aggregates of large numbers of crystals radiating from a point; such aggregates are known as spherulites. Some spherulites have an obviously radial, hedgehog-like appearance: individual needle-like crystals, which may even show normal prism faces, can be seen radiating from a centre where evidently a number of crystal nuclei formed. An example is sodium sesquicarbonate, $Na_2CO_3.NaHCO_3.2H_2O$. In others, individual needle crystals cannot be seen, though the radial character is usually indicated by a spherical external shape, by radial markings, or even sometimes by concentric circular markings. The absence of very specific morphological features limits the scope of study of such growths; it is necessary to observe their optical properties or to resort to X-ray methods to study their structure or to identify them effectively. Spherulites are well known in mineralogy; and in the products of inorganic chemical reactions, even a substance like calcium carbonate is sometimes found in spherulitic form. Among organic substances, good examples are cholesteryl acetate and 1,1,1-trichloro-2,2-bis ($p$-chlorophenyl) ethane (DDT). This type of crystal growth is very common in high polymers like polythene and nylon, and may indeed be fairly called the normal mode of crystallization of such substances (Bunn, 1953).

Of the morphological phenomena mentioned in the last few paragraphs, that of twinning is likely to be of most frequent value in identification problems, but all the phenomena are significant from the point of view of crystal structure and the relation between internal structure and growth characteristics. The subject of crystal morphology in relation to internal structure will not, however, be pursued further at present; it will be taken up again in Chapters VII and VIII. For the present, we shall continue our consideration of the problem of the identification of microscopic crystals; we pass on to discuss crystal optics, the relation between optical properties and crystal shape and symmetry, and the determination of refractive indices and other optical characteristics under the microscope.

# III

# THE OPTICAL PROPERTIES OF CRYSTALS

THE physical properties of crystals, such as refractive index, absorption of light, and conduction of heat and electricity, are in general not the same for all crystal directions; in other words, a three-dimensional graph of any characteristic showing its magnitude for all directions is not, except in certain special cases, a sphere, but a less symmetrical figure, owing to the fact that on passing through a crystal the sequence of atoms encountered depends on the direction taken. The type of shape of the three-dimensional graph is not the same for all characteristics and naturally varies with crystal symmetry, but one generalization that can be made is that the figure must necessarily exhibit a symmetry at least as high as that of the atomic pattern in the crystal. The symmetry of the figure may be higher than that of the atomic pattern (just as the shape of a crystal may have a higher symmetry than that of the atomic pattern), but it cannot be lower. If there is a plane of symmetry in the atomic pattern, then there must be a corresponding plane of symmetry in the figure; if there is an axis of symmetry or a centre of symmetry in the atomic pattern, then these also are necessarily exhibited by the figure.

In this chapter we are concerned chiefly with the refractive indices of crystals and other phenomena depending on the refractive indices. The absorption of light and the rotation of the plane of polarization are also considered briefly. The treatment of crystal optics followed in this book is restricted to those aspects which are most generally useful for purposes of identification or structure determination. The finer points of crystal optics, and aspects which are of physical rather than chemical interest, may be pursued in more comprehensive textbooks, such as Miers's *Mineralogy*, Tutton's *Crystallography and Practical Crystal Measurement*, Hartshorne and Stuart's *Crystals and the Polarizing Microscope*, Wooster's *Crystal Physics*, Preston's *Theory of Light*, Winchell's *Elements of Optical Mineralogy*, and Wahlstrom's *Petrographic Mineralogy*.

The refractive index of a solid is usually defined in terms of Snell's law, which states that when a ray of light changes its direction on passing from one medium to another the ratio of the sine of the angle of incidence to that of the angle of refraction is a constant; this constant is the refractive index of the second medium with respect to the first. For the consideration of the optical properties of crystals, however, it is better to think of the refractive index, not as a measure of the bending of a ray of light when it passes from air into the solid, but as a measure of the velocity of light in the solid: the refractive index of a solid with respect to air is the ratio of the velocity of light in air to the velocity in the solid. By thinking in this way we are focusing our attention on a particular direction in the crystal.

The first point to be made is that in a crystal the refractive index depends not on the direction in which the electromagnetic waves are travelling but on the direction of the electrical disturbances transverse to the line of travel—the 'vibration direction'. We have to consider the shape of the graph connecting refractive index with vibration direction for each crystal system, and the methods available for measuring the refractive indices of crystals in different vibration directions.

**Cubic crystals.** Crystals with cubic unit cells have the same atomic arrangement along all three axial directions; consequently all the properties of the crystal are identical along these three directions. The optical properties are found to be the same, not only along these three directions, but also for all other directions. An attempt at an explanation of this would take us too deeply into the electromagnetic theory of light; we shall therefore simply accept the fact that a cubic crystal is optically isotropic—it behaves towards light just like a piece of glass; its refractive index is the same for all vibration directions of the light. To identify a cubic crystal it is usually sufficient to measure its one refractive index.

**Measurement of refractive index under the microscope.** The measurement of the refractive index of an isotropic transparent solid under the microscope is extremely simple. The principle is to keep a set of liquids of known refractive indices, and to find which liquid has the same (or nearly the same) refractive index as the solid in question. When the solid particles are immersed in this liquid they become invisible; the light, in passing from liquid to solid and from solid to liquid, is not refracted, and consequently the edges of the particles cannot be seen; as far as the light is concerned, the whole complex is a homogeneous medium.

The procedure is to immerse particles of the solid in a drop of liquid of known refractive index on a microscope slide, cover the drop with a thin cover-glass, and observe the particles, using a low or moderate magnification ($\frac{1}{2}$-inch objective and 4 or 10 times eyepiece, for instance) and parallel or nearly parallel light. If the particles show up plainly, their refractive index must differ considerably from that of the liquid; other liquids of different refractive indices are then tried, until a liquid is found in which the particles are invisible or very nearly so. The search for the right liquid is not as laborious as one might suppose, because it is possible, by observing certain optical effects, to tell whether the refractive index of the liquid is higher or lower than that of the crystal; and with experience, one can estimate roughly how much higher or lower. These optical effects are illustrated in Plate III, in which $a$ shows cubic crystals of sodium chlorate (refractive index $n = 1\cdot515$) immersed in a liquid of $n = 1\cdot480$. If the crystals are first of all focused sharply, and if then the objective is raised slightly (by means of the fine adjustment of the microscope), a line of light (the 'Becke line') is seen inside the edges of each crystal; as the objective is raised more and more, the line contracts farther and farther within the boundaries of the crystal. This is what happens when the refractive index of the liquid is less than that of the crystal; but if the reverse is true, as in Plate III $b$, the Becke line appears round the outside of the crystal when the objective is raised and expands as the objective is raised farther. The shape of the particles does not matter; the Becke line always follows the outline of the particle; the determination of the refractive index of irregular fragments of crystals, or of particles of glass, is just as easy as that of well-formed crystals.

The simplest way of regarding the Becke line effect, as well as the best way of remembering which way the line moves, is to think of a particle as a crude lens which, if it has a refractive index higher than that of the medium surrounding it, tends to focus the light at some point above it (Fig. 43 $a$); when the objective is raised it is focused on a plane $PP$ above the particle, and in this plane the refracted light waves occupy a smaller area than they do in a plane nearer the particle, and thus the boundary line of light moves inwards as the objective is raised. If the refractive index of the particle is lower than that of the surrounding liquid, it will have the opposite effect and act as a negative lens (Fig. 43 $b$); consequently on raising the objective the boundary line of light expands. Strictly speaking, the phenomenon is due to diffraction of light at the edges of the particle; for a theoretical treatment of it as a Fresnel diffraction effect, see Faust (1955).

By observing this effect and trying various liquids in turn, it is possible to find in a few minutes a liquid in which the particles are nearly invisible. In practice, it is convenient to keep a set of liquids with refractive indices differing by 0·005. Refractive index values are nearly always given for sodium $D$ light, and the liquids are therefore standardized for this wavelength. (For suitable liquids, see Appendix 1.) Usually, of course, the refractive index of the particles is found to lie between those of two of these liquids; its value can be estimated from the magnitude of the Becke line effects in the two liquids. In this way the refractive index of isotropic particles can be found within limits of ±0·002. It must be mentioned that solid particles are seldom quite invisible in liquids, because the dispersion of the liquid (variation of

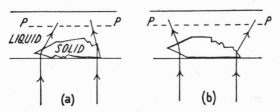

FIG. 43. The 'Becke line' effect.

refractive index with colour of light) is usually different from that of the solid; consequently, if the refractive indices of solid and liquid are equal for yellow light, they are not equal for red or blue light, and therefore in white light, coloured Becke line fringes will be seen round the edges of the crystals. For this reason it is sometimes suggested that monochromatic light should be used for refractive index determinations; in practice, however, sufficient accuracy for identification purposes is usually obtainable by the use of white light, which is also more pleasant in use.

**Tetragonal, hexagonal, and trigonal crystals. Preliminary.** The simple method just described is applicable as it stands only to isotropic solids, that is, to glasses and amorphous solids in general, and to crystals belonging to the cubic system. In all other crystals the refractive index varies with the direction of vibration of the light in the crystal; the optical phenomena are more complex, and it is necessary to disentangle them.

If tetragonal crystals of monammonium phosphate, $NH_4H_2PO_4$ (Fig. 44), lying on the microscope slide on their prism faces, are examined in the way already described with ordinary unpolarized light, it is not possible to find any liquid in which they are nearly invisible. In liquids with refractive indices below 1·479 it is clear that the crystals have a higher index than the liquids; in liquids with indices above 1·525 it is equally clear that the crystals have lower indices than the liquids; but in liquids with indices between 1·479 and 1·525 confusing effects are seen—Becke lines can be seen both inside and outside the crystal edges. This is because the crystal resolves light into two components vibrating in different planes,† and the refractive indices of the two components are unequal; the crystal thus 'shows' two different indices at the same time.

In order to observe one refractive index at a time, we must evidently use polarized light—light vibrating in one plane only—and adjust its plane of vibration to coincide with one of the planes of vibration in the crystal itself. In the polarizing microscope, plane polarized light is obtained by means of a Nicol prism or Polaroid sheet placed between the light source and the microscope slide; it is usually located immediately below the condenser which concentrates light on the slide. The plane of vibration can be adjusted with respect to the crystal either by rotating the polarizer or (on other types of microscope) by rotating the microscope slide; the two cross-wires in the eyepiece indicate planes parallel and perpendicular to the plane of vibration of the light transmitted by the polarizer. If a crystal of monammonium phosphate is immersed in a liquid of refractive index 1·500, and observed in light vibrating along the fourfold axis, the Becke line effect (Plate III d) shows that the index of the crystal is lower than that of the liquid; if the polarizer is turned through 90°, the index of the crystal is seen to be higher than that of the liquid (Plate III c). (At intermediate positions, confusing effects are seen; Becke lines appear both inside and outside the crystal outline.)

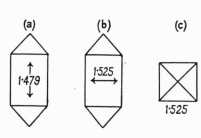

Fig. 44. Refractive indices of monammonium phosphate, $NH_4H_2PO_4$. Arrows indicate vibration directions.

If now we immerse the crystals in various liquids, and observe each crystal in light vibrating parallel to its fourfold axis, we observe consistent effects as in the case of isotropic solids in ordinary light, and we find the refractive index is 1·479. If we use light vibrating perpendicular to the fourfold axis of the crystal, we again observe consistent effects and this time find the refractive index to be 1·525 (Fig. 44 a and b).

That tetragonal crystals should have one refractive index for light

† The plane of vibration is the plane containing the direction of propagation and the direction of the electrical disturbances associated with the waves (the 'electric vector').

PLATE III

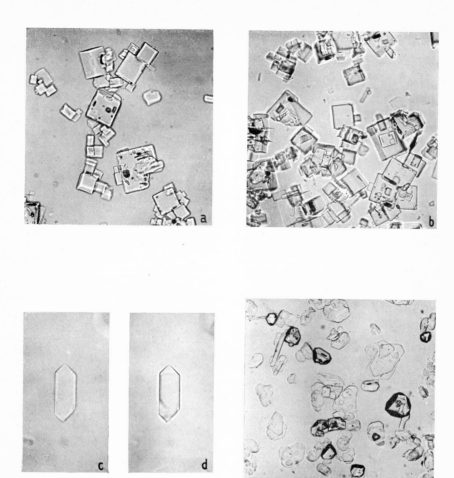

*a*. Crystals of sodium chlorate, NaClO₃, in liquid of refractive index 1·48; objective raised.
*b*. The same substance in liquid of refractive index 1·55; objective raised. *c*. Crystal of
monammonium phosphate, NH₄H₂PO₄, in liquid of refractive index 1·500; polarized
light, vibration direction horizontal; objective raised. *d*. The same, vibration direction
vertical; objective raised. *e*. Mixture NaBr.2H₂O and NaBrO₃ in liquid of refractive
index 1·54. The NaBrO₃ crystals show up in relief

vibrating along the fourfold axis and a different index for vibration directions perpendicular to this axis is only to be expected, since the arrangement of atoms along the $c$ axis (the fourfold axis) is different from that along the $a$ and $b$ axes. The same is true for hexagonal and trigonal crystals; the refractive index for light vibrating along the unique sixfold or threefold axis is different from the index for light vibrating in directions perpendicular to this axis. The only new and perhaps unexpected phenomenon to be grasped is that the crystal actually resolves the light into two components vibrating at right angles to each other, and that the crystal therefore 'shows' two different refractive indices simultaneously except when the incident light is polarized and vibrates along one of the crystal's vibration directions.

**Use of crossed polarizers. Extinction directions. Interference colours.** To set the polarizer's vibration plane parallel to one of the crystal's vibration planes is simple for crystals such as those already considered. But suppose we have crystals which are irregular fragments, so that there are no edges to guide us? The vibration planes of such crystals are found by making use of a second polarizer, the 'analyser', which is placed somewhere between the crystal and the observer's eye; in the polarizing microscope it is located either in the tube of the microscope or above the eyepiece. The vibration plane of the analyser is set perpendicular to that of the polarizer, so that the light passed by the polarizer, as long as it continues to vibrate in the plane imposed on it by the polarizer, will be completely stopped by the analyser.† If we look through the microscope with the polarizers 'crossed' in this way we shall see a dark background. If the particles we are observing happen to be isotropic we shall see nothing at all; but if, like monammonium phosphate crystals, they are birefringent—that is, have two different refractive indices—we shall see that most of the crystals are illuminated, often with beautiful colours. Moreover, if we rotate the polarizers together (keeping them exactly crossed all the time), or alternatively rotate the microscope slide, we shall see that each crystal is 'extinguished' at a certain position, only to reappear as the polarizers or the slide are rotated further. It will be found that the extinction positions for any one crystal are 90° apart; extinction occurs four times during a complete revolution.

The explanation of these phenomena is as follows. Suppose the

---

† When light is resolved into a vibration plane which makes an angle $\theta$ with its original vibration plane, the resolved part has an intensity equal (apart from absorption effects) to a fraction $\cos^2\theta$ of the original intensity.

polarizer transmits light vibrating in the plane $P$ (perpendicular to the page), Fig. 45 $a$; when it gets to a crystal of monammonium phosphate which happens to be lying in such a position that its vibration directions are not parallel to either of the cross-wires (vibration directions of the polarizers), it is resolved by the crystal into two components, vibrating in the crystal's own vibration directions $X$ and $Z$. When this light, which now consists of the two components $X$ and $Z$, passes through the

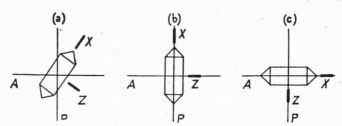

Fig. 45. Crystals of monammonium phosphate between crossed polarizers.

analyser, each component is again resolved by the analyser into *its* own vibration direction $A$, so that the light emerges from the analyser as a single component but now vibrating in plane $A$. In this position, therefore, the crystal transmits light. But now consider Fig. 45 $b$ in which the crystal's vibration directions coincide with the vibration directions of the polarizers. Light from the first polarizer, vibrating in plane $P$, on arriving at the crystal continues vibrating in plane $P$ since this is also the crystal's own vibration plane $X$; the resolved part in plane $Z$ is zero. On arriving at the analyser, all the light is necessarily stopped, since it is still vibrating in plane $P$ and the analyser cannot transmit it, the resolved part in the analyser's vibration plane $A$ being zero. In this position, therefore, the crystal is extinguished. The same thing occurs when the fourfold axis of the crystal is parallel to $A$ (Fig. 45 $c$), and this position, 90° from the first-mentioned position, is thus also an extinction position. At all intermediate positions the crystal will be illuminated, the intensity of illumination being greatest at the 45° position.

Thus, extinction occurs when the vibration directions of the polarizers coincide with those of the crystal.

This explains illumination and extinction; but what of the colours? To understand the production of colours we must consider the relative velocities of the two components $X$ and $Z$ in the crystal. We have already seen that in a crystal of monammonium phosphate the refractive index for component $Z$ is greater than for component $X$; this means that light vibrating along $Z$ travels through the crystal more slowly than light vibrating along $X$, the ratio of the velocities being inversely proportional to the ratio of the refractive indices. The frequency $\nu$ of any monochromatic component of the white light naturally remains constant; therefore, since $\nu\lambda$ = velocity, the wavelength $\lambda$ is smaller for component $Z$ than for component $X$. The two components start in phase with each other at the bottom of the crystal (Fig. 46), but when

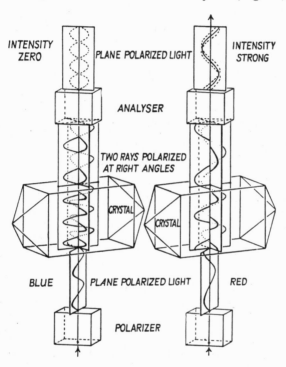

FIG. 46. Birefringent crystal between crossed polarizers, in 45° position.

they reach the top of the crystal it is likely that they are no longer exactly in phase with each other. When they reach the analyser they are resolved into the same plane of vibration and are able to interfere with each other. Whether or not they entirely cancel each other out depends on the difference of phase. Now, for a given thickness of a particular crystal, one particular wavelength of light will be completely cut out by interference; for other wavelengths there will be only a diminution of intensity. If the thickness of the crystal and the values of the two refractive indices are such that blue light is entirely cut out by interference, the colour we shall see will consist of the rest of the spectrum—a yellowish colour; if red light is cut out, we shall see a greenish colour, and so on. For increasing thicknesses of crystal the colours given are in the order known as 'Newton's scale'; it is the same order as that of the interference colours given by very thin films, such as oil films on a wet road. The order can be studied on any birefringent crystal of varying thickness, such as the pyramidal ends of the crystals of monammonium phosphate; the colours appear as bands like contour lines on the crystals. The colour produced is determined by the birefringence of the crystal (the difference between the two refractive indices) and its thickness.

To return to the extinction phenomenon. We now know how to set the polarizer so that its vibration direction coincides with one of the vibration directions of the crystal: we make use of the extinction phenomenon in the following way. Keeping the polarizer always in the illuminating beam, focus a particular crystal; introduce the analyser (crossed with respect to the polarizer) and rotate either the crystal or the coupled pair of polarizers until extinction occurs; then remove the analyser and observe the Becke line effect. Reintroduce the analyser, and turn either polarizers or crystal through 90° to the other extinction position; after removing the analyser once again, observe the Becke line effect for the second time. These observations reveal the relations between the refractive indices of the crystal and that of the liquid. Suppose one index of the crystal is lower and the other higher than that of the liquid (Plate III c, d). Try liquids of lower index until one is found whose index is equal to the lower of the two indices of the crystals; and subsequently, seek the higher of the two indices of the crystals in a similar way.

Crystals which are all lying in the same position, such as monammonium phosphate crystals lying on their prism faces, give consistent results when examined in this way; but if these crystals are crushed to provide irregular fragments capable of lying on the microscope slide in any orientation, and these fragments are examined in the same way, it will be found that although the upper index of each fragment is constant and equal to 1·525, the lower index is different for each fragment, and may have any value between 1·479 and 1·525. This brings us to a general consideration of the refractive indices for all possible orientations with respect to the transmitted light.

**The indicatrix.** Imagine a point within a crystal, and from this point lines drawn outwards in all directions, the length of each line being proportional to the refractive index for light vibrating along the line. It is found that for all crystals the ends of these lines fall on the surface of an ellipsoid, a solid figure all sections passing through the centre of which are ellipses. This ellipsoidal three-dimensional

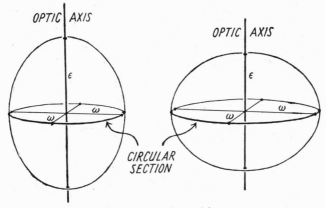

FIG. 47. Left: positive uniaxial indicatrix. Right: negative uniaxial indicatrix.

graph of refractive indices is called the 'indicatrix'. For monammonium phosphate crystals and for all tetragonal, hexagonal, and trigonal crystals the indicatrix is a special type of ellipsoid (Fig. 47) in which two of the principal axes are equal to each other and the third different in length (it may be longer or shorter); it is an 'ellipsoid of revolution' obtained by rotating an ellipse round one of its principal axes—in the case of monammonium phosphate, round the minor axis. The ellipsoid thus has one circular section perpendicular to the unique axis. The unique axis of this ellipsoid of revolution necessarily coincides with the unique (fourfold, sixfold, or threefold) symmetry axis of the crystal.

The vibration directions and refractive indices of crystal fragments of monammonium phosphate lying on a microscope slide in any orientation

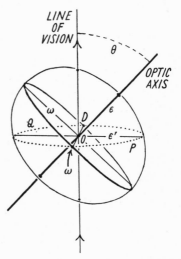

FIG. 48. Uniaxial indicatrix— general orientation.

are given by the indicatrix in the following way. A crystal fragment, oriented with its unique axis at any angle $\theta$ to the line of vision, is mentally replaced by the indicatrix (Fig. 48). Perpendicular to the line of vision, imagine a section $PQ$ passing through the centre of the ellipsoid; this section is an ellipse, and its principal axes (the maximum and minimum radii of the ellipse) represent the vibration directions and refractive indices of the crystal fragment. Now the maximum radius $OD$ of every such ellipse is also a radius $\omega$ of the one circular section of the indicatrix.† The minimum radius $\epsilon'$ of the ellipse, however, varies with the angle $\theta$. In general, the length $\epsilon'$ lies between $\epsilon$ and $\omega$; when $\theta = 90°$, as it is for well-formed monammonium phosphate crystals lying on their prism faces as in Fig. 44 $a$, $\epsilon'$ is equal to $\epsilon$, the unique axis of the indicatrix; when $\theta = 0°$, as it is for crystals of this substance standing on end as in Fig. 44 $c$, $\epsilon$ is equal to $\omega$, the radius of the one circular section. The observed refractive indices of crystal fragments of monammonium phosphate are in line with this: every fragment has an upper index equal to 1·525, but the lower index varies in different fragments between 1·479 and 1·525.

The method of finding the principal refractive indices of such crystals even when quite irregular is therefore simple: numerous fragments are examined, each fragment being observed in its two extinction positions; the two principal refractive indices are the extreme upper and lower values observed. The upper principal index is (for this particular substance) the easier to find because every fragment, however oriented, gives this value as its upper index. The lower principal index is the lowest of the lower values of all fragments.

When we are looking along the unique axis, both indices of the crystal or fragment are equal to 1·525; the crystal will therefore not show any interference colours when examined between crossed polarizers; it will appear to be isotropic. This direction of apparent isotropy is called the optic axis; there is only one such direction in the crystals we have hitherto dealt with—tetragonal, hexagonal, and trigonal crystals —and such crystals are therefore described as optically uniaxial. The optic axis necessarily coincides with the principal symmetry axis.·

The principal refractive indices of uniaxial crystals are usually symbolized $\omega$ or $n_\omega$ for the more important of the two, the one which is constant for all orientations, and $\epsilon$ or $n_\epsilon$ for the other one. When $\epsilon$ is less than $\omega$ (as in monammonium phosphate) the crystal is described as uniaxial negative; when $\epsilon$ is greater than $\omega$, as in quartz, $SiO_2$ ($\omega = 1·544$, $\epsilon = 1·553$), the crystal is described as uniaxial positive.

The method for the determination of the principal refractive indices

† Wire models will make this and other features of the optical indicatrix clearer than plane diagrams can possibly do.

of irregular fragments has been described, not only because such material may often be encountered in chemical work, but also for another reason. Well-formed crystals of many uniaxial crystals are of such a shape that, when lying on any one of their faces on a microscope slide, they do not show both the principal indices. Rhombohedra or bipyramids, for instance, do not show $\epsilon$; they necessarily show $\omega$ as one of their indices, but the other index lies between $\omega$ and $\epsilon$. In such circumstances it is advisable to break the crystals so as to provide irregular fragments, and to seek $\epsilon$ in the way already described.

**Orthorhombic crystals.** The symmetries of the orthorhombic classes—either three mutually perpendicular planes of symmetry, or

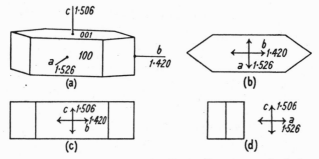

FIG. 49. Refractive indices of sodium carbonate monohydrate, $Na_2CO_3 . H_2O$.

three mutually perpendicular twofold axes, or two perpendicular planes intersecting in a twofold axis—demand that the indicatrix, which is of the most general type with all three principal axes of unequal length, has these three axes parallel to the crystallographic axes. The inequality of the refractive indices for light vibrating along the three crystallographic axes is a consequence of the fact that the arrangements of atoms encountered along these axes are all different from each other. Any one indicatrix axis may coincide with any crystallographic axis.

For well-formed crystals of suitable shape the three principal refractive indices can be found quite easily. Crystals of sodium carbonate monohydrate (Fig. 49), which can be made by evaporating a solution of sodium carbonate above 40° C, are suitable for demonstration because they lie on a microscope slide either on their 001 faces or their 100 faces (Fig. 49 *b* and *c*). It will be found that the extinction directions —that is, the vibration directions—are parallel and perpendicular to the long edges of the crystals for both orientations; crystals lying on 001 give refractive indices of 1·420 for light vibrating along the crystal and 1·526 for light vibrating across the crystal; those lying on 100 give 1·420 for the vibration direction along the crystal and 1·506 for the other vibration direction. If crystals standing on end can be found on the microscope slide, they will give indices of 1·506 and 1·526 for the vibration directions shown in Fig. 49 *d*. These three values 1·420, 1·506, and 1·526 are the principal refractive indices, and are symbolized $\alpha$ or $n_\alpha$ for the lowest, $\beta$ or $n_\beta$ for the next, and $\gamma$ or $n_\gamma$ for the highest.

Many orthorhombic crystals are of such a shape that, when lying on one of their faces on a microscope slide, they do not show any of the

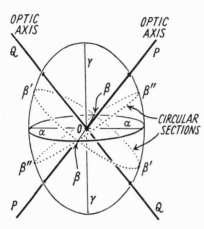

FIG. 50.  Biaxial indicatrix.

principal refractive indices. Such crystals may be broken to provide fragments which lie in a variety of orientations. If fragments of crystals of sodium carbonate monohydrate oriented in all possible ways are examined, both indices of each fragment being observed, it will be found that the lower of the two indices may have any value between $\alpha$ and $\beta$, while the upper index lies between $\beta$ and $\gamma$. The determination of $\alpha$ and $\gamma$ for identification purposes is in principle quite simple : $\alpha$ is the lowest index for any vibration direction, and $\gamma$ is the highest index for any vibration direction.

To find the intermediate principal index $\beta$ is less simple. One method of finding it makes use of the fact that in any ellipsoid having three unequal axes there are two circular sections. Thus, referring to Fig. 50, there is, somewhere between $\alpha$ and $\gamma$ on the surface of the ellipsoid, a point $\beta'$ such that $O\beta' = O\beta$, and the section passing through this point and the centre of the ellipsoid is evidently a circle. Further, there is another point $\beta''$ for which $O\beta''$ is equal to $O\beta$, and $\beta\beta''$ is therefore another circular section. This means that crystals seen along either of the two directions $OP$ and $OQ$ which are perpendicular to these circular sections (directions known as 'optic axes') have one refractive index only and will appear isotropic. Moreover, this one refractive index is equal to $\beta$. Therefore, to find $\beta$, search for fragments which appear isotropic or nearly so (giving very low order interference colours); these fragments give $\beta$ or values very near it.

It is not always easy to find crystals or fragments oriented so that one is looking along an optic axis; hence it is necessary to mention another method of finding $\beta$. This method depends on the fact that no crystal, whatever its orientation, can give two refractive indices above $\beta$ or two refractive indices below $\beta$. One index must be between $\alpha$ and $\beta$ (for particular orientations it may be equal to $\alpha$ or $\beta$), and the other must be between $\beta$ and $\gamma$ (for particular orientations it may be equal to $\beta$ or $\gamma$). Therefore, to find $\beta$ we observe upper and lower values for numerous fragments, and $\beta$ is the highest of the lower values or the lowest of the higher values.

To sum up, the method of determining the three refractive indices of an orthorhombic crystal is to observe the upper and lower indices (for the two extinction directions) of numerous fragments. $\alpha$ is the lowest of the lower values, $\gamma$ the highest of the higher values, while $\beta$ is the highest of the lower values or the lowest of the higher values. If we find fragments oriented so that we are looking along an optic axis, upper and lower values are both equal to $\beta$.

Since orthorhombic crystals have two optic axes (that is, two directions of apparent isotropy), they are termed optically biaxial. The angle between the optic axes is known as the optic axial angle. The three principal axes of the indicatrix are known as the acute bisectrix (of the optic axes), the obtuse bisectrix, and the third mean line. The last-mentioned—the third mean line—is in all cases the vibration direction of $\beta$. The acute bisectrix is either the vibration direction of $\gamma$—in which case the crystal is known as biaxial positive—or else it is the vibration direction of $\alpha$, in which case the crystal is known as biaxial negative. Note that this nomenclature conforms with that of uniaxial crystals. If we regard a uniaxial crystal as having an optic axial angle of $0°$, we may say that both optic axes coincide with the acute bisectrix. This unique direction is the vibration direction of $\epsilon$, and when this is the highest index (corresponding to $\gamma$ for a biaxial crystal), the crystal is known as a uniaxial positive crystal. For weakly or moderately birefringent biaxial crystals it is nearly correct to say that a positive crystal has $\beta$ nearer to $\alpha$ than to $\gamma$, while a negative crystal has $\beta$ nearer to $\gamma$ than to $\alpha$. But for strongly birefringent crystals $(\gamma-\alpha > 0\cdot1)$ the dividing line between positive and negative crystals (where the optic axial angle is $90°$) occurs when $\beta$ is appreciably different from $\frac{1}{2}(\alpha+\gamma)$.

**Monoclinic and triclinic crystals.** The indicatrix for monoclinic and triclinic crystals is of the same type as that for orthorhombic crystals—an ellipsoid with all its three principal axes unequal in length. (This is the least symmetrical type of ellipsoid, so that any diminution of crystal symmetry below orthorhombic cannot alter the form of the ellipsoid.) The measurement of the three principal refractive indices of a monoclinic or triclinic crystal is therefore carried out in the manner described for orthorhombic crystals, random orientation being assured by crushing the crystals if necessary.

The orientation of the indicatrix with respect to the unit cell axes, however, obviously cannot be the same as for orthorhombic crystals,

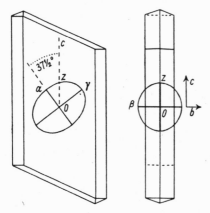

since the unit cell axes in mono-clinic and triclinic crystals are not all at right angles to each other.

In monoclinic crystals the $b$ axis is either an axis of twofold symmetry or is normal to a plane of symmetry (or both); therefore, since the orien-tation of the indicatrix must conform to the crystal symmetry, one axis of the indicatrix (it may be either $\alpha$, $\beta$, or $\gamma$) must coincide with the $b$ axis of the unit cell. This is the only restriction on indicatrix orientation;

Fig. 51. Orientation of indicatrix in gypsum crystal. (The differences between the refractive indices—for example, the lengths $O\alpha$ and $O\gamma$—are greatly ex-aggerated.)

its other two axes must obviously lie in the plane normal to $b$—the $ac$ plane, but they may be in any position in this plane, though of course remaining at right angles to each other. This is illustrated in Fig. 51, which shows a gypsum crystal lying on its 010 face, the $b$ axis being normal to the paper. The vibration direction of $\beta$ happens to be the one which coincides with the $b$ axis, hence $\alpha$ and $\gamma$ lie in the $ac$ plane, and it is found that the vibration direction of $\alpha$ makes an angle of $37\frac{1}{2}°$ with the $c$ axis. If gypsum crystals are examined under the microscope, it will be found that the extinction directions are inclined to the crystal edges, and refractive index $\alpha$ (1·521) is shown when the vibration direction of the light from the polarizer makes an angle of $37\frac{1}{2}°$ with the long edge of the crystal, in the direction shown in the diagram, while $\gamma$ (1·530) is shown for the direction at right angles to $\alpha$, $52\frac{1}{2}°$ to the $c$ axis. If these crystals can be observed edgewise (in a crowd of crystals, especially when immersed in a viscous medium, some may be found suitably oriented) it can be seen (Fig. 51, right) that the extinction directions are parallel and perpendicular to the long edges of the crystal, and that refractive index $\beta$ (1·523) is shown when the vibration direction of the light is perpendicular to the long edges, that is, along the $b$ axis; for the vibration direction parallel to the long edges the index lies between $\alpha$ and $\gamma$, its value being given by the length $OZ$.

One consequence of the freedom of position of the indicatrix in the $ac$ plane is that the extinction position need not be the same for all wavelengths of light; its position for red light may be, and often is, appreciably different from that for blue light; consequently some monoclinic crystals, when lying on the microscope slide on their 010 faces, do not show complete extinction at any position of the crossed polarizers; the illumination passes through a minimum on rotation of the polarizers, and in the region of the minimum, abnormal interference colours may be seen, reddish for one setting of the polarizers (where blue light is extinguished) and bluish when the polarizers are turned a degree or two (when red light is extinguished). This occurs in crystals of sodium thiosulphate pentahydrate, $Na_2S_2O_3.5H_2O$, and sodium carbonate decahydrate, $Na_2CO_3.10H_2O$. This phenomenon does not occur in orthorhombic crystals lying on faces parallel to crystallographic axes,[†] since the indicatrix axes are fixed by symmetry along the crystal axes and are therefore unable to vary in position with the wavelength of light. Nor does it occur for monoclinic crystals lying on any face parallel to $b$, since one ellipsoid axis is fixed by symmetry along $b$.

In triclinic crystals there are no restrictions at all on the position of the indicatrix with respect to the crystal axes. No axis of the ellipsoid need coincide with any one of the crystal axes. Consequently the position of the ellipsoid may vary with the light wavelength for all crystal orientations; incomplete extinction with abnormal interference colours at the position of minimum illumination may therefore be seen for any crystal orientation.

If crystals large enough to be handled individually are available, the determination of their optical properties is facilitated by the use of a stage goniometer, a simple instrument fitting on the stage of a microscope, consisting of a horizontal rotating spindle on which a crystal can be mounted (Wood and Ayliffe, 1935; Bernal and Carlisle, 1947; Hartshorne and Swift, 1956). The crystal, mounted on the spindle, is held just above the microscope slide and covered with a drop of a suitable liquid; observations are made in the usual way by observing for each

† Orthorhombic crystals lying on $hkl$ faces such as (111) may, however, show this phenomenon.

extinction direction in turn. The crystal can be rotated until it appears
to be giving either maximum or minimum indices (whichever is being
sought), or to a position showing $\beta$; the liquid can then be changed, one
drop being removed with filter paper before another is tried (Joel, 1950).
By a few changes of liquid, together with readjustments of the rotating
spindle, the principal indices are found, and at the same time valuable
observations of extinction directions in relation to the crystal edges are
gathered.

   **Use of convergent light.** The phenomena so far described are those
which are seen when approximately parallel light is used. For any
particular crystal orientation they give information about the properties
of the crystal for one particular direction of propagation of light (the
line of vision). If strongly convergent light (given by a high power
condenser) is used, phenomena can be seen which give information
about a wide range of directions of propagation of light: in fact, in
some circumstances, the phenomena show at a glance whether a crystal
is uniaxial or biaxial, and if it is biaxial, they indicate the magnitude
of the optic axial angle.

   A bundle of parallel rays which all take the same direction through
the crystal and then pass through the objective lens of the microscope
are necessarily brought to a focus at a point a little above the objective
(in the focal plane of the objective, the plane in which the image of a
distant object would be produced); all the rays taking another direction
through the crystal are focused at a different point in the same plane.
Consequently, if we look at the optical effects in this plane we shall see
a pattern which represents the variation of optical properties over the
range of directions taken by the objective lens. When the crystal is
between crossed polarizers the pattern of colours indicates the variation
of birefringence with direction in the crystal.

   This pattern, known as the 'interference figure', 'convergent light
figure', 'directions image', or 'optic picture', may be seen by removing
the eyepiece of the microscope and looking straight down the tube; it
appears to be just above the objective lens. If the microscope is fitted
with a Bertrand lens—a special auxiliary lens which can be inserted in
the tube—it is not necessary to remove the eyepiece. For the observation of small crystals a Bertrand lens with a small diaphragm, located
just below the eyepiece, is most suitable, as it picks out the convergent
light figure produced by a small crystal which occupies only a small
fraction of the field of view. The objective lens used should have a
high numerical aperture, so that it takes in a wide angular range of

directions; a 6- or 4-mm lens of numerical aperture 0·7–0·8 is suitable. The crystals are preferably immersed in a liquid whose refractive index is not far from $\beta$ or $\omega$.

A uniaxial crystal with its optic axis along the line of vision gives a convergent light figure consisting of a black cross with concentric coloured rings (Fig. 52 $a$, left). The centre of the figure is dark because

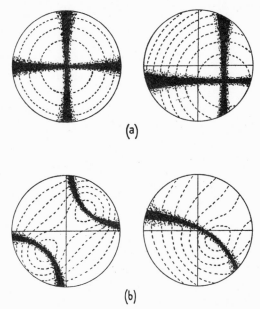

(a)

(b)

FIG. 52. Convergent light figures. $a$. Uniaxial crystal with optic axis parallel (left) and slightly inclined (right) to line of vision. $b$. Biaxial crystal with acute bisectrix parallel (left) and inclined (right) to line of vision.

it represents the direction of the optic axis—a direction of apparent isotropy. The arms of the black cross represent the vibration directions of the crossed polarizers, while the rings show interference colours whose order (see p. 72) increases with their radius, owing to the rising bire-fringence of the crystal for directions increasingly inclined to the optic axis. Suitable crystals for demonstrating this type of figure are the hexagonal plates of cadmium iodide, $CdI_2$, which lie correctly oriented on the microscope slide. Crystals lying so that the optic axis is a little inclined to the line of vision give a convergent light figure displaced from the centre of the eyepiece field.

Biaxial crystals under similar optical conditions produce convergent light figures like that shown in Fig. 52 $b$, when the acute bisectrix of the optic axes lies along the line of vision and the vibration directions of the crossed polarizers are at 45° to the extinction directions. There are black hyperbolae and coloured lemniscate rings. A sheet of muscovite mica is a suitable specimen for demonstration. The distance between the black hyperbolae is a measure of the optic axial angle. If various crystals of known optic axial angle are observed, and the distances between the black hyperbolae are measured by means of a micrometer eyepiece, a calibration can be made so that the optic axial

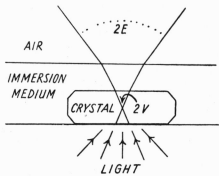

Fig. 53. Optic axial angle in crystal (2V) and in air (2E).

angle of any crystal can subsequently be determined. The angle thus measured is the angle the optic axial directions make with each other on emerging from the crystal into air (Fig. 53); this angle $2E$ is related to the true optic axial angle $2V$ by the expression $\sin E = \beta \sin V$.

The optic axial angle $2V$ is related to the three refractive indices by the expression

$$\tan V_\gamma = \frac{\gamma}{\alpha} \sqrt{\left/ \left(\frac{\beta^2 - \alpha^2}{\gamma^2 - \beta^2}\right)\right.}$$

for positive crystals (denoted by $V_\gamma$, meaning that the acute bisectrix is $\gamma$), or

$$\tan V_\alpha = \frac{\alpha}{\gamma} \sqrt{\left/ \left(\frac{\gamma^2 - \beta^2}{\beta^2 - \alpha^2}\right)\right.}$$

for negative crystals, in which the acute bisectrix is $\alpha$. When the birefringence is low (less than 0·02), the simpler approximate formulae

$$\tan V_\gamma = \sqrt{\left(\frac{\beta - \alpha}{\gamma - \beta}\right)} \quad \text{and} \quad \tan V_\alpha = \sqrt{\left(\frac{\gamma - \beta}{\beta - \alpha}\right)}$$

are adequate.

If three of these quantities are known, the fourth can be calculated. Thus, when it is possible to measure all three principal refractive indices, the measurement of the optic axial angle is, strictly speaking, superfluous. But in some cases it may be possible to measure only two of the principal refractive indices. For instance, some organic crystals have $\gamma$ higher than any available immersion liquid. In such circumstances a measurement of the optic axial angle gives the necessary information for calculating the third index; this measurement of the optic axial angle must include the determination not only of its magnitude but also of its sign. The distinction between positive and negative crystals can be made by the use of the quartz wedge; this forms the subject of the next section.

When the optic axial angle is small and $\gamma$ is very much higher than $\alpha$ and $\beta$, this method of obtaining $\gamma$ from $\alpha$, $\beta$, and $2V$ gives inaccurate results. In these circumstances better results can be obtained by using a stage goniometer in the manner described by Wood and Ayliffe (1936). The crystal, mounted with $\beta$ as the axis of rotation, is immersed in a series of liquids whose indices increase in steps of 0·01. The crystal is rotated about the horizontal axis until a match for each liquid is obtained, and the angle $\theta$ from the position in which $\alpha$ is parallel to the stage is measured. If $n$ is the refractive index of the liquid which matches the crystal for a setting $\theta$, then

$$\frac{1}{n^2} = \frac{1}{\gamma^2} + \left(\frac{1}{\alpha^2} - \frac{1}{\gamma^2}\right)\cos^2\theta;$$

thus $1/n^2$ varies linearly with $\cos^2\theta$. The observed values of $1/n^2$ are plotted against $\cos^2\theta$, and the straight line thus obtained is extrapolated to $\theta = 90°$ to give $\gamma$. $\alpha$ and $\beta$ are given by the values of $n$ corresponding to $\theta = 0°$ and $\theta = V$ respectively.

**Use of the quartz wedge.** When needle crystals of a uniaxial substance such as urea (tetragonal—uniaxial positive) are being examined between crossed polarizers, it may be seen that when one crystal lies across another of similar thickness, and at right angles to it, the apparent birefringence (as shown by the interference colour) at the point where they cross is very low or actually zero. The effect is seen perhaps most conveniently by examining thin threads of fibres such as rayon or nylon which behave optically like uniaxial crystals; in a yarn of such materials the threads are of uniform diameter, and where they cross each other at right angles, the apparent birefringence is zero. But if one thread lies on another parallel to it, the interference colour is of much higher order than that given by a single thread. The interference effects are thus subtractive when the threads or crystals are at right angles to each other, and additive when they are parallel. This is because crystal 1 (Fig. 54 a) retards waves vibrating along $A$ relative to those along $B$; but subsequently, when the waves go through crystal 2, the waves vibrating along $B$ are retarded relative to those along $A$, thus neutralizing or compensating the effect of crystal 1, so that no interference colours are shown for the crossed position. Conversely, if the crystals are parallel, the retardation effects are additive and a higher order interference colour is produced.

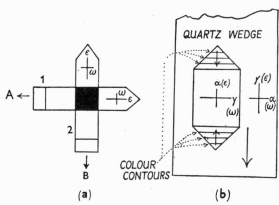

FIG. 54. *a*. Two urea crystals of the same thickness, crossed at right angles. At the centre overlapping portion the combination appears isotropic. *b*. Effect of quartz wedge on crystal of $NH_4H_2PO_4$. As the wedge advances, the colour contours move towards the thicker part of the crystal.

This effect can be used for finding which vibration direction gives the higher index for any birefringent crystal. It is most convenient to use the quartz wedge, a thin slice of quartz with its length parallel to the hexagonal axis of the crystal (the vibration direction which has the higher index) and uniformly tapering in thickness.† If it is pushed into the polarizing microscope at 45° to the vibration directions of the polarizers (a slot is provided for the purpose), the interference colours of Newton's scale can be seen—grey near the thinnest part of the wedge, and passing through near-white, brownish-yellow, red, and violet of the first order, then peacock blue, yellowish-green, yellow, magenta, and violet of the second order, then emerald green, yellowish, and pink of the third order, and thence through alternating, progressively paler shades of green and pink of the higher orders. If a crystal of monammonium phosphate is examined, and the quartz wedge pushed in parallel to the fourfold axis (Fig. 54 *b*), it can be seen that the interference

† This is the commonest type. But quartz wedges having the opposite orientation (with the vibration direction for the lower index parallel to the length of the wedge) are also made. The phenomena they give are naturally opposite to those described.

colours decrease in order as an increasing thickness of quartz overlaps the crystal. This shows at once that the optical character of this crystal is opposite to that of quartz—the waves vibrating along the crystal have the lower refractive index. Perhaps the best method of observation is to watch the colour contours on the pyramidal ends of the crystal; these contours retreat towards the thicker part of the crystal as the quartz wedge advances and neutralizes the retardation. The effect may be checked by pushing the wedge in at right angles to the fourfold axis of the crystal; the birefringence effects are now additive, and the colour contours move towards the pointed ends of the crystal as the quartz wedge advances.

The distinction between the vibration directions of higher and lower refractive indices can always be made in this way for crystals having inclined extinction no less than for those with parallel extinction. When refractive indices are measured by the methods already given, the use of the quartz wedge is hardly necessary (unless for confirmation of conclusions already reached); but in other circumstances (for instance, when crystals are being examined in their mother liquor), quartz wedge observations are useful clues to optical character.

The quartz wedge may be used in a quantitative manner for finding the magnitude of birefringence of a crystal, that is, the difference between the two refractive indices the crystal is showing. For this purpose it is necessary to know the thickness of the crystal. The quartz wedge is pushed in until the birefringence of the crystal is just neutralized; the interference colour given by the wedge alone at this point is noted, and the corresponding retardation can then be read off on a chart like that given by Winchell (1931). The relation between the retardation of one wave behind the other $(R)$, the birefringence $(\gamma' - \alpha')$, and the thickness $t$ is $(\gamma' - \alpha')t = R$. Such measurements can be done more conveniently and accurately by using some form of mechanically adjustable compensator mounted in the microscope. The best-known and perhaps the most widely used is the Babinet, in which two quartz wedges slide over each other in response to the turn of a screw; but there are other types, such as the Berek, in which a calcite plate is tilted. (For a review of compensating devices, see Jerrard, 1948.) Compensator methods are very useful when it is difficult or impossible to measure individual refractive indices, and when the birefringence is very small. The birefringence of stretched sheets of rubber has been measured in this way (Treloar, 1941).

The optic sign of a crystal can be discovered by observing the effect of the quartz wedge on the interference figure. For a uniaxial positive crystal the vibration directions of higher index lie along the radii of the coloured circles (Fig. 55 a). Consequently, when the quartz wedge moves across the figure, additive effects occur along the radii parallel to the wedge (since the direction of higher index for the wedge is along its length), and subtractive effects along the radii perpendicular to the wedge; the coloured circles therefore move inwards along radii parallel

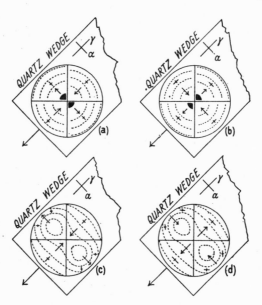

FIG. 55. Effect of quartz wedge on convergent light figures. a. Uniaxial positive. b. Uniaxial negative. c. Biaxial positive. d. Biaxial negative.

to the wedge and outwards along radii perpendicular to the wedge. The converse is true for uniaxial negative crystals. Similar effects for biaxial crystals are illustrated in Fig. 55 b.

Such observations may be useful in those cases when complete refractive index measurements by the methods already described are not possible; for instance, when the maximum refractive index of an organic crystal is too high to be matched by any available liquid.

**Dispersion.** The principal refractive indices of a crystal vary in magnitude with the frequency of light; and in crystals of monoclinic or triclinic symmetry, the vibration directions of the principal indices may vary with frequency. Such variation is known as dispersion.

The indicatrix for a cubic crystal is a sphere; the only variation which can occur is a change in the size of the sphere with the frequency of light. The colour fringes often seen round the edges of a crystal when it is immersed in a liquid of nearly the same refractive index are due to a difference between the dispersion of the crystal and that of the liquid.

For uniaxial crystals (those of tetragonal, trigonal, and hexagonal symmetry) the indicatrix is an ellipsoid of revolution, the orientation of which is fixed by symmetry (see earlier section). But the magnitudes of $\omega$ and $\epsilon$ may vary with frequency in different degrees, so that the birefringence varies with wavelength. This is not likely to give rise to noticeable phenomena under the microscope unless the birefringence is very low, when abnormal interference colours may be seen when the crystals are observed between crossed polarizers in parallel light. For instance, the mineral rinneite, $FeCl_2.3KCl.NaCl$, is practically isotropic for yellow light, but appreciably birefringent for blue light; fragments of suitable thickness do not show first-order yellow, but a bluish tinge. In benzil, $C_6H_5.CO.CO.C_6H_5$, the changes of $\omega$ and $\epsilon$ with frequency are such that it is positive for most of the visible spectrum, isotropic in the violet, and negative for the far violet end of the spectrum (Bryant, 1943).

In orthorhombic crystals the vibration directions of the three principal indices are fixed by symmetry, but their magnitudes may vary independently, and this may lead to appreciable variation of optic axial angle with frequency. This effect modifies the appearance of the convergent light figure. The acute bisectrix of the optic axes (to which the centre of the convergent light figure corresponds) is fixed by symmetry along one of the crystal axes, and the plane of the optic axes (the $\alpha\gamma$ plane of the indicatrix) is one of the faces of the unit cell. Consequently the two planes of symmetry of the convergent light figure are fixed in the same positions for all frequencies. Therefore the hyperbolae which indicate the positions of the optic axes may move towards or away from each other with change of frequency, but always symmetrically with respect to the fixed lines $AB$ and $CD$ in Fig. 56 a. For small dispersions the convergent light figure produced by white light will show a red fringe on one side of the hyperbola (where blue light is missing) and a blue fringe on the other side (where red light is missing), both hyperbolae being the same. When the red fringes are on the side nearer to the acute bisectrix, as in the diagram, the optic angle for blue light is evidently smaller than for red light. The usual symbol for recording this condition is $\rho > v$. In extreme cases, as in brookite (the orthorhombic form of titanium dioxide, $TiO_2$), the optic axial angle narrows to zero and then opens out again in a plane at right angles to the first, as the frequency of the light is changed (see Fig. 56 *b–d*). This means that the refractive index for vibration direction *CD*, which for red light is $\beta$, approaches that for the vibration direction *AB* ($\alpha$ for a positive crystal), becomes equal to it for green light (so that the crystal is fortuitously uniaxial), and falls below it for blue light, so that the index for vibration direction *CD* is now called $\alpha$, while that for *AB* is called $\beta$. The convergent light figure produced by white light in such circumstances is very abnormal; to elucidate the relation between optic axial angle and frequency, it is necessary to make observations in mono-chromatic light of variable frequency. (See Bryant, 1941.)

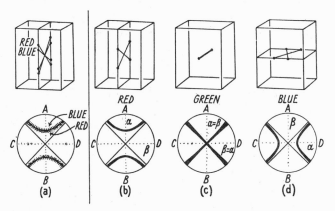

FIG. 56. Dispersion of optic axes in orthorhombic crystals. *a.* $\rho \succ v$.
*b–d.* Crossed axial plane dispersion.

In monoclinic crystals the indicatrix may not only change its dimen-sions, but may rotate round whichever axis coincides with the *b* crystal-lographic axis; and in triclinic crystals it may rotate in any direction whatever, with change of frequency. These movements may give rise to less symmetrical types of dispersion of the optic axes, though it is only rarely that the magnitude of the effect is great enough to render the phenomenon a useful criterion for identification. These types of dispersion will therefore not be described in detail; it will merely be observed that the type of dispersion is conditioned by the symmetry of the crystal, and that when appreciable dispersion occurs, the sym-metry of the polychromatic convergent light figure, or the movement of the monochromatic figure as the frequency is changed, is a reliable indication of maximum crystal symmetry. A polychromatic figure which has only a centre of symmetry, or is symmetrical about only one line, can only be produced by a crystal having monoclinic or triclinic symmetry; a figure having no symmetry can only be produced by a triclinic crystal. For further information, see Miers (1929) and Hartshorne and Stuart (1960).

**Pleochroism.** When crystals absorb light, the positions of the absorption bands and their intensities are likely to vary with the vibration direction of the light, and therefore, when the absorption bands are in the visible region, the colour shown is likely to depend on the vibration direction of the light. All coloured anisotropic crystals— that is, all coloured crystals except those belonging to the cubic system —are likely to show, in polarized light, colours which vary as the polarizer is rotated. This will be noticed when the refractive indices of coloured crystals are being measured. Thus, when crystals of potassium ferricyanide $K_3Fe(CN)_6$ are examined in polarized light, rotation of the polarizer causes the colour of some of the crystals to change from yellow to orange-red; crystals 'showing' the refractive index $\alpha$ are yellow, while those 'showing' $\gamma$ are orange-red. Such crystals are said to be 'pleochroic'. These absorption effects, which are shown when only the polarizer of the microscope is in use, should not be confused with the interference colours produced when crossed polarizers are in use.

The three-dimensional graph showing the variation in the absorption of any frequency with crystal direction is, like that of the refractive indices, an ellipsoid. Cubic crystals necessarily have the same absorption for all vibration directions, just as they have a constant refractive index. For optically uniaxial crystals (those belonging to the tetragonal, hexagonal, and trigonal systems) the absorption for the $\omega$ vibration direction may be different from the absorption for the $\epsilon$ vibration direction—different in respect of both the proportion of light absorbed and the wavelength ranges of the absorption bands; and when an index between $\omega$ and $\epsilon$ is shown, the absorption is intermediate. (Strictly speaking, the phenomenon in uniaxial crystals should be termed dichroism, since there are only two different absorptions.) For biaxial crystals, $\alpha$, $\beta$, and $\gamma$ may all show different colours. Thus in crystals of $Fe_3(PO_4)_2.8H_2O$ (the mineral vivianite) $\alpha$ is cobalt blue, $\beta$ is nearly colourless, while $\gamma$ shows a pale olive-green colour (Larsen and Berman, 1934).

The observation of the colour and the degree of absorption associated with each index is of obvious value for identification purposes; the larger the number of characteristics observed, the more certain the identification. Observations of pleochroism may also be useful as indications of certain features of molecular structure. (See Chapter VIII.)

Very strongly pleochroic crystals, which absorb almost completely for one vibration direction and hardly at all for another, can be used as polarizers. Tourmaline, a complex aluminosilicate mineral of trigonal symmetry, has a very low absorption for light of all colours vibrating along the trigonal axis, and a very high absorption for vibration directions perpendicular to this axis; when unpolarized light passes through the crystal, it is resolved in the usual way into two components vibrating parallel and perpendicular to the threefold axis; but the component vibrating perpendicular to this axis is almost completely absorbed by even very thin crystals, while the other component is transmitted with little loss of intensity; consequently the light which emerges from the crystal is practically completely plane polarized. The polarizing sheets known as 'Polaroid' have similar characteristics. The first material used for this purpose consisted of sub-microscopic crystals of 'herapathite', strychnine sulphate periodate, all oriented parallel to each other and embedded in a suitable medium. Later, a complex of highly oriented polyvinyl alcohol and iodine was found to be even better. These materials owe their extreme pleochroism and their usefulness as polarizers to the strings of iodine atoms which very strongly absorb light vibrating parallel to the iodine chains.

**Rotation of the plane of polarization.** When plane polarized light passes through crystals belonging to certain classes, the plane of polarization may be rotated. The phenomenon is readily observed only in cubic crystals and in birefringent crystals seen along an optic axis; these, when examined between crossed polarizers, using parallel white light, do not appear dark (as they would if no rotation occurred), but coloured; and when the crossed polarizers are rotated, no extinction occurs, the intensity and colour of the light remaining constant. Light is transmitted because the plane of vibration of the light from the polarizer is rotated by the crystal, so that it is no longer extinguished by the analyser; and the reason for the colour is that the amount of rotation usually varies considerably with the wavelength of the light, and consequently the proportion of light passed by the analyser (resolved into its own plane of vibration), is different for each wavelength, the net transmitted light being therefore coloured. The rotation is usually greatest for the blue end of the spectrum; consequently for thin crystals in which the amount of rotation is much less than 90° for all wavelengths, the light which passes the analyser is predominantly blue. Thus, for microscopic crystals, rotation of the plane of polarization is indicated by the appearance of a bluish light which does not extinguish as the crossed polarizers are rotated, but remains of constant colour and intensity. As a check, the analyser should be rotated so that it is no longer exactly crossed with the polarizer; the colour should change, and the sequence of changes shows the sense of rotation of the plane of polarization; if the analyser is rotated clockwise, a change of colour in the order blue, violet, yellow shows that the crystal is rotating the plane of polarization of the light to the right (clockwise).

If monochromatic light is used, polarizers exactly crossed will transmit some of it, but by rotating the analyser extinction can be achieved.

Rotation of the plane of polarization naturally modifies convergent light figures. When rotation occurs in a uniaxial crystal the black arms of the convergent light figure fade towards the centre, and the centre itself is coloured, not black; and if rotation occurs along the optic axial directions of a biaxial crystal the image will show coloured 'eyes', the black hyperbolae being interrupted at these points.

Such evidence of rotation of the plane of polarization is not likely to be detected in microscopic crystals unless the specific rotation is exceptionally large. The phenomena mentioned above are usually exhibited only by crystals at least several millimetres thick. Suitable subjects for observation are sodium chlorate (cubic), quartz (trigonal, uniaxial), and cane sugar (monoclinic, biaxial).

The crystal classes which may rotate the plane of polarization of light are, first of all, the enantiomorphous classes—those which lack planes of symmetry, inversion axes, and a centre of symmetry. But in addition to these, crystals of certain other non-centrosymmetric classes, even though they possess planes of symmetry, are expected to be capable of exhibiting the phenomenon, though it must be admitted that no authentic examples are known. These classes are $m$, $mm2$, $\overline{4}$, and $\overline{4}2m$. (One crystal which appeared to belong to class $m$ was at one time said to exhibit the phenomenon (Sommerfeldt, 1908), but it has since been shown by X-ray diffraction methods that it belongs to the centrosymmetric class $2/m$, and that the apparent evidence for rotation of the plane of polarization was due to confused optical effects in twinned crystals (Rogers, 1953).) To a chemist, familiar with the conditions necessary for rotation of the plane of polarization by dissolved molecules (that is, absence of planes, inversion axes, and a centre of symmetry in the molecular geometry), rotation in a crystal containing a plane of symmetry may appear surprising; but the surprise disappears when it is realized that the two situations—on the one hand, a mass of randomly oriented molecules, and on the other, a single crystal composed of precisely oriented molecules—are not comparable. Reconciliation of ideas is effected by the following considerations. A crystal or a single molecule having a plane of symmetry but no centre of symmetry can rotate the plane of polarization, but the rotation varies with the direction in which the light travels, and if there is left-handed rotation along any selected direction on one side of the plane of symmetry, there must be, along the mirror-image direction on the other side of the plane of symmetry, right-handed rotation of the same magnitude. Therefore in a mass of randomly oriented molecules (or crystals) some will rotate in one direction and others (differently oriented) in the opposite direction, the net rotation being exactly zero. Thus it is not true to say that a single molecule or a single crystal having a plane of symmetry cannot rotate the plane of polarization of light; provided it has no centre of symmetry, it can and does cause rotation for light travelling in any direction except those parallel and perpendicular to the plane of symmetry; it is the mass of randomly oriented molecules in a liquid or solution which fails to show any net rotation.

For a fuller discussion of the phenomenon, and a list of the crystal classes which (according to current theories) may exhibit it, see Wooster (1938) and *International Tables* (1952). Rotation of the plane of polarization, though difficult to observe and measure except in large isotropic and uniaxial crystals, and therefore of rather limited application in identification or structural investigations, is a phenomenon of great interest that has played an important part in the historical development of chemistry and crystallography.

**Optical properties of twinned crystals.** Each individual in a twin exhibits its own optical characteristics. If a gypsum twin is seen along its *b* axis and examined between crossed polarizers, it can be seen that each individual extinguishes independently. The twin plane (100) is a plane of symmetry of the composite whole, and the vibration directions of the two individuals, like all the other properties, are related to each other by this plane of symmetry (see Fig. 57 *a*).

The relations between the optical properties of the two individuals are clear in the case of gypsum because the crystals lie on the microscope slide on their (010) faces, so that the (100) twin planes are parallel to the line of vision. In some crystals the twin planes are inclined to the line of vision when the crystals are lying on their principal faces so that one is looking through two crystals in which the vibration directions are not parallel to each other. In these circumstances, in the overlapping regions extinction does not occur when the polarizers are rotated. When observations are being made for refractive index determination it is necessary to confine the observations to those portions of crystals which are not overlapped by other individuals.

Observations of crystals between crossed polarizers are particularly valuable in the case of some of those twin combinations which in their external shape simulate a single crystal having a symmetry higher than that of one of the individuals. The observation of different extinction directions in different regions demonstrates at once that the crystal is

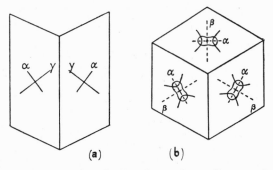

FIG. 57. Optical properties of twinned crystals. *a*. Gypsum. *b*. Calcium sulphate subhydrate. Note orientations of convergent light figures in the three sectors.

not a single individual but a twinned combination. The hexagonal prisms of ammonium sulphate mentioned on p. 59 are in this way shown to be mimetic triplets, since adjacent sectors extinguish at 60° to each other. Similarly, crystals of calcium sulphate subhydrate grown in nitric acid solution are hexagonal plates which, however, are not single crystals but triplets (Fig. 57 *b*): three sectors have extinction directions at 120° to each other, and, moreover, biaxial convergent light figures at 120° to each other can be seen by examining each sector in turn.

Some crystal species grow as plates which are twinned on a plane parallel to the plane of the plate; such crystals, lying naturally on a microscope slide, may give confusing optical effects, such as very unusual and complex convergent light figures. Plates composed of several thin lamellae associated by repeated twinning are not uncommon, and these too may give confusing optical effects. A side view of the plates, obtained either by searching in a crowd of crystals on a slide, or by mounting one crystal on a stage goniometer and turning it about, should reveal the nature of the twinning and make it possible to measure the principal refractive indices and other optical characteristics.

A twin plane inclined to the direction of vision, so that differently oriented individuals overlap, also leads to confusing effects, and in parallel light between crossed polarizers, the overlapping portions may not extinguish for any position of the polarizers. The same effect is often seen in a crowd of single crystals oriented at random : the overlapping portions do not extinguish.

**Optical properties of spherulites.** A spherulite, composed of many crystals radiating from a point, shows between crossed polarizers in parallel light a general illumination interrupted by a black cross : those crystals that are in extinction positions do not transmit light, while those in intermediate positions are illuminated, so that two directions at right angles (the vibration directions of the polarizers) are dark while intermediate regions show interference colours. The maltese-cross effect looks superficially like the convergent light figure of a uniaxial single crystal, but obviously has a different origin, since it is produced in parallel light. In isolated spherulites it may be possible to measure the principal refractive indices—those for the radial and tangential directions—by immersion methods, and this information, by comparison with the properties of single crystals of the same substance, may reveal which crystal direction is the radial growth direction of the spherulite. In a solid composed of a mass of joined spherulites—as in many crystalline high polymer specimens—this cannot be done, but it is at any rate possible to determine by means of the quartz wedge which vibration direction, the radial or the tangential, has the higher refractive index, and this information is sometimes useful in revealing the molecular orientation in the spherulite (Bunn, 1953).

Spherulites of certain substances—monomeric and inorganic substances as well as high polymers—when grown under certain conditions show between crossed polarizers a zigzag black cross instead of the usual straight-armed one ; evidently the extinction direction is not consistently parallel to the radius but veers regularly as one proceeds from the centre outwards. Others show, in addition to a straight-armed black cross, a series of concentric dark rings with illuminated regions between them (Wallerant, 1907; Gaubert, 1908, 1916, 1927; Keller, 1955). These curious optical effects are due to twisted or helical growth of the crystals instead of the more usual straightforward radial growth. It is curious that crystal distortion should take this regular form ; it has not been satisfactorily explained, though the fact that it occurs when growth takes place in a viscous melt or gel would appear to be a useful clue (Morse and Donnay, 1936).

# IV

## IDENTIFICATION OF TRANSPARENT
## CRYSTALS UNDER THE MICROSCOPE

In this chapter the sequence of observations followed in the microscopic method of identification is outlined. The immersion method for the identification of small separate crystals forms the main subject of this chapter, though some remarks on methods for large aggregates will be found at the end. When the immersion method is to be used aggregates may be crushed or ground carefully.

A preliminary observation is made in ordinary transmitted light to see whether the solid is transparent or not. It must be remembered that the amount of light transmitted is greatest when the solid is immersed in a medium of similar refractive index; transparent solids of very high refractive index, in air or in a liquid of low index, may appear opaque, especially if they are aggregates of small particles, on account of the total internal reflection of light at inclined surfaces. Therefore, if the particles appear opaque when immersed in a liquid of refractive index 1·4–1·5, a liquid of much higher index—say 1·7–1·8—should be tried. (The polarizer of the microscope, though not necessary for this observation, may be left in position; in fact, it is hardly ever necessary to remove it.)

In general chemical work the great majority of substances encountered, when in the form of small microscopic particles, are likely to be in some degree transparent, and can therefore be studied by methods employing transmitted light. For completely opaque particles it must be admitted that the chances of identification by any microscopic method are rather small, unless well-formed crystals large enough to be handled individually are available: such crystals may be mounted on a microscope stage goniometer, and if sufficient angular measurements can be obtained it may be possible to use Barker's morphological method of identification. (See Porter and Spiller, 1951, 1956.)

For opaque crystals too small to be handled individually, only general observations of shape can be made, and for this purpose it is best to use diffused light illuminating the crystals from above on one side of the microscope. Such observations will not carry us very far—we may be able to recognize cubes or octahedra or hexagonal prisms or other shapes, but in the absence of angular measurements or indeed measurements of any characteristics at all, identification in the strict sense of the word is scarcely possible. In case any readers happen to be metallurgists, I hasten to add that experience in dealing with a particular system (in the phase rule sense of the word) may show that certain characteristic shapes or formations recognizable by simple observation are indicative of the presence of certain phases. In metallurgy the body of experience built up by a large number of observations of polished and subsequently etched surfaces of metal specimens is used with great effect in 'spotting' particular constituents. Metallurgical textbooks, such as Rosenhain's *Introduction to Physical Metallurgy* (1935), should be consulted for further information on this highly specialized branch of crystallography. Similar methods may be used, and often are used, for non-metallic systems, once the necessary experience has been gained. But experience obviously has to be built up for every different system individually; if a new consti-tuent is added, the picture may be entirely changed, because new phases may be formed or familiar phases may grow in unfamiliar shapes and will have to be identified by methods of general validity before the necessary experience for specialized inspection methods can be built up. It is with the methods of general validity that we are concerned in this book.

When a solid substance is seen to be transparent, the next step is to observe whether it is isotropic or not. The analyser is introduced (crossed with respect to the polarizer), and the polarizers (or alterna-tively the particles) are rotated. If the particles remain dark for all positions of the crossed polarizers they are isotropic, and their refractive index can be measured by the method described at the beginning of the previous chapter. Note at this point that crystals belonging to the optically uniaxial systems which happen to grow as thin plates (of tetragonal, hexagonal, or trigonal outline) tend to lie flat on the micro-scope slide, and in this position their optic axes lie along the line of vision and the crystals therefore appear isotropic. If, however, the iris diaphragm of the substage condenser is opened to give strongly con-vergent light, such crystals will show interference colours, thus betray-ing their birefringent character; and an observation of the convergent light figure will confirm that they are uniaxial. In any case, it is un-likely that all the crystals will be lying flat; in a crowd of crystals some will almost certainly be tilted or even standing on edge, and in parallel light these will show interference colours, revealing their birefringent character. In case of doubt the crystals may be deliberately tilted. If a 'universal stage' is available the microscope slide may be readily tilted in any direction. If not, the crystals should be immersed in a viscous liquid such as glycerol or dibutyl phthalate; if the microscope is tilted so that its stage is not horizontal, or in any case if the cover-glass is disturbed, the liquid will flow slowly and the crystals will turn over; observation between crossed polarizers while the crystals are moving will show whether they are birefringent or not. (This is also a useful way of studying the shapes of microscopic crystals, the analyser being removed for this purpose.)

**Cubic crystals and amorphous substances.** Isotropic solids, if they are truly isotropic (not merely aggregates of very small birefringent crystals too small to show interference colours), are either crystals belonging to the cubic system or amorphous substances like glasses or gels in which there is no regular arrangement of atoms. Crystalline substances are likely to show some signs of regular structure; if they are well formed and their shape is obvious, isotropic crystals should have a shape consistent with cubic symmetry (see Fig. 37). Even broken fragments of crystals are likely to show occasional edges, corners, or cleavage surfaces suggesting the original shape. Substances such as ammonium chloride and bromide which grow in skeletal forms often have rounded surfaces, but the occurrence of fragments branching at right angles does give an indication of an ordered internal structure.

The magnitude of the refractive index of an isotropic crystal usually leads to unequivocal identification. In the tables published by Winchell (1931) and Lange (1956) for inorganic laboratory products and Larsen and Berman (1934) and Winchell (1951) for minerals, crystals are arranged in order of their principal refractive index, and it is therefore a straightforward matter to find which crystal has the refractive index which has been measured. It may happen that the measured value does not correspond with any in the lists; in this case, there are two possibilities. One is that the substance is a mixed crystal or crystalline solid solution, the refractive index of which varies continuously with the composition (the tables mentioned indicate the known variations); a hint of such variation is often given by the sample itself—some crystals may have a slightly higher index than others. The second possibility is that the substance is one whose refractive index has not previously been measured, in which case it obviously cannot be identified by this method.

Glasses may reveal their nature by exhibiting conchoidal (curved, shell-like) fractures. The composition of a one- or two-component glass may be deduced from its refractive index if the system has previously been studied; the indices of a number of glasses are given in Winchell's tables. For three-component glasses the refractive index alone cannot give the composition; but if the refractive index and one other property —say the density—can be measured, it may be possible to specify the composition.

Precipitated amorphous substances usually appear to be irregular isotropic masses. They usually tend to hold varying amounts of solvent and therefore show variable refractive indices. Usually they cannot be identified with certainty.

Irregular masses which appear isotropic may consist of aggregates of anisotropic crystals which are individually too small to show inter-ference phenomena between crossed polarizers; each crystal may be of submicroscopic size. The single measurable refractive index is an average value lying between the principal indices of the crystal in question. Weakly birefringent substances are the most likely to appear in this form, but any substance may do so provided the individual crystals are small enough; the higher the birefringence, the smaller the individual crystals must be in order to appear isotropic. Slaked lime, $Ca(OH)_2$, which has a moderate birefringence ($\omega = 1 \cdot 57$, $\epsilon = 1 \cdot 54$), sometimes forms apparently isotropic masses; in such cases it is always advisable to increase the intensity of illumination (still using crossed polarizers) by opening the iris diaphragm of the condensing lens of the microscope, when it may happen that vague patches of feeble interference colours (greys of the first order) indicate the presence of minute birefringent crystals. Strained glass may also show weak birefringence, but the glassy character will probably be betrayed by conchoidal fractures. In any such case the specimen should be referred to the higher court of inquiry by X-ray examination; this method is dealt with in the next chapter.

**Optically uniaxial crystals.** When a crystalline substance is found to be birefringent one proceeds with the determination of its principal refractive indices by the methods already described. If the crystals are flat plates, apparently isotropic when lying flat on the slide, they are evidently uniaxial;† the principal index $\omega$ is given by the apparently isotropic plates, while plates standing on edge give $\omega$ for light vibrating in the plane of the plate and $\epsilon$ for light vibrating normal to the plate.

For crystals which are not plate-like it may not be possible to decide

---

† Flat biaxial crystals in which one of the optic axes happens to be precisely normal to the plane of the plate will appear isotropic; but this situation is rare.

from the appearance of the crystals whether they belong to one of the uniaxial systems (tetragonal, hexagonal, trigonal) or one of the biaxial systems (orthorhombic, monoclinic, triclinic). It should then be assumed initially that there are three principal indices $\alpha$, $\beta$, and $\gamma$ to be measured; evidence of uniaxial or biaxial character is bound to turn up in the course of the observations. Thus, the general procedure is to observe the upper and lower indices (for the two extinction positions) of numerous fragments in a range of liquids, random orientation being assured by crushing if necessary. The index $\alpha$ is the lowest of the lower values, $\gamma$ is the highest of the upper values, while $\beta$ is the highest of the lower values or the lowest of the upper values. If the crystals happen to be uniaxial positive, then $\beta$ will be found to be equal to $\alpha$—that is to say, every crystal will give a constant lower value: $\beta = \alpha = \omega$. If the crystals are uniaxial negative, $\beta$ will be found to be equal to $\gamma$—every crystal will give a constant upper value: $\beta = \gamma = \omega$.

The uniaxial character may be checked, if possible, by observing (on a crystal which appears isotropic or nearly so) the convergent light figure, either by introducing the Bertrand lens or by removing the eye-piece. It is useful to do this because some biaxial crystals have two indices so close together that it is scarcely possible to detect the difference by the immersion method. Thus, potassium nitrate has $\alpha = 1\cdot335$, $\beta = 1\cdot505_6$, $\gamma = 1\cdot506_4$. The convergent light figure shows, however, not the black cross of a uniaxial crystal, but (for the 45° position of the polarizers) the two black hyperbolae of a biaxial crystal; careful observation is necessary to confirm this, because the hyperbolae are very close together (the optic axial angle $2V$ being only 7° and $2E$ $10\frac{1}{2}°$).

If a uniaxial convergent light figure is seen, the optical sign of the crystal may be checked by the use of the quartz wedge in the manner described in the previous chapter. This is not necessary (except as confirmation) unless for any reason it is not possible to obtain actual measurements of both $\omega$ and $\epsilon$.

Needle-like crystals naturally lie on the microscope slide with their long axes parallel to the slide, and it may not be possible to find tilted crystals; and even crushing may not yield fragments which lie in all possible orientations. However, even when the needle axis is invariably parallel to the slide, all orientations obtainable by rolling a needle are likely to be encountered, and observations of a number of crystals should be sufficient to give all the information required. The first thing to do is to observe the extinction direction; if extinction is consistently parallel to the length, the crystals may be uniaxial, the direction of elongation being necessarily the unique geometrical axis and therefore also the optic axis; but they may also be biaxial—either orthorhombic, the direction of elongation being any one of the three axes, or monoclinic elongated along the $b$ axis (since the $b$ axis of a monoclinic crystal is the only direction which has an axis of the indicatrix coincident with it). For all these types the refractive index for light vibrating along the needle axis is constant; but for light vibrating perpendicular to the needle axis the refractive index is constant only for uniaxial crystals; for biaxial types it is variable. We return to the biaxial types in the next section; meanwhile the position is that needle crystals with parallel extinction which give two constant refractive indices are uniaxial. It only remains to discover which of these indices is $\omega$ and which $\epsilon$. The latter is the value for light vibrating along the needle axis (the optic axis); if the vibration direction of the polarizer is known, it will be obvious which of the two measured indices is $\epsilon$; if not, the use of the quartz wedge will decide the question.

Uniaxial bipyramids and rhombohedra (usually recognized by shape and symmetrical extinction), when lying on the slide on their faces, will not give $\epsilon$ but a value lying somewhere between $\omega$ and $\epsilon$. Hence the need for breaking the crystals to give random orientation. Crystals having good rhombohedral or pyramidal cleavages (like calcite) may, even when crushed, give many fragments which still lie inconveniently on the cleavage faces; nevertheless, irregular-shaped fragments which will lie in random orientation are sure to be produced in sufficient numbers for the determination of $\epsilon$.

Optically uniaxial crystals may be tetragonal, hexagonal, or trigonal. If it is possible to recognize a shape characteristic of a particular system this information is useful supplementary evidence; but it must be emphasized that the refractive index values by themselves are usually sufficient for identification.

**Optically biaxial crystals.** The measurement of the three principal refractive indices of a biaxial substance presents no difficulties when the crystals are large enough to be crushed to provide irregular fragments which will lie on the slide in random orientation. When the crystals are too small for crushing to be desirable or effective, and are bounded by a very few plane faces, some caution is necessary; one must make sure of observing not only those crystals which are lying on their principal faces but also crystals tilted in various ways (because crystals lying on their principal faces may not give their principal indices). If a universal stage is available this presents no difficulty; but even without the universal stage it is not as difficult as might be supposed to find suitably oriented crystals; even thin plates, the worst type of crystals in this respect, may be found tilted at various angles or standing on edge, especially in a crowd of crystals.

Crushing has been recommended as a primary method because it is safe and will lead to the determination of the principal refractive indices of any crystalline substance, provided a sufficient number of randomly oriented fragments is observed; it is a beginner's method. But the more experienced worker may often dispense with it, when the crystals being examined have a well-defined polyhedral shape. If the relation between crystal shape and optical properties is properly understood, it is possible to determine the principal indices by a limited number of observations on crystals selected because they lie in such positions that they necessarily show their principal indices.

For instance, crystals which appear to possess three mutually perpendicular planes of symmetry, or two planes intersecting in a twofold axis, or three twofold axes, are probably orthorhombic, with rectangular unit cells; and if, on looking along the presumed axial directions, extinction is parallel to crystal edges or bisects the angles between crystal edges, this conclusion is confirmed. Any crystal lying so that an axial direction lies along the line of vision necessarily shows two of the principal refractive indices; and views down two different axial directions yield the three principal refractive indices. Crystals such as those of sodium carbonate monohydrate (Fig. 49) are ideal for such observations. At the same time, these observations yield a knowledge of the orientation of the principal vibration directions (the principal axes of the indicatrix) with respect to the crystal axes; thus, for sodium carbonate monohydrate the vibration direction for $\alpha$ is the direction of elongation of the crystal, while the vibration direction for $\beta$ is the zone axis of the terminal faces.

Crystals which appear to possess one twofold axis, or one plane of symmetry, or both (the twofold axis $b$ being normal to the plane of symmetry) are probably monoclinic; if so, crystals lying with their presumed $b$ axes parallel to the microscope slide will show extinction parallel to this $b$ axis, and the refractive index for this vibration direction is one of the principal refractive indices. The other two principal indices will be shown by crystals lying with their $b$ axes along the line of vision; for this aspect of the crystal, extinction is not parallel to a principal edge or to the bisector of edge angles.†

† Note that in rare cases extinction angles may be so small as to escape detection.

Crystals which appear to possess only a centre of symmetry or no symmetry at all are probably triclinic, and will probably not show their principal refractive indices when lying on their faces; such crystals should be crushed.

Biaxial crystals of inorganic substances can usually be identified by their refractive indices alone; it is true that biaxial crystals are far more numerous than uniaxial ones, but this is balanced by the fact that they have three principal refractive indices—three different measurable characteristics—as against two for the uniaxial types; it is rare to find two substances having their three principal refractive indices equal within the limits of experimental error. Nevertheless, it is always desirable to discover, if possible, the crystal system and the relation between the principal vibration directions and the crystal axes. This information will often be simply confirmatory, but for certain mineral systems in which considerable variation of composition (and therefore of refractive indices) may occur, the magnitudes of the refractive indices alone are not enough for unequivocal identification; it is necessary to discover the crystal symmetry and the orientation of the indicatrix with respect to the crystal axes. For orthorhombic crystals the principal axes of the indicatrix necessarily coincide with the unit cell axes, and it is simply a matter of observing which vibration directions lie along characteristic axial directions (such as a direction of elongation, a principal prism zone, or a polar axis). For monoclinic crystals it is necessary to find which vibration direction lies along the $b$ axis, and the angles made by the other vibration directions with respect to the $a$ and $c$ axes. For triclinic crystals the indicatrix is not fixed in any way by symmetry; it may be possible to determine extinction directions with respect to characteristic morphological directions, though not to define precisely the orientation of the indicatrix, unless a universal stage is available. The necessary information for these purposes is normally gathered in the course of the determination of the refractive indices; it is applied to the operation of identification by the use of the tables of Larsen and Berman (1934) and Winchell (1951) for minerals and Winchell (1931) and Lange (1952) for laboratory chemicals.

For organic substances, the available information has been collected and arranged by Winchell (1954). For some substances the only refractive indices which have been recorded are those given by crystals lying on their principal faces; these are not, of course, always principal indices, but they may be equally useful for identification purposes. Such information is included in Winchell's tables.

If the crystals being examined are not well-formed polyhedra, the scope of such observations is naturally more limited. Perhaps the commonest type of partly defined shape is a rod somewhat rounded so that there are no definite faces on it. The only definite morphological feature here is a single direction—the long axis of the rod. If extinction is consistently parallel, and it is found that the crystals are biaxial (see pp. 100–101), they are almost certainly† either orthorhombic or else monoclinic with the $b$ axis as the direction of elongation. It is possible to determine which vibration direction lies parallel to the rod by the methods already given (for instance, by the use of the quartz wedge). If extinction is inclined, the crystals are either monoclinic with $a$ or $c$ as the direction of elongation, or else triclinic. The extinction angle will vary with the orientation of the rod-like crystal on the slide. If it is found that crystals which show the maximum extinction angle also show two of the principal indices, then the substance is probably monoclinic, and the maximum extinction angle represents the angle made by one of the principal vibration directions with the direction of elongation. Otherwise, the crystals are triclinic.

The observation of convergent light figures may often provide confirmation of the orientation of the indicatrix. The plane of the optic axes is the $\alpha\gamma$ plane, while the normal to this plane is the $\beta$ vibration direction. For a positive crystal the acute bisectrix is the $\gamma$ vibration direction, while for a negative crystal it is the $\alpha$ vibration direction.

Even when the crystals being examined are quite irregular fragments, it may be possible to obtain some information on their symmetry, if certain types of dispersion of the optic axes are observed (see pp. 86–9).

The optical properties of crystals are usually quite reliable criteria for identification; but occasionally crystals have submicroscopic cracks and cavities, and although appearing quite normal, give refractive indices lower than those of an entirely solid crystal. This phenomenon, which is obviously very misleading, is fortunately very rare, but has been observed in anhydrite (calcium sulphate) and calcite (calcium carbonate) prepared in the laboratory. In cases of doubt, X-ray powder photographs should be taken—see Chapter V.

**Mixtures.** When the constituents of a mixture differ markedly from each other in appearance the refractive indices and other optical properties of each can be determined without difficulty. This is very frequently the case even when the shapes of the crystals are not very well defined; for instance, a mixture may consist quite obviously of

† See footnote to p. 101.

three constituents, one in the form of comparatively large, rounded, roughly equidimensional crystals, another in the form of small rod-like crystals, and a third in the form of small rectangular or cubic crystals. There is no difficulty in measuring the properties of each constituent in such a mixture as this. Even when the differences between constituents are much slighter and less easy to specify, they may be none the less obvious.

Even when there are no morphological distinguishing features, how-ever, it is very often possible to measure the refractive indices of different constituents. Two or more isotropic substances can be identified, provided that their refractive indices are not closer than 0·002. A mix-ture of one anisotropic substance with one, two, or more isotropic sub-stances likewise presents no difficulty. Plate III e shows a mixture of sodium bromate (cubic, $n = 1·616$) and sodium bromide dihydrate (monoclinic, $\alpha = 1·513$, $\beta = 1·519$, $\gamma = 1·525$) immersed in a liquid of refractive index 1·54. In this case the constituents are distinguishable by two features—one substance (sodium bromate) is not only isotropic but also its refractive index is much higher than those of the other substance. Two anisotropic constituents can be identified if the refrac-tive indices of one lie wholly above those of the other; and in fact, any number of anisotropic constituents can be identified if their respective ranges of refractive indices are quite distinct. Serious difficulties only occur if there are present in a mixture two or more anisotropic consti-tuents whose refractive index ranges overlap—for instance, if the $\gamma$ of one constituent is higher than the $\alpha$ of another. It will be evident that there are two (or more) constituents in the mixture, since two (or more) values of $\beta$ are observed; but, unless there are some distinguishing features (such as differences of shape or size, or the presence of striations or other marks on one constituent, or differences of dispersion), it will not be possible to measure the other indices. Identification may some-times be achieved on the basis of the $\beta$ values alone or perhaps by $\beta$ values aided by measurements of optic axial angles; if not, the mixture is one of those which cannot be identified by microscopic methods. This situation is most likely to arise when one of the constituents is a very strongly birefringent substance such as a carbonate or a nitrate.

**Identification when it is not possible to measure refractive indices.** In some circumstances it may be desired to identify sub-stances without removing them from their mother liquor. Direct identifi-cation—that is, by measuring properties and looking up the measured values in tables—is not possible, and the evidence obtainable is confined to shape, vibration directions, optic axial angles, and the like; but if such characteristics of all the substances likely to be formed in the particular circumstances are known, it may be possible to conclude that the crystals can only be one of the likely substances. For instance, it may be known that one of the possible substances grows as plate-like crystals of a certain shape, which when lying flat on the slide give a convergent light figure showing part of a biaxial figure, oriented in a particular way with respect to the crystal edges; if none of the other likely substances has similar characteristics, these obviously form a good criterion for identification. Hartshorne and Stuart (1960) give numerous examples of the value of such observations.

The value of measurements of the magnitude of the optic axial angle has been urged by Bryant (1932); and where dispersion of the optic axes occurs, the variation of the optic axial angle with light frequency is a highly characteristic feature which is valuable evidence for identity. (See Bryant, 1941, 1943.)

These methods of 'spotting' constituents of particular systems (in the phase rule sense of the word) are akin to those of the metallurgist, but have far greater scope on account of the wealth of observable or measurable characteristics in transparent crystals. They are most closely allied, however, to those of the petrologist, who by observing birefringence, extinction directions, optic axial angles, and the like in thin slices of rocks, and referring the information to his knowledge of the characteristics and occurrence of mineral species, is able to identify such species with rapidity and certainty. For information on these methods, see Rogers and Kerr's *Optical Mineralogy* (1942).

The thin-section methods of the petrologist may be used for artificial specimens which are in the form of large aggregates—specimens of such materials as refractories, bricks, and boiler scales. Instead of powdering them and using immersion methods, it is possible to grind thin sections and examine them. When it is simply a question of distinguishing between a few possible constituents of known characteristics, this is a useful method. But in unfamiliar systems the powder method is likely to be more useful for identification purposes; the principal function of the thin-section method in such circumstances is to provide information on the distribution, orientation, or size of the crystals of the different constituents.

Substances which are too opaque for the use of transmitted light methods are rare, apart from metals; they include chiefly sulphides and a few oxides. Aggregates of such materials may be examined by the metallurgist's method of grinding and polishing a flat surface. The scope of such methods is much greater for non-cubic than for cubic substances, since by the use of reflected polarized light it is possible to measure birefringence. (See Phillips, 1933.)

**Fusion methods and chemical methods under the microscope.** Observation of the changes that take place when crystalline substances are heated or cooled can form the basis of effective methods of identification and characterization. The material, between microscope slide and cover-glass in a temperature-controlled enclosure on the microscope stage, is observed, for instance, while the temperature rises; the melting-point, which is of course widely used in the identification of organic substances, can be measured accurately and conveniently in this way. A mixed melting-point can show whether two substances are the same or not, while observations of polymorphic changes during heating or cooling, and the growth habits of the crystals (for every different crystalline species has its idiosyncrasies) may provide additional useful information. The methods are described in McCrone's *Fusion Methods in Chemical Microscopy* (1957). The measurement of melting-points under the microscope is also much used in the characterization of high polymers, the melting-points of which vary with minor changes of molecular structure (Bunn, 1957).

For inorganic substances, chemical reactions may be carried out on a small scale on microscope slides, the crystallization of reaction products being watched. Tests for particular ions or atom groups have been devised, the criterion of identity being, not solubility or colour, as in macroscopic qualitative chemical analysis, but crystallographic properties. For information on such methods, see *Handbook of Chemical Microscopy*, by Chamot and Mason (1958).

# IDENTIFICATION BY X-RAY
# POWDER PHOTOGRAPHS

SOLID substances cannot always be identified by measuring crystal shapes and optical properties. In the first place, the crystals in a specimen may be too small to be studied as individuals under the microscope. Secondly, even if the individual crystals are large enough, the information obtainable by microscopic methods may not be sufficient for unequivocal identification. The measured refractive indices may be (within the limits of error of measurement) equal to those of two different substances; this is rare, but may occur if for any reason only rough measurements can be made. Or it may happen that the measured refractive indices do not correspond exactly with those of any known substance, either because the specimen in question is an unfamiliar substance whose optical properties have not previously been recorded, or because it is a mixed crystal whose refractive indices lie between those of the pure constituents. Finally, if crystals are completely opaque (as in metals and alloys), microscopic technique is limited to observations by reflected light. In metallurgical specimens, often the only evidence available is that provided by the shapes of the intergrown constituents in the polycrystalline aggregate; in familar systems, such evidence may be sufficient for identification, but in unfamiliar systems (especially the more complex ones) it is likely to be inadequate. In any of these circumstances, examination by X-ray methods may provide an answer to the problems involved.

**The production of X-rays.** X-rays are electromagnetic waves of very high frequency and short wavelength, and are produced when rapidly moving electrons, accelerated by potentials of some tens of thousands of volts, collide with atoms; the energy released when the electrons are suddenly stopped is given out in the form of electromagnetic waves having a wavelength of around 1 Å ($10^{-8}$ cm), the order of magnitude of interatomic distances.

In X-ray tubes the electrons are produced either by ionization of air at a moderately low pressure (in 'gas tubes') or by emission from a heated filament at a much lower pressure (in 'hot cathode' or Coolidge tubes). In most commercially obtainable X-ray tubes, one of which is

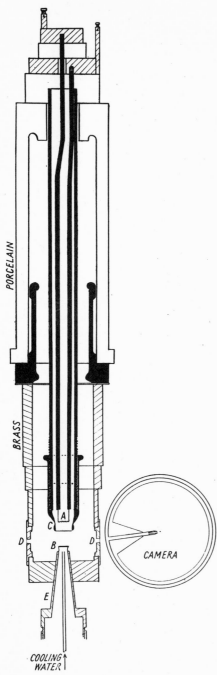

COOLING
WATER

illustrated in Fig. 58, the latter method is used. An electrically heated tungsten filament $A$ emits electrons, which are accelerated by a high voltage of some tens of thousands of volts maintained between the filament and the target $B$. (In some generators, high-voltage A.C. is applied, but only one-half of the cycle is passed by the one-way electron stream. In other generators, D.C. obtained by full-wave rectification and smoothing is used, for there are some advantages to be gained by this arrangement; see Peiser, Rooksby, and Wilson, 1955.)

In practice the anode, which is water-cooled, is kept at earth potential, while the filament is at a negative high voltage. A metal shield $C$ surrounding the filament and kept at the same potential has the effect of focusing the electron stream on a small area of the target. The acceleration of the electrons by the high voltage gives them sufficient energy to bring about the emission of X-rays on striking the metal target $B$. The part of the tube surrounding the filament and target is made of brass (the rest being porcelain), and is cooled by a water-jacket. The tube illustrated in Fig. 58 is continuously evacuated, through a wide tube, by a diffusion pump using

FIG. 58. A demountable X-ray tube. $A$, filament; $B$, target; $C$, focusing shield; $D$, windows; $E$, target holder.

low-vapour-pressure oil, backed by a rotary pump. The X-rays are emitted from the target in all directions, but only a small proportion is used: windows $D$ of thin aluminium foil allow the exit of only those rays which make a small angle with the target face. This type of X-ray tube is demountable: the target and windows are readily detachable, and the whole of the porcelain part of the tube can be taken off to fit a new filament. All joints are simply flat or conical surfaces in contact, sealed by 'plasticine' made from low-vapour-pressure grease. Targets of different materials can be mounted in duplicate holders such as $E$, so that rapid changes may be made. Sealed glass X-ray tubes can also be obtained; their advantage is that they do not have to be continuously evacuated, require no attention during operation, and demand no expenditure of time for maintenance; on the other hand, if more than one type of target must be used, extra complete tubes are required; also the emission decreases during the useful life of the tube owing to the deposition of a solid containing tungsten (from the filament) all over the inside of the tube, including the target and the insides of the windows; and the X-ray beam may be contaminated with undesired wavelengths from this same deposit.

In the X-ray tube illustrated the filament is a close helix of tungsten wire, set horizontally; the shield surrounding it brings the electrons to a focus along a horizontal line. For most crystallographic purposes a narrow X-ray beam is taken at a small angle 5–7° to the plane of the target; at this angle the line focus appears foreshortened so that the source is effectively a point—or, more precisely, a small area, not much larger than the collimating systems used in X-ray cameras. Ideally, the X-ray source should be as small as possible, but in practice, if the focus is made too sharp, a hole is burnt in the target after a short period of use.

**X-ray wavelengths.** The wavelength distribution in the X-ray beam depends on the material of the target and on the accelerating voltage used. Fig. 59 shows the sort of wavelength distribution given by a copper target when bombarded by electrons accelerated by 50,000 volts. There is a continuous band of wavelengths, often referred to as 'white' radiation; these waves are produced when the rapidly moving electrons lose energy, and since the energy is usually not all lost at once but may be released in a series of collisions and secondary processes, a whole range of wavelengths is produced. The limit of this range on the short wavelength side is rigidly determined by the quantum relation $Ve = h\nu$, where $V$ is the accelerating potential, $e$ the electronic charge, $h$ Planck's constant, and $\nu$ the frequency of the shortest waves. If the potential is expressed in volts $(V)$, the shortest wavelength in Å is given by $1 \cdot 234 \times 10^4/V$. In addition to the continuous band, and superimposed on it, are very narrow peaks of great intensity, the wavelengths of which are rigidly determined by the nature of the target material. They are produced by a secondary process of energy release: the innermost $(K)$

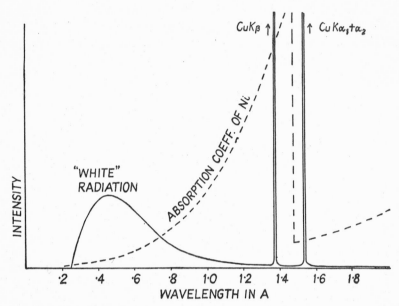

FIG. 59. Intensity distribution in X-ray beam from copper target; accelerating voltage, 50,000 V. $K\beta$ has about 1/6 the intensity of $K\alpha$. A nickel filter 0·021 mm thick reduces this ratio to 1/600 owing to the form of the absorption curve. $K\alpha$ is actually a very close doublet.

electrons of the copper atom are ejected during the primary collision, leaving the $K$ low-energy levels vacant; electrons of various high-energy levels then fall into these vacant low-energy $K$ levels, releasing energy in the form of X-rays of sharply defined wavelengths. The set of radiations produced in this way is known as the $K$ series of copper; by far the strongest peaks are $\alpha_1$, $\alpha_2$, and $\beta$ components; the wavelengths of $\alpha_1$ and $\alpha_2$ are so nearly identical that resolution of them occurs only in special circumstances. The intensity of $\alpha_1$ (1·5405 Å) is twice that of $\alpha_2$ (1·5443 Å).

For most crystallographic purposes a monochromatic beam, that is, a beam consisting of one wavelength only, is desirable. Actually the $\alpha$ components are so strong in comparison with all other wavelengths present that the unfiltered beam may be used for some purposes; the 'white' radiation merely increases the background intensity of X-ray diffraction photographs, and this may not constitute a serious disadvantage; the $\beta$ component produces its own diffraction effects, but provided $\alpha$ and $\beta$ diffractions are readily distinguished, the presence of the latter can be tolerated. For powder photographs it is best always

TABLE II

*Targets, Wavelengths, and Filters*

| Target | | | | $\beta$ Filter | | |
|---|---|---|---|---|---|---|
| Element with atomic number | Line | Wavelength in $\mathring{A}$ | Peak kV | Element and absorption edge ($\mathring{A}$) | $gm/cm^2$ | Thickness in mm necessary to reduce $K\beta/K\alpha$ to 1/600 |
| Mo, 42 | $K\alpha_1$ $K\alpha_2$ $K\beta_1$ | 0·70926 0·71354 0·63225 | 80 | Zr, 0·689 | 0·069 | 0·108 |
| Cu, 29 | $K\alpha_1$ $K\alpha_2$ $K\beta_1$ | 1·54051 1·54433 1·39217 | 50 | Ni, 1·488 | 0·019 | 0·021 |
| Ni, 28 | $K\alpha_1$ $K\alpha_2$ $K\beta_1$ | 1·65784 1·66169 1·50010 | 50 | Co, 1·608 | 0·015 | 0·018 |
| Co, 27 | $K\alpha_1$ $K\alpha_2$ $K\beta_1$ | 1·78892 1·79278 1·62075 | 45 | Fe, 1·743 | 0·014 | 0·018 |
| Fe, 26 | $K\alpha_1$ $K\alpha_2$ $K\beta_1$ | 1·93597 1·93991 1·75653 | 40 | Mn, 1·896 | 0·012 | 0·016 |
| Cr, 24 | $K\alpha_1$ $K\alpha_2$ $K\beta_1$ | 2·28962 2·29351 2·08480 | 35 | V, 2·269 | 0·009 | 0·016 |

to remove the $\beta$ component, and this may be done by placing a suitable filter in the beam; the absorption coefficient of any chemical element suddenly changes at a particular wavelength corresponding to the resonance frequency (see Fig. 59), and by choosing an element whose absorption edge lies between the wavelengths of the $\alpha$ and $\beta$ components in the X-ray beam, the intensity of the $\beta$ component may be reduced to a negligible level. For the very frequently used copper radiation, nickel foil accomplishes this end; if it is of thickness 0·021 mm, it reduces the intensity of $K\beta$ to 1/600 that of $K\alpha$, and at the same time reduces the intensity of some of the 'white' radiation in comparison with $K\alpha$. Information for targets of other metals is given in Table II. The filter may, if desired, be made the window of the X-ray tube; or, if the window is aluminium, the filter may be placed in a holder in front of the window or on the camera. If it is necessary to remove 'white' radiation altogether, this is accomplished by reflecting the X-ray beam by a particular face of a large crystal set at the correct angle; sodium chloride, lithium fluoride, pentaerythritol, and urea nitrate have been used for this purpose because they give very strong reflections (Fankuchen, 1937; Lonsdale, 1941; Brindley, 1955). A simple method of mounting is described by Lipson, Nelson, and Riley (1945), who also give useful information on the relative merits of various crystals and their special applications. Urea nitrate gives the strongest reflected beam, but is liable to be distorted, and on this account to give not very sharp reflections; it also, like pentaerythritol, deteriorates rapidly in the X-ray beam. Sodium chloride is more stable, and is therefore much used; but Brindley (1955) recommends lithium fluoride for general purposes. The reflected beam consists of $K\alpha_1$ and $K\alpha_2$, with negligible proportions of other wavelengths; its intensity is much reduced in comparison with the primary beam, so much so that exposures must be increased tenfold or more; this is the price of strict monochromatism. The intensity of the reflected beam is increased by a factor of 1·5–1·6 by grinding an artificial flat surface on the reflecting crystal at a suitable angle (Fankuchen, 1937; Evans, Hirsch, and Kellar, 1948). Johannson (1933) and Guinier (1937) achieved a focusing effect by using a curved crystal as monochromator; but the benefits of the focusing effect can only be effectively used in special focusing cameras, which are mentioned later (p. 129).

For the less frequently used wavelengths, see Peiser, Rooksby, and Wilson (1955). Useful information on the preparation of filters is given by Edwards and Lipson (1941).

To reduce exposures, high-power X-ray tubes have been developed; the limiting factor here is the heat generated at the focal spot on the target. To avoid melting, the target is rotated so that the heat is spread over an increased area (Müller, 1929; Astbury and Preston, 1934; Peiser, Rooksby, and Wilson, 1955).

The wavelength of the $K\alpha$ radiation is determined by the atomic number of the target material; the higher the atomic number, the shorter the wavelength. (The wavelength $\lambda$ is given almost exactly by the expression $\lambda = K/(N-1)^2$, where $N$ is the atomic number and $K$ a constant.)

**Powder diffraction patterns.** When a narrow monochromatic beam of X-rays passes through a small specimen of a powdered crystal-

line solid, or through any polycrystalline specimen in which the crystals
are oriented at random, numerous cones of diffracted beams emerge
from the specimen, and they can be recorded either as circles on a flat
photographic plate or film placed behind the specimen at right angles
to the X-ray beam, or, better still, as arcs on a strip of film encircling
the specimen as in Fig. 60. The latter is preferable because the angular
range of diffracted cones which can be recorded on a circular film is
much greater than on a flat film. The powder method was first used
by Debye and Scherrer (1916) and independently by Hull (1917).

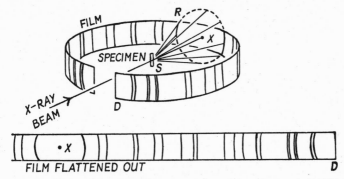

Fig. 60. Arrangement for taking powder photographs. The angle $RSX$ is $2\theta$,
where $\theta$ is the angle of incidence on a set of crystal planes.

With regard to the origin of the diffraction cones, it is sufficient for
the present to remark that each cone consists of a large number of small
diffracted beams, each from a small crystal; and that all the diffracted
beams in any one cone are 'reflections' by one particular type of crystal
plane. Any particular crystal plane can reflect monochromatic X-rays
only when it is at a particular angle $\theta$ to the primary beam; all the little
crystals which happen to lie with this plane at this angle $\theta$ to the
primary beam give a reflection. The angle of reflection is equal to the
angle of incidence; hence the reflected beam makes an angle $2\theta$ with
the primary beam. The reflected beams from all the little crystals which
happen to be suitably oriented therefore form a cone of semi-vertical
angle $2\theta$ having the primary beam as its axis. Each different type of
crystal plane requires a different angle of incidence, and therefore gives
a reflected beam at a different angle to the primary beam; thus,
numerous cones of reflected beams are produced at specific angles, each
cone coming from a different crystal plane.

For the present we shall not inquire into the reason why reflections
are produced only at specific angles, nor into the type of crystal plane

responsible for each cone; we shall merely accept the fact that each crystalline species produces its own characteristic pattern which is different from the patterns given by other species. It is possible to identify substances by means of their X-ray powder photographs without any knowledge of the structures of the crystals or of the theory of diffraction, just as it is possible to use optical emission spectra for the identification of elements without any knowledge of the electron transitions responsible for the emitted rays.

**Powder cameras.** A powder camera consists essentially of an aperture system to define the X-ray beam, a holder for the specimen, and a framework for holding the photographic film. For most identification purposes a camera 9–10 cm in diameter is found satisfactory; an X-ray beam about 0·5 mm wide is generally used, the powder specimen being a little narrower than this—of the order of 0·3 mm.

X-ray cameras are usually made almost entirely of brass; this material is not ideal for the aperture system, as its absorption of the commonly used wavelengths is only moderate; but in practice it is usually found satisfactory. The best aperture system (see Fig. 61) consists of a circular hole 0·5 mm in diameter drilled through a brass cylinder $A$. To prevent X-rays scattered by the edges of the aperture from reaching the film there is a guard tube $B$, 1 mm in diameter. Using this aperture system, powder photographs like that shown in Plate IV are produced. It is found that not much deterioration of quality of the photograph occurs if a slit up to 2 mm long (and still 0·5 mm wide) is used instead of the circular 0·5 mm tube. For instance, in Plate IV, the photographs of zinc oxide and α alumina were taken with the smaller aperture system, while those of sodium sulphite and dickite were taken with the slit system 2 mm long; in the latter the ends of the arcs are a little diffuse, but the centres do not suffer much, except at very small angles. The time of exposure is reduced by using the slit; the whole brass cylinder $AB$ can be withdrawn and replaced by the slit system when required.

Several methods of mounting specimens are used. Ideally, the only solid material in the X-ray beam should be the specimen material itself, but this is only possible if the specimen is a coherent piece of material such as a metal wire; usually, a powder specimen must be held together in some manner, using as little extraneous material as possible. It is sometimes mixed with a trace of adhesive and stuck to a hair or fine glass fibre; the hair must be kept taut by hanging a small lead weight on it. Another method is to mix the powder with some adhesive to form

PLATE IV

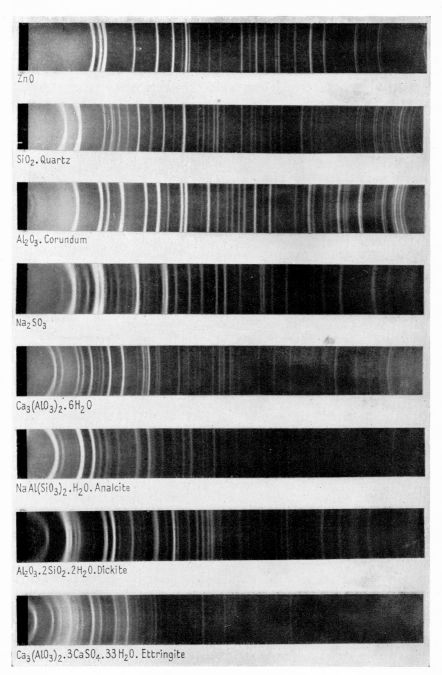

ZnO

SiO₂. Quartz

Al₂O₃. Corundum

Na₂SO₃

Ca₃(AlO₃)₂.6H₂O

NaAl(SiO₃)₂.H₂O. Analcite

Al₂O₃.2SiO₂.2H₂O.Dickite

Ca₃(AlO₃)₂.3CaSO₄.33H₂O. Ettringite

X-ray powder photographs

a paste, and extrude a rod of this from a capillary tube. Substances which are affected by solvents, or are deliquescent, are packed into capillary tubes of lithium beryllium borate glass ('Lindemann glass') which can then be sealed. Lithium beryllium borate is used because it contains only elements of low atomic number, and consequently does not absorb X-rays to any great extent.† Powders containing heavy elements may be mixed with a light diluent such as powdered gum tragacanth (Rooksby, 1942) to reduce the absorption. Metals and alloys are usually examined in the form of filings, and the preparation of uncontaminated specimens thoroughly representative of the lump from which they were filed presents special problems of its own (Hume-Rothery and Raynor, 1941).

The specimen $P$ (Fig. 61), however it is made, should be not more than 0·5 mm wide. It is best to rotate it to ensure random orientation of the crystals (otherwise discontinuous spotty arcs may be produced on the photograph), and for this purpose it is mounted on a rotating holder. Centring may be done by hand, or better, by using a holder fitted with adjusting screws.

To prevent fogging of the film by the primary beam a trap is provided. Its construction is sufficiently explained by Fig. 61; the edges $D$ must be so placed that X-rays $XE$ scattered in the trap cannot reach the film. At the back of the trap is a screw which can be removed ($a$) for centring the specimen by looking through the hole at a light placed at $A$, and ($b$) for adjusting the camera in relation to the X-ray tube, for which purpose a fluorescent screen is placed at $C$. (This must be done before the photographic film is put in the camera.) It is sometimes useful to have the position of the primary beam recorded on the film, but its strength must be very much reduced to avoid fogging. This can be done by drilling out the screw just mentioned until the thickness of brass remaining to obstruct the beam is 1·5 mm; this reduces the primary beam to about the same level of intensity as a strong diffraction arc on an average powder photograph.

The film is in contact with the cylindrical brass frame of the camera and is held in position by springs $S$. Sharp edges $E$ terminate the exposed part of the film abruptly. Light is excluded by a brass cover which fits over the whole camera; the X-ray beam is admitted through a hole covered with black paper. Further details of the construction and use of Debye–Scherrer powder cameras can be found in a paper by

† Lithium beryllium borate glass capillaries become devitrified in moist air in a few days, but will keep indefinitely if stored over anhydrous calcium chloride.

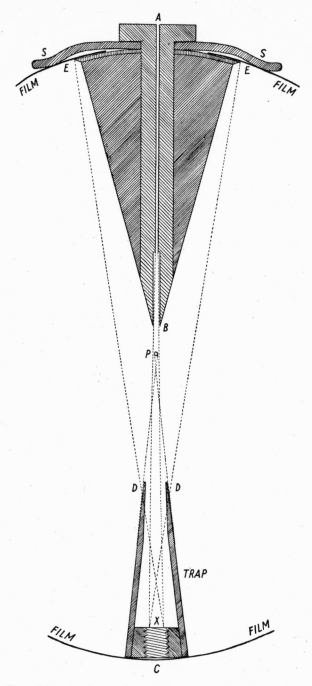

FIG. 61. Essential parts of a powder camera. *A*, aperture system; *B*, guard tube; *CD*, trap; *E*, knife edges; *P*, specimen; *S*, springs; *XE*, path of scattered X-rays.

Bradley, Lipson, and Petch (1941). (See also Peiser, Rooksby, and Wilson, 1955.)

Cameras in which powder photographs of substances maintained at high temperatures may be taken are much used, especially in metallurgy; other special cameras have been designed for low temperatures. For reviews of high and low temperature cameras, see the chapters by Goldschmidt and Steward in *X-ray Diffraction by Polycrystalline Materials*, ed. Peiser, Rooksby, and Wilson (1955). A powder camera for high pressures is described by Frevel (1935).

**Quantum counter methods of recording diffraction patterns.** An alternative method of recording an X-ray diffraction pattern is to use some form of radiation detector which is moved either continuously or in steps across the pattern. The most commonly used detector is the Geiger–Müller counter, in which each quantum of radiation causes an electric pulse to flow between electrodes across which a high voltage is maintained; an amplifier and counting arrangement records the number of quanta in a given time, and so measures the X-ray intensity. The counter is mounted on an arm which can be rotated to record the intensity of diffracted X-rays over a chosen angular range. Since the pattern is not all recorded simultaneously, it is necessary either to minimize fluctuations in the incident X-ray intensity within narrow limits by stabilizing circuits in the X-ray generator, or to use a second counter which monitors the primary beam and to incorporate a circuit which records the ratio of the number of quanta in the diffracted beam to that in the primary beam. The results are usually registered on a chart recorder.

In counter diffractometers it is customary, for the sake of attaining a high sensitivity, to use an extended flat specimen rather than the small cylindrical specimen used in photographic methods, and to irradiate it with a divergent beam. Good resolution is preserved by mounting the flat specimen at the axis of rotation of the counter arm, and rotating it at half the speed of the counter arm; approximate focusing is attained by this arrangement, which is known as the Bragg–Brentano system. Accurate focusing can only be obtained if the surface of the specimen is curved so that it lies on the circle passing through the point of divergence of the X-rays (usually the target of the X-ray tube) and the counter entrance slit, as indicated in Fig. 62; but in practice a sufficient degree of focusing is obtained with a flat specimen (Brentano, 1925, 1937). An additional advantage in sensitivity is obtained by using a line focus in the X-ray tube; the divergence of the

beam in the plane perpendicular to the focusing plane is limited by
Soller slits, which are multiple slits consisting of equally spaced flat
pieces of thin metal foil a fraction of a millimetre apart; the arrangement
is made clear in Fig. 63.

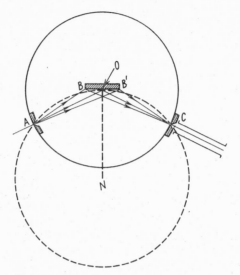

FIG. 62. Bragg-Brentano focusing system.

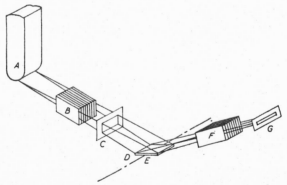

FIG. 63. X-ray optical system of a Geiger-counter diffractometer by North American
Philips Co. Inc. *A*, X-ray tube target; *B*, Soller slits; *C*, scatter slit; *D*, specimen; *E*,
diffractometer axis; *F*, Soller slits; *G*, counter entrance slit.

At its best, the counter diffractometer can give more accurate intensity measurements than photographs measured by a microdensitometer,
and can give results more rapidly; but the equipment is more complex
and requires more effort in maintenance. The accuracy of the results
depends on the number of quanta counted at any angle of diffraction;

small numbers mean large random errors, and for weak diffraction intensities it may be advisable to dispense with automatic working with a chart recorder, and to take separate counts at fixed angles for whatever time is necessary for statistical reliability. For further information see Klug and Alexander (1954), Arndt (1955).

**General characteristics of X-ray powder photographs.** A few examples of X-ray powder photographs, all taken with copper $K\alpha$ radiation, are shown in Plate IV. They vary greatly in complexity; chemically simple crystals of high symmetry give strong patterns containing few arcs, while crystals of complex chemical constitution or of low symmetry give patterns consisting of a large number of less strong arcs. The time of exposure necessary to produce a photograph of convenient intensity is related to the complexity. Under typical conditions —for instance, when a self-rectifying X-ray tube is passing 20 mA and the unsmoothed peak voltage is 60 kV—well-exposed photographs of metals can usually be taken in 10–15 min, using the 2 mm slit aperture in the 9 cm camera just described, while a complex silicate may require over an hour under the same conditions.

Exposures may be shortened by putting a fluorescent screen behind and in contact with the film, so that the optical fluorescence reinforces the direct X-ray effect on the photographic emulsion; or two screens might be used, one in front and one behind the film. (Note that the intensity relations are much changed by the optical fluorescence: weak reflections come out relatively much too weak.)

There is always a certain background intensity on X-ray powder photographs, due partly to the presence of 'white' radiation, which gives diffracted rays over a wide angular range from each crystal plane, partly to a certain amount of incoherent scattering of the $K\alpha$ radiation by the crystals themselves, and partly to X-ray fluorescence of the crystals, which absorb the primary rays and re-emit the energy in the form of longer waves. The last effect may in some circumstances be so strong that serious fogging of the film occurs, and for this reason the wavelength of the primary beam used must be chosen with this effect in mind. X-ray fluorescence is strongest when the wavelength of the absorption edge of the irradiated element (which is almost equal to that of $K\beta_1$ for the element) is slightly longer than the wavelength of the irradiating beam; under these circumstances, in addition to the part of the primary beam diffracted by the crystals another part is converted into the $K$ series of the irradiated element. For instance, the shortest wavelength of the $K$ series (and the absorption edge) of iron is not much longer than that of copper $K\alpha$, and consequently iron-containing crystals fluoresce strongly in copper $K\alpha$ radiation. For substances containing iron, therefore, copper $K\alpha$ radiation is quite unsuitable; cobalt or iron $K\alpha$ should be used. The elements preceding iron in the periodic table also fluoresce in copper $K\alpha$ radiation, but less strongly than iron, the effect diminishing with the atomic number; for calcium, for instance, it is practically negligible.

Fluorescent radiation, when it is not too serious, may be partly absorbed by placing a suitable filter between the specimen and the film. For instance, titanium compounds in copper radiation give rather foggy photographs owing to X-ray fluorescence; the fog is reduced by putting the nickel filter (necessary in any case for removing copper $K\beta$) between the specimen and the film, instead of in the more usual position in front of the camera; it absorbs titanium radiation much more than it does copper $K\alpha$, and the background intensity is therefore reduced in comparison with the diffraction arcs.

Some substances, such as alkaline-earth sulphides, emit visible light when irradiated by X-rays; for these substances it is essential to have a sheet of optically opaque material (such as black paper) between the specimen and the film.

The wavelength used does not, in general, affect to any serious extent the relative intensities of the various arcs in a pattern, but it does control the scale of the pattern; the longer wavelengths spread out the pattern, while the shorter wavelengths contract it.

The simplest procedure in identifying a substance by an X-ray method is to compare its powder photograph with those of known substances taken in the same camera with X-rays of the same wavelength. The patterns given by different substances are usually so obviously different that visual comparison is sufficient for certainty. Often, however, it may not be possible to obtain the reference substances required; nor is this necessary in many cases, for a limited amount of interpretation makes it possible to use published results, obtained, maybe, with cameras of different radius or X-rays of different wavelength. Interpretation of powder photographs for this purpose usually need go only as far as the calculation of the spacings of the crystal planes responsible for the various arcs. This demands no knowledge of the crystal structure, but only the use of a simple equation, the derivation of which forms the subject of the next section.

**Diffraction of X-rays by a crystal.** Diffraction by a three-dimensional array of atoms might be expected to present a complex geometrical problem, but in actual fact the fundamental equation, known as Bragg's law, turns out to be extremely simple:

$$\frac{d}{n} = \frac{\lambda}{2 \sin \theta},$$

where $\lambda$ is the X-ray wavelength, $d$ the distance between successive identical planes of atoms in the crystal, $\theta$ the angle between the X-ray beam and these atomic planes, and $n$ any whole number. (W. L. Bragg, 1913.) It may seem curious that the arrangement of the atoms *in* each atomic plane does not come into the expression, which contains merely $d$, the distance *between* the atomic planes. The reason for this can be appreciated by considering, first the diffraction of rays by a row of points, then by a plane arrangement of points, and finally by a three-dimensional array of points.

If a train of waves, whose wave-front is perpendicular to the direction of propagation, is scattered by an array of points, the scattered rays interfere with each other except when they happen to be in phase, that is, when the difference between the path-lengths of rays scattered by different points is either zero, or one wavelength, or two wavelengths, or any whole number of wavelengths. If a single row of equally spaced points (spacing $= a$) is perpendicular to the beam (Fig. 64 *a*), ray II is $a \cos \phi$ behind ray I, and thus the rays will be in phase only when $n\lambda = a \cos \phi$. For particular values of $n$ and $\lambda$, $\phi$ is constant, that is, the diffracted rays form a cone with the point-line as axis—or rather, two cones, one on each side of the incident beam. The second-order diffractions form a narrower cone than the first-order diffractions. The zero-order cone is a plane surface (Fig. 64 *b*). If the incident beam is not perpendicular to the point-line (Fig. 64 *c*) the diffraction surfaces are still cones, but their semi-vertical angles $\phi$ are given by

$$n\lambda = a(\cos \phi - \cos \theta),$$

and the upward and downward cones for the same value of $n$ have different angles. Note that for diffracted rays having the *same* path-length ($n = 0$), $\phi$ will equal $\theta$, and the angle of this (zero-order) cone of diffracted beams is independent of the point-spacing $a$, and depends only on $\theta$, which may have any value; in other words, an X-ray beam falling on a line of equally spaced diffracting points at any angle gives rise to a zero-order cone of diffracted beams whose semi-vertical angle $\theta$ is the same as the angle between the incident beam and the point-line —in other words, the incident beam forms part of the cone.

Consider now a regular array of points in a plane, such as that in

Fig. 65; this may be divided into rows of points in many different ways; each type of point-row would, by itself, produce its own diffraction surfaces, but the diffracted rays from different types of point-rows such as *BAC* and *DAE* will not co-operate except where the different surfaces

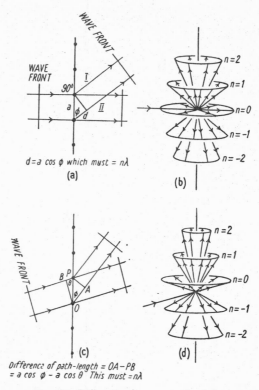

$$d = a \cos \phi \text{ which must } = n\lambda$$
(a)

(b)

Difference of path-length = $OA - PB$
$= a \cos \phi - a \cos \theta$ This must $= n\lambda$

(c)          (d)

FIG. 64. Diffraction by a row of points.

intersect—that is, along certain straight lines. We need not consider this in detail, except to show that the zero-order diffracted beam ($n = 0$) is a sort of reflection of the incident beam by the point-plane. The incident beam *OA* strikes the surface at an angle $\theta$, Fig. 65. One row of points (suppose it is *BAC*) is bound to lie exactly under the incident beam; that is, $\angle OBA = \angle OBD = 90°$. This point-row would, by itself, give a zero-order diffraction cone of angle $\theta$. Any other row of points such as *DAE* is at a larger angle $\phi$ to the incident beam, and by itself would give a zero-order diffraction cone of angle $\phi$. The two cones cut in a line, and this will be the direction of the diffracted beam produced by both point-rows together. We have to find the direction of this line *AP*. Make $AP = OA$, $AC = AB$, and $AE = AD$; join *PC*,

$PE$, and $CE$. Now the solid figure $PCAE$ has three angles $\theta$, $\phi$, and $\omega$ (meeting at $A$) equal to corresponding angles of the figure $OBAD$, and the three sides enclosing these angles ($AP$, $AC$, and $AE$) also equal to the corresponding sides of the figure $OBAD$; hence the two solid figures are similar in all respects; therefore the angle $PCE = OBD = 90°$,

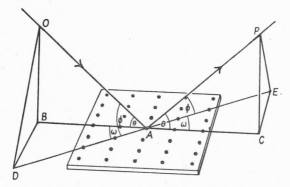

FIG. 65. 'Reflection' by a regular array of points in a plane.

and thus $AP$ lies in the plane $OAB$. The same could be shown for every possible point-row; hence all the points acting together produce a zero-order diffraction along a single direction, the angle of diffraction being equal to the angle of incidence, with both incident and diffracted beams lying in a plane perpendicular to the point-plane: the zero-order diffraction is, in fact, a 'reflection' of the incident beam by the point-plane. Such a 'reflection' can be produced for any angle of incidence of the primary beam; and it is important to notice that the spacing and arrangement of the points in the plane do not affect the process.

If a *three*-dimensional point-array is to produce a diffracted beam, the diffracted waves from all the points must be in phase; some of them will have the same path-length, those from other points will be one wavelength behind the first set, still others will be two wavelengths behind, and so on. It has just been shown that any plane of points by itself would be capable, at *any* angle of incidence, of producing a diffracted beam consisting of waves all of the same path-length, and this beam would be a reflection of the primary beam by the plane; but if the waves from the next lower plane of points are to be in phase with those from the first-mentioned plane, this imposes strict limitations on the permissible angles of incidence. Thus in Fig. 66, $P$, $Q$, and $R$ are successive planes of points seen edgewise. Plane $P$, if it were alone, would reflect the primary beam $AX$ in $XD$, the angle of reflection $DXP'$

being equal to $AXP$ $(= \theta)$; this would happen whatever the value of $\theta$, and does not depend at all on the spacing and arrangement of the points in the plane. Plane $Q$ likewise, if it were alone, would also reflect the beam at this same angle; but since $Q$ is lower than $P$, the path $BYE$ traversed by waves reflected in $Q$ is longer than the path $AXD$ traversed by waves reflected in $P$, and if the two sets of waves are to be in phase,

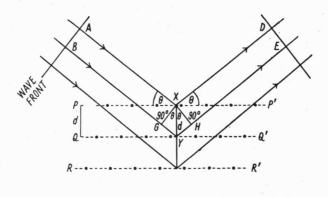

Fig. 66. The condition of 'reflection' by a crystal lattice. Difference of path $= GY + YH = 2d \sin \theta$, which must $= n\lambda$.

then the difference of path-length must be a whole number of wave-lengths. The difference in path-length is $GY + YH$, where $XG$ and $XH$ are perpendicular to $BY$ and $YE$ respectively. $XY$ is drawn perpendicular to $PP'$ and $QQ'$, so that its length is $d$, the spacing of the planes. It follows that $GY$ and $YH$ are each equal to $d \sin \theta$, hence

$$GY + YH = 2d \sin \theta = n\lambda.$$

This equation is Bragg's law.

A crystal is not, in actual fact, a simple array of points, each of which is a pattern-unit. In the first place, an atom is not a point; its electrons, which scatter the X-rays, are distributed over distances commensurable with the interatomic distances. Secondly, each pattern-unit in a crystal often consists, not of one atom, but a group of atoms. The pattern-unit is thus not a point, but has a diffuse and often irregular form. However, for the purpose of diffraction theory, as far as it is carried in this chapter, the diffuse pattern-unit may be mentally replaced by a point. It will be shown in Chapter VII that the form of the pattern-unit affects the intensities of the diffracted beams; but it does not affect their positions, which depend only on the space-lattice, the fundamental arrangement of identical pattern-units.

Each of the many different sets of planes in a crystal may produce a 'reflected' beam, but only if it is at the appropriate angle $\theta$ to the primary beam, this angle $\theta$ being determined by $d$, the spacing of the set of planes in question. The angle between the reflected beam and the primary beam will be $2\theta$. The Bragg equation means that if we turn a crystal about at random in an X-ray beam, in general no reflected beam will be produced; but at certain definite positions of the crystal, when the condition $n\lambda = 2d\sin\theta$ is satisfied for a particular set of planes, a reflected beam flashes out. A set of planes having a large spacing $d$ produces a first-order reflection close to the primary beam (that is, $\theta$ is small), and higher-order reflections ($n = 2$, 3, and so on) at larger angles. A set of closely spaced planes produces its first-order reflection at a large angle. For any particular X-ray wavelength there is a lower limit to the possible values of $d/n$, set by the fact that $\sin\theta$ cannot be greater than 1. The lower limit for $d/n$ is equal to $\lambda/2$.

In a crystalline powder the crystals are oriented at random. If a narrow X-ray beam is sent through the powder, most of the crystals will give no diffracted beams, because none of their planes makes a suitable angle with the beam. Some crystals, however, lie in such positions that a particular set of crystal planes—say the 100 set—is at exactly the appropriate angle for giving the first-order reflection (the angle must be within a few minutes of arc of the angle specified by the Bragg equation; see p. 223); all the little crystals which reflect with their 100 planes give a reflected beam at the same angle, this angle depending on the spacing of the 100 planes. The locus of all directions making a particular angle with the primary beam is a cone having the primary beam for its axis. Other crystals in the powder happen to lie in such a way that they can reflect with their 110 planes, and all these will produce a cone of reflected rays, but the 110 cone will have a different angle from the 100 cone, since the spacing of 110 planes is different from that of 100 planes. (See Fig. 67.) Each cone of rays cuts the photographic film in an arc.

This, therefore, is the origin of the arcs on a powder photograph; each arc represents the combined diffracted beams from all the crystals which happen to be suitably oriented for reflecting with one particular set of planes.

**Measurement of powder photographs.** From the measured position of each arc on a powder photograph, $\theta$ can be calculated, and thence $d/n$ by the Bragg equation. Since on powder photographs the position of the undeviated primary beam is usually not precisely defined, it is necessary to measure from an arc on one side of the photograph to the corresponding arc on the other side, the distance $x$ between which represents $4\theta$. If the radius of the film when it was in the camera was $r$, the circumference $2\pi r$ represents 360°, or, since we are to divide through by 4, $2\pi r$ represents a Bragg angle of 90°; $\theta$ for each arc is thus obtained, and $d/n$ is calculated from $\theta$, $r$, and the known X-ray wavelength used

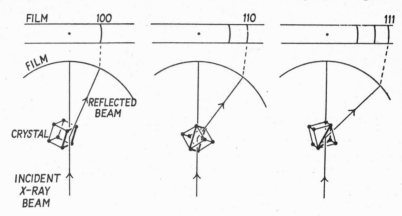

FIG. 67. Each arc on a powder photograph represents
a 'reflection' by a particular crystal plane.

for the photograph. If many films have to be measured, it is best in the long run to make a table giving $d/n$ for all values of $x$. The effective radius $r$ of the camera is best determined by the methods mentioned in the section on high-precision methods (p. 193).

The X-rays used are not strictly monochromatic; copper $K\alpha$ radiation consists not of one wavelength but of two slightly different wavelengths, 1·5405 and 1·5443 Å. These produce reflected beams from any particular crystal plane at slightly different angles; but in ordinary powder cameras the two reflections are not resolved except at angles near 90°, as may be seen by inspecting the powder photographs in Plate IV; the last few reflections are plainly doublets, resolution at large angles being a consequence of the fact that when $\theta$ is near 90°, a small difference of $\sin \theta$ (produced by a small difference of $\lambda$) means a comparatively large difference of $\theta$. Therefore, for the arcs at small angles a weighted average† value (1·5417 Å for copper) must be assumed for calculations, while for the doublets at large angles calculations can be made for both individual wavelengths. For identification purposes measurement with a steel rule graduated in millimetres or half-millimetres is usually sufficiently accurate, but for precision work a travelling microscope may be used.

---

† The $\alpha_1$ wavelength is given twice the weight of $\alpha_2$, since it is twice as strong.

For still greater precision photometric measurement of the distribution of blackening on the film may be made; each reflection appears as a hump on the blackness-distance curve, and the position of the peak can be taken as the 'position' of the reflection. In work of such precision as this, some account must be taken of several sources of error arising from the particular experimental circumstances.

**Spacing errors in powder photographs.** Owing to the appreciable thickness of the powder specimen and the absorption of X-rays

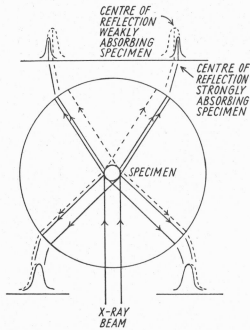

FIG. 68. Apparent displacement of reflections owing to absorption. (Much exaggerated.) Reflections at large angles are less affected than those at small angles.

in it, the diffraction arcs are produced more by the outer layers of the specimen than by its centre (Fig. 68); on this account, corresponding arcs on opposite sides of the photograph tend to be slightly too far apart, and spacings $d/n$ calculated from the arc angles therefore tend to be low. Such errors are greatest for small angles of reflection (large values of $d/n$), and diminish towards zero for large angles. For specimens containing only light atoms, such as carbon, oxygen, aluminium, or sodium, they are very small at all angles; but for specimens containing large proportions of heavy elements, such as iodine or lead, they are appreciable, though not sufficiently large as to be likely to cause confusion in identification. The diameter of the specimen should be as small as possible (not more than 0·3 mm for the camera described here) to minimize such errors. An effect often produced by strongly absorbing specimens is the splitting of small-angle reflections into narrow doublets, owing to the beam passing round both sides of the specimen but not through its centre; at larger angles, only the outer component of the doublet is present, as in Fig. 68. Other errors may occur if the specimen is not strictly in the centre of the film or if a long slit is used. Correction

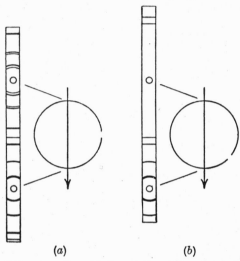

(a)                                    (b)

Fig. 69. Methods of film mounting. (a) Conventional Straumanis–Ieviņš arrangement. (b) Wilson's modification.

terms can be calculated if certain factors are known (Warren, 1945; Taylor and Sinclair, 1945; Wilchinsky, 1947; Nelson, 1955). Finally, photographic films shrink on development and drying; errors from this cause can be avoided by printing fiducial marks on the film. In the type of camera shown in Fig. 61 (Bradley and Jay, 1932) the exposed part of the film (always defined by the general background blackening) is terminated by a knife edge whose position represents a definite angle which can be accurately measured; assuming uniform shrinkage, the true angle for any arc can be calculated by simple proportion.

Film shrinkage errors can be avoided in another way, by mounting the film in the way first described by Straumanis and Ieviņš (1936), with its free ends at one side of the camera (Fig. 69 a); Bragg angles of 0° and 90° are defined by the mid-points between corresponding diffractions in the small and large angle regions respectively, so that no independent measurement of the camera constant is necessary. Since some substances do not give well-defined arcs in the high angle region, the modified position of Fig. 69 *b* suggested by Wilson (1949) is preferable.

One method of correcting for all possible errors is to mix the substance with a standard substance whose spacings are accurately known; the X-ray photograph shows both patterns superimposed. For this purpose it is desirable to use a simple substance giving few lines, otherwise overlapping of arcs will be frequent; sodium chloride is often used. Measurement of the sodium chloride arcs gives a calibration curve, which can then be used for interpolating the precise spacings of the substance under investigation.

A different approach to the problem of obtaining precise spacings of crystal planes is to use some form of focusing camera. In the earliest type of focusing camera, introduced by Seeman (1919) and Bohlin (1920), a divergent X-ray beam from a small source is used, and a focusing effect is obtained by making the powdered specimen and the recording film parts of the same circle, which passes through the point of divergence of the X-ray beam (Fig. 70 *a*). The focusing effect depends on the fact that all angles subtended by the same arc of a circle are equal. Thus, if the angle of reflection for a particular crystal is $2\theta$, the reflections from crystals at two points $A$ and $B$ on the arc-shaped specimen reach the film at the same point $R$, since

$$\angle OAR = \angle OBR = 180° - 2\theta;$$

sharp reflections are thus produced. The powder must, of course, be attached by a trace of adhesive to a suitable film mounted on the circumference of the camera. Accurate angular measurements are assured by calibrating the camera with a standard substance such as sodium chloride or quartz. The specimen $AB$ need not be diametrically opposite to the point of entry $O$ of the X-ray beam; it may be anywhere on the circumference of the circle; indeed, if measurements of diffractions at small angles are required it *must* be asymmetrically placed, as in Fig. 70 *b*, for the symmetrical position of Fig. 70 *a* gives only the high angle diffractions. These cameras have been effectively used for accurate work on metals and alloys by Owen and his collaborators; see, for instance, Owen and Iball (1932), Owen, Pickup, and Roberts (1935). For further information, see Hägg and Regnström (1944), Brindley (1955).

There are distinct advantages in using a focusing camera in conjunction with a curved-crystal focusing monochromator; the convergent

X-ray beam can be passed *through* the curved specimen as in Fig. 70 c
(not reflected from the surface, as in Fig. 70 a), and so the low-angle
reflections are produced without using an asymmetric arrangement.
The other arrangements shown in Fig. 70 d, e, and f can also be used.

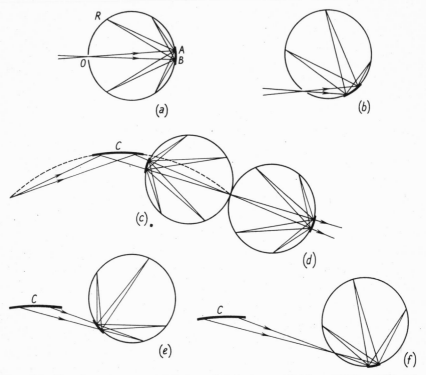

FIG. 70. Focusing cameras. (a) Seeman–Bohlin type; $\angle OAR = \angle OBR = 180° - 2\theta$.
(b) Asymmetric arrangement to give reflections at $2\theta < 90°$. (c), (d), (e), and (f) Arrangements of curved-crystal focusing monochromator (C) with focusing camera.

Sharp photographs with a low background intensity are produced by
such cameras. Focusing cameras, however, are used less for identification than for special purposes such as the accurate determination of
unit cell dimensions. Further information on this subject will be
found on p. 193.

In any work aiming at high accuracy in the determination of crystal
plane spacings, it is advisable to state the values of X-ray wavelengths
which have been assumed; and in using published figures for plane
spacings it is likewise advisable to take note of the wavelengths assumed,
if they are explicitly stated. In recent years there have been alterations
in the scale of X-ray wavelengths, owing to adjustments in the values

of some of the fundamental constants. Before 1943, Siegbahn's X-ray wavelengths, expressed as Ångström units (Å = $10^{-8}$ cm) or X units ($10^{-11}$ cm), and based on the cleavage spacing of calcite at 18° C taken as 3·02904 Å, were used. But later measurements by a ruled-grating method revealed a discrepancy of about 0·2 per cent; Siegbahn's wavelengths were retained and called kX units, which were still used because the relative values of the various X-ray wavelengths were known with more confidence than the absolute values. (See Lipson and Riley, 1943; Siegbahn, 1943; Wilson, 1943 *b*.) Later work has confirmed that kX figures must be multiplied by 1·00202 to convert them to Å. The wavelengths quoted in this book are in Å by this standard, which are Cauchois and Hulubei's kX figures (1947) multiplied by 1·00202. For further information, see Lonsdale (1955), who has this to say on published figures for crystal spacings: 'No reliance can be placed on statements published prior to about 1945 (in crystallographically active countries) or 1950 (elsewhere) that a measurement is expressed in Å; statements that measurements are expressed in kX are usually reliable. The unit used can sometimes be ascertained if the author quotes values of $\theta$ or $\sin\theta$ in addition to calculated spacings or lattice parameters.'

Further information on high precision methods will be found on p. 193.

**Identification of single substances, and classification of powder photographs.** Each crystalline substance has its own set of plane-spacings, which is different from those of other crystalline substances. The relative intensities of the various reflections are also characteristic. Each substance thus gives its own characteristic powder photograph, the scale of which, however, depends on the wavelength of the X-rays used and the diameter of the camera.

The indirect method of identification, in which the pattern of the unknown is compared with those of likely substances, has been much used; but to eliminate the chances of possible substances being overlooked, and to deal with the occurrence of quite unexpected substances, a direct method is desirable, in which 'key' spacings of the unknown are looked up in an index, in the manner used in the identification of optical emission spectra. In the direct method of identification the main 'key' is the spacing of the strongest arc; a card index is made, in which all substances are arranged in order of the spacing of the strongest arc. If two or more arcs appear equally strong to the eye, the innermost— the one with the greatest spacing—should be used as the key. To identify an unknown substance, the spacing of its strongest arc is measured; reference to the index may indicate several substances having the correct key spacing within the possible limits of error of the photograph. Some will be out of the question, in view of the origin of the specimen; for the rest, the remaining arcs will decide.

In addition to the sets of crystal plane spacings from many powder diffraction patterns scattered in many published papers on particular substances, collections of powder patterns have been published by Hanawalt, Rinn, and Frevel (1938)—a collection of 1,000 patterns— Mikheev and Dubinina (1939) for minerals, and Harcourt (1942) for ore minerals. These and many more gleaned from published papers, as well as many which have not been published elsewhere, are included in the very comprehensive card index known as *The X-ray Powder Data File*, published by the American Society for Testing Materials and compiled under the auspices of that body, together with the American Crystallo-graphic Association, the (British) Institute of Physics, and the National Association of Corrosion Engineers. In this index, to which supplemen-tary sets of cards are added at intervals, and which can be obtained in Great Britain from the Institute of Physics, there are three cards for each substance, one for each of the three strongest arcs; these three spacings may lead to unequivocal identification, which, however, should only be accepted as final when the whole pattern is compared with that in the index and found to agree, both in spacings and relative intensities. Visual estimates of relative intensities classified as 'very strong', 'strong', 'medium', 'weak', and so on, are usually sufficient for identi-fication purposes. A collection of 137 patterns of steroids has been published by Parsons, Beher, and Baker (1958).

If the spacings of the arcs on a powder photograph do not lead to identification, the determination of unit cell dimensions from the powder photograph may be attempted; the methods are described in Chapter VI. If crystals large enough to be handled individually can be picked out of the specimen, single-crystal rotation photographs may be taken and used for identification; this also is dealt with in Chapter VI.

**Identification and analysis of mixtures.** A mixture of two or more substances gives a pattern consisting of the superimposed patterns of the individual components, provided that these components exist as separate crystals in the powder specimen (see Plate V). The identifica-tion of simple mixtures, therefore, does not differ in principle from that of single substances. The principle is to find the spacing of the strongest arc; reference to the index may result in identification of one—probably the main—constituent, and this accounts for some of the arcs. The spacing of the strongest of the remaining arcs is then used in the same

PLATE V

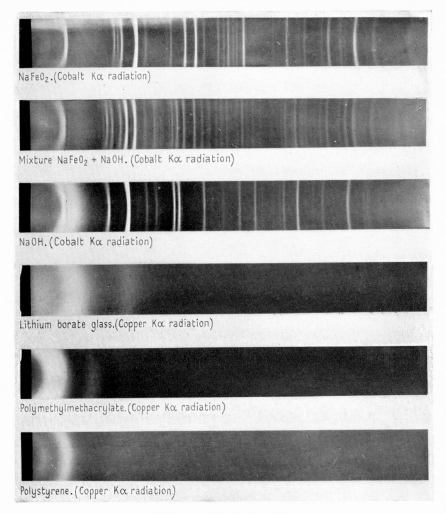

NaFeO$_2$.(Cobalt Kα radiation)

Mixture NaFeO$_2$ + NaOH.(Cobalt Kα radiation)

NaOH.(Cobalt Kα radiation)

Lithium borate glass.(Copper Kα radiation)

Polymethylmethacrylate.(Copper Kα radiation)

Polystyrene.(Copper Kα radiation)

X-ray powder photographs

way for identifying the second constituent, and this procedure is repeated until every arc on the photograph has been accounted for. Overlapping of the arcs of different constituents may sometimes cause confusion.

If a mixture is found to give a very complex pattern which appears to consist of several superimposed patterns, many of the arcs of which overlap, it may be desirable to attain greater resolution, and this can be done either by using X-rays of longer wavelength to spread out the diffraction pattern or by using a larger camera or a smaller specimen.

Chromium $K\alpha$ radiation ($\lambda = 2 \cdot 29$ Å) is suitable for the first method; but the absorption of this wavelength by air is appreciable, and it is desirable either to evacuate the camera or to fill it with hydrogen. Even longer wavelengths, such as the characteristic $K$ radiation of calcium or even magnesium, have been used for special purposes, but it is doubtful whether identification problems would ever call for the use of such long waves. Their use entails further experimental difficulties; owing to the high absorption of these waves by air, the camera should be evacuated and built straight on to the X-ray tube, forming part of the same evacuated system (Clark and Corrigan, 1931; Hägg, 1933).

The second method is preferable. Either the specimen and aperture system may be reduced in size or the camera increased in size. The preparation of very narrow powder specimens is not easy, and the tendency now is to use larger cameras (Bradley, Lipson, and Petch, 1941). Exposures are necessarily increased, but this is the unavoidable price of greater resolution.

X-ray powder photographs are now very widely used for identification. Two typical investigations will be mentioned. The first is the identification of the crystalline constituents of Portland cement, one of the more important building materials of the present day. It is made by heating to a high temperature such raw materials as chalk or limestone, clay, and sand. Its chemical composition may be expressed in terms of lime, silica, alumina, and ferric oxide, but its actual constitution cannot be deduced by stoichiometric methods. X-ray powder photographs, together with evidence obtained by the determination of optical properties under the microscope, have shown that the principal crystalline constituents are $Ca_3SiO_5$ and $\beta\ Ca_2SiO_4$, together with smaller amounts of $Ca_3(AlO_3)_2$, $4CaO \cdot Al_2O_3 \cdot Fe_2O_3$, and $MgO$ (Brownmiller and Bogue, 1930; Insley, 1937; Insley and McMurdie, 1938). It may be said that the recent great progress in our understanding of the chemistry of the setting of cements is largely due to crystallographic investigations of this type. (See *The Chemistry of Cement and Concrete*, by Lea and Desch, 1935.)

The second example is the investigation of the constitution of 'bleaching powder', which is made by the action of chlorine gas on slaked lime. The constitution of this widely used material had remained obscure for many years, since, although it contains calcium chloride as well as hypochlorite $(2Ca(OH)_2 + 2Cl_2 \longrightarrow Ca(OCl)_2 + CaCl_2 + 2H_2O)$, it is not deliquescent; moreover, it is difficult to carry chlorination to completion. These features had led to many suggestions of the existence of double compounds—suggestions which could not be tested by older methods of investigation, on account of the small size of the crystals. X-ray powder photographs showed that bleaching powder consists of two substances—a crystal of variable composition consisting chiefly of $Ca(OCl)_2$, and the basic chloride $CaCl_2 . Ca(OH)_2 . H_2O$. It is the latter, a very stable non-deliquescent substance, which is responsible for the difficulty of complete chlorination and the non-deliquescent nature of the material. (Bunn, Clark, and Clifford, 1935.)

In both these investigations the X-ray method was not used alone; measurements of the optical properties of crystals under the microscope supplied evidence on certain points. The desirability of using microscopic and X-ray methods in conjunction with each other cannot be too strongly emphasized. This applies also in another field where the X-ray method of identification has been widely used—the determination of phase boundaries in metallurgical equilibrium diagrams. (Bradley, Bragg, and Sykes, 1940; Hume-Rothery and Raynor, 1941; Lipson, 1943.)

It is possible not only to identify the components of a mixture, but also to estimate the proportions of the different components from the relative intensities of the patterns. No simple mathematical relationship between the proportions of the components and the relative intensities of particular diffraction arcs can be given, and therefore the method of analysis must be empirical; when the constituents have been identified, powder photographs of mixtures containing known proportions of the constituents must be taken, and that of the unknown mixture compared with them. Estimates of proportions to within 5 per cent. can be made by visual comparison, but the probable error can be reduced to the order of 1 per cent. by measuring the intensities of selected diffraction arcs by means of a micro-photometer; the relation between known composition and the relative photographic densities of particular arcs is found empirically, and the composition of the unknown mixture interpolated from these results. On account of the somewhat variable characteristics of X-ray films and the circumstance that the relation between photographic density and X-ray exposure is not linear except at low densities, it is better for this purpose to print on each film a strip giving a series of known X-ray exposures, and from this to calibrate the mixture patterns in terms of X-ray exposure rather than photographic density. (See Chapter VII.) The necessary information on the relative intensities of the chosen diffraction peaks can be obtained more rapidly and conveniently by the use of a counter diffractometer and chart recorder. It should be noted that for mixtures of substances having very different absorption coefficients for the X-rays used, the relative intensities of the diffraction peaks may depend on the sizes of the crystals, unless the crystals are very small. (See Brindley, 1945; A. Taylor, 1955.)

This method of analysis is particularly valuable when chemical methods are inadequate or inapplicable. For instance, for complex mixtures where the different elements or ions may be associated in many different ways, all compatible with the analytical figures; or for mixtures of polymorphous forms of the same substance, such as the three crystalline forms of $CaCO_3$ (calcite, aragonite, and vaterite) or the three crystalline forms of $FeO(OH)$ (goethite, lepidocrocite, and $\beta$ $FeO(OH)$—see Bunn, 1941)—mixtures for which chemical analytical methods are irrelevant.

One limitation in the use of X-ray powder photographs for the identification and analysis of mixtures must be mentioned. It is very often not possible to detect less than 5 per cent. of a constituent. The minimum proportion of a substance which can be detected varies enormously; it is usually specific for each crystalline substance, and depends on many factors, such as the symmetry of the crystal and the diffracting power of the atoms composing it. Highly symmetrical crystals of simple substances such as sodium chloride (cubic) and the rhombohedral form of calcium carbonate (calcite) can be detected even when present to the extent of only 1 per cent. or even less, but less symmetrical crystals such as monoclinic $CaSO_4 . 2H_2O$ (gypsum) can be detected only if 5 per cent. or more is present. This statement is valid under normal conditions, that is, when the X-rays used contain a certain proportion of 'white' radiation in addition to the principal $\alpha$ wavelengths; but the figures given can be reduced by using strictly monochromatic radiation, thus diminishing the background intensity of the photographs and making it possible to detect weaker arcs.

'Mixed crystals' or 'crystalline solid solutions' (see p. 61) present different problems from those of straightforward mixtures. A mixed crystal gives a diffraction pattern which is in general intermediate, in respect of both the positions and the intensities of its arcs, between those of the pure constituents. Identification of the crystal species can be effected if this relation between a given pattern and those of known pure constituents is recognized, and quantitative analysis is possible if the relation between composition and arc position and intensity is known for the system in question. An interesting example is given by Rooksby (1941). Preparations of zinc and cadmium sulphides are used as luminescent powders, the colour of the emitted light depending on the proportions of the two constituents. The X-ray diffraction patterns show that the solids are mixed crystals: there is a complete range of mixed crystals, as is shown by the fact that the positions of the arcs change gradually with composition. (Rooksby shows a range of patterns for the whole series.) The composition of the mixed crystal phase can be determined to within 1–2 per cent. from the X-ray pattern, and the X-ray method has the advantage over chemical analysis that it is not affected by the presence of oxide. Mixtures of different mixed crystals are also used to give other luminescent colours; and in these the composition of each mixed crystal phase can be determined from the X-ray pattern; this probably could not be done at all by any other method.

Interpretation of the diffraction patterns of mixed crytals, as far as the determination of unit cell dimensions, may be desirable. This is described in Chapter VI.

**Non-crystalline substances.** Some solid substances, such as silicate glasses and certain organic polymers like polystyrene, are not crystalline; the atoms of which they are composed are not arranged in a precise way, though there may be some approach to regularity. The X-ray diffraction patterns of these 'amorphous' solids, like those of liquids and gases, consist of broad diffuse bands with perhaps two or three intensity maxima at definite angles. Examples are shown in Plate V. It is obvious that such diffuse patterns afford less scope for identification or interpretation than crystal patterns. Nevertheless, something may be done; the difference between the patterns of polymethylmethacrylate and polystyrene, for instance, is so great that the substances could easily be distinguished from each other in this way.

It has been pointed out (Randall, Rooksby, and Cooper, 1930; Randall and Rooksby, 1931, 1933) that, when a substance is capable of existing in both amorphous and crystalline forms, the X-ray pattern given by the amorphous form may be regarded as a very diffuse version of the crystal pattern. There is, in fact, no sharp distinction between 'crystalline' and 'amorphous' states; if, starting with a coarsely crystalline solid, we could reduce the size of the crystals by stages, taking an X-ray diffraction photograph at each stage, we should find that when the crystal size fell below about $10^{-5}$ cm the photographs would become diffuse; the effect is analogous to the imperfect resolution of an optical diffraction grating containing only a few lines. With reduction of crystal size, the reflections become increasingly diffuse until the limit is reached at $10^{-7}$ to $10^{-8}$ cm—the region of atomic dimensions, where the word 'crystal', with its implication of precise pattern-repetition, ceases to be appropriate. One cannot speak of a crystal only one unit cell in diameter, for the term 'unit cell' implies repetition; this is the justification for the use of the term 'amorphous' in describing glass-like substances.

The breadth of X-ray reflections may be used to calculate crystal size within the range in which broadening occurs; the method is mentioned in Chapter XI. The interpretation of amorphous patterns in terms of atomic structure is also referred to in the same chapter.

This brings us to the end of the section of this book concerned primarily with identification problems. This does not mean that these problems will not reappear later; they do reappear in Chapter VI. But from this point onwards the book is concerned mainly with the determination of the arrangements of atoms in crystals.

# PART II.  STRUCTURE DETERMINATION

## VI

# DETERMINATION OF UNIT CELL DIMENSIONS

I f it were possible to produce, by means of a supermicroscope, images of atomic structures, it would not be necessary to undertake the lengthy processes of reasoning and calculation which form the subject-matter of the greater part of this book.  Up to the time of writing (1958), how-ever, this very desirable objective has not been reached.  Enormous magnifications have been achieved by means of the electron microscope, but the resolving power still falls short of atomic dimensions.  The very great extension of our range of vision that has been achieved has been based, for the most part, on the principles of the optical microscope, and X-rays have not been used, because although they have sufficiently short wavelengths to respond to the details of atomic structures, they cannot be refracted† and focused as visible light can.  Electron beams, however, since they consist of streams of charged particles, can be refracted and focused by magnetic or electric fields; since they also behave as wave-trains having (with a suitable accelerating voltage) effective wavelengths short enough to respond to the details of atomic structure, it might be possible, by their use, to produce images of atomic structures.  The difficulties, especially that of making corrected electron 'lenses' suitable for the enormous magnifications involved, are serious, however, and although progress has been very rapid, the resolution attained by 1958 was still about 10 Å.  Some of the larger molecules have been seen individually, but not individual atoms; a resolution of 1–2 Å is required to distinguish atoms.  Images of molecules, and even of atoms in certain metal crystals, have been obtained by a different method, in what is called the 'field emission microscope'; this is a highly evacuated tube in which electrons or gas ions emitted from the very minute tip of a pointed electrode fall on a fluorescent screen; the pattern represents the structure of the electrode tip, enormously magnified by the radial spread from the minute tip of the electrode to the comparatively enormous

† X-rays are refracted when they pass through matter, but to such a slight extent that it is not possible to make lenses of short focal length. They can be reflected and focused by curved crystals, but it is not practicable to obtain high magnifications.

PLATE VI

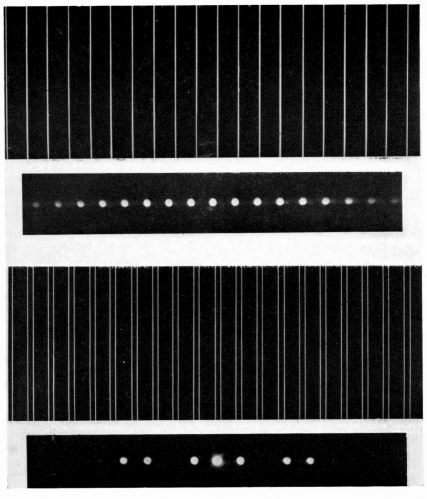

Diffraction of light by line gratings. Above: grating of evenly spaced lines, with diffraction pattern. Below: grating in which the unit of pattern is a pair of lines (repeat distance same as in the first), with diffraction pattern screen (Müller, 1956). This method is, however, of very limited application.

At present, therefore, the details of most atomic structures must be discovered indirectly. The experimental material for the purpose is the X-ray diffraction pattern. Electron diffraction patterns and neutron diffraction patterns are similar, and have been used for the same purpose; but the great majority of investigations of crystal structure are based on X-ray diffraction patterns. The interpretation of these diffraction patterns falls into two stages—first, the determination of the shape and dimensions of the unit cell (see Chapter II), and second, the discovery of the positions of the atoms in the unit cell.

It has been assumed, in the previous chapter, that the positions of diffracted beams depend only on the repeat distances in the crystal—that is, on the unit cell dimensions—while the intensities of the diffracted beams depend on the positions of the atoms in the unit cell. This can be demonstrated in principle by means of a simple one-dimensional optical analogy. In Plate VI is shown, first of all, a grating in which the lines are evenly spaced. (It was made by drawing black lines on white card, and taking a very small photograph on which the lines are 0·2 mm apart.) A beam of monochromatic light, on passing through it, produces a set of diffracted beams,† the intensities of which fade off regularly in the successive orders. In the lower half of Plate VI is another grating having the same repeat distance as the first; but in this grating the unit of pattern is not one line but two. It can be seen that in the diffraction pattern the diffracted beams have the same spacing as those of the first pattern, but the intensities of the successive orders do not diminish regularly. The diffraction of X-rays by crystals is more complex than this, but not different in principle. Thus, in the determination of unit cell dimensions, only the positions of the diffracted beams need be considered; the intensities may be ignored.

From a powder photograph all we can obtain (apart from the intensities of the arcs, which are irrelevant to the present problem) is a set of values of $d$ $(= \lambda/(2 \sin \theta))$. Each arc represents a 'reflection' from a particular set of parallel crystal planes, but there is nothing to tell us which set of crystal planes produces which arc; nothing, that is, except the magnitudes and ratios of the spacings themselves. We cannot deduce the unit cell of the arrangement of pattern-units directly; our only course is the indirect one of thinking what arrangement of pattern-

† The experimental arrangement used for photographing the diffraction pattern is described on p. 294.

units has spacings of the observed magnitudes. This can only be done for the more symmetrical arrangements; for those of low symmetry, the number of variables defining the unit cell is too great for such a method to be possible, but for arrangements whose unit cells are defined by not more than two variables—that is to say, for cubic, tetragonal, and hexagonal (including trigonal) crystals—it is readily accomplished.

**Cubic unit cells.** In a crystal having a simple cubic unit cell—that is, a crystal in which identically situated points lie at the corners of cubes, as in Fig. 71—the distance between the 100 planes of pattern-units is evidently $a$, the length of the unit cell edge; that between 010 and 001 planes is also $a$. For other sets of lattice planes it is a matter of simple geometry to show that the spacing $d = a/\sqrt{(h^2+k^2+l^2)}$, where $h$, $k$, $l$ are the indices of the planes. (For a general derivation of the expression for the plane-spacings in all crystals having rectangular and hexagonal unit cells, see Appendix 2.) Thus the powder photograph of a substance such as ammonium chloride which has

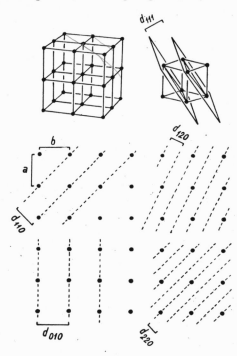

FIG. 71. Spacings of some simple planes of a cubic lattice.

a simple cubic unit cell shows a set of arcs whose positions correspond with plane-spacings in the ratios $1:1/\sqrt{2}:1/\sqrt{3}:1/\sqrt{4}:1/\sqrt{5}$, and so on. The first arc on the photograph—the one with the smallest angle of reflection—is produced by the planes having the greatest spacing—the 100, 010, and 001 planes; the others follow in order of diminishing spacing.

Whenever the arc positions in a powder photograph are found to correspond with spacings in these ratios, it is evident that the substance producing the photograph has a simple cubic unit cell. This is indeed usually obvious from a mere inspection of the photograph, which shows regularly spaced arcs as in the pattern of ammonium chloride in Plate XI.

Note that the gaps in this photograph are due to the fact that not all whole numbers are values of $h^2+k^2+l^2$; for instance, no combination of the squares of three whole numbers is equal to 7, and therefore there is a gap following the sixth arc.

Some cubic crystals—sodium chloride, for instance—give powder photographs in which there are many more gaps than those in the ammonium chloride pattern. It will be shown later, in Chapter VII, that such absences are due to the fact that the crystal in question has a compound (face-centred or body-centred) unit cell, or to certain symmetries in the arrangement of atoms in the unit cell. For the determination of cell dimensions these absences need not be considered; we need only note that if a pattern shows spacings in the ratios of the various values of $1/\sqrt{(h^2+k^2+l^2)}$, even though some of the values are missing, the crystals producing the pattern have cubic unit cells.

The calculations necessary to show that a crystal has a cubic unit cell show in addition which crystal plane is responsible for each arc. Thus, the 100, 010, and 001 planes are responsible for the first arc in the ammonium chloride pattern, the 110, 011, and 101 planes for the second arc, and so on.

Note that the fourth arc, which is the second-order 'reflection' from 100 planes, is labelled '200', the order being included in the index description. Similarly the second-order 'reflection' from the 110 planes is called 220, and the third-order 'reflection' from 312 would be called 936. This practice of including the order in the index numbers has become standard, as it makes for uniformity and avoids confusion. Looking at it in another way, we may regard 220 as the first-order 'reflection' from a set of planes having half the spacing of 110 (see the bottom right-hand corner of Fig. 71). This fits in with the definition of the indices of crystal planes given in Chapter II (p. 24)—the number of planes crossed between one lattice point and the next, along each axial direction. Another meaning of the indices of X-ray reflections is also important. All 'reflections' are first-order 'reflections' from planes defined in the above manner; this means that there is a phase-difference of one wavelength between waves from successive planes. Counting the number of planes crossed between one lattice point and the next is therefore the same thing as counting the number of wavelengths phase-difference between waves scattered by neighbouring lattice points. The indices thus represent the phase-differences between waves diffracted by neighbouring lattice points along the three axial directions. Thus, if we take any one atom as the reference point, the 936 'reflection' is produced when waves diffracted by the next similarly situated atom along the $a$ axis are 9 wavelengths in front of those from the reference atom, those from the next similarly situated atom along the $b$ axis are 3 wavelengths in front, and those from the next along the $c$ axis 6 wavelengths in front. The indices are thus the three order numbers which characterize diffracted beams produced by a three-dimensional grating. For an optical line grating—a one-dimensional pattern—we speak of 'first', 'second', and succeeding orders of diffraction, the one order number being appropriate to the one-dimensional character of the pattern; but for a three-dimensional pattern, three order numbers are necessary to describe diffracted beams. The X-ray beam which we have called, rather loosely, the 936 'reflection', or the 'third-order reflection from the 312 plane', is, strictly speaking, the diffracted beam whose order numbers are 936.

The length $a$ of the unit cell edge can be calculated from the spacing of any arc from the expression $a = d_{hkl}\sqrt{(h^2+k^2+l^2)}$. The results from arcs at large angles are more accurate than those from the first few arcs for two reasons: firstly, the errors due to the thickness and absorption of the specimen diminish with increasing diffraction angle (see p. 127), and secondly, on account of the form of the Bragg equation $n\lambda = 2d \sin \theta$, the resolving power increases with $\theta$ (see p. 126), as is obvious from the fact that the $\alpha_1 \alpha_2$ doublets are only resolved at large values of $\theta$.

Although the interpretation of patterns from cubic crystals can be done by way of calculations as above, it is more convenient to use the graphical methods described in the next section.

**Tetragonal unit cells.** In crystals of tetragonal symmetry the unit cell is a rectangular box with two edges equal ($a$) and the third ($c$) different from the first two. The spacings of $hk0$ planes—those parallel to $c$—are in the same ratios as those of the $hk0$ planes of cubic crystals, that is, in the ratios $1/\sqrt{1^2} : 1/\sqrt{(1^2+1^2)} : 1/\sqrt{2^2} : 1/\sqrt{(2^2+1^2)}$, and so on. But the 001 spacing is not related in any simple way to $a$; the ratio $c/a$ may have any value and is different for every tetragonal crystal; and $hkl$ spacings in general are given by $d_{hkl} = 1 \bigg/ \sqrt{\left(\dfrac{h^2+k^2}{a^2} + \dfrac{l^2}{c^2}\right)}$. The diffraction patterns of tetragonal crystals are thus less simple than those of cubic crystals, and there is no regular spacing of the arcs, as may be seen in the pattern of urea, Fig. 72 and Plate XI; the relative spacings are different for every different tetragonal crystal, except for the $hk0$ spacings.

It would be possible to find the unit cell of a tetragonal crystal by first picking out those arcs whose spacings are in the ratios $1:1/\sqrt{2}:1/\sqrt{4}$, etc. (these being the $hk0$ reflections), and then assigning likely indices to the remaining reflections by trial. But this would be a laborious process, and there is no need to proceed in this way, since the problem can be solved graphically. The relative spacings of the different planes are determined by the axial ratio $c/a$; if two crystals happened to have the same axial ratio but different actual cell dimensions, their patterns would show the same relative spacings, though one pattern would be more spread out than the other if the same X-ray wavelength were used. Graphs connecting the relative values of $d$ and $c/a$ can be constructed, and the whole set of arcs in a powder pattern identified by finding where their relative spacings fit the chart. In order to deal only with *relative* spacings so that only the shape (not the actual size) of the cell enters into the problem, the chart is made logarithmic with respect to $d$. The first such charts were published by Hull and Davey (1921), who plotted $\log d$ for each crystal plane against $c/a$. These charts are rather small, and for small values of $c/a$ do not extend far enough for some purposes. A method of constructing such a chart entirely without calculation is given in an appendix. The method of using these charts is to plot on a strip of paper the values of $\log d$ (or $-2\log d$ for the new form of chart) for all the arcs on the photograph, and move the strip about on the chart, keeping it always parallel to the $\log d$ axis, until a good match between strip points and chart lines is found; this is illustrated in Fig. 72. (Some reflections may be absent; this feature may be ignored.) More than one matching position will be found; the position giving the simplest indices will naturally refer to the simplest unit cell. When the correct position is found, the indices of all arcs can be read off on the chart. The axial ratio can also be read off approximately, but it is better to calculate $a$ and $c$ from the spacings of selected arcs. The length $a$ can be obtained from the spacing of any $hk0$ arc, and $c$ from any of the $00l$ arcs, the most accurate results being obtained from the arcs at the largest reflection angles. Arcs representing two or more different crystal planes with about the same spacing should naturally be avoided. If unambiguous $hk0$ and $00l$ arcs are not available, both $a$ and $c$ can be calculated from the spacings of any two arcs having different $hk$ and $l$ values from the equations

$$(d_{h_1 k_1 l_1})^2\left(\frac{h_1^2+k_1^2}{a^2}+\frac{l_1^2}{c^2}\right) = (d_{h_2 k_2 l_2})^2\left(\frac{h_2^2+k_2^2}{a^2}+\frac{l_2^2}{c^2}\right) = 1,$$

the most accurate results being obtained from a pair of arcs (such as 211 and 102 in the urea photograph, Fig. 72), one of which comes from a plane with high *hk* and low *l*, and the other from a plane with low *hk* and high *l*; they should be fairly near together on the photograph so

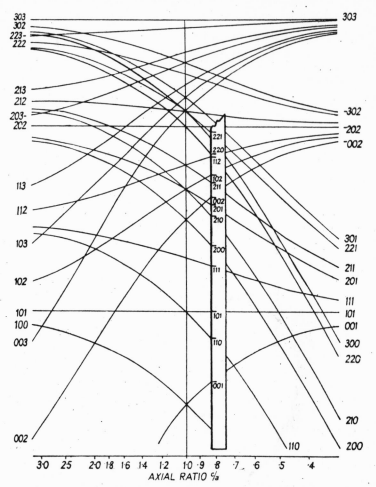

FIG. 72. Graphical method for indexing the powder pattern of a tetragonal crystal. The pattern shown is that of urea.

that absorption and other errors are about the same for both. Calculations should be made from several pairs of arcs, and the results averaged. Reflections at large angles give more accurate results than those at small angles—see Fig. 68. (For high precision methods, see p. 193.)

Note that a tetragonal cell with an axial ratio of 1 is cubic, and the chart at this position can therefore be used for cubic crystals.

**Hexagonal and rhombohedral unit cells.** In many crystals of hexagonal and trigonal symmetry the unit cell has a diamond-shaped base, $a$ and $b$ being equal in length and at $120°$ to each other; $c$ is perpendicular to the base and different in length from $a$ and $b$. The axial ratio $c/a$ is different for each crystal. The spacings $d$ of the planes are given by

$$d_{hkl} = 1\Big/\sqrt{\left(\frac{4}{3}\frac{(h^2+hk+k^2)}{a^2}+\frac{l^2}{c^2}\right)}.$$

The indices for the arcs on a powder photograph can be found graphically on a suitable chart (see Appendix 3) in a way similar to that described for tetragonal crystals, and the axial lengths calculated from the spacings of suitable pairs of arcs by the above equation.

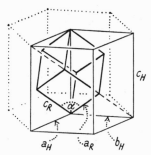

Fig. 73. Rhombohedral cell (bold lines) with corresponding hexagonal cell (narrow lines) and hexagonal prism (dotted).

For some trigonal crystals, the unit cell is a rhombohedron—a figure which has three equal axes which make equal angles not $90°$ with each other; the cell is, so to speak, a cube either compressed or elongated along a body diagonal. The spacing $d$ of any set of atomic planes $hkl$ is given, in terms of the unit cell edge $a$ and the interaxial angle $\alpha$, by the expression

$$d_{hkl} = a\sqrt{\left\{\frac{1+2\cos^3\alpha-3\cos^2\alpha}{(h^2+k^2+l^2)\sin^2\alpha+2(hk+kl+lh)(\cos^2\alpha-\cos\alpha)}\right\}}.$$

It is not easy to determine directly $a$ and $\alpha$ from a powder photograph by the use of this rather unwieldy expression; fortunately, however, the atomic arrangement in rhombohedral crystals can always be referred to a larger hexagonal cell (Fig. 73) whose dimensions $a_H$ and $c_H$ are related to those of the rhombohedral cell, $a_R$ and $\alpha$, by the relations

$$a_R^2 = \frac{a_H^2}{3}+\frac{c_H^2}{9}; \qquad \sin\frac{\alpha}{2} = \frac{3}{2\sqrt{\left\{3+\left(\frac{c_H}{a_H}\right)^2\right\}}}.$$

Hexagonal indices $h_H k_H l_H$ are related to rhombohedral indices $h_R k_R l_R$ by the relations

$$3h_R = h_H - k_H + l_H,$$

$$3k_R = h_H + 2k_H + l_H,$$

$$3l_R = -2h_H - k_H + l_H.$$

The procedure is to find the simplest hexagonal indices on the chart already mentioned, to calculate the dimensions of the hexagonal cell, and finally to find the dimensions of the true rhombohedral cell by the above expressions.

If it is not known whether a crystal has rhombohedral symmetry or not, this question may be settled by assigning hexagonal indices to the reflections and then surveying these indices to see whether all of them are such that $h_H - k_H + l_H$, $h_H + 2k_H + l_H$, and $-2h_H - k_H + l_H$ are divisible by 3; if they are, the true unit cell is rhombohedral.

**Orthorhombic, monoclinic, and triclinic unit cells.** The determination of the dimensions of orthorhombic, monoclinic, and triclinic unit cells from powder photographs is usually a problem of some complexity. The number of variable parameters is too great to permit the use of charts for finding the indices of the arcs. Three-dimensional figures of the required type are impracticable. It is therefore necessary to proceed by trial—to postulate simple indices for the first few arcs, to calculate the unit cell dimensions on these assumptions, and then to find whether the spacings of the remaining arcs fit this cell. If external evidence, such as the axial ratios and angles deduced from goniometric microscopic measurements, is available, this will suggest possible indices for the first few arcs, and so may lead to the successful indexing of the rest of the pattern; it may be necessary to halve or double one of the morphological axes in relation to the other two, to account for the pattern. The cell first chosen may be too large; if, for instance, all the $h$ indices are found to be even, then the length of the true $a$ axis is half that first chosen: the change to this true $a$ axis will halve all the $h$ indices.

The spacings of the various planes for these crystals are given by the following expressions:

Orthorhombic
$$d_{hkl} = \frac{1}{\sqrt{\left(\dfrac{h^2}{a^2} + \dfrac{k^2}{b^2} + \dfrac{l^2}{c^2}\right)}},$$

Monoclinic    $d_{hkl} = \dfrac{1}{\sqrt{\left(\dfrac{\dfrac{h^2}{a^2}+\dfrac{l^2}{c^2}-\dfrac{2hl\cos\beta}{ac}}{\sin^2\beta}+\dfrac{k^2}{b^2}\right)}}$.

For triclinic crystals the expression is so unwieldy that it is not worth while attempting to use it; a graphical method based on the conception of the reciprocal lattice should be used (see pp. 154 ff). The reciprocal lattice method is also more rapid than calculation for monoclinic crystals.

If no external evidence is available, it is still possible to determine the unit cell dimensions of crystals of low symmetry from powder diffraction patterns, provided that sharp patterns with high resolution are available. Hesse (1948) and Lipson (1949) have used numerical methods successfully for orthorhombic crystals. (See also Henry, Lipson, and Wooster, 1951; Bunn, 1955.) Ito (1950) has devised a method which in principle will lead to a possible unit cell for a crystal of any symmetry. It may not be the true unit cell appropriate to the crystal symmetry, but when a possible cell satisfying all the diffraction peaks on a powder pattern has been obtained by Ito's method, the true unit cell can be obtained by a reduction process first devised by Delaunay (1933). Ito applies the reduction process to the reciprocal lattice (see p. 185), but *International Tables* (1952) recommend that the procedure should be applied to the direct space lattice.

The difficulties in the interpretation of powder photographs of crystals of low symmetry lie in the fact that in a powder photograph all the information is crowded along one line, and this information consists only of the spacings of the planes, without any geometrical indication of the relative orientations of the crystal planes producing the various arcs. This is inevitable in a powder photograph on account of the random orientation of the crystals in the specimen. Only by departing from the randomness of orientation can we obtain X-ray diffraction photographs which give geometrical indications of the orientation of the crystal planes producing the various reflections. Obviously it is best to use a single crystal set in some definite way with regard to the X-ray beam, so that the reflections from differently oriented planes shall fall on different parts of the recording film.

**Single-crystal rotation photographs.** The method found most convenient for finding the unit cell dimensions of crystals of low symmetry is to send a narrow monochromatic X-ray beam through a single crystal at right angles to one of its axes, to rotate the crystal round this axis during exposure in order to bring a number of different crystal planes successively into reflecting positions, and to record the reflections either on a flat plate or film perpendicular to the primary beam (Fig. 74 a), or better still (because more reflections are registered) on a cylindrical film surrounding the crystal, the cylinder axis coinciding with the crystal's axis of rotation (Fig. 74 b). A single-crystal camera

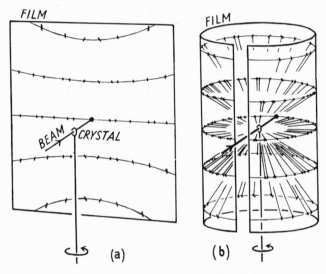

FIG. 74. Arrangements for taking single-crystal rotation photographs (a) on flat films, (b) on cylindrical films.

differs from a powder camera only in the necessity of having arrangements for the accurate adjustment of the crystal and the use of a much longer cylinder of photographic film. The crystal is mounted on the stem of a goniometer head; whenever possible, accurate adjustment is effected by making use of the reflection of light by the faces, in the manner described in Chapter II. (Ill-formed crystals may be set accurately by X-ray methods; the procedure cannot be given at this stage—it will be found on p. 186.) Aperture systems for defining the X-ray beam are the same as in powder cameras; a 0·5 mm channel in a brass tube, with the usual guard tube, is suitable for most purposes. Fogging by the primary beam is avoided either (as in the powder camera, Fig. 61) by the provision of a trap or by making a small hole in the film through which the primary beam passes. Goniometer cameras are not usually made light-tight; instead, the film is contained in an envelope of black paper or other material which stops light but not X-rays.

PLATE VII

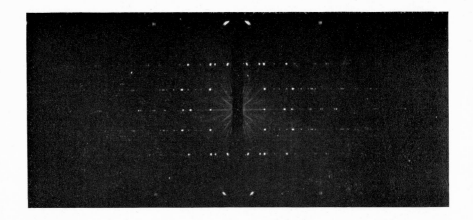

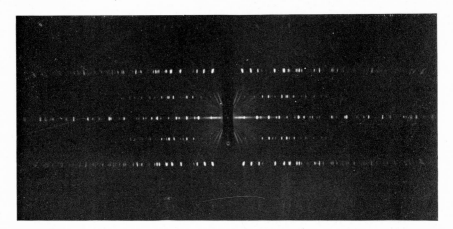

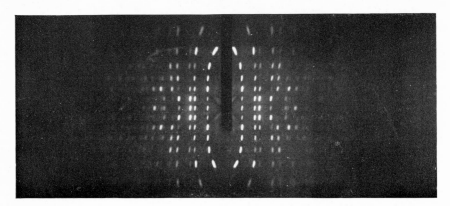

Single-crystal rotation photographs. Above: potassium nitrate (orthorhombic; rotation axis, c). Centre: gypsum (monoclinic; rotation axis, c). Below: benzil (hexagonal; rotation axis, c)

X-ray goniometers are usually fitted, not only for complete rotation of the crystal, but also for oscillations over limited angular ranges; this is usually effected by heart-shaped cams controlling the angular movement. For further details, see Buerger (1942).

The crystal is mounted by sticking it to a glass hair (preferably lithium borate glass) by a trace of plasticine, shellac, or wax; the glass hair in turn is stuck to the goniometer stem. Crystals which are deliquescent, efflorescent, or rather volatile must be sealed inside lithium borate tubes (Robertson, 1935 a). It is in some cases necessary to take X-ray photographs of crystals immersed in their own mother liquor; here again, thin-walled capillary tubes must be used (Bernal and Crowfoot, 1934 a).

The type of X-ray photograph given by a crystal rotated round a principal axis is illustrated in Plate VII, which shows the diffraction pattern of the orthorhombic crystal potassium nitrate rotated round its $c$ axis. The most obvious feature of this photograph is the arrangement of the diffraction spots on a series of straight horizontal lines. The reason for this will be apparent when it is remembered that along the $c$ axis there are identical diffracting units (groups of atoms) spaced a distance of $c$ apart. It has already been shown (p. 121) that a row of identical, equally spaced diffracting units perpendicular to an X-ray beam produces cones of diffracted rays at angles given by $n\lambda = c \cos \phi$, where $\lambda$ is the X-ray wavelength, $c$ the distance between the diffracting units, $\phi$ the semi-vertical angle of the cone of diffracted rays, and $n$ a whole number. On a cylindrical film having the point-row for its axis, these cones of rays would be registered as a series of straight lines. A crystal is not a single row of diffracting units, but consists of many identical rows of such units, all parallel to each other and packed side by side in a precise way, and on account of the three-dimensional character of the assemblage of diffracting units, diffracted beams are produced, not all along each cone, but only along specific directions lying on the cone, the directions being such that the Bragg equation $\lambda = 2d \sin \theta$ is satisfied; thus we get on the cylindrical film, not continuous straight lines, but spots lying on straight lines. The lines of spots are usually called 'layer lines'.

The length of $c$ can be obtained very simply from this photograph by measuring the distance $y$ of any layer line from the equator; if the camera radius is $r$, then $r/y$ is $\tan \phi$; $c$ is then given by $n\lambda/\cos \phi$, $n$ being the number of the layer line selected (the equator having $n = 0$). For the potassium nitrate crystal, $c$ is 6·45 Å. If a flat film is used instead of a cylindrical film, the layer lines are shown, not as straight lines but as hyperbolae. $\tan \phi$ is given by $r/y'$, where $y'$ is the shortest distance from the hyperbola to the equator—the distance at the meridian.

**Unit cell dimensions from rotation photographs.** The simplest way of measuring the lengths of the three edges of the unit cell of an orthorhombic crystal is evidently to take three rotation photographs, the crystal being rotated round a different axis for each photograph; the axial directions are chosen on the basis of morphological measurements, and these directions are necessarily, by symmetry, parallel to the true unit cell edges. For the potassium nitrate crystal the lengths of the edges of the unit cell were found by D. A. Edwards (1931) to be:
$a = 5 \cdot 42 \text{ Å}; b = 9 \cdot 17 \text{ Å}; c = 6 \cdot 45 \text{ Å}.$

The same method can be used for all crystals, irrespective of symmetry; axial directions are chosen, and interaxial angles determined, by measurements of interfacial angles, while the lengths of the axes are determined from X-ray rotation photographs. There are pitfalls here, however; the directions selected as crystal axes on the basis of morphological measurements may not always be parallel to the edges of the simplest unit cell, which will be referred to here as the 'true unit cell'—the smallest cell which has the correct symmetry and accounts for all the X-ray reflections. Consider first the most highly symmetrical crystals—those belonging to the cubic, tetragonal, and hexagonal (including trigonal) systems. (Although, as we have seen, the unit cell dimensions of such crystals can usually be determined from powder photographs, nevertheless it may happen that faint reflections not seen on powder photographs are registered on single-crystal photographs, and these may necessitate revision of cell dimensions; hence, single-crystal photographs should be taken whenever possible.)

Axial directions in cubic crystals are fixed by symmetry, as in the orthorhombic crystals already considered. But in tetragonal crystals, although there is no doubt about the direction of the unique $c$ axis, on the other hand the morphologically chosen $a$ axis may be at 45° to the true $a$ axis: the prism face selected as 100 may really be 110 (see Fig. 75 $a$), and thus an X-ray photograph with direction 1 as rotation axis would give (from the layer-line spacing) the repeat distance $a_1$, which is $\sqrt{2}$ times the true unit cell edge $a_2$. Therefore, to find the true $a$ for a tetragonal crystal by this method, it would be necessary to take two rotation photographs, one with the morphological '[100]' direction 1 and the other with the morphological '[110]' direction 2 as rotation axis; one repeat distance will be found to be $\sqrt{2}$ times the other, and the smaller of these lengths is evidently the true $a$. Similarly, for hexagonal crystals (Fig. 75 $b$) it is necessary to take two photographs with directions 1 and 2 respectively as rotation axes; one repeat distance ($a_1$) will be found to be $\sqrt{3}$ times the other ($a_2$), and the latter is evidently the correct $a$.

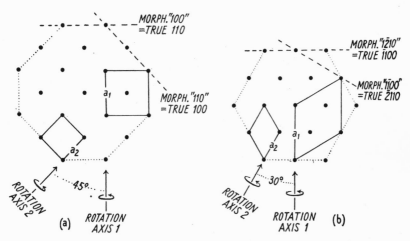

FIG. 75. Determination of unit cell dimensions by rotation photographs, (a) for tetragonal, (b) for hexagonal crystals.

Monoclinic crystals may present more serious difficulties of a similar type: the $b$ axis is fixed by the symmetry (it coincides with the single twofold axis or is perpendicular to the single plane of symmetry); but the $a$ and $c$ axes are not fixed in any such way. We may encounter the state of affairs illustrated in Fig. 76, where the morphological '001' plane is really 101 of the true unit cell, and the morphological '100' is really $10\bar{1}$; and in addition the true angle $\beta$ would be different from the morphologically determined $\beta'$. Here we should evidently have to take X-ray photographs with the crystal rotating round directions parallel to $OP$ and $OQ$ in order to obtain the dimensions of the simplest unit cell. Note that the alternative cell defined by $a''$, $c$, and $\beta''$ has the same size as that defined by $a$, $c$, and $\beta$, and has an equal claim to be regarded as the true unit cell, but may be less convenient because its $\beta$ is greater. It is possible that the relations between the morphologically chosen axial directions and the edges of the simplest unit cell might be more remote, in which case it would be difficult to find the latter by the simple method hitherto described. In the triclinic system, still more difficulties may be encountered. In crystals of rhombohedral symmetry the simplest unit rhombohedron may be one with quite different values of $a$ and $\alpha$ from those of the morphologically selected rhombohedron; this is so for calcite, for instance (Fig. 77).

The straightforward way out of these difficulties is to accept provisionally the cell edges selected on morphological evidence, and to find the indices of all the reflections on this basis; then to survey the indices to see whether any smaller cell will account for all the reflections, thus simplifying the indices. The smallest cell which has a shape appropriate

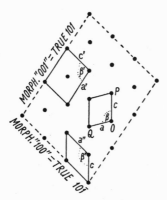

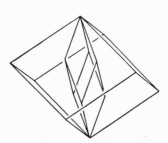

FIG. 76. Alternative monoclinic cells (*b* projection).

FIG. 77. Large (32-molecule) unit rhombohedron of calcite based on cleavage rhomb. The true unit cell is the small (2-molecule) steep rhombohedron shown inside.

to the crystal system and will account for all the reflections is the true unit cell. This procedure may appear very laborious, but the graphical methods now to be described greatly simplify and shorten the work.

For the determination of unit cell dimensions, detailed indexing of the reflections on single-crystal rotation photographs is only necessary in certain cases, as indicated in the foregoing discussion; the complete indexing of rotation photographs of all types of crystals is, however, necessary whenever an investigation is to be carried beyond the determination of unit cell dimensions (to the discovery of the symmetry of the arrangement of atoms in the crystal, or to the elucidation of the arrangement in detail), and it will be appropriate to deal with the whole subject at this stage.

One further remark must be made before taking up this subject. Morphological features are useful in suggesting possible unit cell edges, but it is possible to proceed with very meagre evidence of this sort (such as a single direction, as in rod-shaped crystals lacking well-defined faces), or even with none at all. There are initial difficulties in setting such crystals in a suitable orientation on the goniometer, but these can be solved by X-ray methods; see p. 186. As soon as a single crystal has

been set sufficiently well to give an X-ray rotation photograph showing recognizable layer lines, the unit cell dimensions and the indices of all the reflections can be found by the methods now to be described.

**Indexing rotation photographs. Preliminary consideration.** The spots on the equator of a rotation photograph are obviously reflections from atomic planes which were vertical during the exposure. In Plate VII the equatorial spots are reflections from planes parallel to the $c$ axis, that is, $hk0$ planes: the third or $l$ index for these reflections is 0 by inspection. The other two indices, $h$ and $k$, of all the equatorial reflections may be found from the spacings of the planes, which are worked out from the reflection angles $\theta$ by the Bragg equation. The spacing $d$ of any $hk0$ plane of an orthorhombic crystal is given

by $d = 1 \Big/ \sqrt{\left(\dfrac{h^2}{a^2} + \dfrac{k^2}{b^2}\right)}$; the simplest

way of finding $h$ and $k$ for all the reflections is to plot $\log d$ for each spot on a strip of paper and fit this on a chart (Fig. 78) similar to, but simpler than, the charts used for indexing powder photographs. The construction of such a chart (which shows $\log d$ for all values

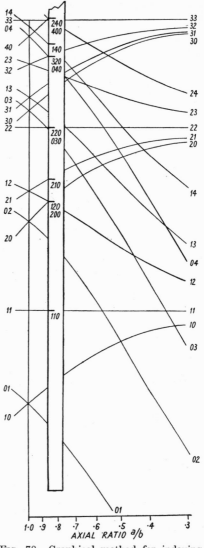

Fig. 78. Graphical method for indexing equatorial reflections on rotation photographs when the projected cell-base is rectangular. The pattern shown is that of polychloroprene ($hk0$ reflections).

of $h$ and $k$ and a wide range of axial ratios $a:b$) is described in Appendix 3. The $h$ and $k$ indices for each reflection are read off on the chart when the match position is found. Note that in some cases, owing to the absence of many equatorial reflections (see pp. 233–58), the simplest match position is not correct. As a guide to the correct match position, $\log d_{100}$ and $\log d_{010}$ (already known from the other two rotation photographs) should be marked on the strip.

For the spots on layer lines above and below the equator, one index ($l$) is given by inspection. It should be remembered that the indices of reflections represent phase-differences between waves diffracted by neighbouring units along the three axial directions (see p. 141). The spots on the first layer line above the equator lie on a cone for which $n$ in the equation $n\lambda = c \cos \phi$ (see p. 149) is 1; this means that waves coming from any one diffracting unit are one wavelength behind those from the next diffracting unit above it; in fact, $n$ in the cone equation is $l$, the third index number. Thus, all spots on the fourth layer line (fourth cone) above the equator are from $hk4$ planes (those on the fourth layer line below the equator are from $hk\overline{4}$ planes), and so on.

The $l$ index of every spot is thus obvious by mere inspection. The other two indices are best obtained by a graphical method. Just as all spots with the same $l$ indices (in the present example) lie on definite lines, so all spots with the same $hk$ values lie on definite curves. But these '$hk$ curves' have a form less simple than the '$l$ curves'. The form of these curves is most readily determined by introducing a piece of mental scaffolding known as the 'reciprocal lattice'—a conception which has proved to be a tool of the greatest value for the solution of all geometrical problems concerned with the directions of X-ray reflections from crystals. It was introduced by Ewald (1921).

**The 'reciprocal lattice'.** From a point within a crystal imagine lines drawn outwards perpendicular to the lattice planes; along these lines points are marked at distances inversely proportional to the spacings of the lattice planes. The points thus obtained form a lattice —that is, they fall on sets of parallel planes. (For a simple proof that they do form a lattice, see Appendix 4.) This imaginary lattice is known as the 'reciprocal lattice'. An example is shown in Fig. 79; all points having the same $l$ index fall on a plane, and the plane containing all $hk1$ points is parallel to that containing the $hk2$ points, and so on. By thinking of this imaginary lattice, in which the planes of the real lattice are symbolized by points, we are obviously brought nearer to the single-crystal X-ray diffraction pattern with its array of spots, especially as the layers of points in the reciprocal lattice correspond with the layers of spots on the diffraction pattern. In fact, a rotation photograph such as one of those in Plate VII is, as we shall see, strongly similar to the pattern we should get by rotating the reciprocal lattice round the $c$ axis

of the crystal and marking off the positions where the reciprocal lattice points pass through a plane through the $c$ axis (Fig. 80). The resemblance between this 'reciprocal lattice rotation diagram' and the X-ray photograph is closest near the centre of the photograph; elsewhere the X-ray photograph is a somewhat distorted version of the reciprocal lattice rotation diagram.

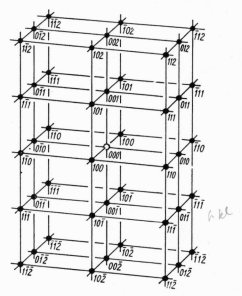

FIG. 79. Reciprocal lattice of an orthorhombic crystal.

The process of reflection by the real lattice cannot be visualized in terms of the reciprocal lattice; but the condition for reflection by the real lattice (the Bragg equation) naturally has its precise geometrical equivalent in terms of the reciprocal lattice. This is illustrated in Fig. 81, in which $XY$ represents the orientation of a set of crystal planes which we will suppose is in a reflecting position. Along the normal to this

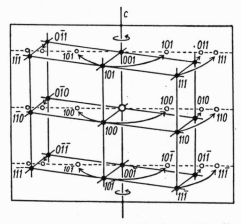

FIG. 80. Formation of reciprocal lattice rotation diagram.

set of planes is the corresponding reciprocal lattice point $P$, the distance of which from the reciprocal lattice origin $X$ is inversely proportional to

$d$, the spacing of the planes in question (defined as on p. 141 so as to include the 'order' of reflection); the unit of length is chosen so that $XP$ is equal to $\lambda/d$ rather than $1/d$ for a reason which will presently appear ($\lambda$ is the characteristic X-ray wavelength, which in any particular experiment is constant). The X-ray beam $QX$ is reflected by the plane at an angle $\theta$, the reflected beam $XR$ making an angle $2\theta$ with the primary beam. If $Y$ lies in the plane $QXR$, the angle $QXY = \theta$.

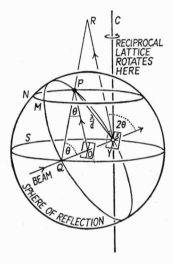

At $P$ draw a line perpendicular to $XP$ to meet the primary beam at $Q$. $R$ must also lie on this line, since primary beam, reflected beam, and the normal to the reflecting plane all lie in a common plane. $QR$ and $XY$ are parallel to each other (since both are at right angles to $XP$ and are in the same plane), hence the angle $PQX = QXY = \theta$. Since the angle $QPX$ is a right angle,

FIG. 81. The condition for reflection in terms of the reciprocal lattice. Reflection occurs when a reciprocal lattice point $P$ touches the surface of the sphere of reflection.

$$PX/QX = \sin \theta;$$

therefore

$$QX = \frac{PX}{\sin \theta} = \frac{\lambda/d}{\sin \theta} = \frac{\lambda}{d \sin \theta}.$$

But the Bragg equation states that when a set of crystal planes reflects X-rays,

$$\frac{\lambda}{d \sin \theta} = 2.$$

Hence $QX = 2$. Thus, for every different set of crystal planes when in a reflecting position, the above construction brings us the line $QX$ of constant length 2 units. For every possible position of $P$ the angle $QPX$ is a right angle, hence $P$ always lies on a circle which has $QX$ (= 2) as its diameter. To plot the positions occupied by all reciprocal lattice points when the planes they symbolize are in reflecting positions, rotate the circle $QPX$ about its diameter $QX$; the sphere $QSXP$ is obtained. (The reason why the reciprocal lattice is made on the scale $XP = \lambda/d$ is now apparent; it is to give the sphere $QXSP$ unit radius.)

In other words, the condition for reflection, in terms of the reciprocal lattice, is this: construct a sphere of unit radius having the primary beam along its diameter. Place the origin of the reciprocal lattice at the point where the primary beam emerges from the sphere. As the crystal turns, the reciprocal lattice, in turning about its origin, passes through the sphere (Fig. 82), and whenever a reciprocal lattice point (distant $\lambda/d$ from the origin) just touches the surface of the sphere (the 'sphere of reflection') a reflected beam flashes out, being reflected by the crystal plane corresponding to the reciprocal lattice point.

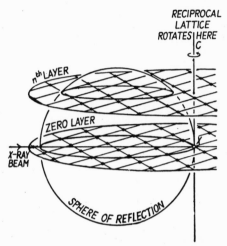

FIG. 82. Reciprocal lattice passing through sphere of reflection
as it rotates.

Note that if in Fig. 81 we join $O$, the centre of the sphere, to $P$, the angle $OQP = OPQ = \theta$, and thus the angle $XOP = 2\theta$; $OP$ is therefore parallel to $XR$ and, equally with $XR$, represents the direction of the reflected ray. The problem of finding the position of any reflected spot on an X-ray photograph therefore resolves itself into (1) finding where the reciprocal lattice point for the plane in question touches the surface of the sphere of reflection, and then (2) finding where the (produced) radius through this point strikes the film. This procedure is valid for all types of single-crystal X-ray photographs. In the particular case of a crystal rotating round a principal axis (say $c$) which is perpendicular to the X-ray beam, the reciprocal lattice points are in layers parallel to the equatorial section of the sphere of reflection (Fig. 82), and remain on the same level as the reciprocal lattice rotates round $XC$; consequently all the points on any one layer—that is, all points having the same $l$ index—pass through the surface of the sphere at various points lying on the circle $PNM$ (Fig. 81) which is parallel to $QSX$. If we joined the centre of the sphere to each of these points we should get a set of lines lying on the surface of a cone. We have thus arrived, by way of the conception of the reciprocal lattice, at the same conclusion as that already drawn from a consideration of diffraction by a row of scattering points, namely, that when a single crystal is rotated round its c axis and an X-ray beam passes through it perpendicular to its c axis, all reflected rays from planes having the same l index lie on a cone. The semi-vertical angle of this cone, $\phi$, we have already seen is given by $l\lambda = c \cos \phi$; this is also obvious from Fig. 83:

$$OU = l\lambda/c = \cos \phi.$$

When the reflections are recorded on a cylindrical film the height $y$ of each layer of spots above the equator is $r \cot \phi$, where $r$ is the radius of the cylinder.

Since the directions of reflected rays are obtained by joining the centre of the sphere to points on its surface, the crystal itself may be regarded as rotating in the centre of the sphere of reflection, while the reciprocal lattice of this same crystal rotates about a different point—the point where the beam emerges from the sphere. If this seems odd, it must be remembered that the reciprocal lattice

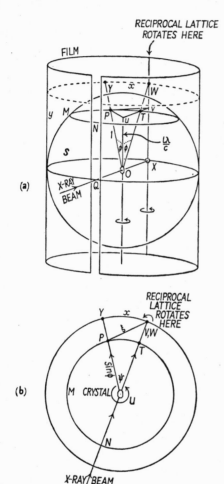

FIG. 83. Sphere of reflection surrounded by cylindrical film of unit radius. *a*. Elevation. *b*. Plan.

is a geometrical fiction and should not be expected to behave other than oddly; the fact is, the reciprocal lattice is concerned with *directions*; its magnitude and the location of its origin are immaterial.

As for the precise position of each reflected beam, and the point at which it strikes the film, this evidently depends (for any one layer of reciprocal lattice points, any one cone of reflections) on the distance of the reciprocal lattice point from the axis of rotation. A point whose distance from the axis of rotation is equal to the shortest distance from this axis to the circle $PNM$ would just touch the sphere at $T$ (Fig. 83 $a$ and $b$), which lies on the line $UV$, parallel to the primary beam; the reflected beam for this plane would travel along $OT$, striking a film of unit radius at $W$ on the meridian of the film, directly above the central spot $X$. Points nearer the axis of rotation than $T$ would never touch the sphere at all, and the planes they represent would never reflect. Other points whose distance $\xi$ from the axis of rotation lies between $TV$ and $NV$ touch the sphere at points such as $P$; what we want to know is the angle $PUV$ (or $\psi$), since this angle determines the distance $x$ of the reflected spot from the meridian of the film. To find $\psi$ we have to solve the triangle $PUV$. Now $UV$ is 1 (the radius of the sphere). $UP$, the radius of the circle of contact, is

$$\sin \phi \left( = \sqrt{\left\{1 - \left(\frac{l\lambda}{c}\right)^2\right\}} \right).$$

Therefore, if we know $\xi$, all three sides of the triangle are known and the angle $\psi$ can be found. $\psi$ is $x/r$ radians.

In practice, we want to find the coordinates of a reciprocal lattice point from the measured position of a spot on the film. This is most simply done by a graphical method, as described below. If, however, it is desired to do it by calculation, for the sake of greater accuracy, the following expressions are required. If the coordinates of a spot on a cylindrical film are $x$ (along the equator) and $y$ (along the meridian), the distance $\zeta$ of any reciprocal lattice point from the equatorial plane (the circle $QSX$) is $\cos \phi = \cos(\cot^{-1} y/r)$. The distance $\xi$ of the point from the axis of rotation is (solving the triangle $PUV$ having two sides of length 1 and $\sin \phi$, and the included angle $\psi$) given by

$$\xi = \sqrt{(1 + \sin^2\phi - 2 \sin \phi \cos \psi)}$$
$$= \sqrt{[1 + \sin^2\{\cot^{-1}(y/r)\} - 2 \sin\{\cot^{-1}(y/r)\}\cos(x/r)]}.$$

Bernal (1926) worked out $\xi$ and $\zeta$ for all positions on a cylindrical film, and gave a chart (illustrated in Fig. 84). Transparent charts of this type, suitable for a cylindrical film 6 cm in diameter, can be obtained from the Institute of Physics (47 Belgrave Square, London, S.W. 1); it is only necessary to place a rotation photograph on the chart, and read off the $\xi$ and $\zeta$ coordinates for every spot on the film. Similar charts for flat films (specimen to film distance 4 cm) can also be obtained. Greater accuracy is obtained by measuring the positions of

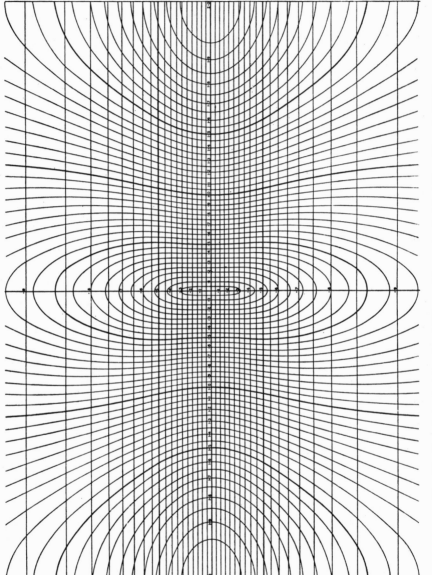

Fig. 84. Bernal chart giving $\xi$ and $\zeta$ for positions on cylindrical film. (Bernal, 1926.)

spots on the photograph, using a travelling microscope, and then plotting these positions on a large-scale Bernal chart; for such precision, the camera constant must be accurately determined.

For the purpose of visualizing the geometry of the reciprocal lattice in terms of the actual camera dimensions, it is perhaps useful to multiply the dimensions of the reciprocal lattice and of the sphere of reflection

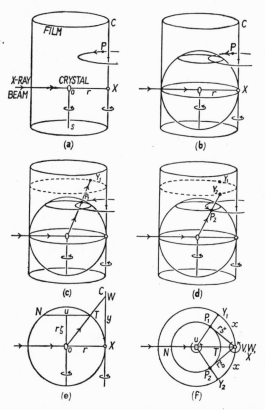

Fig. 85. $a$–$d$. See text. $e$ and $f$ illustrate graphical construction of a Bernal chart.

by $r$, the radius of the cylindrical film, since in this case the origin of the reciprocal lattice is the point where the primary X-ray beam strikes the film, and the axis of rotation of the reciprocal lattice is the vertical line through this point. Let us recapitulate the geometrical construction on this scale.

We have, first of all (Fig. 85 $a$), the primary beam passing through the crystal at right angles to its axis of rotation and striking the cylindrical film (radius $r$) at the point $X$. Erect the axis $XC$ parallel to the

M

cylinder axis; the reciprocal lattice will rotate round $XC$ (its origin being at $X$) while the crystal itself rotates round $OS$. In the cylinder, describe a sphere having the same radius $r$ (Fig. 85 $b$); this will be the sphere of reflection. Any reciprocal lattice point $P$ (distance from the origin $= r\lambda/d$) rotates round $XC$; as soon as it touches the surface of the sphere (Fig. 85 $c$), a reflected beam flashes out, and strikes the film at $Y_1$. On further rotation (Fig. 85 $d$), the point passes again through the surface of the sphere at $P_2$, and a reflection again flashes out, striking the film at $Y_2$.

A Bernal chart for a cylindrical camera of any radius may be constructed graphically by drawing the plan and elevation of this model. Thus, if the height of any reciprocal lattice point above the origin is $r\zeta$ and its distance from the axis of rotation is $r\xi$, the position of the reflection on the film is obtained in the following way. Draw a circle of radius $r$ (Fig. 85 $e$), and then a chord $NUT$ at a distance $r\zeta$ from the centre (this is the circle of contact seen edgewise); $UT$ is the radius of the circle of contact for this reciprocal lattice point. Join $OT$ and produce to $W$ on the line $XC$ which is parallel to $OU$. $WX$ is then the ordinate $y$ of the spot on the film. Now draw the plan, that is, draw another circle of radius $r$ (Fig. 85 $f$) and in it describe a circle of radius $UT$. On this circle $NT$ mark off the points $P_1$, $P_2$ which are at a distance $r\xi$ from $X$, and produce $UP_1$ to $Y_1$ and $UP_2$ to $Y_2$. The arcs $XY_1$ and $XY_2$ are the abscissae $x$ of the two reflections on the film produced by this plane. By doing this for a number of different values of $r\zeta$ and $r\xi$, the complete chart is obtained.

**Indexing rotation photographs by reciprocal lattice methods. Orthorhombic crystals.** First of all, the coordinates $\zeta$ and $\xi$ for each reflection on the photograph (Fig. 86) are found in one of the ways just described; these coordinates may be plotted as in Fig. 87 $a$ to form the reciprocal lattice rotation diagram. The problem now is to decide which point of the reciprocal lattice itself corresponds to each spot on the rotation diagram.

Consider first the equatorial reflections. For a crystal rotated round its $c$ axis, the equatorial reflections are those of $hk0$ planes. To assign correct indices it is only necessary to make a diagram (Fig. 87 $b$) of the zero level of the reciprocal lattice (the dimensions being already known from layer-line spacings on other photographs), and to measure with a ruler the distance $\xi$ of each point from the origin; it is then obvious which reciprocal lattice point corresponds to each spot on the rotation diagram.

As for the upper and lower layer lines of the rotation diagram, it is immediately obvious that the spots on them lie exactly above or below equatorial spots—the $\xi$ values for spots on all layer lines are the same (except where certain spots are missing). The reason is that the 101 point of the reciprocal lattice is at the same distance from the axis of rotation as 100 (Fig. 80), and in general a point $hkl$ is at the same

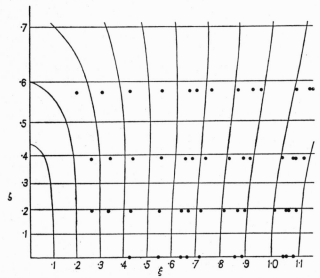

FIG. 86. Coordinates of spots on rotation photograph of orthorhombic crystal.

distance from the axis of rotation as the corresponding $hk0$ point. Therefore, knowledge of the indices of the equatorial spots immediately leads to the correct indices for all the remaining spots. The vertical lines of spots having the same $hk$ indices are known as 'row lines'. The row lines are often obvious on the photograph itself, though they are not straight lines—see the photograph of benzil in Plate VII.

It should be noted that some reflections may be missing from the photograph on account of certain symmetries in the atomic arrangement (see Chapter VII), others because they are so weak that they do not produce a perceptible blackening on the film. Still others (such as 001, 002) are absent because the crystal planes have not been in reflecting positions; the reciprocal lattice points which do pass through reflecting positions are contained within a circular area of radius 1, corresponding to the boundary of the sphere of reflection (see Fig. 87 a). It is useful to remember that the distance from the origin to each point on the rotation diagram is $\lambda/d$ for the corresponding crystal plane.

**Monoclinic crystals.** The procedure already described is followed
as far as the determination of $\zeta$ and $\xi$ for each point and the construction

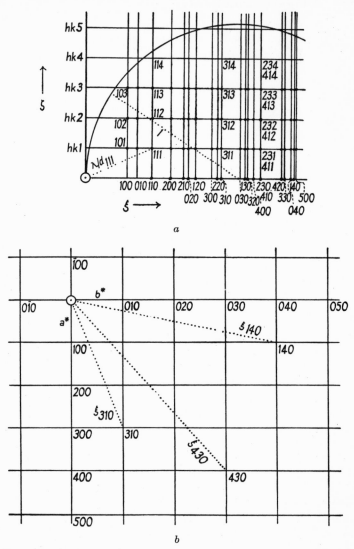

Fig. 87. *a*. Reciprocal lattice rotation diagram corresponding to Fig. 86.
*b*. Graphical determination of $\xi$ values for an orthorhombic crystal.

of the reciprocal lattice rotation diagram. But, on account of the lower
symmetry of the monoclinic cell, the rotation diagram is less simple than
that of an orthorhombic crystal.

A monoclinic unit cell has its *a* and *c* axes at an angle $\beta$ not 90°, and its $b$ axis normal to the $ac$ plane. The reciprocal lattice has a similar form, but it should be noted that, whereas in the orthorhombic system all three reciprocal axes are parallel to the real axes, in the monoclinic system only the $b^*$ axis of the reciprocal lattice is parallel to the real $b$ axis. The $a^*$ and $c^*$ reciprocal axes are not parallel to the $a$ and $c$ axes of the real cell: $a^*$ (length $= \lambda/d_{100}$) is perpendicular to $c$, and $c^*$

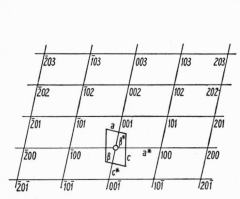

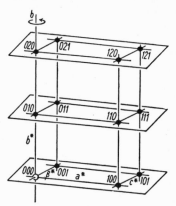

FIG. 88. Reciprocal lattice ($h0l$ plane) of monoclinic crystal. The $b$ projection of the real cell is also shown $(a, c, \beta)$.

FIG. 89. Monoclinic reciprocal lattice rotated round $b$.

(length $= \lambda/d_{001}$) is perpendicular to $a$ (Fig. 88); and the angle $\beta^*$ of the reciprocal cell is the supplement of the angle $\beta$ of the real cell.

If the crystal is rotated round its $b$ axis (Fig. 89) the equatorial spots are reflections from $h0l$ planes. The $\xi$ values for these spots are found as before by measuring the distance from the origin to each point of the (non-rectangular) $h0l$ net plane (Fig. 88). Note that the indexing of equatorial reflections in this case cannot be done by a log $d$ chart, since there are three variables, $a$, $c$, and $\beta$; the reciprocal lattice method is essential. Once the indices for the equatorial reflections have been found, those of the reflections on upper and lower layer lines follow at once, since all reciprocal lattice points having the same $h$ and $l$ indices (such a set as 201, 211, 221, 231, and so on) are at the same distance $\xi$ from the axis of rotation and thus form row lines.

Rotation round the $a$ or $c$ axis of a monoclinic crystal (Fig. 90) results in a different type of photograph; the spots fall on layer lines, as always when a crystal is rotated about a principal axis, but not on row lines. Consider first the equatorial spots on a photograph obtained by rotating the crystal round the $c$ axis; these are from $hk0$ planes. The zero ($hk0$) level of the reciprocal lattice is a rectangular array of points, from which

$\xi$ values are obtained as before by measurements from the origin. The other levels are also rectangular networks, but they do not lie directly above or below the zero level, being displaced in the direction of $a*$ by distances which are multiples of $c* \cos \beta*$. The 101 point, for instance, is not the same distance from the axis of rotation as the 100 point, and hence $10l$ reflections on the photograph do not lie on row lines but on

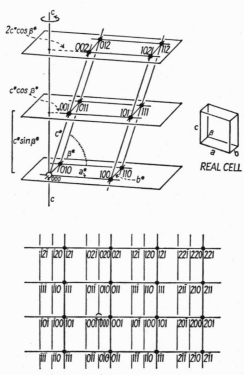

Fig. 90. Monoclinic reciprocal lattice rotated round normal to $a*b*$ plane ($c$ axis of real cell). Above: general view. Right: real cell, same orientation. Below: view (on smaller scale) looking straight down $c$ axis.

curves whose form depends on $\beta*$. The distances of the non-equatorial points from the axis of rotation might be obtained by drawing the projections of the various levels on the equatorial plane, as in Fig. 90; but it is simpler to use the same network—the already drawn zero level— for all layers, marking off along $a*$ a set of new origins, one for each level (Fig. 91). It is important to note that the origins for the upper layers (positive values of $l$) lie along the negative direction of $a*$. The $\xi$ values for all $hk1$ points are found by measuring the distance from the origin for $l = \pm 1$ to the appropriate $hk0$ point; and so on for other layers. Note that $\xi$ for $10\bar{1}$ (or $\bar{1}01$) is smaller than $\xi$ for 101. The rotation diagram produced in this way is shown in Fig. 92. Only $00l$ points, and $h0l$ points having $h$ constant, lie on straight lines (inclined to the $\xi$ axis at the angle $\beta^*$), all others lying on curves.

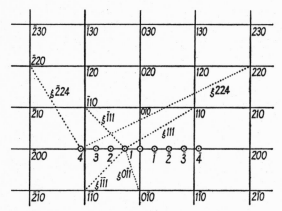

FIG. 91. Graphical method for determining $\xi$ values for non-equatorial reflections of monoclinic crystal rotated round $c$.

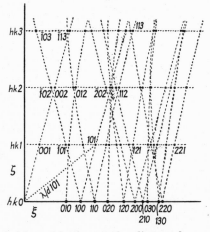

FIG. 92. Part of reciprocal lattice rotation diagram for monoclinic crystal rotated round $c$ axis, constructed by measurement of Fig. 91.

The rotation diagrams of monoclinic crystals can also be used for graphical determination of the spacings of the planes; this is done (as in Fig. 92) by measuring the distance of each point to the origin. This graphical method is much more rapid than calculation.

**Triclinic crystals.** None of the angles of a triclinic cell are right angles; in consequence, none of the axes of the reciprocal lattice are parallel to those of the real lattice, and the angles $\alpha^*$, $\beta^*$, and $\gamma^*$ of the reciprocal lattice are all different from those ($\alpha$, $\beta$, and $\gamma$) of the real lattice. The relations between these quantities are as follow:

$$\cos\alpha^* = \frac{\cos\beta\cos\gamma - \cos\alpha}{\sin\beta\sin\gamma},$$

$$\cos\beta^* = \frac{\cos\gamma\cos\alpha - \cos\beta}{\sin\gamma\sin\alpha},$$

$$\cos\gamma^* = \frac{\cos\alpha\cos\beta - \cos\gamma}{\sin\alpha\sin\beta},$$

$$a^* = \frac{\lambda}{D}bc\sin\alpha,$$

$$b^* = \frac{\lambda}{D}ca\sin\beta,$$

$$c^* = \frac{\lambda}{D}ab\sin\gamma,$$

where $D = abc\sqrt{(1 + 2\cos\alpha\cos\beta\cos\gamma - \cos^2\alpha - \cos^2\beta - \cos^2\gamma)}$.

These formulae are so unwieldy that it is better to derive the reciprocal lattice elements directly from the spacings and angles of the planes:

$$a^* = \frac{\lambda}{d_{100}}, \qquad b^* = \frac{\lambda}{d_{010}}, \qquad c^* = \frac{\lambda}{d_{001}},$$

and

$$\alpha^* = \angle\,(010):(001), \qquad \beta^* = \angle\,(100):(001), \qquad \gamma^* = \angle\,(100):(010).$$

If a triclinic crystal is rotated round any axis of the real cell (Fig. 93), the photograph exhibits layer lines (since the various levels of the reciprocal lattice are normal to the axis of rotation), but not row lines, since none of the points on upper or lower levels are at the same distance from the axis of rotation as corresponding points on the zero level. The indices for points on the zero level are found in the same way as for photographs of monoclinic crystals rotated round the $b$ axis: for the zero level of a triclinic crystal rotated round $c$, a net with elements $a^*$, $b^*$, and $\gamma^*$ is constructed (Fig. 94), and distances $\xi$ of points from the origin are measured. The other levels, projected on to the equator, are displaced with regard to the zero level in a direction which does not lie along an equatorial reciprocal axis; the simplest way of measuring $\xi$ values is, as before, to use the zero level network, marking off a set of alternative origins, one for each level, along a line *OL* in Fig. 94. The angle δ this line makes with $a^*$ is given by

$$\tan \delta = \frac{\cos \alpha^* - \cos \beta^* \cos \gamma^*}{\cos \beta^* \sin \gamma^*},$$

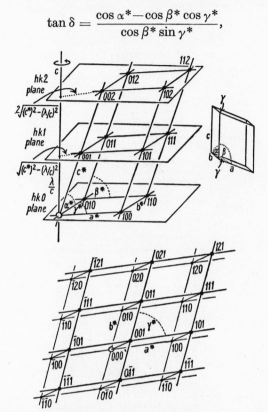

FIG. 93. Triclinic reciprocal lattice. Above, left: general view. Right: real cell. Below: view looking straight down *c*, showing zero and first layers only.

and the distances of the alternative origins are multiples of

$$\sqrt{\left\{(c^*)^2 - \left(\frac{\lambda}{c}\right)^2\right\}}.$$

The rotation diagram has the appearance of Fig. 95; the only points lying on a straight line (apart from the layer lines) are the 00*l* set. Note that the ξ values for *hkl*, *hkl̄*, *h̄k̄l*, and *h̄kl* are all different.

The spacings of the planes of a triclinic crystal are best determined from the rotation diagram, by measuring the distance of each point from the origin.

**Oscillation photographs.** It often happens that on rotation photographs the positions of two or more possible reflections are so close together that it is impossible to decide whether a particular spot is produced by one of the crystal planes in question, or the other, or indeed both together. For the purpose of determining unit cell dimensions

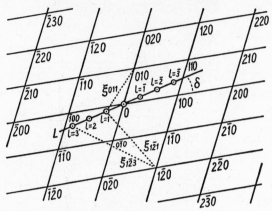

Fig. 94. Graphical determination of $\xi$ values for non-equatorial reflections of triclinic crystal rotated round $c$.

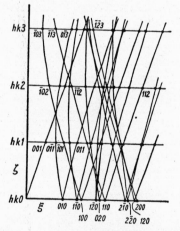

Fig. 95. Reciprocal lattice rotation diagram for triclinic crystal, constructed by measurements on Fig. 94.

this usually does not matter, but if the investigation is to be carried further, to the determination of atomic positions (see Chapter VII), it is important to identify every reflection unequivocally and to measure its intensity.

One method of separating reflections is to take photographs while the crystal is, not rotating completely, but oscillating through a limited angular range. A set of several photographs is required to cover all reflections; on each photograph only certain spots appear, because only certain sets of crystal planes pass through their reflecting positions in the course of the oscillation of the crystal through the selected angular range. Thus, it is usually possible to decide that because a particular spot appears on one photograph and not on others it must have been produced by one crystal plane and not another.

The orientation of the crystal necessary for the production of each reflection is determined graphically by a method (Bernal, 1926) which

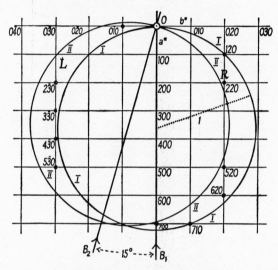

Fig. 96. Reciprocal lattice diagram for oscillation photograph. Orthorhombic crystal, equatorial level.

follows naturally from the reciprocal lattice methods already described. Consider first the equatorial reflections given by an orthorhombic crystal oscillated about its $c$ axis. These reflections are produced as the zero level of the reciprocal lattice (containing the $hk0$ points) passes through the sphere of reflection. In Fig. 96 the axis of rotation $O$ is normal to the plane of the paper. Suppose that the crystal is oscillated through 15°, one extreme position being with the X-ray beam $B_1$ normal to the 100 plane. At this position the circle of contact, which for the zero level is the equator of the sphere (radius = 1), has its diameter along $a*$ (position I). When the crystal rotates, the reciprocal lattice rotates about $O$, but it is simpler for graphical purposes to keep the reciprocal lattice still and rotate the beam (in the opposite direction), and with it the circle of contact, which for the other extreme position of the 15° oscillation reaches position II. During this movement the only reciprocal lattice points which pass through the circumference of the circle are those marked with spots; therefore the only equatorial reflections which appear on this photograph are those from planes having the indices of these points, and if we look at the photograph as if looking along the beam, reflections $0\bar{1}0$, $2\bar{3}0$, $3\bar{3}0$, $4\bar{3}0$, and $5\bar{3}0$ appear on the left of the film, while reflections 120, 220, 520, 620, 710, and 700 appear on the right.

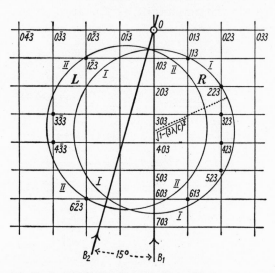

FIG. 97.  Reciprocal lattice diagram for oscillation photograph.
Orthorhombic crystal, third layer line.

Consider now the reflections on an upper layer line—say the third. These are produced when the points on the third (upper) level of the reciprocal lattice pass through the sphere of reflection. The circle of contact ($MNP$ in Figs. 81–83) has a radius less than that of the sphere; the radius is actually $\sqrt{\{1-(3\lambda/c)^2\}}$. (For the $n$th layer the radius would be $\sqrt{\{1-(n\lambda/c)^2\}}$.) During the oscillation of 15° (see Fig. 97) this circle of contact moves from position I to position II; the only crystal planes which reflect during this movement are those whose reciprocal lattice points lie in the areas $L$ and $R$—that is, $1\bar{2}3$, $3\bar{3}3$, $4\bar{3}3$, and $6\bar{2}3$, giving spots on the left of the photograph, and 113, 223, 323, 423, 523, and 613, giving spots on the right.

All reciprocal lattice levels and all angles of oscillation can be dealt with in this way, care being taken always to use the correct radius for the circle of contact. In the same way, if for any purpose it is desired to know at what angle any plane reflects, it is only necessary to draw the circle of contact on tracing-paper, and rotate it until the appropriate reciprocal lattice point touches the circumference; the position of the diameter *BO* then gives the necessary orientation of the beam with respect to the reciprocal lattice net and thus to any chosen reference direction in the crystal. Bernal, in the paper already mentioned (1926), gives a transparent chart showing the circles of contact for various reciprocal lattice levels.

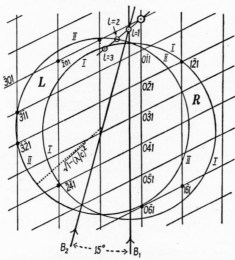

FIG. 98. Reciprocal lattice diagram for oscillation photograph. Triclinic crystal, first layer line.

The same procedure is followed for all crystals. In dealing with photographs of monoclinic crystals oscillated round *a* or *c*, or triclinic crystals oscillated round any axis, care should be taken to use the appropriate origin for each reciprocal lattice level. (See Figs. 91 and 94.) As an example, the procedure for the first (*hk*1) level of a triclinic crystal is illustrated in Fig. 98.

The oscillation method just described is essentially a method of checking indices which have already been assigned on the basis of $\xi$ values, and of separating those reflections which on complete rotation photographs are found to overlap. It defines the positions of reciprocal lattice points only within the 15° or 10° angle used for the oscillation photograph. It would be possible to define the angular positions of these points more closely by oscillating through smaller angles, or by taking photographs covering slightly overlapping angular ranges; but this would be tedious. It is better to use one of the methods which have been devised to define the *precise* positions of reciprocal lattice points—in other words, methods whereby the reciprocal lattice may be plotted *directly* from the coordinates of reflections on the photographs. The best methods of doing this are those (to be described later) in which the film is moved while the crystal is rotating, so that one coordinate of a spot on the film is related to the position occupied by the crystal when that reflection was produced. If, however, a moving-film goniometer is not available, it is often possible to achieve the same result by using the ordinary rotation-and-oscillation goniometer in a special way:

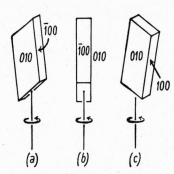

the crystal, instead of being rotated round a principal axis, is rotated round a direction inclined at an angle of a few degrees to a principal axis.

**The tilted crystal method.** Crystals rotated ·round a direction inclined at a few degrees to a principal axis give X-ray diffraction photographs in which the spots are displaced from the layer lines. But the amount of displacement is different for each reflection; on the equator of Plate VIII (upper photograph), it can be seen that some reflections are doublets,

FIG. 99.  Rotation of a tilted crystal.

one above and one below the equator, the separation being different for each pair of reflections; a few lie actually on or very near the equator and are therefore not resolved; others are quadruplets, the separation being again variable. The reason is illustrated in Fig. 99, which shows a crystal tilted in a direction lying in the 010 plane; this particular plane is still vertical (see Fig. 99 *b*) and therefore gives reflections lying *on* the equator. But the reflections from plane 100 will not lie on the equator; a reflection to the right when the crystal is in position *a* will lie above the equator, while on turning through 180° (position *c*) the reflection to the right will appear below the equator. The reflections from other planes in the $hk0$ zone will be displaced from the equator by an amount which depends on the orientation of the reflecting plane with respect to the plane of tilt, as well as on the angle of reflection.

The problem is best treated by reciprocal lattice methods. Fig. 100 gives a general view of the zero layer of the reciprocal lattice of a crystal tilted in an arbitrary direction. Fig. 101 is a plan; the axis of rotation is normal to the plane of the paper; the normal to the zero

PLATE VIII

X-ray diffraction photographs of a gypsum crystal rotated round a direction inclined $8\frac{1}{3}°$ to the $c$ axis in an arbitrary direction. Above, complete rotation; below, 90° oscillation

layer, as it comes out above the paper, lies a little to the right in the plane $OT$. All the reciprocal lattice spots to the right of $AA'$ lie a little below the equatorial level, while those to the left of $AA'$ lie a little above the equatorial level. Now since all the points on this net lie in a plane, the distance $\zeta$ of any point from the equatorial level is proportional to the distance $x$ from the line $AA'$; if $\phi$ is the angle of tilt, $x = \zeta \operatorname{cosec} \phi$ (see Fig. 100). Hence, if $\phi$ and $\zeta$ are known, $x$ can be calculated. The angle of tilt $\phi$ can be fixed experimentally by first setting the

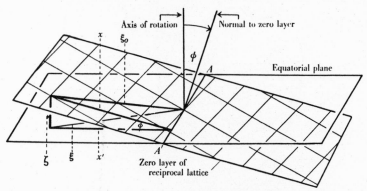

FIG. 100. Reciprocal lattice of a tilted crystal. Zero layer (general view).

crystal with a principal axis accurately parallel to the axis of rotation, and then tilting it $\phi°$ by one of the goniometer arcs. The coordinate $\zeta$ of each spot can be determined either by using a Bernal chart or more accurately by calculation (p. 159). It is also possible to determine the distance $\xi_0$ (Fig. 100) from the origin of the reciprocal lattice: the coordinate $\xi$ of each spot is determined, either on the Bernal chart or by calculation, and from this $\xi_0$ is given by $\sqrt{(\xi^2 + \zeta^2)}$.

The two coordinates $x$ and $\xi_0$ fix the position of each reciprocal lattice point in its own net plane, except in one particular: the sign of the $y$ coordinate (Fig. 101) is not determined; in other words, any reciprocal lattice point $P$ may be on either side of the tilt plane $OT$. Points $P$ and $Q$, for instance, in Fig. 101 are on opposite sides of the tilt plane $OT$, but there is nothing in the treatment so far to tell us which side each is on. This ambiguity can be avoided by taking, not a complete rotation photograph, but an oscillation photograph in such a way that all reflections on one side of the photograph correspond with reciprocal lattice points all lying on the same side of $OT$. For instance, the crystal is oscillated through 90° so that the tilt plane $OT$ moves anti-clockwise from a position normal to the X-ray beam to a position parallel to the beam, and back again. On Fig. 101, in which the reciprocal lattice is stationary, this is equivalent to a rotation of the X-ray beam clockwise from *OB* to *OC* and back again. Reflections on the right-hand side of this photograph correspond to reciprocal lattice points through which the semicircle† *ODB* (radius = 1) passes as it rotates to *OFC* and back

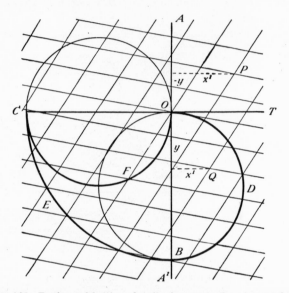

FIG. 101. Reciprocal lattice of a tilted crystal. Zero layer (plan).

again; all these points (lying within the heavily outlined area *ODBECF*) are on the same side of the tilt plane *OT*. (The left-hand side of the same photograph is not free from ambiguity.) The oscillation may, if desired, be through a smaller angle within the 90° range mentioned; but the X-ray beam may oscillate only between *OB* and *OC* if ambiguity is to be avoided—and it is only avoided on the right-hand side of the photograph.

In this way the coordinates of all reciprocal lattice points on the zero layer lying within the area *ODBECF* are directly determined. Fig. 102 shows the results obtained from a 90° oscillation photograph (Plate VIII) of a gypsum crystal set with its $c$ axis inclined $8\frac{1}{3}°$ to the axis of rotation; in spite of the limited precision in the determination of $x$, there is no doubt about where to draw the net. If the remaining

† Strictly speaking, owing to the tilt of the net plane with respect to the plane of the paper all 'circles' in Fig. 101 should be slightly elliptical, with the major axis parallel to *AA'* (eccentricity = sin $\phi$).

points are required, the simplest plan is to restore the crystal to the untilted position, and then tilt it in a direction at right angles to the first by using the second of the arc movements of the goniometer head.

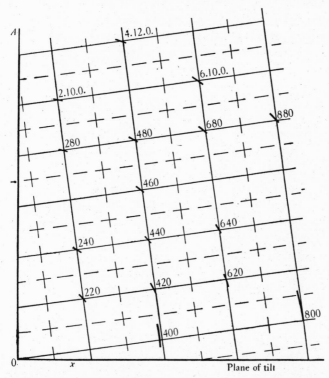

FIG. 102. $hk0$ plane of reciprocal lattice of gypsum crystal, determined from the photographs in Plate VIII. The length of each arc represents the possible error.

A second 90° oscillation photograph is then taken, the plane of tilt being oscillated as before in relation to the X-ray beam.

The coordinates of reciprocal lattice points corresponding to spots on the upper and lower layers of the same photograph can also be determined directly. For these layers it can be shown (Bunn, Peiser, and Turner-Jones, 1944) that if $z$ is the distance of a layer from the equatorial layer,

$$x = z \cot \phi - \zeta \operatorname{cosec} \phi.$$

The other coordinate necessary for the determination of the position of a reciprocal lattice point is $\xi_0$, the distance of the point from the normal to the net plane (i.e. the real axis of the crystal); this can be obtained either from a photograph of the untilted crystal (in which circumstance $\xi_0 = \xi$) or, alternatively from the tilt photograph, using the expression $\xi_0 = \sqrt{(\xi^2+\zeta^2-z^2)}$. It is thus possible to determine the whole reciprocal lattice directly from one or two tilt photographs, without any previous knowledge of the unit cell edge-lengths or angles.

The tilted crystal method can only be used if the layers of reflections, though somewhat dispersed, are distinct from each other: it must be possible to recognize at a glance that a particular reflection belongs to a particular level of the reciprocal lattice. For this reason, the method is most suitable for crystals having at least one short axis. Rotation about a direction inclined by a few degrees to the short axis gives a photograph in which the layer lines are well separated; the shorter the axis, the larger the angle of tilt which can be used, and therefore the greater the displacement of the spots and the more accurate the determination of $x$. This condition is fulfilled by many crystals of aromatic substances, since flat molecules often pack parallel to each other; one crystal axis is approximately normal to the plane of the molecules and may be as short as 4–5 Å. Moreover, the crystals of such substances are often needle-like, the short axis lying along the needle axis; these crystals can be conveniently set up on the goniometer with the needle axis inclined by a few degrees to the axis of rotation.

**Moving-film goniometers.** The advantage of moving the photographic film during its exposure to the diffracted X-ray beams from a rotating crystal (the movement of the film being synchronized with that of the crystal) has already been mentioned: it is that one coordinate of a spot on the film is related to the position occupied by the crystal when that reflection was produced, and in practice this means that the coordinates of reciprocal lattice points can be derived directly from the coordinates of the spots on the film. It is true that this can be done by means of the ordinary rotation-and-oscillation goniometer if the tilted crystal method is used; but the scope of this method is limited by the necessity of keeping the layer lines separate from each other, and even in the most favourable circumstances the displacements of the spots from the average layer-line levels are small. In moving-film goniometers a crystal axis is set accurately parallel to the axis of rotation, and one cone of reflections only is allowed to reach the film, which is moved through a comparatively large distance during the rotation of the crystal.

The earliest of the moving-film goniometers, the one which up to the present has been most widely used, is that of Weissenberg (1924), in which (see Fig. 103 a), while the crystal is rotated, a cylindrical film is moved bodily along the axis of rotation, a complete to-and-fro cycle taking place during the rotation of the crystal through 180° and back again. A slotted screen is adjusted to permit the passage of any selected cone of reflections. Details of the design of this type of gonio-

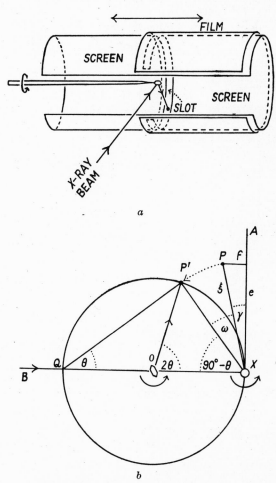

FIG. 103. *a*. Principle of the Weissenberg moving-film goniometer, arranged for recording equatorial layer by normal-beam method. *b*. Determination of reciprocal lattice coordinates for spots on equatorial layer.

meter are to be found in papers by Robertson (1934 *b*), Buerger (1936), and Wooster and Martin (1940).

The interpretation of Weissenberg photographs is quite simple. Consider first the zero layer of reflections, the X-ray beam being perpendicular to the axis of rotation of the crystal—in other words, the reflections which would lie on the equator of a fixed-film, normal-beam rotation photograph, but which in a Weissenberg photograph are spread out as in the example in Plate IX. Imagine the film at one extreme end of its range of travel, the crystal being in a corresponding position, and in Fig. 103 *b*, let *XA* (perpendicular to the X-ray beam) and *XB* (*along* the beam) be the axes of reference of the reciprocal lattice. *P* is any

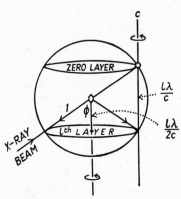

reciprocal lattice point, whose position with respect to *XA* is given in polar coordinates by $\xi$ (the distance *PX*) and the angle $\gamma$ ($\angle PXA$). When the crystal rotates anti-clockwise, reflection occurs when *P* reaches *P'* on the surface of the sphere of reflection, the direction of the reflected ray being *OP'*. To reach this position, the reciprocal lattice has rotated through an angle $\omega$ ($\angle PXP'$); and the film has simultaneously moved a distance *d* which is related to the total travel *D* by the

FIG. 104. Scheme for equi-inclination method. When $\cos \phi = \dfrac{l\lambda}{2c}$, the *l*th cone includes the direction of the primary beam.

relation $\dfrac{d}{D} = \dfrac{\omega}{180°}$.

We wish to find $\xi$ and $\gamma$ for the spot corresponding to the reciprocal lattice point *P*. $\xi$ is obtained from the distance *x* of the spot from the centre line of the film (corresponding to the distance along the equator of a fixed-film rotation photograph): if the radius of the cylindrical film is *r*, $\dfrac{x}{\pi r} = \dfrac{2\theta}{180°}$, where $\theta$ is the Bragg angle; $\xi$ is then given by $\xi = 2 \sin \theta$. The angle $\gamma$ is given very simply by the fact that $\angle P'XA$ ($= \omega + \gamma$) is equal to $\theta$ (since $P'XQ = 90° - \theta$): thus

$$\gamma = \theta - \omega = \theta - \frac{d}{D} \times 180°.$$

The whole zero layer of the reciprocal lattice can thus be plotted directly, using the polar coordinates $\xi$ and $\gamma$. Cartesian coordinates *e* and *f* are usually more convenient, however; these are given by $e = \xi \cos \gamma$ and $f = \xi \sin \gamma$. It is a simple matter to construct a chart giving Cartesian coordinates for all positions on the film; such a chart is illustrated in Plate IX. Transparent copies of such charts can be obtained from the Institute of Physics (47 Belgrave Square, London, S.W. 1).

PLATE IX

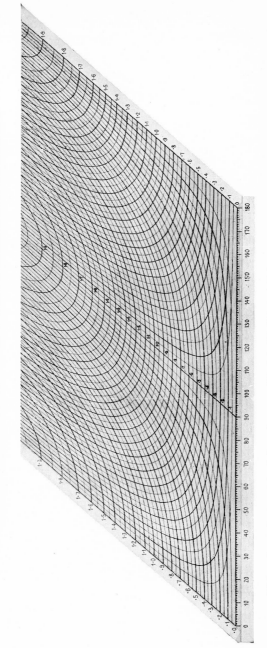

Weissenberg photograph of the substance (Et₃As)₂(HgCl₂)₂ (triclinic; rotation axis, $c$; zero level), with chart for reading off reciprocal lattice coordinates. (R. C. Evans and H. S. Peiser)

For other cones of reflections it is best to use the 'equi-inclination' method (Fig. 104), in which the X-ray beam is inclined to the axis of rotation of the crystal at such an angle that it actually lies on the cone of reflections being studied. This occurs when cos $\phi = l\lambda/2c$ (for rotation round the $c$ axis). The advantage of the equi-inclination method (see Buerger, 1934) is that the chart for the zero layer can be used for the other layers; it is only necessary to remember that to obtain reciprocal lattice coordinates on the same scale as those of the zero layer, the figures on the chart must be multiplied by the factor $\sqrt{\{1-(\zeta/2)^2\}}$. For further information on the interpretation of Weissenberg photographs, see Buerger (1935, 1942) and Crowfoot (1935).

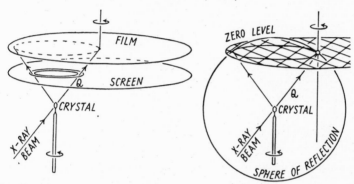

Fig. 105. De Jong and Bouman's goniometer for undistorted photography of reciprocal lattice net planes. Left: camera arrangement. Right: reciprocal lattice equivalent.

Several forms of moving-film cameras using flat films have been devised; the earlier types have been superseded by those which, by ingenious systems of coupled movements of the crystal and the film, give photographs which are undistorted representations of reciprocal lattice layers. The principle of the simplest of these, that of De Jong and Bouman (1938), is illustrated in Fig. 105 (see also De Jong, Bouman, and De Lange, 1938; Torroja, Pajares, and Amoros, 1951). The X-ray beam is inclined to the axis of rotation of the crystal, and a flat film is rotated at the same speed in its own plane about an axis parallel to, but not coincident with, the axis of rotation of the crystal (Fig. 105). One cone of reflections is selected by means of a screen with an annular slot. Reflections corresponding to the zero level of the reciprocal lattice lie on the cone containing the direction of the X-ray beam, and for photography of this cone the beam must pass through the centre of the rotating film. When these conditions are fulfilled the spots on the film are found to be arranged in a network exactly as in the reciprocal lattice;

in fact, it may be said that the film shows an undistorted photograph of the zero level of the reciprocal lattice. The reason is demonstrated in Fig. 105. The scale of the reciprocal lattice and its attendant sphere of reflection may be made whatever we choose. Suppose we make the radius of the latter equal to $Q$, the distance from the crystal to the centre of the film. We have seen that the origin of the reciprocal lattice lies at the point where the beam emerges from the sphere of reflection; evidently, then, the centre of the film is the origin of the reciprocal lattice, and, in fact, since the film is normal to the axis of rotation of the crystal, the plane of the film is the plane of the zero level of the reciprocal lattice. Moreover, we have seen that when the crystal rotates on its axis, the reciprocal lattice rotates about its own origin; hence, when crystal and film rotate together at the same speed, the film keeps pace exactly with the reciprocal lattice—in fact, the film *is* the zero level of the reciprocal lattice. Reflections are produced when reciprocal lattice points touch the surface of the sphere, which they do at various positions in the circle of contact. The circle of contact for the zero level of the reciprocal lattice is, in this camera, defined by the annular slot in the screen. The directions of reflected beams are lines joining the crystal (the centre of the sphere) to reciprocal lattice points when the latter touch the circle of contact; hence the reflected beams make spots on the films at positions corresponding exactly to reciprocal lattice points. We may imagine the reciprocal lattice points as already existing in the film, only waiting to be printed (as latent images) when reflected beams flash out from the crystal.

The foregoing description refers to the photography of the zero level of the reciprocal lattice. But De Jong and Bouman show that in a camera in which both the inclination of the beam and the position of the axis of rotation of the film are variable, the various levels of the reciprocal lattice may be recorded successively, all on the same scale. The advantages of such photographs are obvious: no charts or graphical constructions are needed for indexing the spots, the indices being obvious by inspection. This is a considerable advantage for crystals with very large unit cells, for which the indexing of Weissenberg photographs is difficult. A disadvantage of the De Jong and Bouman camera is that the angular range of reflections which can be registered on any one film is more limited than in the Weissenberg camera.

Buerger (1944) developed a very ingenious variant of the same basic idea in his precession camera. In this camera, the crystal does not rotate; instead, its axis performs a precessing movement (Fig. 106).

What the crystal does, the film, representing a layer of the reciprocal lattice, must do also, and so its normal performs the same precessing motion; the film thus, so to speak, rolls around and through the sphere of reflection, picking up diffracted beams on the way, as it cannot fail to do if the film slavishly repeats the movement of the crystal. (The

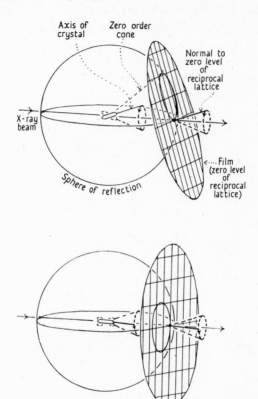

Fig. 106. Principle of Buerger's precession camera. The crystal does not rotate; its axis precesses. The lower diagram shows the situation 90° after the upper diagram.

cone of reflections comes through an annular slot in a screen as in the De Jong and Bouman camera.) Levels other than the zero level can be photographed by suitably adjusting the angle of the X-ray beam to the crystal, the film position, and the layer-line screen; the spacing of the reciprocal lattice levels must of course be known. An advantage of the precession camera over the De Jong and Bouman arrangement is that since the tilted crystal does not rotate but merely precesses, it need only be perfect in a small cylindrical volume, not over the whole crystal;

it is thus useful for soft plastic crystals which may be distorted, and for twinned crystals, since during the small changes of direction of the crystal during precession, the X-ray beam need not touch the surrounding imperfect regions.

**The simplest unit cell.** When the indices of all reflections on the X-ray photographs of a crystal have been obtained by any of the methods described—indices based, it will be remembered, on morphologically chosen axes—the whole set of indices can be surveyed to see whether any simpler cell would account for all the reflections. One way of doing this is to look at reciprocal lattice diagrams or models. For instance, in Fig. 107 it is obvious that the larger, heavily outlined

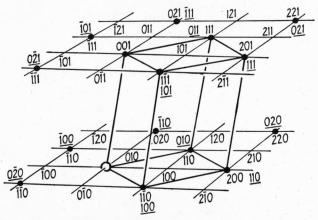

Fig. 107. The systematic absences in this reciprocal lattice indicate that a larger reciprocal cell (that is, a smaller real cell) can be chosen. The new reciprocal cell is heavily outlined. The new indices (underlined) are simpler than the old.

reciprocal cell—extended to form a network—accounts for all the reflections, and therefore should be accepted in preference to the original network based on morphologically chosen axes. The larger reciprocal cell represents a smaller real cell, and gives smaller indices for the reflections than the old cell—for instance, the former 110 becomes *010*, the former 1$\bar{1}$0 becomes *100*, and the former 200 becomes *110*.

The true unit cell is not necessarily the *smallest* unit that will account for all the reciprocal lattice points; it is also necessary that the cell chosen should conform to the crystal symmetry. The reflections of crystals with face-centred or body-centred lattices can be accounted for by unit cells which have only a fraction of the volume of the true unit cell, but the smallest unit cells for such crystals are rejected in favour of the smallest that conforms to the crystal symmetry. The reciprocal lattice of the true unit cell of such a crystal will show that many of its points (in the form of a definite pattern) are missing: the reflections corresponding to them do not appear on the photographs. The subject of missing reflections in relation to the lattice type and in relation to internal symmetries will be taken up in the next chapter.

There is also a numerical reduction process first introduced by Delaunay (1933), which leads automatically from the possible unit cell to the smallest unit cell. Moreover, when the reduction process is complete, the characteristics of the smallest cell, revealed in diagrams which are used as part of the reduction process, show the symmetry and indicate how the true unit cell is related to the smallest unit. Details of the process are given in *International Tables* (1952). (See also Patterson and Love (1957).)

Rhombohedral crystals are best treated as if they were hexagonal. When hexagonal indices have been assigned to all reflections, and the simplest hexagonal cell has been chosen, hexagonal indices may be transformed to rhombohedral indices by the formulae given on p. 146. If, however, a rhombohedral crystal is rotated round an axis of the (morphologically chosen) cell, the photographs must be indexed by the methods given for triclinic crystals. Examination of a sketch or model of the reciprocal lattice deduced in this way will show whether or not a smaller, differently shaped rhombohedral cell would account for all the reflections.

Where there is more than one cell of the same volume (and shape appropriate to the crystal system) which will account for all the reflections, as in monoclinic and triclinic crystals (see Fig. 76), the most nearly rectangular cell will usually prove the most convenient to accept. There has been much discussion of conventions in the triclinic system; the convention recommended by *International Tables* (1952) is that all three angles of the cell should be obtuse, and the direction cosines of the axes with the [111] zone axis should all be positive.

When an investigation is to be carried only as far as the determination of unit cell dimensions, it may not be necessary to index the whole of the reflections; it will often be sufficient to index reflections up to a Bragg angle of 30–40°, or even less for crystals having large unit cells. Moreover, photographs taken for only one setting of the crystal are usually sufficient; it is not necessary to take rotation photographs for three settings as in the method mentioned on p. 150. For a single setting a straightforward rotation photograph gives the cell dimension along the axis of rotation (from the layer-line spacing); the other cell dimensions and angles are obtained from the positions of individual spots, either on moving-film photographs or, if a moving-film goniometer is not available, on tilted crystal photographs.

So far it has been assumed that well-formed crystals with plane faces, suitable for accurate setting by the optical method, are available. Such crystals form the ideal experimental material for any detailed crystallographic investigation; but it is possible, even when the crystal symmetry is low, to proceed with far less promising material—with ill-formed crystals, or with irregular crystal fragments, or even with polycrystalline specimens. The additional problems presented by such specimens will now be considered.

**The accurate setting of ill-formed crystals.** Some crystals have imperfect faces which give diffuse optical reflections; or it may happen that the only crystals available have partially defined shapes such as those considered in the chapter on microscopic methods of identification—they may be rod-like or plate-like, with fairly well-defined edges but too few well-formed faces to permit precise setting by the optical method. In such circumstances it is possible to set the crystal by preliminary X-ray photographs. The chosen direction is first set approximately parallel to the axis of rotation by the optical method, and a small-angle (10–15°) oscillation photograph is taken, one of the arcs of the goniometer head being parallel to the beam for the mean position of the crystal. The zero-layer reflections are found to lie, not exactly on the equator, but on a curve, and from the form of the curve it is possible to deduce in what direction, and by how much, the chosen axis is mis-set. This, like all such problems, is best appreciated in terms of the reciprocal lattice.

If, as in Fig. 108 $a$, the $c$ axis of the crystal is displaced from the axis of rotation in the plane normal to the beam (for the mean position of the crystal), the zero layer ($hk0$) of the reciprocal lattice is tilted in this same direction, and its plane cuts the sphere of reflection in the circle $AD$. During the 15° oscillation a number of $hk0$ points pass through the surface of the sphere, and thus X-rays reflected by these $hk0$ planes of the crystal strike the film at corresponding points; on the flattened-out film (Fig. 108 $b$) the spots fall on a curve $BAD$, whose distance from the equator is a maximum at a Bragg angle $\theta = 45°$ and zero at $\theta = 90°$. If, on the other hand, the displacement of the $c$ axis is in the plane containing the beam (Fig. 108 $c$), the spots on the film fall on a curve whose maximum distance from the equator is at $\theta = 90°$ (Fig. 108 $d$). When the displacement of the $c$ axis has components in both directions, an intermediate form of curve is obtained (Fig. 108 $e$). Note that the angle $\phi$ gives the component of displacement in the plane perpendicular to the X-ray beam—that is, the component for one setting arc; $\phi$ is unaffected by the other component. From the curve ($e$) it is theoretically possible (Kratky and Krebs, 1936; Hendershot, 1937 $b$) to calculate both components, at any rate for crystals having large unit cell dimen-

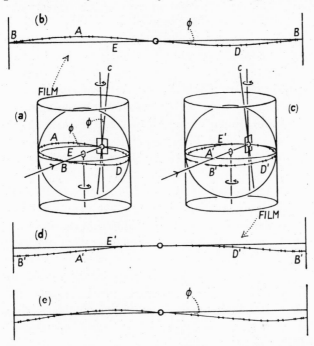

FIG. 108. Oscillation photographs for setting ill-formed crystals.

sions in the equatorial plane (so that there are sufficient spots on the photograph to define the curve of the equatorial layer line). In practice it is usually better to take two small-angle oscillation photographs: for one of them one of the setting arcs is, at the mean position of the oscillation, perpendicular to the X-ray beam; the angle $\phi$ of the equatorial layer (Fig. 108 $b$) gives the correction to be applied to this setting arc. For the other photograph, the second setting arc is, at the mean position of the oscillation, perpendicular to the X-ray beam; the angle $\phi'$ on this photograph gives, as before, the correction to be applied to this arc. This simple method has the advantage that only short exposures need be given, since only the strong reflections at small angles are used. Another point worth remembering is that unfiltered radiation may be used; the 'white' streak on the equatorial layer helps to define the angle $\phi$.

If the only crystal available is quite irregular in shape, it may be set up on the X-ray goniometer in any position, and trial oscillation photographs may be taken; if recognizable layer lines are produced, accurate setting may be achieved by the method just given; if not, the setting may be altered at random until recognizable layer lines *are* produced. Examination under the microscope between crossed Nicols may be useful: an extinction direction may coincide with, or lie near to, a possible crystal axis.

Finally, if setting proves difficult, it is quite possible (and without inordinate difficulty) to index the diffraction pattern of a crystal in a completely random setting, by a procedure (Turner-Jones and Bunn, 1944) based on the same principle as the tilted crystal method described on p. 174. This may be useful for crystals grown in sealed tubes, when the orientation taken up by the crystal happens to be inconvenient for axial setting.

**Oriented polycrystalline specimens.** Not every substance occurs naturally in the form of single crystals which can be dealt with by the methods already described, or can be induced in the laboratory to grow in such a form. In certain fibrous minerals—for instance, chrysotile, $3MgO . 2SiO_2 . 2H_2O$ ('asbestos')—even very thin fibres are found to be, not single crystals, but bundles of crystals all having one axis parallel to the fibre axis but randomly oriented in other respects (Warren and Bragg, 1930). And among organic substances the long-chain polymers —to which class many biologically important substances as well as many useful synthetic substances belong—usually cannot be obtained in the form of single crystals. Fortunately, however, these substances can usually be obtained in the form of fibres in which all the little crystals have one axis parallel or nearly parallel to the fibre axis (as in chrysotile). Substances such as cellulose, keratin (the protein of hair), and fibroin (the protein of silk) occur naturally in this form (Polanyi, 1921; Astbury and Street, 1931; Astbury and Woods, 1933; Kratky and Kuriyama, 1931). Synthetic polymers such as polyethylene and the polyesters and polyamides can be drawn out to form fibres in which the same type of orientation occurs (Fuller, 1940); and some of the rubber-like substances, although amorphous when unstretched, crystallize on stretching, the crystals so formed all having one axis parallel to the direction of stretching (Katz, 1925; Sauter, 1937; Fuller, Frosch, and Pape, 1940).

PLATE X

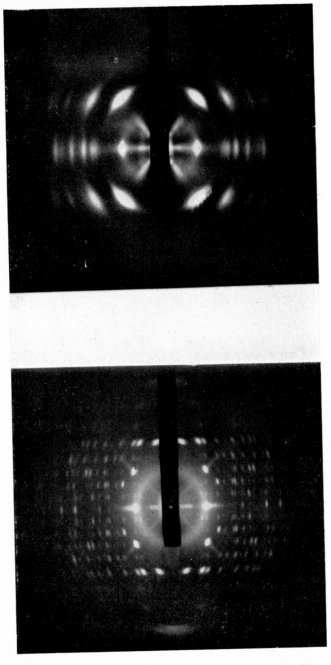

X-ray diffraction photographs of a fibre of poly-vinylidene chloride ($-CCl_2-CH_2-$)$_n$ (above) and a stretched thread of poly*iso*butene ($-C(CH_3)_2-CH_2-$)$_n$ (below)

When an X-ray beam passes through such a fibre perpendicular to its length, the pattern produced is of the same type as that given by a single crystal rotated about a principal axis. All orientations perpendicular to the fibre axis are already present in the specimen, so that the effect of rotation is produced. Examples are shown in Plate X. The reflections are less sharp than those produced by single crystals, for two reasons: firstly, the orientation of the crystals in the fibre is not perfect, so that each spot is drawn out to the form of a short arc, and secondly, in most polymer fibres the crystals are so small that the reflections are inevitably more diffuse than those of large crystals (see p. 437).

The unit cell dimensions can often be deduced from such a pattern by the methods already described; it is true that only one rotation photograph is available, but this may be sufficient for the purpose. The length of the unit cell edge which is parallel to the fibre axis is given directly by the spacing of the layer lines. The other dimensions, and the angles, are less easy to discover; the degree of difficulty depends on the symmetry of the crystals. The procedure is first to discover, from the spacings of the equatorial planes, the shape and size of the projected cell area seen along the fibre axis. Naturally the simplest possibility—a rectangular projection—is considered first; this is best done by calculating $\log d$ for each spot, plotting the values on a strip of paper, and attempting to find a match point on the $\log d$ chart (see Fig. 78, p. 153).

Assuming that the equatorial reflections have been shown to fit a rectangular reciprocal lattice net, attention may be turned to the upper and lower layer lines. The $\xi$ values for all the spots are read off on Bernal's chart, and the reciprocal lattice rotation diagram is constructed from these values; if the $\xi$ values for the upper and lower layer lines correspond with those of the equator—that is, row lines as well as layer lines are exhibited as in Fig. 86—then the unit cell must be orthorhombic. It should be noted that some spots may be missing from the equator, and it may be necessary to halve one or both of the reciprocal axes previously found to satisfy the equatorial reflections. The dimensions of the unit cell, and the indices of all the spots, follow immediately from the reciprocal lattice diagrams.

Suppose, however, that although the equatorial reflections fit a rectangular projected cell-base—that is, a rectangular zero-level reciprocal lattice net—the rest of the spots do not fall on row lines. This must mean that the remaining axis of the reciprocal lattice is (as in Fig. 90) not normal to the zero level; in other words, the unit cell is monoclinic, the fibre axis being the $c$ or $a$ axis of the cell. (It is customary to call the fibre axis $c$ rather than $a$.) Indexing is done by trial—that is, by postulating simple indices for the innermost spots and then testing the rest to see whether they fit the reciprocal lattice defined in this way. The solution is often indicated very simply by the fact that in the rotation diagram several orders of $00l$ (or $h00$) are seen to lie obviously on a straight line starting at the origin; the slope of this line at once gives $\beta^*$. (This line may be obvious in the fibre photograph itself, though the line is not straight; see Fuller and Erickson, 1937; Fuller and Frosch, 1939.) This line gives the slope of $c^*$, but not its orientation with respect to the zero-level net. To discover this, and to test the remaining $\xi$ values, mark off, on the zero-level net, values of $nc^* \cos \beta^*$ along one axis, the points to serve as origins for their respective layer lines; measure $\xi$ values as in Fig. 91. If the

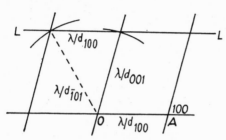

FIG. 109. Determination of non-rectangular equatorial net-plane by trial.

measured values do not correspond with those on the rotation diagram, these alternative origins should be marked off along the other axis of the zero-level net to test the alternative orientation of $c^*$. It may be necessary to halve one of the zero-level reciprocal axes to account for all spots on other levels.

If the equatorial reflections do not fit a rectangular net, the crystals must be either monoclinic (with $b$ parallel to the fibre axis) or triclinic. The shape and size of the projected cell-base must be found by trial. Simple indices such as 100, 001, 101, $\bar{1}01$ are postulated for the first few reciprocal lattice points; thus, mark off along a line the value of $\lambda/d$ for the first spot and call it 100 (Fig. 109); from the origin draw arcs of circles with radii equal to $\lambda/d$ for the second and third spots, which will be called 001 and $\bar{1}01$; then find the position where a line $LL$ (parallel to $OA$) cuts these two arcs at points whose distance apart is equal to $\lambda/d_{100}$. This defines a possible net, which can then be extended to mark a sufficient range of additional points, the distances of which from the origin are compared with the values of $\lambda/d$ for the remaining spots. If this does not account for all the spots, it is necessary to try halving first one, then the other, and finally (if necessary) both axes of the net to account for the whole of the equatorial spots.

This done, consider the other layer lines on the photograph. A reciprocal lattice rotation diagram is prepared as before from the $\xi$ and $\zeta$ values of all the spots. If row lines are exhibited, then the remaining axis of the reciprocal lattice is normal to the zero-level net, as in Fig. 89; in other words, the crystals are monoclinic with their $b$ axes parallel to the fibre axis. It is again necessary to remember that one or both reciprocal axes of the zero-level net may have to be halved to account for all the points on other levels.

If row lines are not shown, then the crystals are triclinic. The inclination of $c^*$ to the vertical may be shown by a row of spots in line with the origin; but the orientation of $c^*$ with regard to the zero-level net must be found by trial. Distances equal to the $\xi$ values for $00l$ planes are marked off along a line on a strip of paper pivoted at the origin of the zero-level net, and this line is swung round until the distances measured, as in Fig. 94, correspond with the $\xi$ values on the rotation diagram. This process is not so difficult or lengthy as it may seem.

Expressions for calculating the dimensions of the real cell from those of the reciprocal cell are given in *International Tables* (1952), and by Buerger (1942).

When sheets of certain crystalline polymers are thinned by being passed through rollers, or when sheets of certain rubber-like substances are stretched, a double orientation of the crystals is effected; not only does one crystal axis become approximately parallel to the direction of rolling or stretching, but also a particular crystal plane tends to lie in the plane of the sheet. For rubber the best double orientation is obtained by stretching a sheet which is short (in the direction of stretching) in comparison with its width (Gehman and Field, 1939). Double orientation in keratin has been achieved by compressing horn in steam, in a direction at right angles to the fibre axis (Astbury and Sisson, 1935). If the structure is orthorhombic and the favoured plane happens to be a face of the unit cell, then the whole specimen may simulate a single crystal; in other circumstances (Fig. 110) there may be two or more different orientations of the unit cell in the specimen (for instance, for a triclinic unit cell there are four different orientations of the unit cell in a doubly oriented specimen). Such doubly oriented specimens are more useful than singly oriented fibres; they give photographs which are like the oscillation photographs of single crystals or twinned crystals, and although the limits of crystallite orientation are naturally somewhat indefinite, the photographs can be used like oscillation photographs to provide clues to the orientation of crystal planes giving particular spots, or to confirm or disprove indices already selected. Photo-

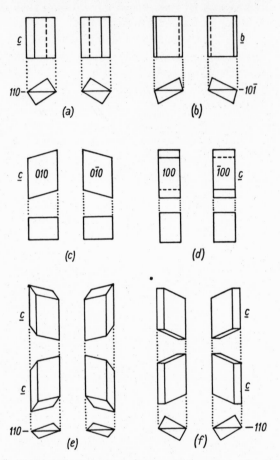

Fig. 110. 'Twinned' orientations of unit cell in specimens having both axial and planar orientation.

(a) Orthorhombic, fibre axis c, favoured plane 110 (or any hk0; h, k ≠ 0). Twins.
(b) Monoclinic, fibre axis b, favoured plane 10$\bar{1}$ (or any h0l; also 100, 001). Twins.
(c) Monoclinic, fibre axis c, favoured plane 010. Twins.
(d)    ,,     ,,    c,       ,,       100     ,,
(e) Triclinic     ,,    c,       ,,       110 (or any hk0; also 100, 010). Quadruplets.
(f.) Monoclinic, fibre axis c, favoured plane 110 (or any hk0; h, k ≠ 0). Quadruplets.

graphs of such specimens may also be taken, one layer at a time, in moving-film cameras; instead of the spots given by single crystals, streaks are produced, and the position of maximum intensity on any streak may be taken as an indication of the position of the reciprocal lattice point for the plane in question.

In fibres of some polymers, made under certain conditions, the crystalline regions are found to be tilted with respect to the fibre axis in a well-defined crystallographic direction. This is a very valuable feature, because the diffraction patterns of specimens in which this type of orientation occurs are of precisely the same form as tilted crystal diffraction patterns of single crystals rotated round a direction inclined to a principal axis. The unit cell cannot be obtained directly, for 90° oscillation tilted crystal photographs are required for direct interpretation, but unit cells obtained by trial can be checked by the displacements of diffraction spots from the layer lines; this is a severe check, and consistent displacements would leave no doubt of the correctness of a unit cell. This procedure played an effective part in the determination of the unit cell of polyethylene terephthalate (Daubeny, Bunn, and Brown, 1954).

In drawn metal wires the fibre axis is usually not a crystal axis. The problem of the determination of crystal orientation in such specimens (and in rolled metal sheets), though closely related to those dealt with here, is outside the scope of this book. (The unit cell dimensions, and indeed the complete structures of such crystals, are usually known, and the problems that arise are questions of correlation of physical properties with orientation.) See Schmid and Boas, 1935; Orowan, 1942.

**Determination of unit cell dimensions with high precision.** The greatest precision in the determination of the spacings of crystal planes is attained when the angle of reflection ($\theta$) is near 90°. This is in the first place a consequence of the form of the Bragg equation $d = \dfrac{\lambda}{2 \sin \theta}$; near 90° a very small change of $\sin \theta$ (corresponding to a very small change in $d$) means a large change in $\theta$. Hence a certain error in the measurement of $\theta$ means a much smaller error in the determination of $d$. In addition to this circumstance, the possible error due to the absorption of X-rays in the specimen (see Fig. 68) tends towards zero as $\theta$ approaches 90°.

In powder photographs, whether taken with a Debye–Scherrer camera or one of the focusing cameras, the reflection angles of several arcs (they are all $\alpha_1 \alpha_2$ doublets in the large-angle region) are determined from their positions in relation to the fiducial marks; values of $d$ are calculated from the angles, and from these values the axial dimensions are worked out for each arc. By plotting the several different calculated values of the axial dimensions against $\cos^2\theta$ and extrapolating to $\cos^2\theta = 0$ (that is, $\theta = 90°$), the most probable values are obtained (Bradley and Jay, 1932). If the only likely errors are those due to absorption and the divergence of the X-ray beam (not eccentricity of the specimen), it may be better to plot against $\cos^2\theta/\sin\theta$ or $\cos^2\theta/\theta$ (Taylor and Sinclair, 1945). An analytical least-squares method of finding the most probable value has also been suggested (Cohen, 1935; Hess, 1951). Determination of the camera constant (the angle which the fiducial marks represent) can be done either by an optical method or by taking a powder photograph of quartz, silicon, or aluminium, the lattice dimensions of which are accurately known (Wilson and Lipson, 1941; Edmunds, Lipson, and Steeple, 1955). In favourable cases axial dimensions may be determined in this way with a possible error of no more than 1 part in 50,000. (The small deviations from the Bragg equation caused by refraction of X-rays are usually negligible —Hägg and Phragmen, 1933; but see also Wilson, 1940, and Lipson and Wilson, 1941.) A precision of even 1 part in 200,000 has been claimed for the unit cell of diamond by Straumanis and Aka (1951), though this may be unduly optimistic. For methods suitable for focusing cameras and counter spectrometers, see Edmunds, Steeple, and Lipson (1955).

For cubic, tetragonal, hexagonal, and trigonal crystals, powder photographs alone may be used. The same method may be used for crystals of orthorhombic or even lower symmetry, provided that the indices of the reflections at large angles can be found.

Single-crystal rotation photographs may also be used for very accurate determinations of lattice dimensions, by using the same principles as those described for powder photographs: equatorial reflections at Bragg angles near 90° are used, first of all for calculating the axial ratio (see p. 143), and then for determining axial lengths by the extrapolation method. A Weissenberg camera suitable for the purpose is described by Buerger (1937). For further details of procedure, see Farquhar and Lipson (1946) and Henry, Lipson, and Wooster (1951). This of course gives, for any one rotation photograph, the precise dimensions of the projected cell-base. The length of the cell edge along the axis of rotation can be determined only roughly from layer-line spacings on cylindrical films, but Mathieson (1957) has pointed out that a great improvement can be made by mounting a piece of photographic film on the top of the camera to record high layer lines which usually escape through the top of the cylinder; since the length of the cell edge is given by $n\lambda/\cos\phi$ (see p. 149), there is an increase of sensitivity as $\phi$ approaches 0°, analogous to that already mentioned in equatorial reflections at Bragg angles near 90°. Alternatively, the crystal can be reset to rotate round another axis, the equatorial reflections on the resulting rotation photograph being used in the way already mentioned to give accurate lengths for a different pair of cell edges. For orthorhombic crystals, the precise lengths of the three edges define the unit cell accurately; for monoclinic and triclinic crystals, additional calculations are required (always, of course, based on large-angle reflections, unambiguously indexed) to determine the non-orthogonal angles as well as the axial ratios. The publication of precise lattice dimensions should always be accompanied by a statement of the wavelength figures used (see p. 130).

**Applications of knowledge of unit cell dimensions.** 1. *Identification*. The use of powder photographs for identification has been described in Chapter V; the simplest method is to calculate the spacings of the crystal planes from the positions of the reflections, and to use these spacings together with the relative intensities as determinants. If this information does not lead to identification, it may be worth while to attempt to discover the unit cell dimensions, since for many substances unit cell dimensions have been determined and published, but the details of the X-ray diffraction photographs have not been recorded.

For powder photographs, the use of the charts described on p. 143 and in Appendix 3 will show whether the substance is cubic, tetragonal, or hexagonal; if it is not, the numerical methods of indexing the patterns of crystals of low symmetry may be tried; or, if it is possible to pick out single crystals, or if the specimen can be recrystallized to give suitable crystals, the unit cell dimensions may be determined by the methods described earlier. A search may then be made in the tables of Donnay and Nowacki (1954), in which, for each crystal system, the species are arranged in order of the axial ratios.

Single-crystal photographs are extremely sensitive criteria for identification, much more sensitive than powder photographs. The set of spacings and intensities given by a powder photograph is quite sufficient for the unequivocal identification of most substances, but complex organic compounds which are closely related to each other (for instance, large molecules differing only in the position of a single substituent atom) may give very similar powder photographs. The single-crystal photographs of such substances are, nevertheless, sure to display some differences. Many reflections which would overlap on powder photographs are separated on single-crystal photographs, which show not only the spacings of the crystal planes and the intensities of the reflections, but also the relative orientations of the planes. Even if the unit cell dimensions of two substances are closely similar, the relative intensities of some of the reflections are likely to be different, since, as we shall see in the next chapter, the intensities of reflections change rapidly with small changes in atomic positions.

As an example of the use of single-crystal photographs for identification, vitamin B4 was shown by Bernal and Crowfoot (1933 *b*) to be identical with adenine hydrochloride. The extensive survey of the crystallography of substances of the sterol group by Bernal, Crowfoot, and Fankuchen (1940) gives a vast amount of information on these crystals, including unit cell dimensions; this paper also contains a discussion of the identification problems in this group.

If single crystals cannot be obtained, and the only available X-ray photograph is a powder photograph which cannot be interpreted directly, the possibilities of identification are not exhausted. Indirect methods may perhaps be used. For instance, it may be suspected on chemical grounds that a substance is one which is known to form monoclinic crystals whose single-crystal photographs or unit cell dimensions have been published; from the published information it may be possible to calculate the spacings and intensities which would be shown on powder photographs. To do this for a large number of reflections would be a task of considerable magnitude, for which the knowledge in the next chapter is required; but calculation of the spacings of a few of the strongest reflections would soon show whether it is worth while to proceed further.

Another possibility is that the suspected substance has not previously been studied by X-ray methods, but morphological axial ratios have been published. The axial ratios of the simplest unit cell are either the same as, or are closely related to, those selected by morphological methods. Consequently, a determination of unit cell dimensions by whatever X-ray method is practicable may give the clue to identification.

For chain compounds, such as the paraffin wax hydrocarbons, fatty acids, and other derivatives, it is possible to use a single spacing, or the various orders of diffraction from one particular crystal plane, for purposes of identification. A thin layer of the substance is crystallized on a glass plate; the leaf-like crystals grow with their basal planes parallel to the glass surface, so that if an X-ray beam grazes the surface while it is oscillated through a small angle, the various orders of diffraction from the basal plane are recorded. The long molecules are either normal to the basal plane or somewhat inclined to the normal; the spacings are thus related to the lengths of the molecules, and can thus be used for identifying particular members of a series of homologues. The relative intensities of the different orders may be used to locate substituent atoms, as in the ketones. (See Piper, 1937.)

2. *Determination of composition in mixed crystals.* The unit cell dimensions of mixed crystals—crystals in which equivalent positions in the lattice are occupied indiscriminately by two or more different types of atom or molecule—are intermediate between those of the separate constituents. If the relation between composition and unit cell dimensions has previously been established, then in practice the unit cell dimensions may be used to determine the composition of the mixed crystal. For instance, certain metals form mixed crystals, often over a wide range of composition. The crystals are usually highly symmetrical—cubic or hexagonal—and therefore powder photographs may yield very precise unit cell dimensions, which lead to an accurate determination of composition. Of course, for a simple two-component system the composition could be determined chemically. But if other constituents are present, it may not be known which of them crystallize together; there might be a double compound of $A$ and $B$ and mixed crystals of $A$ and $C$, and in such a case the X-ray method would be very valuable. Even in a simple two-component system the results may not be as simple as might be expected. For instance, mixed crystals of copper and nickel were prepared by co-precipitation of the hydroxides, conversion to oxides by heat, followed by low-temperature reduction. But in one experiment the resulting solid was shown by its X-ray powder photograph to consist of two different compositions of mixed crystal, one rich in copper and the other rich in nickel; the two patterns of cubic type appeared together on the film, and the lattice dimensions gave the compositions of the two phases.

Whenever the composition of a crystal lattice varies, and with it the lattice dimensions, this method may be used. Certain 'interstitial' compounds, such as iron nitrides and carbides, come under this heading (though they are not usually called 'mixed crystals'); in these crystals varying numbers of carbon or nitrogen atoms fit into the holes between metal atoms (Hägg, 1931). Zeolitic crystals, in which the water content may vary without essential change of crystal structure, are also of this type (Taylor, 1930, 1934). A simpler substance of the same type is calcium sulphate subhydrate, $CaSO_4 . 0–\frac{2}{3}H_2O$; the water content may be determined from the lattice dimensions (Bunn, 1941).

In certain circumstances it may be possible to use accurate values of lattice dimensions as criteria of the purity of a substance. If the impurities likely to be present in small quantities are such as form mixed crystals with the main substance, then the lattice dimensions determined by a high-precision method form sensitive criteria of purity. No generalizations can be made on the sensitivity of the test, which is entirely specific to each substance and each possible impurity.

3. *Determination of molecular weight.* The standard physico-chemical methods of determining molecular weight are not always effective: for very sparingly soluble substances, for instance, the elevation of the boiling-point or depression of the freezing-point of the strongest solution obtainable may be so small that only an approximate estimate of the molecular weight is obtained. In such circumstances, a more accurate figure may be obtained if crystals suitable for the determination of unit cell dimensions are available. From the unit cell dimensions, the volume $V$ of the unit cell may be calculated. Multiplying the volume $V$ (in cm³) by the density $\rho$ (g/cm³), we get the weight of matter in the unit cell, which is the weight of either one or a small whole number $n$ of molecules: $V\rho = nm$, where $m$ is the weight of one molecule. Therefore, if we know the approximate weight of a molecule—and this knowledge is usually available from chemical evidence—we can find the number of molecules $n$ constituting the unit of crystal pattern. Having found $n$, we can then calculate an accurate value for $m$, which $= V\rho/n$. The molecular weight $M$ on the chemical scale (which accepts the atomic weight of oxygen as 16·000) is equal to $m \times 0{\cdot}6023 \times 10^{24}$. $M$ thus equals

$$\frac{V\rho}{n} \times 0{\cdot}6023 \times 10^{24}.$$

The volume of a rectangular cell (cubic, tetragonal, or orthorhombic) is, of course, the product of the three edge-lengths. For non-rectangular cells the following expressions give the volume:

Hexagonal:      $V = abc \sin 60°$;

Rhombohedral:   $V = a^3 \sin^2\alpha \sin \delta'$, where $\sin\dfrac{\delta'}{2} = \dfrac{1}{2\cos(\alpha/2)}$;

Monoclinic:     $V = abc \sin \beta$;

Triclinic:      $V = abc \sin \beta \sin \gamma \sin \delta$, where

$$\sin\frac{\delta}{2} = \sqrt{\left\{ \sin\frac{(\alpha-\beta+\gamma)}{2} \sin\frac{(\alpha+\beta-\gamma)}{2} \right\}}.$$

It is worth remembering that to determine the volume of the unit cell of a monoclinic or triclinic crystal it is not necessary to find all the edge-lengths and angles of the unit cell. The volume of such a unit cell is, for instance, the area of the $c$ projection multiplied by the length of the $c$ axis (Fig. 111). Consequently, if the crystal is set up with $c$ as the axis of rotation, determination of the dimensions of the projected cell-base (from the equatorial reflections) and the length of the $c$ axis (from the layer-line spacing) gives all the information required to calculate $V$. It is not necessary to find $\beta$ for the monoclinic cell,† or any of the real angles of the triclinic cell.

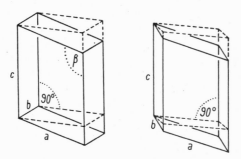

Fig. 111. Volume of unit cell $= c \times$ area of $c$ projection.
Left: monoclinic.    Right: triclinic.

The following is an actual example. The molecular weight of a dye-stuff could only be estimated roughly by standard methods to be between 400 and 500 on the chemical scale. A rotation photograph of a small crystal gave the following dimensions for the provisional unit cell: $c$ (rotation axis) $= 3 \cdot 866$ Å; projected cell-base non-rectangular with $a' = 13 \cdot 36$ Å, $b' = 10 \cdot 44$ Å, and $\gamma' = 76°$. The volume of the provisional unit cell therefore $= 3 \cdot 866 \times 13 \cdot 36 \times 10 \cdot 44 \sin 76° \times 10^{-24}$ cm$^3$ $= 523 \cdot 2 \times 10^{-24}$ cm$^3$. Multiplying by the density $1 \cdot 528$, we get the mass of the unit cell $= 799 \cdot 3 \times 10^{-24}$ g $= 799 \cdot 3 \times 10^{-24} \times 0 \cdot 6023 \times 10^{24}$ or 484 on the chemical scale. This is about equal to the approximate molecular weight, so that there is evidently only one molecule in the provisional unit cell, and the precise molecular weight is therefore 484 on the chemical scale. The estimated error was $\pm 5$ units.

The most convenient method of measuring the density of crystals is to suspend them in a liquid mixture, the composition of which is adjusted by adding one of the constituents until the crystals neither float nor

† For a monoclinic cell centred on the 100 face (symbol $A$—see p. 239) the equatorial reflections alone yield an apparent projected cell-base having a $b$ axis half the true length. For molecular weight determination this does not matter: the method gives the weight of matter associated with each lattice point, which is either the molecular weight itself or a multiple of it.

sink. The use of the centrifuge increases the sensitivity of this method (Bernal and Crowfoot, 1934 *b*). The density of the liquid is then determined by the standard pycnometer method.

The X-ray method is often the most accurate way of finding the molecular weight of a substance. Usually the chief error is likely to be in the value for the density.

It should be noted that in crystals of long-chain polymers, the unit cell shown by the X-ray photographs contains only sections of molecules. A small group of atoms, often only one or two monomer units, is repeated many times along a chain molecule, and the precise side-by-side packing of these chains gives rise to the crystalline pattern of atoms. By a 'crystal' of a long-chain polymer is meant a repeating pattern of monomer units, not of whole molecules (see Fig. 136). Chain molecules thread their way through the unit cell. A calculation of the foregoing type leads, for such substances, to a knowledge of the number of monomer units in the unit cell. It should also be noted that the measured density of specimens of such substances is lower than the true density of the crystalline regions, on account of the presence of a certain amount of less dense amorphous material (Mark, 1940; Bunn, 1942 *c*); therefore the calculated value of $n$ (assuming $M$) is always a little low; but if it comes to 3·8, for instance, it is obvious that there are really four monomer units in the cell. In such circumstances, the true density of the crystalline regions can be calculated from $M$, $n$, and $V$.

4. *Determination of the proportions of crystalline and amorphous material in partially crystalline polymers.* Knowledge of the unit cell dimensions in high polymer crystals leads to a knowledge of the density of the crystalline regions. If the density of amorphous regions is also known, either by measurement of the density of an entirely amorphous specimen (if this can be obtained) or by extrapolation of the liquid density/temperature curve, it is possible to calculate, from the measured density of any partially crystalline specimen, the proportions of crystalline and amorphous material. Since the physical properties of polymer specimens are profoundly influenced by the degree of crystallinity, X-ray determinations of crystallinity are much used in such studies (see Bunn, 1957).

5. *Shapes of molecules, and orientation in the unit cell.* A knowledge of the dimensions of the unit cell does not, by itself, lead to a knowledge of molecular shape, even when there is only one molecule in the cell and all the molecules in the crystal are therefore oriented in the same way. For instance, Fig. 112 shows how a projected cell of given dimen-

sions can accommodate molecules of very different shapes. In conjunction with other evidence, however, unit cell dimensions may lead to valuable conclusions on molecular structure and orientation. For instance, alternative formulae for a particular substance may be suggested on chemical grounds; models can be made, using the known interatomic distances and bond angles, and these may be packed together to see which will fit the known unit cell.

FIG. 112. Molecules of very different shapes, packed in identical unit cells.

The evidence from optical and other physical properties (see Chapter VIII) is likely to be very useful in conjunction with unit cell data. It is often possible to form a general idea of the shape and orientation of molecules from such evidence; after which the actual overall dimensions follow from the unit cell dimensions.

One-molecule unit cells are, however, not common. Usually there are two, four, or more molecules in the unit cell, and in such circumstances it is necessary to discover the manner of packing ('space-group symmetry'—see pp. 241–51) before considering molecular dimensions.

6. *Chain-type in crystals of linear polymers.* In drawn fibres of these substances the molecules are approximately parallel to the fibre axis, and the unit cell dimension along the fibre axis is also the identity-period of the molecule itself. The fact that it is possible so simply to determine intra-molecular distances has far-reaching consequences. The magnitude of this identity-period may lead directly to a knowledge of

the geometry of the chain, and sometimes to a knowledge of the geometry of the whole molecule, including side-substituents. For instance, it is known that the fully extended zigzag form of the saturated carbon chain has an identity-period of 2·53 Å (Bunn, 1939). In polyvinyl chloride ($-CH_2-CHCl-)_n$, the identity-period is twice this length, 5·1 Å, which suggests that the chain has a plane zigzag configuration,

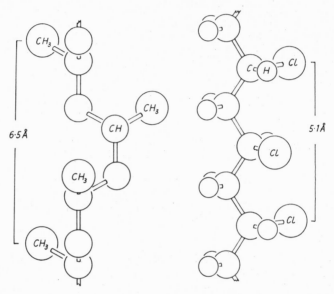

Fig. 113. Left—polypropylene (H atoms omitted). Right—polyvinyl chloride.

but that the chlorine atoms occupy alternating stereo-positions, as in Fig. 113. In a similar way the identity-period of poly-hexamethylene adipamide (nylon 66) is 17·3 Å. Assuming the usual interatomic distances (C—C 1·53 Å, C—N 1·47 Å) and tetrahedral bond angles, the chain must be a fully extended (or very nearly fully extended) zigzag, and the geometry of the whole molecule is therefore approximately settled (Fuller, 1940).

The chains of some polymer molecules are not fully extended; the identity-periods leave no doubt of that. By rotation round the single bonds the chains are crumpled and shortened. The magnitude of the identity-period may by itself indicate the geometry of the chain, but more probably it will not be possible to draw unambiguous conclusions without the aid of further stereochemical considerations. Examples of the use of identity-periods in conjunction with stereochemical considerations to deduce possible molecular structures for chain polymers are (1) the prediction (subsequently confirmed by detailed structure determination—Bunn and Garner, 1942) of the chain-form of rubber hydrochloride (see p. 356), and (2) the deduction from the chain repeat distance of 6·5 Å that the molecules of isotactic polypropylene, polystyrene, and some other α-olefine polymers have helical chain-forms (Fig. 113, left) in which chain-bonds take up alternately trans and gauche positions—a deduction that was confirmed by detailed structure determination (Natta and Corradini, 1955 ; Natta, Corradini, and Cesari, 1956 ; Natta, Corradini, and Bassi, 1956). It must be emphasized that such conceptions, in the case of chains with long periods, are suggestions only ; they cannot be accepted as proved unless and until detailed structure determination is achieved.

Conclusions of this sort have also been drawn from the X-ray diffraction patterns of the remarkable urea-hydrocarbon adducts. With many chain hydrocarbons, urea forms crystalline complexes in which a framework of urea molecules holds the hydrocarbon chains in long parallel channels. Single crystals of these substances, rotated round their c (channel) axes, give X-ray diffraction patterns showing an ordinary spot arrangement due to the urea framework, and layer-line streaks due to hydrocarbon molecules packed end-to-end in the channels. The length of the hydrocarbon molecules is calculated from the distances of these streaks from the equator. Such measurements, for the adduct of urea with squalene, a chain hydrocarbon consisting of six isoprene units and containing six double bonds, led Nicolaides and Laves (1954) to the conclusion that all the double bonds have a *trans* chain configuration.

# VII

## DETERMINATION OF THE POSITIONS OF THE ATOMS IN THE UNIT CELL BY THE METHOD OF TRIAL AND ERROR

HITHERTO only the *positions* of the X-ray beams diffracted by crystals have been considered; unit cell dimensions are determined from the positions of diffracted beams without reference to their intensities. To discover the arrangement and positions of the atoms in the unit cell it is necessary to consider the intensities of the diffracted beams.

The ideal method would be to measure these intensities, and then combine them, either by calculation or by some experimental procedure, to form an image of the structure. Unfortunately it is usually not possible to proceed in this direct manner. To appreciate the reason for this, and to approach the whole subject in a simple way, it is useful to refer once more to the one-dimensional optical analogy already introduced at the beginning of Chapter VI (Plate VI). This experiment demonstrates the fact that the relative intensities of the successive orders of diffraction depend on the details of the grating pattern; the problem now is how to recombine the diffracted beams to give an image of the original grating. The possibility of doing this is suggested by the fact that, if this grating were put on the microscope stage and illuminated by monochromatic light, diffracted beams would be produced; it is these diffracted beams which are collected by the objective lens of the microscope. The formation of the magnified image in the microscope is obviously the recombination of the diffracted beams; so, one would suppose, if the diffracted waves do, as an experimental fact, recombine, it ought to be possible to combine them by calculation. The difficulty here, however, is to know the phase relations between the various diffracted waves: to combine waves by calculation we must obviously know their phase relations as well as their intensities. The best way of thinking of the situation is to trace back all the diffracted waves to some one particular point in the pattern, taking this particular point as the origin of the 'unit cell' of the one-dimensional pattern. This is illustrated in Fig. 114, the chosen origin being $O$. Monochromatic light passing through the patterned grating at right angles is scattered at each line; interference occurs, except where the path-difference between waves from successive similar points in the pattern ($P$ and $Q$, for instance) is a whole number of wavelengths. In the upper diagram the path-difference is one wavelength, while in the lower diagram it is three wavelengths. When waves from $P$ and $Q$ are in phase (and so on all along the grating), then $R$ and $S$ are also in phase with each other; but what decides the intensity of the diffracted beam is the phase relationship between $R$ and $P$ (or $S$ and $Q$). In both cases chosen the resultant diffracted beam is strong; but the point of interest at the moment is that, if we choose a particular moment, and trace back the resultant diffracted beams to the point of reference $O$, we find that for the first-order diffraction there is a trough at this point, while for the third order there is a crest. In recombining the diffracted waves by calculation this would have to be taken into account; if the wrong phase relations were assumed, the wrong picture would be obtained. (Some *other* pattern would give first and third orders having the same phase at the origin.)

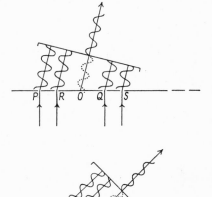

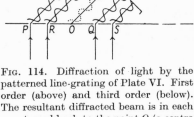

Fig. 114. Diffraction of light by the patterned line-grating of Plate VI. First order (above) and third order (below). The resultant diffracted beam is in each case traced back to the point $O$ (a centre of symmetry); the phases (referred to this point) of the first and third orders are opposite.

Turning back to X-ray diffraction patterns, the problem is quite analogous; it is more complex, because a three-dimensional diffraction grating is involved, but exactly the same in principle; and the difficulty is that we cannot determine experimentally the phases of the diffracted X-ray beams, and usually have no means of knowing anything about them. In certain circumstances the phase relations can be deduced directly, using crystallographic evidence, and when this is so an image of the atomic structure can be calculated directly; or alternatively, by substituting light waves for X-rays, an image can be formed experimentally; the methods are described in Chapter X. For the great majority of crystals, however, the phases are not known. It is therefore necessary to use indirect methods. The method of postulating a likely structure, calculating the intensities of diffracted beams which this structure would give, and comparing these with the observed X-ray intensities, was used for all the earlier structure determinations, and must still be used for many crystals. But although, in absence of a knowledge of the phases, atomic *positions* cannot be obtained, nevertheless an appropriate synthesis in which all the beams have the same phase can give atomic *vectors*, that is, interatomic distances coupled with directions. From vector diagrams it may be possible to deduce some at least of the atomic positions; or, in rare cases, all of them. The methods are also described in Chapter X.

The present chapter deals first with all the preliminary steps which must be taken to obtain suitable data for structure determination (whether by direct or indirect methods)—the measurement of the intensities of diffracted beams, and the application of the corrections necessary to isolate the factors due solely to the crystal structure from those associated with camera conditions. It then goes on to deal with the effect of atomic arrangement on the intensities of diffracted beams, the procedure in deducing the general arrangement, and finally the methods of determining actual atomic coordinates by trial. It follows from what has been said that, as soon as atomic positions have been found to a sufficient degree of approximation to settle the phases of the diffracted beams, then the direct method can be used; this, in fact, is the normal procedure in the determination of crystal structures.

**Measurement of X-ray intensities.** The method first used by W. H. and W. L. Bragg (1913) for the measurement of the intensities of X-ray reflections makes use of the fact that X-rays ionize gases, and the resulting conductivity is a measure of the intensity of the X-ray beam. The gas—the inert gas argon is most suitable (Wooster and Martin, 1936)—is contained in a chamber, to which the narrow X-ray beam is admitted through a fine aperture. A voltage is applied between an internal electrode and the wall of the chamber; the current is measured, and this is proportional to the intensity of the beam entering the chamber. The chamber is mounted on the rotating arm of a spectrometer, the central table of which is occupied by the single crystal or block of crystal powder (Wyckoff, 1930) under investigation. By suitable movements of the specimen and ionization chamber, reflections at all angles may be explored, for one crystal zone at a time; and the primary beam itself may be measured in the same way. The record produced—a curve relating X-ray intensity to angle of reflection—shows peaks, each representing the reflection of X-rays by a different set of internal planes. The 'intensity' of each reflection is the integrated intensity, which is proportional to the area under the peak (W. H. Bragg, 1914). This is the most direct method for the measurement of 'absolute' intensities—the intensities of crystal reflections in relation to that of the primary beam.

The great convenience and rapidity of photographic methods, how-ever, has led to their development and widespread use. Many crystal structure determinations have been based on the relative intensities of the reflections among themselves, measured photographically. It is sometimes desirable to put the whole set of intensities on an absolute basis, and this too may be done photographically by comparing a few of the strongest reflections with some of the reflections of sodium chloride (James and Firth, 1927) or anthracene (Robertson, 1933 a). If the intensity of the X-ray beam can be kept constant, known exposures may be given, first to one specimen and then to another in the same camera, using two pieces of the same film which are subse-quently developed together. If the intensity of the X-ray beam cannot be kept constant over a long period, the safest method is to use a special camera in which the two crystals are admitted alternately into the beam. Wooster and Martin (1940) have designed a two-crystal Weissenberg goniometer for this purpose.

These experimental methods of measuring absolute intensities work best when the crystals are so small that absorption is negligible. In practice this means that hydrocarbon crystals should be not larger than 0·1 mm in diameter, while more strongly absorbing crystals should be even smaller. For larger crystals, absorption corrections should be calculated: see p. 221.

The procedure in the photometry of X-ray photographs depends on the type of photograph and the type of photometric equipment avail-able. It is simplest for powder photographs. On the margin of the film (which was shielded from X-rays during the taking of the diffraction photograph) is printed a calibration strip consisting of a row of patches exposed to X-rays for known relative times. By measuring the light transmission of each patch on a microphotometer the relation between X-ray exposure and light transmission is established; and since the calibration strip is printed on the same film as the photograph, and thus passes through the same development process, any possible errors due to variation of film characteristics or development conditions are avoided. The series of patches may be obtained conveniently by means of a brass sector wheel rotating in front of a slit in a brass plate (Fig. 115 a). For visible light such a method cannot be used, but for X-rays it is sound (Bouwers, 1923). Alternatively, a strip showing a continuously varying opacity may be printed by using an appropriately shaped cam in place of the sector wheel (Fig. 115 *b*); in this case the distance along the strip indicates the X-ray exposure. In taking a photometer record of a powder photograph each arc is traversed. In the simplest type of photoelectric photometer (Jay, 1941) the light

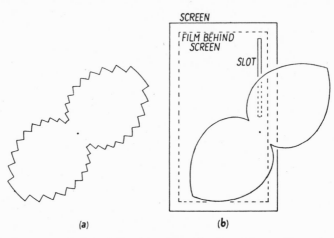

FIG. 115. Arrangements for printing intensity calibration strips on X-ray photographs. *a.* Sector wheel to give a stepped wedge. *b.* Cam to give a continuous wedge.

transmission at any point on the film is proportional to a galvanometer deflexion. In the better types of photometer the light transmission through the film is balanced against a known light intensity adjusted by an optical wedge. When the variation of X-ray intensity with angle of diffraction has been obtained and plotted, the area of each peak above the background intensity is measured; this is most conveniently done with a planimeter.

For single-crystal photographs the requirements are different. It is necessary to obtain the integrated intensity over the whole of each spot. In B. W. Robinson's photometer (1933; also Dawton, 1937) the calibration strip itself (of the continuously varying type) is used as an optical wedge, against which the light transmission through any point on a spot is balanced by means of a pair of opposed photocells coupled to an amplifier and galvanometer. Each spot is traversed at several levels and the readings at a number of points all over the spot are added mechanically. The X-ray intensities measured by this instrument compare very well with those given by the ionization spectrometer. The measurement of the intensities of several hundred spots is, however, a lengthy task; to accelerate such work Dawton has devised a photometer in which each spot is scanned in the manner used in television, the integrated intensity being given as a single galvanometer reading (Robertson and Dawton, 1941).

Another integrating method, due to Wiebenga (1947), is based on a specially designed Weissenberg goniometer, in which the film carrier is shifted slightly after each cycle, in such a way that a set of overlapping spots is produced in place of the single spot for each reflection given by the normal instrument; a single photometric measurement of the intensity at the centre of this multiple exposure represents the integrated intensity of the reflection; the integration is performed by the film carrier during its progress, and occurs of course simultaneously for all reflections of a zone (Wiebenga and Smits, 1950).

Many of the simpler structures have been solved by consideration of the relative intensities estimated visually. The intensities of X-ray reflections are very sensitive to small changes of atomic positions; comparatively small movements of atoms mean large changes in the relative intensities of the various reflections. Consequently, by adjusting postulated atomic positions until mere qualitative agreement between calculated and observed intensities is attained—that is, the arrangement of the calculated intensities in order of strength is the same as that observed on the photographs—a surprisingly good approximation to the truth can be achieved. Visual estimates may even be used for moderately complex structures; comparison of reflections with calibration spots of known relative intensity is a method capable of yielding a set of reflection intensities suitable for all but the most precise investigations (Hughes, 1935).

Whatever photographic method is used for estimating intensities, it will be found that the range of intensities is far too great to be recorded satisfactorily on a single film: an exposure suitable for recording weak reflections at convenient strength would show the strongest reflections so opaque that measurement would scarcely be possible. A suitable set of films may be obtained in a single X-ray exposure by placing several films one behind the other in the camera; successive photographs are related by a constant exposure ratio of about 2:1. Much additional information on the measurement of intensities by photographic methods can be found in a paper by Robertson (1943).

When quantum counter methods are used instead of photographic recording, the whole of each diffracted beam can be allowed to enter the counter for a definite time, and the intensity is thus measured.

Diffractometers have been designed for completely automatic operation (Bond, 1955; Benedict, 1955; Furnas and Harker, 1955). The most accurate measurements of single crystal reflections are obtained in this way.

**Calculation of intensities. Preliminary.** Each spot or arc on an X-ray diffraction photograph may be regarded as the 'reflection' of X-rays by a particular set of parallel crystal planes. The intensity of this reflection is controlled by several factors—the diffracting powers of the atoms, the arrangement of the atoms with regard to the crystal planes, the Bragg angle at which reflection occurs, the number of crystallographically equivalent sets of planes contributing towards the total intensity of the spot or arc, and the amplitude of the thermal vibrations of the atoms. In any powder photograph—for instance, that of ammonium chloride (Plate XI)—two features immediately strike the eye; firstly, there is a general diminution of intensities with increasing reflection angle, and secondly, the intensities vary from one arc to the next in an apparently irregular manner. The general diminution of intensities with increasing reflection angle is due to a decrease in the diffracting powers of atoms with increasing angle $\theta$, to the polarization of the X-rays on reflection (to a degree depending again on $\theta$), to a geometrical factor, and to the thermal vibrations of the atoms. The apparently irregular variation of intensity from one arc to the next is due to the effect of the relative positions of the atoms in space—the 'structure factor'—and to the variation in the number of equivalent sets of planes contributing to the spot or arc—a number which depends on the type of plane. It is the structure factor in which we are chiefly interested, but in order to isolate it we must allow for all the other factors. Each factor will now be considered.

**The diffracting powers of atoms.** X-rays are diffracted, not by the positively charged core of an atom, but by the cloud of electrons forming the outer parts of the atom. The diffracting power of an atom is determined, in the first place, by the number of electrons surrounding the central nucleus, that is, by the atomic number of the element—its place in the periodic table. Atoms such as iodine and lead, which have high atomic numbers, have much higher diffracting powers than those like sodium and oxygen, which have low atomic numbers; in fact, at small angles the diffracting power of an atom is proportional to the number of electrons in the atom. In the ammonium chloride crystal the ammonium ion $NH_4^+$ may be treated as a single entity; at room temperature the whole ion is rotating and in effect has spherical

PLATE XI

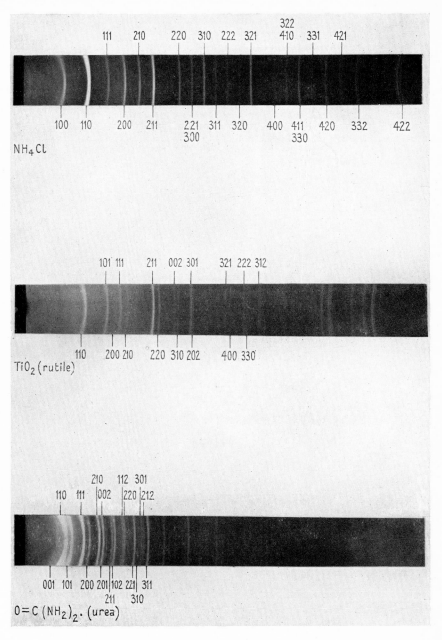

Powder photographs of $NH_4Cl$ (room temperature form), $TiO_2$ (rutile), and urea $O=C(NH_2)_2$. (All taken with copper $K\alpha$ radiation)

symmetry. The total number of electrons in this ion is 10: there are 7 contributed by the nitrogen atom, plus 4 from the hydrogen atoms, minus 1 which is given up to the chlorine. Since the Cl⁻ ion has $17+1 = 18$ electrons, the diffracting power of Cl⁻ is nearly twice that of $NH_4^+$; if the ions behaved as scattering points, or if the variation in diffracting power with angle (see later section on 'angle factors') were the same for both ions, the ratio would be exactly 18/10. Actually, the diffracting powers of the two ions vary with the angle of diffraction in slightly different degrees; but the difference is not great, and in fact the ratio of diffracting powers is never far from 18/10.

**The structure amplitude, $F$.** In an ammonium chloride crystal the unit cell is a cube containing one $NH_4^+$ and one Cl⁻ ion. If the centre of a chlorine ion is taken as the corner of the unit cell, then the ammonium ion lies in the centre of the cell (Fig. 116).

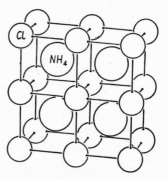

Fig. 116. Structure of ammonium chloride. (The sizes of the spheres are arbitrary; they do not represent effective packing sizes.)

Consider the reflection of X-rays by the 001 plane of the crystal; it is this reflection, together with the exactly similar reflections by the 100 and 010 planes, which gives rise to the first arc on the powder photograph (Plate XI), an arc of moderate intensity. The 001 reflection is produced when X-rays from one plane of chlorine ions ($M$ in Fig. 117) are exactly one wavelength behind those from the next plane of chlorine ions $N$. But when this happens, waves from ammonium ions in plane $P$ must be exactly half a wavelength behind those from the chlorine ions $N$, since the ammonium plane $P$ is exactly half-way between the chlorine planes $M$ and $N$. Waves from ammonium ions are thus exactly opposite in phase to those from chlorine ions, and this is true throughout the crystal. Interference will occur, but the intensity of the resultant diffracted beam will not be zero, because the diffracting power of the ammonium ion $f_{NH_4}$ is little more than half that of the chlorine ion $f_{Cl}$, and the amplitude of the resultant wave $(= f_{Cl} - f_{NH_4})$ is thus reduced to slightly less than half what it would be if chlorine ions alone were present. The intensity of a beam is, for an 'imperfect'† crystal such as ammonium chloride, proportional to the square of the amplitude of

† See p. 223.

the waves, hence the intensity for 001 is less than one-quarter what it would be for chlorine ions alone.

But now consider reflections by planes of type 101 (such as $10\bar{1}$, 110, 011, and so on), which give rise to the second arc—a very strong one. Here, the ammonium ions lie on the same planes as the chlorine ions (Fig. 117), the 101 reflection being produced when waves from plane $L$

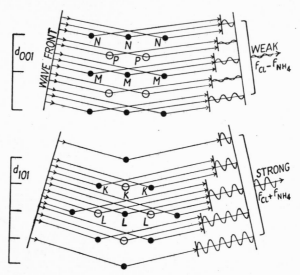

Fig. 117. Reflection of X-rays by 001 and 101 planes of ammonium chloride.

are one wavelength behind waves from plane $K$; the waves from all the ions in the crystal are therefore in phase with each other, and the resultant amplitude $(f_{Cl}+f_{NH_4})$ is about $1\frac{1}{2}$ times what it would be for chlorine ions alone; the intensity is therefore about twice what it would be for chlorine ions alone. The intensity of a 101 reflection is thus something like eight times as great as that of a 100 reflection. This, then, is the principal reason why the second arc on the photograph is so very much stronger than the first. (There is another reason, but this will be considered later.)

The third arc is composed of reflections from 111 planes. The sheets of chlorine ions which define these planes are interleaved by sheets of ammonium ions (Fig. 118); hence, the situation is the same as for 001: waves from the ammonium ions oppose those from the chlorine ions, and a weak reflection is the result.

The fourth arc consists of 200+020+002. These reflections occur when waves from chlorine plane $M$ (Fig. 119) are two wavelengths behind those from the next chlorine plane $N$; but, since the ammonium ions in plane $P$ are half-way between planes $M$ and $N$, waves from $P$ are one wavelength behind those from $N$ and one wavelength in front of those from $M$; therefore they are in phase with those from $M$ and $N$, and a strong reflection is the result.

A rough idea of the relative intensities of all the reflections may be

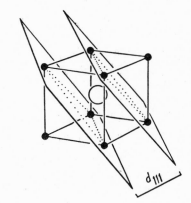

. Fig. 118.  111 planes of ammonium chloride.

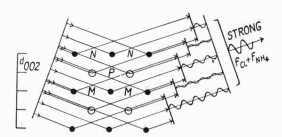

Fig. 119.  Reflection of X-rays by 002 planes of ammonium chloride.

gained in this way. On account of the position of the ammonium ions in the centres of the unit cells defined by the chlorine ions, it is found that, for all planes in which the sum of the indices $h+k+l$ is even, waves from ammonium and chlorine ions are in phase with, and therefore co-operate with, each other, giving a strong reflection, while for all planes having $h+k+l$ odd, waves from ammonium ions oppose those from chlorine ions, and the reflection is therefore relatively weak.

The ammonium chloride crystal forms a particularly simple example of the effect of atomic arrangement on the intensities of the various reflections. The structure amplitude will be treated more generally in a later section.

**The number of equivalent reflections,** $p$. The statement just made is true in a general way, but it may be noted (in Plate XI) that, for instance, 211 (the sixth arc) is stronger than 002 (the fourth arc), though $h+k+l$ is even for both. This is because there are more planes of type 211 than there are of type 002. There are only three different planes of type 002—namely, 002, 020, and 200; a crystal turned to all possible orientations would give reflections from this type of plane for six different orientations with respect to the X-ray beam (002 and 00$\bar{2}$ being reflections in opposite directions from the same plane). But there are twelve different planes of type 211—namely 211, 121, 112, 21$\bar{1}$, 2$\bar{1}$1, 2$\bar{1}\bar{1}$, $\bar{1}$21, 12$\bar{1}$, $\bar{1}$2$\bar{1}$, $\bar{1}$12, 1$\bar{1}$2, $\bar{1}\bar{1}$2, and therefore twenty-four reflections. Stated generally, there are six reflections of type $h$00, twelve of type $hh$0, twenty-four of type $hk$0, eight of type $hhh$, twenty-four of type $hhl$, and forty-eight of type $hkl$. In a powder there are crystals oriented in all possible ways; the number of them which happen to lie in a position suitable for reflection by a particular type of plane is evidently proportional to the number of differently oriented, crystallographically equivalent planes.

TABLE III

*Numbers of equivalent reflections (multiplicity)*

| Point group symmetry | Type of reflection, and multiplicity† | | | | | | |
|---|---|---|---|---|---|---|---|
| Triclinic: 1, $\bar{1}$ | All types: 2 | | | | | | |
| Monoclinic: $m$, 2, 2/$m$ | 0$k$0 — 2 | $h0l$ — 2 | $hkl$ — 4 | | | | |
| Orthorhombic: $mm$, 222, $mmm$ | $h$00, 0$k$0, 00$l$ — 2 | | | $hk$0, 0$kl$, $h0l$ — 4 | | | $hkl$ — 8 |
| Tetragonal: 4, $\bar{4}$, 4/$m$ | 00$l$ — 2 | $h$00, $hh$0 — 4 | $hk$0 — 4+4 | 0$k$0 — 8 | $hhl$ — 8 | | $hkl$ — 8+8 |
| $\bar{4}$2$m$, 4$mm$, 42, 4/$mmm$ | 2 | 4 | 8 | 8 | 8 | | 16 |
| Trigonal and hexagonal: 3, $\bar{3}$ | 00$l$ — 2 | $h$00, $hh$0 — 6 | $hk$0 — 6+6 | 0$kl$ — 6+6 | $hhl$ — 6+6 | | $hkl$ — 6+6+6+6 |
| 3$m$, 32, $\bar{3}m$ | 2 | 6 | 12 | 6+6 | 12 | | 12+12 |
| 6, $\bar{6}$, 6/$m$ | 2 | 6 | 6+6 | 12 | 12 | | 12+12 |
| $\bar{6}$2$m$, 6$mm$, 62, 6/$mmm$ | 2 | 6 | 12 | 12 | 12 | | 24 |
| Cubic: 23, $m$3 | $h$00 — 6 | $hh$0 — 12 | $hk$0 — 12+12 | $hhh$ — 8 | $hhl$ — 24 | $hkl$ — 24+24 | |
| $\bar{4}$3$m$, 43, $m$3$m$ | 6 | 12 | 24 | 8 | 24 | 48 | |

† Where the multiplicity is given as, for example, 6+6, this signifies that there are two sets of reflections at the same angle but having different intensities.

In Table III, the numbers of equivalent reflections in crystals of all possible symmetries are set down. These numbers are applicable to powder photographs, in which all planes having the same spacing give reflections on the same arc. For single-crystal normal-beam rotation photographs the situation is different: planes parallel to the axis of rotation give reflections in two places on the equator of the photograph, one each side of the meridian, while the reflections from other planes are distributed among four positions, one in each quadrant. The multiplicities for single-crystal rotation photographs are therefore given in another Table (IV). These multiplicities depend on the symmetry of the

TABLE IV

| Laue symmetry | Axis vertical | Maximum equatorial multiplicity† | Maximum layer-line multiplicity† |
|---|---|---|---|
| $\bar{1}$ | | 2 | 1 |
| 2/m | Twofold | 2 | 2 |
| mmm | Twofold | 4 | 4 |
| $\bar{3}$ | Threefold | 6+6 | 3+3+3+3 |
| $\bar{3}m$ | Threefold | 12 | 6+6 |
| 4/m | Fourfold | 4+4 | 4+4 |
| 4/mm | Fourfold | 8 | 8 |
| 6/m | Sixfold | 6+6 | 6+6 |
| 6/mmm | Sixfold | 12 | 12 |
| m3 | Twofold (c) | 4+4 | 4+4 (8 for hkk's and hhl's) |
| m3m | Fourfold | 8 | 8 |

† Where the multiplicity is given as, for example, 4+4, this signifies that there are two sets of spots on the same layer line and at the same Bragg angle, but having different intensities.

axis round which rotation occurs; they are obvious by inspection in tilted crystal photographs. It should be noted that in some cases there are two or more sets of reflections having the same spacing but different intensities; this depends on the 'Laue symmetry' of the crystal—see p. 260. These features also are obvious in tilted crystal photographs.

**Angle factors.** The two factors already mentioned—the crystal structure amplitude and the factor for the number of similar planes—give a general idea of the reason for the variation of intensity from one arc to another in the powder photograph of ammonium chloride. We have now to consider the general diminution with increasing angle.

Atoms in crystals cannot be regarded as scattering *points*; the 'diameter' of the electron cloud of an atom is of the same order of size as the distance between the centres of adjacent atoms—in fact, to a first approximation, the atoms in many crystals may be regarded as spheres of definite radius in contact with each other; the electron clouds of adjacent atoms may be regarded as just touching each other. The consequences of this are illustrated in Fig. 120, in which (in the formation of a particular reflection) waves diffracted by electrons on the equatorial plane $BB$ of one atom are one wavelength behind those diffracted by the equatorial electrons $AA$ of the next atom; in these circumstances, waves diffracted by outer electrons $CC$ and $DD$ of these atoms oppose, to some extent, those from $AA$ and $BB$, and therefore

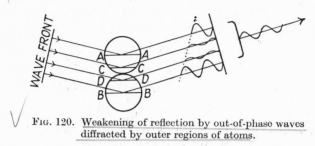

FIG. 120. Weakening of reflection by out-of-phase waves diffracted by outer regions of atoms.

reduce the intensity of the resultant diffracted beam. The reduction of intensity is not considerable in the circumstances mentioned, because the electron density in the outer regions of an atom is low compared with the density near the centre, the electron cloud being in effect a sort of diffuse atmosphere having maximum density in the inner regions and a low density in the outer regions; but for the higher order diffractions (that is, 'reflections' from closely spaced planes), when the phase difference for waves from the inner regions of adjacent atoms is several wavelengths, waves from regions of not very dissimilar electron densities interfere with each other, and the intensity of the resultant diffracted beam is therefore much reduced.

This would appear to introduce considerable complexity into the problem of calculating the intensities of diffracted X-rays; fortunately, however, it can be dealt with in quite a simple way, by treating an atom as if it had all its diffracting matter at a point (the centre of the atom), but with a diffracting power diminishing with the spacing of the reflecting planes. The effective diffracting power of each atom is usually given as a function of $(\sin \theta)/\lambda \ (= n/2d)$, and the diffracting powers of all atoms (symbolized $f$ ) for a wide range of $(\sin \theta)/\lambda$ are to be found in *Internationale Tabellen* (1935) and in James (1948). For many atoms, diffracting powers have been deduced from the measured intensities of reflections from crystals whose structures are firmly established (James and Brindley, 1931), but it is also possible (Hartree, 1928) to calculate the values from the electronic structures of atoms, and these calculated values agree well with the experimental values (James, Waller, and Hartree, 1928). The units used for $f$ are such that for $(\sin \theta)/\lambda = 0$, $f$ is equal to the number of electrons in the atom. For ionized atoms the number is increased or decreased by the magnitude of the charge. In polyatomic ions such as $NO_2^-$ the constituent atoms are charged; the appropriate figures to be used in calculations, for the

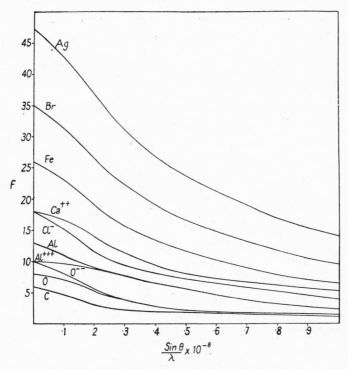

Fig. 121. Diffracting powers of a few common atoms.

nitrite ion taken as example, are those for $O^{-2}$ and $N^{+3}$. Later calculations by McWeeny (1951) and by Hoerni and Ibers (1954) have given diffracting powers slightly different from those previously accepted; McWeeny took into account the effect of the bonding electrons and gives values for light atoms including carbon, nitrogen, and oxygen; Hoerni and Ibers used more recent information on the 'self-consistent fields' of light atoms. Viervoll and Ögrim (1949) have given figures for higher values of $(\sin \theta)/\lambda$ than James. In structural investigations aiming at high precision, the source of the diffracting powers used should be quoted.

It should be remembered that the figures normally quoted for diffracting powers are not valid when appreciable X-ray fluorescence occurs; fluorescence, due to the absorption of X-rays followed by re-emission as longer waves characteristic of the atoms, is intense when the wavelength of the incident X-rays is slightly shorter than $K\beta$ for the atoms, and in these circumstances the intensity of the diffracted beam is naturally reduced (James, 1948).

Another cause of diminution of the intensities of X-rays with increasing angle of reflection is the polarization which occurs on reflection. The intensity of any reflection is reduced by this effect to the fraction $(1+\cos^2 2\theta)/2$.

Yet another angle factor is what is known as the Lorentz factor $L$, which expresses, for rotating crystal photographs, the relative time any crystal plane spends within the narrow angular range over which reflection occurs. When a perfect crystal turns slowly through the reflecting position, reflection occurs only over a range of a few seconds of arc. Most crystals are not perfect, and reflect over a range of some minutes or even as much as half a degree (Bragg, James, and Bosanquet, 1921), but the reason for this is that different portions of the lattice are not quite parallel to each other; this spread may be regarded as part of the rotation of the crystal, and is irrelevant to the present point, which concerns only the angular range within which the small perfect sections of the lattice reflect. In terms of the conception of the reciprocal lattice, each 'point' of the reciprocal lattice has a finite size, and as the reciprocal lattice rotates through the sphere of reflection, each 'point' spends a finite time passing through the surface of this sphere. This factor varies with the distance of the reciprocal lattice point from the origin, which is of course related to the angle of reflection. The Lorentz factor varies with the type of photograph. For the equatorial reflections on a normal rotation photograph, it is $\dfrac{1}{\sin 2\theta}$ (Darwin, 1922). For other layers on normal rotation photographs, it is $\dfrac{1}{\sin 2\theta} \times \dfrac{\cos \theta}{\sqrt{(\cos^2\phi - \sin^2\theta)}}$, where $\phi$ is the angle between the reflecting plane and the axis of rotation; it increases the strength of spots on upper and lower layers in comparison with those on the equator, the increase being greatest near the meridian of the photograph, because here the reciprocal lattice point, during its rotation, grazes the sphere of reflection, while elsewhere it passes through the surface of the sphere of reflection; the contact time is greater for meridional reflections. Cochran (1948) pointed out that the Lorentz factor takes on a simple form if it is expressed in terms of the reciprocal lattice; for normal-beam rotation or Weissenberg photographs it is $(\sin^2 2\theta - \zeta^2)^{-\frac{1}{2}}$, while for equi-inclination Weissenberg photographs it is $(\xi \cos \theta)^{-1}$. Charts giving the combined Lorentz and polarization factors in this form can be obtained from the Institute of Physics (47 Belgrave Square, London, S.W. 1). For the De Jong and Bouman camera, see Bouman and De Jong (1938) and Buerger (1940); and for Buerger's precession camera, see Waser (1951), Burbank (1952), and Grenville-Wells and Abrahams (1952).

It should be noted that the expressions for the Lorentz factor mentioned in the last paragraph become infinite for certain angles (for instance, on the meridian of a normal cylindrical-film rotation photograph); this is because in the derivation of the expressions it is assumed that the angular range of reflection (the size of the reciprocal lattice point) is vanishingly small—an assumption that goes too far. Heide (1951) has calculated the effect of the finite size of the reflecting blocks in the crystal; this effect need only be considered at places very near the special positions.

When diffracted X-ray beams fall on a photographic film at different angles, as the different layer lines in a cylindrical-film rotation photograph do, it is necessary to correct for the absorption of X-rays in different thicknesses of film. (Since double-coated films are normally used, the effect on the back layer depends on the absorption in the film.) This was first considered by Cox and Shaw (1930); Whittaker (1953) gives a formula which is more accurate and deals with greater obliquity and a thicker film; Grenville-Wells (1955) gives the corrections when the multiple film method is used.

For powder photographs it is also necessary to take into account the fact that all the reflected beams from all the little crystals are spread over a cone which is narrow for reflections at small angles but much wider for reflections at larger angles, when $2\theta$ is near $90°$. The fraction of intensity per unit length of arc (which decides the degree of blackening of the film) is thus less at the larger angles than at the smaller ones. The cones are smaller again for 'back reflections' at Bragg angles approaching $90°$ (that is, angles of reflection $2\theta$ approaching $180°$), so that here again there is a greater fraction of intensity per unit length of arc. The effect of this factor at large angles can often be seen on powder photographs as a tendency towards increasing intensity at the very ends of the film where the Bragg angle is approaching $90°$. (See, for instance, Plate IV.) To account for this effect, the expression for the intensity must be multiplied by the factor $1/(\sin^2\theta \cos \theta)$.

**Thermal vibrations.** Atoms in crystals vibrate at ordinary temperatures with frequencies very much lower than those of X-rays; at any one instant, some atoms are displaced from their mean positions in one direction while those in another part of the crystal are displaced in another direction; consequently, diffracted X-rays which would be exactly in phase if the atoms were at rest are actually not exactly in phase, and the intensity of the diffracted beam is thus lower than it would be if all the atoms were at rest. For crystal planes of large spacing (those giving reflections at small angles), the thermal displacements of the atoms are small fractions of the plane-spacing, and therefore do not affect the intensities much; but for the more closely spaced planes (those giving reflections at the larger angles) the atomic displacements may be comparable with the plane-spacing, and therefore the intensities of these reflections may be much reduced. The effect is thus greater, the larger the angle of reflection; and it naturally increases with rising temperature—X-ray diffraction patterns taken at high temperatures are always weaker than those of the same substance at low temperatures.

Note that it is largely in consequence of considerable thermal vibrations that the diffraction patterns of crystals of many organic substances (taken at room temperature) fade away to nothing at Bragg angles of 50–60° (using copper $K\alpha$ radiation, $\lambda = 1\cdot54$ Å), while those of inorganic salts and metals which are far below their melting-points show strong reflections over the whole range to 90°, because the thermal vibrations are very small compared with the interatomic distances.

The ratio $T$ between the actual intensity of a diffracted beam and the intensity which it would have if there were no thermal vibrations is $e^{-2B\left(\frac{\sin\theta}{\lambda}\right)^2}$, where $B$ is a constant for a particular crystal. $B$ is related to the amplitude of vibration of the atoms by the expression $B = 8\pi^2\bar{u}^2$ where $\bar{u}^2$ is the mean square amplitude; it can usually be estimated only approximately (see *Internationale Tabellen*, 1935, p. 569), but this need not deter us from quantitative study of diffraction patterns, since an inaccurate estimation of $B$ would only mean that the intensities of the reflections fall away with increasing Bragg angle rather more slowly or more rapidly than was expected. In practice it is found that uncertainty in the value of $B$ does not lead to appreciable doubt about the interpretation of X-ray diffraction patterns. A typical value of $B$ for an ionic crystal is $1\cdot43 \times 10^{-16}$ for NaCl (*Internationale Tabellen*, 1935, p. 570).

The use of the above expression implies that all the atoms vibrate with equal amplitudes. This is not strictly true: for instance, in sodium chloride the amplitude of vibration of the lighter sodium ion is greater than that of the chlorine ion; and, in general, thermal vibrations must be different for every crystallographically different atom in a unit cell, since they depend on the surroundings of the atom as well as on its inertia.

Instead of making a separate correction for $B$ it is often possible to use experimentally determined values for the diffracting powers of atoms, which include the temperature effect as an additional diminution of the apparent diffracting power with increasing angle of reflection. Empirical diffracting powers for elements occurring in silicate crystals are given by Bragg and West (1929); and for hydrocarbons by Robertson (1935 a).

Another assumption implied in the use of the expression given above (or the empirical diffracting powers referred to in the last paragraph) is that the thermal vibrations of the atoms have the same magnitude in all directions in the crystal. This is not strictly true; it is a sufficient approximation to the truth for many crystals, but there are cases in which the vibrations are markedly anisotropic. For instance, the vibrations of long-chain molecules are almost entirely perpendicular to their long axes, while flat molecules vibrate chiefly in a direction normal to the plane of the molecule.† Furthermore, it has been found that some crystals give diffuse 'extra' reflections, which are undoubtedly due to the thermal vibrations of the atoms. Examples are to be seen in the centre of the Laue photograph of ammonium chloride which is the upper part of Plate XIII. In terms of the conception of the reciprocal lattice, the reflecting power, which hitherto has been assumed to be confined to the *points* of the reciprocal lattice, is actually to some extent spread in varying degrees along the principal lines of the reciprocal lattice. It is as if the diminution of reflecting power referred to at the beginning of this section is not lost, but reappears along the lines of the reciprocal lattice, giving rise to extra spots and streaks on single-crystal photographs. A valuable summary of work on this subject up to 1942 is given in a paper by Lonsdale (1942).

**Absorption.** The effect of absorption of X-rays in a powder specimen is to diminish the intensities of reflections at small angles much more than those of the 'back reflections' (see Fig. 68). Corrections can be calculated for cylindrical specimens of known diameter (Bradley, 1935), these corrections being valid also for cylindrically shaped single crystals. For crystals of natural shape completely bathed in the X-ray beam, it

† For the effect of anisotropic thermal vibrations on the relative intensities of X-ray reflections, see Helmholz (1936), Hughes (1941), and Brindley and Ridley (1938, 1939).

is possible to calculate absorption corrections (Hendershot, 1937 a; Albrecht, 1939), but the calculations are laborious, and it is much better, if possible, to reduce single crystals to cylindrical shape. For rod-shaped crystals this may sometimes be done by rolling them on a ground-glass plate; for soluble substances it may be possible to adjust the crystal on the goniometer, and then rotate it while holding against it a fine paint brush charged with solvent; hard insoluble crystals may be turned on a jeweller's lathe. Pepinsky (1956) uses, for crystal shaping generally, a small ultrasonically oscillated tool mounted on a micromanipulator.

To keep absorption corrections as low as possible it is best, when working with strongly absorbing substances, to use smaller crystals than when working with transparent substances. But a limit is set by the increase in exposure times as well as by difficulties of manipulation: a suitable size for a strongly absorbing crystal is 1/20th to 1/10th mm.

Bradley (1935) points out that, since the effect of the absorption factor is opposite to that of thermal vibrations, the two may in some cases cancel each other approximately; consequently it may be justifiable to ignore both factors. This naturally applies only to crystals of moderate or high absorption; it does not apply to most organic substances, for which absorption is small and thermal vibrations large, so that the effect of the latter far outweighs the absorption effect.

**Complete expression for intensity of reflection. Perfect and imperfect crystals.** If relative intensities are being calculated, it is sufficient to multiply the structure amplitude (which is treated generally in the next section) by all the correction factors mentioned. Thus, for a powder photograph, the intensity of each arc is proportional to

$$F^2 p \frac{1 + \cos^2 2\theta}{\sin^2\theta \cos \theta} \times \text{temperature factor } (T) \times \text{absorption factor } (A),$$

while for a normal-beam single-crystal rotation photograph, the intensity of each spot is proportional to

$$F^2 p \left( \frac{1 + \cos^2 2\theta}{\sin 2\theta} \right) \left( \frac{\cos \theta}{\sqrt{(\cos^2\phi - \sin^2\theta)}} \right) T A.$$

The advantage of using absolute intensities, especially for complex structures, has been urged by Bragg and West (1929). If absolute intensities are being calculated, the following expressions must be used:

(1) For powder photograph on cylindrical film, radius $r$.
   If diffracted energy in a length of arc $l = P'$ and energy of primary
   beam per second per unit area $= I_0$,

$$\frac{P'}{I_0} = \frac{N^2 e^4 \lambda^3 l V}{32\pi m^2 c^4 r} F^2 p \frac{1 + \cos^2 2\theta}{\sin^2 \theta \cos \theta} T A.$$

where $N =$ number of unit cells per unit volume,
   $e, m =$ electronic charge and mass,
   $\lambda =$ X-ray wavelength,
   $V =$ volume of powder in the beam.
   $c =$ velocity of light.

(2) For normal-beam single-crystal rotation photograph, using crystal
   of volume $V$ completely bathed in X-rays:

$$\rho = \frac{N^2 e^4 \lambda^3 V}{4\pi m^2 c^4} \tau F^2 p' \left( \frac{1 + \cos^2 2\theta}{\sin 2\theta} \right) \left( \frac{\cos \theta}{\sqrt{(\cos^2 \phi - \sin^2 \theta)}} \right) T A,$$

where $\rho$ is the integrated reflection, defined thus:

$\rho = E\omega/I_0$, where $E$ is the total energy in a given reflected beam
when the crystal has been rotating for time $\tau$ at constant angular
velocity $\omega$. Some crystal structure determinations (notably those of
complex silicates worked out by W. L. Bragg and his school) have
been based on measurements of reflections from the faces of crystals
much larger than the primary beam, or reflections transmitted through
crystal sections. Formulae appropriate to these experimental conditions will be found in *Internationale Tabellen* (1935).

These expressions containing $F^2$ are valid only for 'ideally imperfect'
crystals, to which class most known crystals belong. It is a curious
fact that really perfect crystals like certain diamonds, in which all
portions of the lattice are parallel to a high degree of precision, give
an integrated intensity which is proportional directly to $F$ (not to its
square), and is thus smaller than that given by an imperfect crystal of
the same substance.

If a perfect crystal is turned slowly through the reflecting position,
using an extremely narrow X-ray beam, reflection occurs only over a
range of a few seconds of arc (Allison, 1932). Reflection, when it occurs,
is total—the whole beam is reflected—but this happens over such a
small angular range that the integrated reflection (which is always
measured in crystal structure determination) is less than that given
by an imperfect crystal which reflects less strongly, but over a much
wider angular range.

Most actual crystals are imperfect; different portions of the lattice are not quite parallel, and the crystal behaves as if it consisted of a number of blocks (of the order of $10^{-5}$ cm in diameter) whose orientation varies over several minutes or even in some cases up to half a degree. This imperfection is perhaps connected with the manner of growth in thin layers (see Chapter II and Plates I and II); each layer may be slightly wavy, and there may be cracks or impurities between the layers. Most crystals are imperfect in this way, and in structure determination it is usually safe to assume that the intensity of any reflection is proportional to the square of the structure amplitude. To make quite sure that a crystal is 'ideally imperfect', it may be dipped in liquid air: the shock-cooling produces imperfections.

The intensities of crystal reflections are in some circumstances reduced by effects known as primary and secondary extinction. If the crystal is not 'ideally imperfect' but consists of rather large lattice blocks, the intensities of the reflections are proportional to a power of $F$ between 1 and 2; this is 'primary extinction'. 'Secondary extinction' affects only the strongest reflections and is due to the fact that the top layer of a crystal (the part nearest the primary beam) reflects away an appreciable proportion of the primary beam, thus in effect partially shielding the lower layers of the crystal; the strongest reflections are therefore experimentally less strong than they should be in comparison with the weaker reflections. The relation between the actual intensity $\rho'$ and the intensity $\rho$ which would be obtained if there were no secondary extinction is, for reflection at a large face,

$$\rho = \frac{\rho'}{1 - 2g\rho'},$$

where $g$ is a constant—the 'secondary extinction coefficient' (Bragg (W. L.), James, and Bosanquet, 1921, 1922; Bragg (W. L.) and West, 1929). For transmission through a plate, see Vand (1955); for small crystals, Jellinek (1958).

Both primary and secondary extinction effects may usually be avoided by powdering a crystal. For this and other reasons the intensities of the arcs on powder photographs are likely to be more reliable than those of other types of photograph; but in practice, in structure determination it is only possible to use 'powder intensities' alone for very simple structures; for complex crystals reflections from different planes overlap seriously.

In most structure determinations small crystals 0·1–0·5 mm across are now used. Primary extinction is rare and not likely to be encountered, while secondary extinction for crystals of this size is usually not serious.

It should be remembered that the strongest reflections which are most seriously affected by secondary extinction occur at small angles and are less likely to overlap on powder photographs; therefore it may often be best to measure the intensities of the small-angle reflections on a powder photograph and the rest on single-crystal photographs. Another useful procedure is to measure the strongest reflections on both powder and single-crystal photographs, and by comparing them (assuming the powder results to be free from extinction effects) to estimate the secondary extinction coefficient which can then be applied to the single-crystal results (Wyckoff, 1932; Wyckoff and Corey, 1934).

**Calculation of absolute intensities from relative intensities.** Although many structures have been solved by interpreting a set of relative intensities, it is always desirable to obtain absolute intensities, and for some purposes the absolute values are essential. Experimental methods of measuring them have been mentioned earlier, but it is also possible to calculate them from a set of relative intensities. For a unit cell with a known content of atoms, *any* arbitrary arrangement of atoms would give a set of reflections of the same average value of $F^2$; in other words, whatever the structure, the average value of $F^2$ is the same; Wilson (1942 $b$) showed that this average $F^2$ is equal to the sum of the squares of the diffracting powers of the atoms : $\overline{F^2} = \sum f^2$. A difficulty in using this relation is that at the beginning of an investigation one does not know the temperature factor; but this difficulty is dealt with by dividing the reflections into groups lying between chosen limits of $(\sin^2\theta)/\lambda^2$; the mean of the observed intensities is evaluated for each range, and this, multiplied by a constant $c$, must equal $\sum f^2$ for the range in question. The constant $c$ will be different for each range, and by plotting $\log c$ against $(\sin^2\theta)/\lambda^2$ and extrapolating to $(\sin^2\theta)/\lambda^2 = 0$, a value of $c_0$ is obtained for zero diffraction angle, where the temperature factor is unity. The figures for relative $F^2$ are then multiplied by $c_0$ to convert them to absolute $F^2$'s. It must be admitted that results obtained by this method are rough, though probably no more so than those obtained by experimental absolute measurements. The method also gives us the temperature factor, for the slope of the curve of $\log c$ against $(\sin^2\theta)/\lambda^2$ is equal to $2B$.

**General expression for the structure amplitude.** We are interested primarily in the arrangement of the atoms in crystals and the effect of the arrangement on the intensities of diffracted X-ray beams.

A general idea of the effect of atomic arrangement on the intensities of various reflections of a very simple crystal has been presented in an earlier section. For this crystal, ammonium chloride, the phase relationships between the waves from the two types of ions are very simple; the waves from ammonium ions are, for every type of crystal plane, either exactly in phase with those from chlorine ions or exactly opposite in phase, owing to the position of the ammonium ion in the exact centre of the cube defined by the chlorine ions.

In most crystals, however, the coordinates of some or all of the atoms are not simple fractions of the unit cell edges, and the phase relationships between waves from different atoms are therefore not simple. Consider, for instance, the atomic arrangement in rutile, one of the crystal forms of $TiO_2$ (Vegard, 1916). The unit cell (Fig. 122 a) is tetragonal ($a = 4·58$ Å, $c = 2·98$ Å) and contains two titanium and four oxygen atoms. Titanium atoms are at the corners and centres of the cells (coordinates 000 and $\frac{1}{2}\frac{1}{2}\frac{1}{2}$ respectively); oxygen atoms lie on the base diagonals and at similar positions half-way up the cells, the coordinates being (1) 0·31a, 0·31b, 0·0c, (2) −0·31a, −0·31b, 0·0c, (3) −0·19a, +0·19b, 0·50c, (4) +0·19a, −0·19b, 0·50c. A powder photograph of this substance, taken with copper $K\alpha$ radiation, is shown in Plate XI. Consider the intensities of some of the reflections.

First of all, no reflection from 001 appears on the photograph; the reason is that when waves from plane $P$ (Fig. 122 a) are one wavelength behind those from plane $M$, then waves from plane $N$ are half a wavelength behind those from plane $M$, and are thus exactly opposite in phase; and since there is exactly the same combination of atoms on $N$ as on $M$ (one Ti and two O per unit cell), the waves from $N$ exactly cancel out those from $M$; and so on throughout the crystal. Reflection 002, however, does appear on the photograph, because a phase-difference of two wavelengths between waves from $M$ and $P$ means a phase-difference of one wavelength between waves from $M$ and $N$, and thus all the waves co-operate. The intensity of 002 is not very great because there are only two reflections of this type (002, 00$\bar{2}$). The 100 reflection is absent because the 100 planes of Ti atoms are interleaved (at exactly half-way) by exactly similar planes of Ti atoms (see Fig. 122 b), which produce waves of exactly opposite phase—and the same is true for the oxygen atoms.

For 110 (see Fig. 122 c), observe first that waves from all Ti atoms are in phase with each other, and that those from two of the oxygens (3 and 4) are also in phase, but that the waves from the other two

(1 and 2) are not in phase. The last-mentioned waves are not exactly opposite in phase to the rest, however; the phase-difference is $(s/d_{110}) \times 360°$, which for O(1) is $0.62 \times 360°$ and for O(2) is $-0.62 \times 360°$.

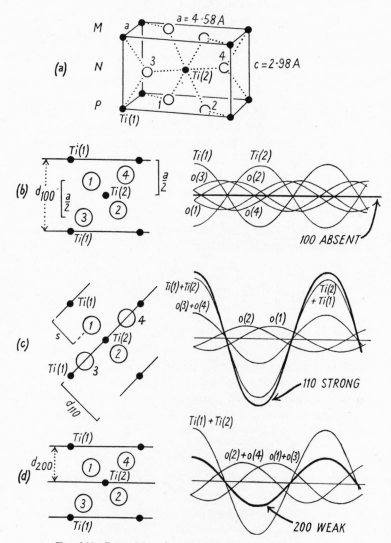

FIG. 122. Intensities of some $hk0$ reflections of rutile, $TiO_2$.

If the waves are represented graphically as in Fig. 122 c, the resultant amplitude (shown by the thicker line) is obtained by adding the ordinates. It is evident that for this particular reflection the partly-out-of-phase waves do not diminish the intensity much, because there are only two oxygens producing them, as against $2(Ti)+2(O)$ producing the rest, and the net result is a strong reflection.

For 200, however (Fig. 122 $d$), waves from all the oxygens oppose, to some extent, those from the titanium atoms, and since the diffracting power of four oxygens is a substantial fraction of that of two titanium atoms, a weak reflection is expected—and found (see the powder photograph, Plate XI); the reflection is, however, not as weak as if the oxygen atoms had been on planes exactly half-way between the titanium planes, which would have meant a phase-difference of $180°$; the actual phase-difference is $2 \times 0.31 \times 2\pi$ ($= 223°$), the waves from two oxygens being $223°$ in front of, and those from the other two $223°$ behind, those from the titanium atoms. Graphical compounding of the waves as in Fig. 122 $d$ shows the result.

In practice the compounding of waves from the different atoms is done by calculation. The expression for compounding waves from different atoms (diffracting power $f$) situated at different points in the unit cell (coordinates $x$, $y$, $z$ in fractions of the unit cell edges) is, quite generally, for any reflecting plane $hkl$,

$$F^2 = A^2 + B^2,$$

where
$$A = \sum f \cos 2\pi(hx + ky + lz),$$
$$B = \sum f \sin 2\pi(hx + ky + lz).$$

This is valid for all crystals, whatever their symmetry; but whenever there is, as in rutile, a centre of symmetry at the origin, there is no need to calculate the sine terms, since in the aggregate they are bound to add up to zero. (For every atom giving a wave of phase angle $\theta$ there is also an identical atom giving a wave of phase angle $-\theta$, and $\sin(-\theta) = -\sin\theta$.)

Apply this to the 200 and 110 reflections of rutile. The spacing $d$ of 200 is $2.30$ Å;

$$\frac{\sin\theta}{\lambda} \left(= \frac{1}{2d}\right)$$

is thus $0.217 \times 10^8$, and, looking up in *Internationale Tabellen* (1935) the diffracting powers of the atoms concerned, we find $f_{Ti} = 14.0$ and $f_O = 5.2$. The phase angles for the two Ti atoms are obviously zero (Fig. 122 $d$) and the net contribution for these atoms is

$$2f_{Ti} \cos 0° = 2f_{Ti} = +28.0.$$

But for oxygen No. 1, $x = 0.31$ and

$$f_O \cos 2\pi(2 \times 0.31) = f_O \cos 223° = 5.2 \times (-0.732) = -3.80.$$

For oxygen No. 2 the phase angle is $-223°$, and its contribution is thus the same as that of the first (since $\cos(-\theta) = \cos\theta$). The other two oxygens are at $x = -0.19$ and $+0.19$ respectively and their phase angles are thus $-137°$ and $+137°$, the cosines of which are the same as those of $223°$ and $-223°$. The net contribution of the four oxygens is thus $4f_O \cos 223° = 4(-3.80) = -15.2$. Adding this to the contribution of the titanium atoms, we get $A (= F) = +28.0-15.2 = 12.8$; the intensity is proportional to the square of $F$.

For 110, $d = 3.25$ Å, $(\sin\theta)/\lambda = 0.154\times10^8$, and $f_{Ti}$ and $f_O$ are $15.7$ and $6.5$ respectively. The phase angles for Ti atoms are again zero, and the Ti contribution is thus $2f_{Ti} = +31.4$. For oxygens 1 and 2 the phase angles are $2\pi(0.31+0.31)$ and $2\pi(-0.31-0.31)$ or $+223°$ and $-223°$; their contributions are therefore

$$2f_O \cos 223° = 13(-0.732) = -9.5.$$

For oxygens 3 and 4 the phase angle is zero, and their contribution is $2f_O = +13.0$. The total is $+31.4-9.5+13.0 = +34.9$. The actual relative intensities of the 200 and 110 arcs on the powder photograph are obtained by multiplying the $F^2$'s by the appropriate angle factor $\dfrac{1+\cos^2 2\theta}{\sin^2\theta \cos\theta}$ and the number of similar reflections $p$ (4 for 200, 4 for 110). In this way it is found that $I_{200} = K\times 9.7\times 10^4$, $I_{110} = K\times 156\times 10^4$, where $K$ is a constant. (The absorption and temperature factors are neglected.)

As a final example the intensity for the general plane 213 will be calculated. Spacing of $213 = 0.888$ Å; $(\sin\theta)/\lambda = 0.566\times 10^8$; $f_{Ti} = 8.0$, $f_O = 1.9$.

| Atom | $hx+ky+lz$ | | | | Phase angle $\omega$ | $\cos\omega$ | $f\cos w$ |
|---|---|---|---|---|---|---|---|
| Ti (1) | 2(0.0) | +1(0.0) | +3(0.0) | = 0.00 | 0° | +1.0 | +8.0 |
| Ti (2) | 2(0.50) | +1(0.50) | +3(0.50) | = +3.00 | 0° | +1.0 | +8.0 |
| O (1) | 2(0.31) | +1(0.31) | +3(0.0) | = +0.93 | +335° | +0.91 | +1.73 |
| O (2) | 2(-0.31) | +1(-0.31) | +3(0.0) | = -0.93 | -335° | +0.91 | +1.73 |
| O (3) | 2(-0.19) | +1(0.19) | +3(0.50) | = +1.31 | +112° | -0.375 | -0.71 |
| O (4) | 2(0.19) | +1(-0.19) | +3(0.50) | = +1.69 | +248° | -0.375 | -0.71 |

$$F = \sum f\cos\omega = +18.04,$$
$$F^2 = 326.$$

Angle of reflection $\theta = 59° 34'$.

$\dfrac{1+\cos^2 2\theta}{\sin^2\theta \cos\theta}$ for $59° 34'$ is $1.443$.

Number of equivalent reflections $(p)$ of type $213 = 16$.

Hence intensity $= F^2 \times$ angle factor $\times p \times K$

$$= 326 \times 1\cdot443 \times 16K = 7\cdot5 \times 10^4 K.$$

The expressions used are valid for crystals of all types, from cubic to triclinic: the structure amplitude depends on atomic coordinates (as fractions of the unit cell edges), irrespective of the shape of the cell.

**Variation of intensities of reflections with atomic parameters.** In the foregoing calculations the general arrangement of Fig. 122 a

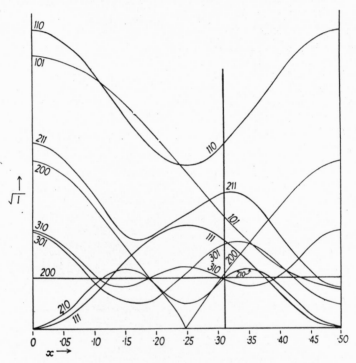

FIG. 123.  Determination of the single parameter in the rutile structure.

was accepted, and the known parameter of the oxygen atoms (0·31) was used; the calculated intensities agree with those actually observed. The accepted value of 0·31 for this parameter was determined by Vegard (1916) by calculating the intensities of a number of reflections for a range of parameters. To demonstrate how sensitively the intensities are related to the parameter $x$, Fig. 123 shows how the calculated intensities for several powder reflections vary with $x$. The curves are shown only for values of $x$ up to 0·5, since they are symmetrical about $x = 0\cdot5$. (The ordinates are not the intensities themselves, but their square roots, which correspond better with visual impressions of intensities on X-ray photographs.) It is evident that, taking into account mere visual impressions of the intensities of the first few powder reflections, the oxygen parameter must be about 0·3, since only for this value are the various intensities in the correct order—110 very strong, 211 strong, 101 fairly strong, 111 and 301 medium, 310 and 002 medium weak, 200 and 210 weak. The intensities of the higher-order reflections vary more rapidly with the value of the parameter, and therefore a more accurate value may be obtained by comparing the intensities of the various high-order reflections.

Fig. 123 thus not only demonstrates how rapidly the relative intensities of different reflections vary with the atomic coordinates, but also indicates the straightforward way in which a single parameter can be determined: when the general arrangement is known, the intensities of a number of reflections are calculated for a range of values of the single parameter. In practice in the example given it would not be necessary to carry out calculations for the complete range of values of $x$, since it is obvious from the start that a weak 200 reflection could only result if the oxygens are about midway between the 200 planes of titanium atoms—that is, if $x$ is not far from 1/4. Calculations would therefore be carried out only for a restricted range round $x = 1/4$.

But how to discover the general arrangement? Calculations such as those just described cannot be made until the general arrangement is known. This problem of the deduction of the general arrangement of atoms in any crystal forms the subject of the next few sections of this chapter. Briefly, the consideration of the relative intensities of the reflections is begun by observing which reflections have zero intensity.

**Atomic arrangements. Preliminary.** For simple structures such as those of many elements and binary compounds the determination of atomic positions by trial presents little difficulty; there are few possible arrangements, and the task of examining them in turn and calculating the intensities of the reflections for a range of coordinates in each arrangement is not a very complex or lengthy one. Some examples are given in Chapter IX. But for complex crystals such as silicate minerals or crystals of most organic substances the problem may seem to be of bewildering complexity. When there are many atoms in the unit cell the number of possible arrangements may be very large, and for each arrangement there may be a number of variable parameters to be considered.

There are two lines of approach to such complex problems. In the first place, a systematic consideration of the possible types of arrangement in crystals in general and the influence of the type of arrangement on the X-ray diffraction pattern as a whole leads to general principles which render the complexities less formidable and save much time and effort.

Atoms, molecules, or ions tend at low temperatures to form that arrangement which has the lowest energy; and the arrangement of lowest energy is a regular repetition of a pattern in space. The pattern usually exhibits symmetries of one sort or another; some types of symmetry, as we have already seen, are displayed in the external shapes of crystals; other types of symmetry, as we shall see in this chapter, affect the X-ray diffraction pattern—they cause certain types of reflection to be absent; systematic absences of certain types of reflection therefore give a straightforward clue to the type of arrangement in the crystal; they may limit the possibilities to two or three arrangements, or even to a single type of arrangement.

The second line of approach to the complexities of crystal structures is by way of the body of existing knowledge of structure types and interatomic distances. The prospects of success in the attempt to find the correct arrangement and parameters in a complex crystal depend to a considerable extent on the amount of knowledge and experience available with regard to related structures previously determined.

When the general arrangement is known it is then necessary to determine precise atomic coordinates. Sometimes the positions of certain atoms are invariant—they are fixed by symmetry considerations—but in complex crystals most of the atoms are in 'general' positions not restricted in any way by symmetry. The variable parameters must be determined by successive approximations; here the work of calculating structure amplitudes for postulated atomic positions can be much shortened by the use of graphical methods, to be described later in this chapter. It cannot be denied, however, that the complete determination of a complex structure is a task not to be undertaken lightly; the time taken must usually be reckoned in months.

The classification of atomic arrangements into types, together with the consideration of the effect of the type of arrangement on the diffraction pattern, will be considered in two stages. First of all, unit cells are either simple, with only one pattern-unit in the cell, or compound, with two or more pattern-units in the cell (see Chapter II). Crystals with compound unit cells give patterns from which many reflections are absent, and the recognition of a compound cell is a very simple matter.

The type of arrangement of pattern-units is called the 'space-lattice'. Secondly, the group of atoms forming a pattern-unit—the group of atoms associated with each lattice point—may have certain symmetries, and some of these symmetries cause further systematic absences of certain types of reflections from the diffraction pattern. The complex of symmetry elements displayed by the complete arrangement is known as the 'space-group'.

**Simple and compound unit cells. The 'space-lattices'.** In Chapter II it has been mentioned that for some crystals it is most appropriate to consider as the unit cell, not the smallest parallelepiped from which the whole crystal could be built up by parallel contiguous repetitions, but a larger parallelepiped containing two or more pattern-units. The examples given (in Figs. 5 c and 6) were the metals iron (in its room-temperature or α form) and copper; the accepted unit cell of α-iron contains two pattern-units of one atom each, and that of copper contains four pattern-units of one atom each. In the first place, it is obviously far more convenient to use these compound unit cells which are cubic in shape than the true structure-units which are not even rectangular. But convenience is not the only basis for accepting the compound unit cells; a more fundamental reason is that the symmetries of these crystals naturally lead to their classification with crystals which have simple cubic cells. For instance, pure α-iron crystals are rhombic dodecahedra and copper crystals octahedra (Groth, 1906–19), and both these shapes are typical of the cubic system; and if the atomic arrangements in these two crystals are examined in the way described on pp. 34–37, it will be found that they possess the same elements of symmetry as caesium bromide which has a *simple* cubic unit cell. All three arrangements possess the highest symmetry possible in the cubic system.

The compound two-atom unit cell of α-iron is termed 'body-centred'. The arrangement is similar to that in ammonium chloride (Fig. 116), with the important difference that in α-iron the atoms in the centres of the cells are the same as those at the corners, whereas in ammonium chloride (which is *not* called 'body-centred') there are weakly diffracting ammonium ions at the cell centres and more strongly diffracting chlorine ions at the cell corners. On account of this difference, all those reflections which are weak in the ammonium chloride pattern (owing to opposition of the waves from corner and centre atoms) are necessarily completely absent from the α-iron pattern (see Plate XII). Thus, for the 010 reflection (Fig. 124), waves from all corner atoms are in phase with each other, while waves from centre atoms are exactly opposite in phase because the planes of centre atoms are exactly half-way between planes of corner atoms. For ammonium chloride this situation merely produces a weak reflection, but for α-iron the diffracting powers of centre atoms are the same as those of corner atoms, and so waves from corner atoms are exactly cancelled by those from centre atoms. (Remember that there are just as many centre atoms as corner atoms.) All planes for which this is true (010, 111, and 210 are examples) have $h+k+l$ odd. (Since the coordinates of the centre atom are $\frac{1}{2}\frac{1}{2}\frac{1}{2}$, the phase angle

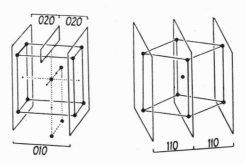

Fig. 124. Planes of body-centred lattice.

$2\pi(hx+ky+lz)$ for this atom is $180°$ when $h+k+l$ is odd.) Therefore, reflections from planes having $h+k+l$ odd are not found in the diffraction pattern of α-iron. On the other hand, all planes such as 110, 200, 310, and 211 which have $h+k+l$ even give strong reflections, because all the atoms lie *on* these planes. (In other words, the phase angle for the centre atom is $0°$ when $h+k+l$ is even.) It is important to note that this is true not only for body-centred cubic crystals but for all other body-centred crystals, whatever their symmetry.

There is another way of realizing the truth of this generalization, which is based on the definition of indices given in Chapter II. The indices $h$, $k$, and $l$ are the numbers of reflecting planes encountered during a journey from one lattice point to another by way of the crystal axes. If we take a journey from the origin to the far corner of the unit cell, passing along cell edges $a$, $b$, and $c$ in turn, the number of planes encountered is $h+k+l$. This is the number of planes crossing the body diagonal of the cell. If $h+k+l$ is even, the body-centre of the cell (half-way along the body diagonal) also lies *on* a plane, which means that waves from the centre atoms are in phase with waves from the corner atom; but if $h+k+l$ is odd, the body-centre of the cell lies half-way between two planes, and this means that waves from the centre atom

PLATE XII

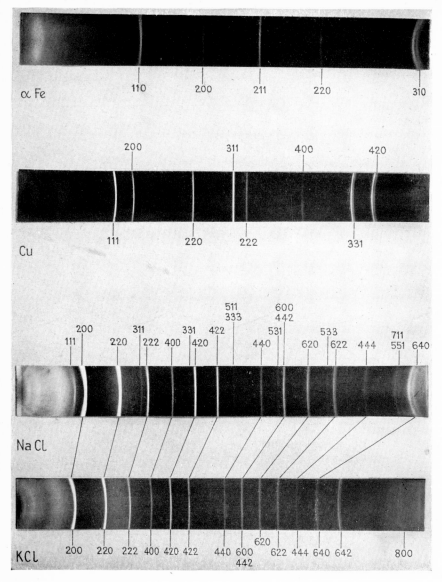

X-ray powder photographs of α iron, copper, sodium chloride, and potassium chloride. The photograph of α iron was taken with cobalt $K\alpha$ radiation, the others with copper $K\alpha$ radiation

are opposite in phase to those from the corner atom, with the result that each cancels the other.

The compound four-atom unit cell of copper is termed 'face-centred'; the cubic unit cell has atoms not only at the corners but also at the centre of each face. If the various planes are examined in the same way as for $\alpha$-iron, it will be seen that in the first place 010 is absent, because the 010 planes (Fig. 125) comprising one corner atom and one of the face-

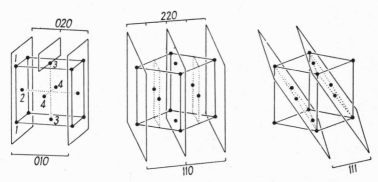

FIG. 125. Planes of face-centred lattice.

centring atoms of each cell (atoms 1 and 2) are interleaved by other planes comprising the other two face-centring atoms of each cell (atoms 3 and 4). For the same reason, 110 is absent. But 111 is strong, and so is 020, because all the atoms lie on these planes. It will be found that all reflections having $h+k$ or $k+l$ or $l+h$ odd are absent, while all planes having $h+k$, $k+l$, and $l+h$ even are present (see Plate XII). The reason can again be seen by counting planes: if we go from the origin to a lattice point at the opposite corner of the $ab$ cell face, the number of reflecting planes encountered is $h+k$; if $h+k$ is even, the atom at the face-centre lies *on* a reflecting plane, and therefore the waves from it are in phase with those from the corner atom, giving a strong reflection; but if $h+k$ is odd, the atom at the face-centre lies half-way between the reflecting planes, and waves from it cancel out the waves from the corner atoms. The same is true for the other faces of the cell, and so all reflections having $k+l$ or $l+h$ odd are also absent. It is easier to remember that the only reflections present are those whose indices are either all even or all odd—for example, 111, 200, 220, 311. This again is true for all cells which are centred on all three faces, irrespective of symmetry.

In the examples just given, one atom is associated with each lattice point, and the lattice points have been chosen for convenience at the centres of these atoms. But the rules are equally true for crystals in which there are several atoms associated with each lattice point; this will be evident when it is remembered that lattice points are defined as those points which have identical surroundings. In such circumstances we must think (in the case of the body-centred lattice) of the combined diffracted wave from the group of atoms associated with the corner lattice point being cancelled by the combined diffracted wave from the identical group of atoms associated with the centre lattice point, for reflections having $h+k+l$ odd.

The recognition of simple or body-centred or face-centred lattices is

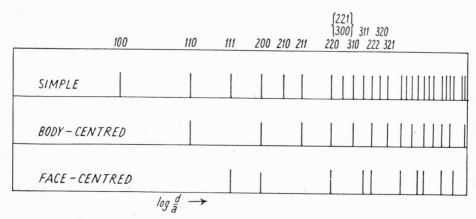

Fig. 126.  Powder patterns of simple, body-centred, and face-centred cubic crystals.

thus quite straightforward. Indeed, for many cubic crystals of elements and binary compounds it is obvious by mere inspection of the powder photograph, provided enough reflections are registered. The grouping of reflections in each of the three types of diffraction pattern is illustrated in Fig. 126: a crystal with a simple cubic lattice gives an X-ray powder pattern like that of ammonium chloride, in which the arcs are regularly spaced up to the sixth, after which there is one gap (because 7 is not a possible value for $h^2+k^2+l^2$); body-centred crystals give patterns in which the regular spacing is maintained beyond the sixth arc; face-centred crystals give the grouping shown in the copper pattern (Plate XII)—two arcs fairly close together (111 and 200), then a gap to the third (220), a similar gap to the fourth (311), and the fifth (222) close to the fourth.

The face-centred cubic lattice is very common. Many metallic elements crystallize in this form; so also do many binary compounds such as alkali halides and the oxides of divalent metals. Thus the powder photograph of sodium chloride (Plate XII) shows the same grouping of arcs as that of copper. Note, however (this is something of a digression, but a useful one at this stage), that while the arcs of copper are all strong, some of those of sodium chloride are much weaker than others. The reason is, of course, to be found in the existence of two types of ion of different diffracting powers, placed in a particular position in relation to each other: in addition to the face-centred lattice formed by the chlorine ions (Fig. 127), there is an equal number of sodium ions which

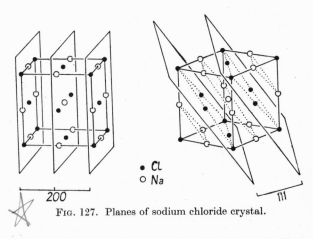

● Cl
○ Na

200                                                          111

Fig. 127.  Planes of sodium chloride crystal.

lie along the edges and in the centre of the cell, always half-way between chlorine ions (forming, by themselves, another face-centred lattice); and these naturally affect the intensities of the reflections. Thus, for the 111 reflection, waves from all the chlorine ions are in phase with each other, but since there are planes of sodium ions midway between the planes of chlorine ions, the waves from the sodium ions oppose those from the chlorine ions and thus weaken the reflection (the diffracting power of sodium being half that of chlorine). On the other hand, all the ions lie *on* the 200 planes, and all the waves therefore co-operate to give a strong reflection. For such reasons, all reflections with odd indices are weak, while those with even indices are strong; that this is so may be seen in Plate XII. Such effects are still more marked in the powder photograph of potassium chloride which is also shown in Plate XII—so much so that the odd type reflections are absent altogether, and the pattern looks like that of a *simple* cubic cell with an edge half the true length. The reason for the complete absence of the odd type reflections is that the diffracting power of the potassium ion is almost exactly equal to that of the chlorine ion, since both ions contain the same number of electrons ($K^+$ 19—1, $Cl^-$ 17+1). The X-ray photograph is in a way misleading, since it appears to indicate a simple cubic cell containing only one atom; but we know, of course, from chemical evidence that there are two sorts of ions, and in view of this the absence of the odd type reflections is really a striking demonstration of the equality of the diffracting powers of $K^+$ and $Cl^-$ and of the effect of ionic positions on the intensities of X-ray reflections.

The three types of lattice which have been mentioned—simple (or primitive), body-centred, and face-centred—are the only ones possible in the cubic system.

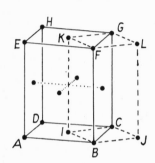

FIG. 128. To a primitive tetragonal lattice $ABCDEFGH$ add extra lattice points at the facecentres. The new lattice is equivalent to the body-centred lattice $BJCIFLGK$.

Note that a lattice centred on one pair of opposite faces, or two pairs, would not have cubic symmetry (the essential elements of which are the four threefold axes running diagonally through the cell). If the possibilities in the other crystal systems are examined, it will be found that there are fourteen kinds of lattice in all. This was first recognized by Bravais in 1848, and the different types are therefore often referred to as 'the fourteen Bravais space-lattices'. Certain kinds of lattice which at first thought might be expected to exist will on examination be found either to have the wrong symmetry or to be equivalent to other kinds. For instance, in the tetragonal system there is no face-centred lattice: if to a simple tetragonal lattice we add extra lattice points at the centres of the faces (Fig. 128), the lattice so formed will be found to have a body-centred unit cell with a square base whose edges are $1/\sqrt{2}$ times the length of those of the original cell. All the fourteen types of lattice are illustrated in Fig. 129.

All body-centred crystals, whatever their symmetry, can give only reflections having $h+k+l$ even, and all face-centred crystals, whatever their symmetry, can give only reflections having either all odd or all even indices. The only additional type of lattice encountered in noncubic crystals is the lattice centred on one face only. If it is the 001 face which is centred, it can easily be seen (by reasoning similar to that used in the foregoing pages) that all reflections having $h+k$ odd must be absent, but that reflections having $k+l$ or $l+h$ odd may be present, provided that $h+k$ is even. Thus 210, 012, 121, and 122 are all absent, because $h+k$ is odd in each case, but 110, 112, and 312 may be present because $h+k$ is even; the values of $k+l$ and $l+h$ do not matter as far as the compound nature of the lattice is concerned.

In referring to the symmetries of atomic arrangements, concise

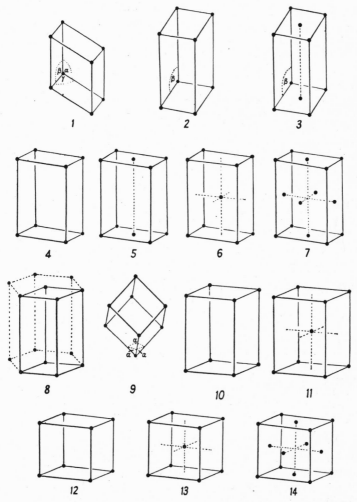

Fig. 129. The fourteen Bravais space-lattices. 1, Triclinic ($P$). 2–3, Monoclinic ($P$ and $C$). 4–7, Orthorhombic ($P$, $C$, $I$, and $F$). 8, Hexagonal ($P$). 9, Rhombohedral ($R$). 10–11, Tetragonal ($P$ and $I$). 12–14, Cubic ($P$, $I$, and $F$).

symbols (similar to those of the point-groups—see Chapter II) are used. In a set of symbols characterizing a space-group, the first is always a capital letter which indicates whether the lattice is simple ($P$ for primitive), body-centred ($I$ for inner), side-centred ($A$, $B$, or $C$), or centred on

all faces (*F*). For the rhombohedral lattice the special letter *R* is used.
In the old *Internationale Tabellen* (1935) the letters *C* and *H* were used
for hexagonal crystals. *C* was used because a hexagonal lattice can be
regarded as an orthorhombic lattice centred on the *c* face (Fig. 130);
but this has now been abandoned in the *International Tables* of 1952,
and *P* is used. The letter *H* referred to a larger cell containing three
lattice points (Fig. 130); it was given for certain space-groups in order
that the secondary axes of symmetry (twofold axes perpendicular to the
sixfold axis) should lie parallel to
unit cell edges, not between them;
but this also has been abandoned,
and all hexagonal lattices are described simply by the letter *P*. This
welcome change makes for simplicity and uniformity. From the
structural point of view it does not
matter that in certain space-groups
the secondary twofold axes are not
parallel to unit cell edges. In structure determination it is simplest to
use the smallest unit cell consistent
with the principal symmetry type,
transforming the indices of reflections if necessary, as described in
Appendix 5.

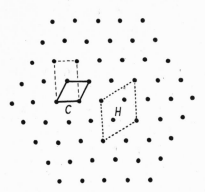

Fig. 130. Alternative cell-bases formerly
used for hexagonal crystals.

The types of absent reflections so far mentioned are those arising
from the compound nature of certain lattices; it is important to note
that a compound lattice causes systematic absences throughout the
whole range of reflections. These are not the only types of systematic
absences; certain other types, which may occur in addition to, or instead
of, those already mentioned, are due to certain types of symmetry in
atomic arrangements. These will be described in the following sections;
for the moment all we need note is that these symmetry elements cause
absences only throughout particular principal zones of reflections, or
among the various orders of reflection from a particular principal plane;
thus they do not affect the determination of the lattice type from the
X-ray diffraction pattern, which is done by examining the list of
reflections for any systematic absences throughout the whole range
of reflections.

The first stage in the determination of the structure of a crystal—
the discovery of the lattice type—is thus quite simple and straight-

forward. In this chapter we will proceed with the story of the further stages in the elucidation of crystal structures in general; but some of the simpler structures can be solved completely by a determination of the lattice type, with perhaps a very limited consideration of the intensities of a few reflections; examples of such structures are given at the beginning of Chapter IX.

**The symmetries of atomic arrangements. Point-groups and space-groups.** Crystals consist of groups of atoms repeated regularly in space. A crystal structure may be imagined as being built up by assembling a particular group of atoms, and then repeating the same grouping in exactly the same orientation at regular intervals in space. The smallest group from which the whole crystal may be constructed in this way is the unit of pattern. Each such group may be regarded as associated with a lattice point; in other words, we mentally replace a group of atoms by a symbolic point. In the previous section the various possible arrangements (both simple and compound) of such lattice points have been mentioned. We now have to consider the arrangement of atoms round each lattice point and the effect of the arrangement on the X-ray diffraction pattern. In speaking of the symmetries of the arrangement of atoms round a lattice point it is customary to use the term 'point-group', and for the symmetries of the complete arrangement in the crystal the term 'space-group'.

Consider first a few of the possible ways of arranging atoms round a point, ignoring crystal structure for the moment and thinking of groups of atoms in isolation. For this purpose we cannot do better than to recall the structures of a few simple molecules and ions. Fig. 131 is a gallery of simple types. (It should be noted that in these drawings the spheres mark the positions of atomic centres; the effective external radii of the atoms are much larger.)

The *trans* form of 1,2 dichlorethylene ClHC=CHCl (Brockway, Beach, and Pauling, 1935) has a single plane of symmetry $(m)$ passing through all the atoms, a twofold axis (symbol 2) normal to this plane and, arising out of this combination, a centre of symmetry; the symmetry of this molecule $(2/m)$ is the same as that of a crystal belonging to the holohedral class of the monoclinic system.

In the carbonate ion $CO_3^-$ (W. L. Bragg, 1914, 1924 $a$) the three oxygen atoms lie at the corners of an equilateral triangle, at the centre of which the carbon atom is situated. The ion has a plane of symmetry $(m)$ passing through all the atoms, and a threefold axis (3) normal to this plane and passing through the carbon atom; this combination is

more concisely described as a hexagonal inversion axis ($\bar{6}$). There are
also three planes of symmetry intersecting in the threefold axis, and
three twofold axes of symmetry, each passing through the carbon atom

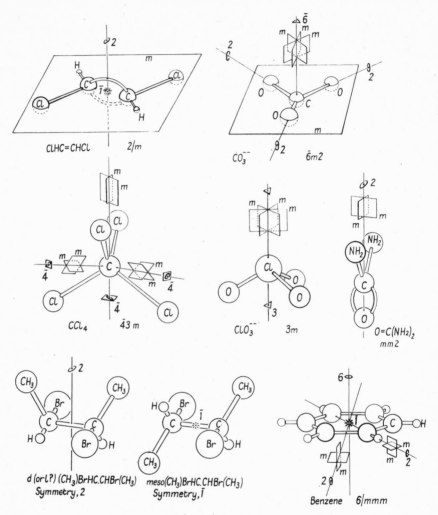

FIG. 131. The symmetries of some simple molecules and ions.

and one oxygen atom. The conventional point-group symbol is $\bar{6}m2$
(though $\bar{6}m$ would be a sufficient description).

In the chlorate ion $ClO_3^-$ the three oxygen atoms form an equilateral
triangle, but the chlorine atom is not in the plane of this triangle
(Dickinson and Goodhue, 1921; Zachariasen, 1929); the whole ion has

a threefold axis with three planes of symmetry intersecting in this axis, like the carbonate ion, but lacks the three twofold axes and the plane of symmetry perpendicular to the threefold axis; its point-group symbol is $3m$.

The urea molecule $O=C(NH_2)_2$ has two planes of symmetry intersecting in a single twofold axis—the symmetry found in crystals belonging to the polar class of the orthorhombic system (Hendricks, 1928 $a$); the point-group symbol is $mm2$.

Molecules of the meso form of 2,3 dibromobutane $Br(CH_3)HC$—$CH(CH_3)Br$ have a centre of symmetry ($\bar{1}$) as their only element of symmetry† (Stevenson and Schomaker, 1939), resembling in this respect crystals belonging to the holohedral class of the triclinic system. It is worth noting that the $d$ and $l$ isomers are not asymmetric; they possess one twofold axis.†

The benzene molecule (Pauling and Brockway, 1934) has a sixfold axis of rotation, together with all the additional symmetry elements possessed by a crystal belonging to the holohedral hexagonal class $6/mmm$.

Finally, the carbon tetrachloride molecule $CCl_4$ has its chlorine atoms arranged tetrahedrally round the carbon atom (Pauling and Brockway, 1934); it has four threefold axes, each passing through the carbon atom and one chlorine atom, three mutually perpendicular fourfold inversion axes which bisect the Cl—C—Cl angles, and six planes of symmetry, each passing through one carbon atom and two chlorine atoms; but it has no fourfold rotation axes or centre of symmetry. The point-group symmetry is that of the tetrahedral class of the cubic system $\bar{4}3m$.

Before considering the placing of point-groups in space-lattices it must be observed that the pattern-unit of which a crystal is built up—the group of atoms associated with each lattice point—is by no means always a single molecule or a pair of ions; more often than not, two or three or four, or perhaps even more, molecules form the pattern-unit. These molecules are often arranged in such a way that the group exhibits some of the symmetry elements already mentioned. There are many ways of grouping molecules round a point; and the general problem confronting those who wish to catalogue all the possible point-groups is to think of all the possible ways of attaining symmetry of one type or another by arranging asymmetric objects round a point. Thus two

† In the gas or liquid, the two halves of these molecules rotate, with respect to each other, round the C—C bond as axis; the remarks on symmetry refer to the most stable configuration, that in which the molecule spends most of its time.

identical asymmetric molecules may be related (Fig. 132) by an axis of symmetry; and two enantiomorphous molecules may be related by a plane of symmetry or a centre of symmetry. Larger numbers of molecules may be arranged to attain higher symmetries. The number of possible symmetries of isolated groups of atoms is unlimited; but we are concerned here only with those symmetries which can also exist in repeating space-patterns; and, as we have already seen, this restricts us to those arrangements having two-, three-, four-, or sixfold axes. There are only thirty-two different symmetry combinations (point-groups) which fulfil these conditions— thirty-two, including the asymmetric case in which only one object is used. This number is the same as the number of crystal classes; in fact, the various possible symmetries of molecules or groups of molecules correspond with the various types of crystal shape which are catalogued in Chapter II; the problem of arranging different types of atoms round a point is formally the same as that of arranging

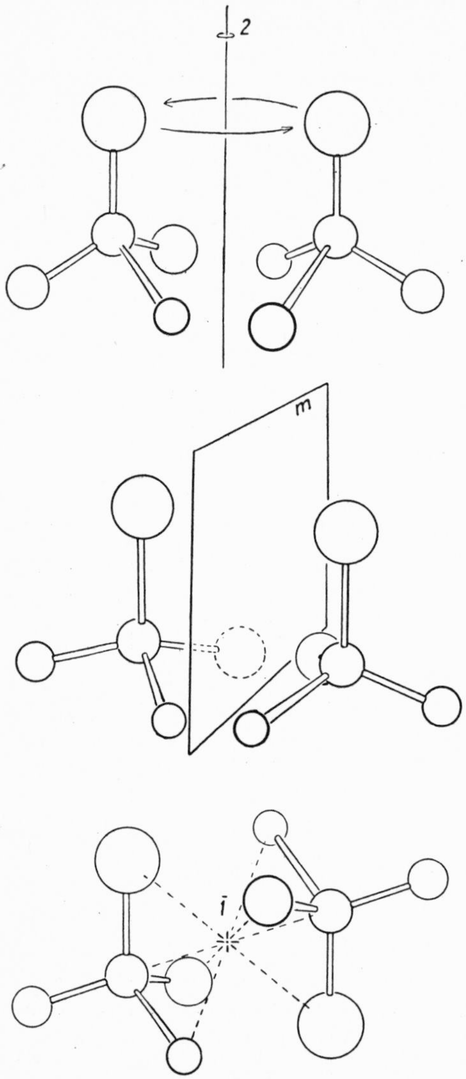

Fig. 132. Arrangements of two asymmetric molecules.

different types of crystal faces round a point.

We have now to think of the possible ways of placing the various types of atomic arrangement in the various types of lattices. Suppose a molecule having certain symmetries is to be associated with each point of a particular space-lattice. The first thing to realize is that the molecule can only be placed in a lattice having the appropriate symmetry—if both molecule and lattice are to retain their original symmetries. Thus a molecule of tetrahedral symmetry such as tin tetra-iodide (Dickinson, 1923) fits appropriately into a cubic lattice, the threefold axes of the molecule lying along the threefold axes of the cubic lattice; and the molecule of s-triazine

which has symmetry $\bar{6}m2$, fits appropriately into a crystal structure having the same symmetry (Wheatley, 1955). But to put a molecule of hexagonal symmetry in a triclinic space-lattice would seem like sheer waste of good symmetry; and since the forces between neighbouring molecules would not be hexagonally disposed, there would be a tendency for all the molecules to distort each other. How much effect this would have would depend on the rigidity of the molecule in relation to the forces around it tending to distort it. Structures of this kind, in which molecules are apparently inappropriately placed, are, however, not uncommon. In fact, the state of affairs just mentioned—a molecule of hexagonal symmetry in a triclinic lattice—actually occurs in the crystal of hexamethylbenzene. In this crystal the rigidity of the molecule is such that no distortion has been detected, but the tendency to distortion must be there. The point is that, from the formal point of view, the molecules in the crystal do *not* possess hexagonal symmetry; the only symmetry element they possess is the only one possible in a triclinic lattice—a centre of symmetry. The reason why hexamethylbenzene molecules arrange themselves to form a triclinic crystal is, no doubt, that intermolecular forces and the requirements of good packing are satisfied better by a triclinic arrangement than they would be by a hexagonal or any other arrangement; though it is difficult to see just why this is so. (See Mack, 1932.) It very frequently happens that some of the symmetry elements possessed by free molecules are not utilized in the formation of crystalline arrangements,† though the neglect is not often so striking as in hexamethylbenzene.

† Note also that non-crystallographic symmetries in molecules are inevitably ignored; thus, in gaseous cyclopentane the molecule may have a fivefold axis (Pauling and Brockway, 1937); this could not be retained in a crystal—in other words, there would be a tendency to distortion.

Conversely, a molecule of low symmetry cannot by itself form the pattern-unit of a crystal of high symmetry. If identical asymmetric molecules were placed singly at the corners of a cell of orthorhombic shape, the result would necessarily be that the asymmetrically disposed forces between the molecules would distort the cell and make it triclinic. The only way of making an orthorhombic crystal out of asymmetric molecules is to group at least four of them together to form a pattern-unit having the symmetry appropriate to the orthorhombic lattice. For instance (confining our attention for the moment to the symmetry elements so far mentioned), two left-handed and two right-handed molecules might be arranged so that the group exhibits two planes of symmetry at right angles to each other (with, arising out of this, a twofold axis at their intersection)—that is, point-group symmetry $mm2$; or four left-handed molecules might be arranged so that the group exhibits three mutually perpendicular twofold axes—that is, point-group symmetry 222. Such groups could be placed at the points of an orthorhombic lattice without changing the symmetry of either the groups or the lattice; they must, of course, be oriented correctly, with twofold axes parallel to cell edges and planes of symmetry parallel to cell faces. These remarks apply to asymmetric molecules; naturally, if molecules themselves possess some symmetry, fewer of them may be required to form an arrangement of particular point-group symmetry, provided that the natural symmetries of the molecules are utilized.

Thus, each of the thirty-two point-groups must be placed, correctly oriented, in a lattice having appropriate symmetry. Bearing in mind the existence of compound lattices having the same symmetries as simple ones, we realize that the number of arrangements possible on this basis is considerably greater than thirty-two.

But this does not end the tale of possible arrangements. Hitherto we have considered only those symmetry operations which carry us from one atom in the crystal to another associated with the same lattice point—the symmetry operations (rotation, reflection, or inversion through a point) which by continued repetition always bring us back to the atom from which we started. These are the point-group symmetries which were already familiar to us in crystal shapes. Now in many space-patterns two additional types of symmetry operations can be discerned—types which involve translation and therefore do not occur in point-groups or crystal shapes.

**Symmetry elements involving translation.** These elements are the glide plane, which involves simultaneous reflection and translation,

and the screw axis, which involves simultaneous rotation and translation. By continued repetition of these symmetry operations we do not
arrive back at the atom from which we started; we arrive at the
corresponding atom associated with the next lattice point, and then the
next, and so on throughout the crystal. These operations will be illustrated first by an isolated molecule—that of polyethylene (Fig. 133), a

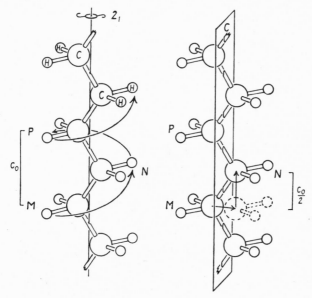

FIG. 133. Left: twofold screw axis. Right: glide plane.

chain polymer molecule so long that it may be regarded for the present
purpose as indefinitely long. This molecule may be constructed in
imagination by repeating a group of two carbon and four hydrogen
atoms—the groups marked $M$ and $N$—over and over again along a
straight line; the distance from any atom to the next similarly situated
atom along the axis—the repeat distance of the molecule—will be
called $c_0$. Some of the symmetries of this molecule are those already
familiar—planes of symmetry, twofold axes, and a centre of symmetry;
these are not marked on the pictures. But now consider how it is
possible to move group $M$ into the position of $N$, and $N$ into the position
of $P$, and so on. One way (Fig. 133, left) is to imagine group $M$ rotated
round the $c$ axis for half a revolution and at the same time moved along
this axis for a distance of $\frac{1}{2}c_0$; in this way we arrive at the next $CH_2$
group $N$; if we repeat the process, we arrive at the next $CH_2$ group $P$,
and so on. Thus, two repetitions of the operation bring us, not to the

original group $M$, but to the next corresponding group along the axis of the molecule. The term 'screw axis' aptly describes the process, and the accepted symbol for this symmetry element is $2_1$.

Another way of going in imagination from group $M$ to groups $N$ and $P$ is (Fig. 133, right) to imagine group $M$ reflected in the plane marked $c$ (at right angles to the plane containing the carbon atoms) and then moved along the molecular axis a distance of $\frac{1}{2}c_0$; this brings us to group $N$, and another repetition of the process brings us to group $P$. This symmetry element is appropriately called the glide plane, and the accepted symbol for it is an italic letter—in this case $c$—indicating the direction along which translation occurs.

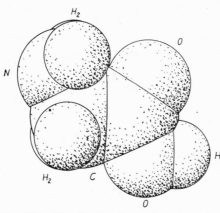

FIG. 134. The effective shape of the molecule of glycine, $NH_2.CH_2.COOH$.

Screw axes and glide planes are of great importance. In molecular crystals the molecules are usually related to each other by these symmetry elements rather than by rotation axes or reflection planes; the reason is presumably that, since atoms are more or less spherical in shape, and when linked by covalent bonds are partly merged in each other, a molecule is a rather knobbly object (Fig. 134) and there is a tendency for the knobs of one molecule to fit into the hollows of its neighbours—an arrangement which is likely to give rise to screw axes, glide planes, or centres of symmetry rather than to rotation axes or reflection planes. (The latter would bring knobs in opposition to each other—see Fig. 132.) An example of a crystal structure exhibiting twofold screw axes and glide planes—the structure of benzoquinone (Robertson, 1935 $a$)—is shown in Fig. 135. Molecule $M$ can be moved into the position of $P$ either by rotation round the screw axis $S_1$ and translation half-way along $b$, or by reflection in the glide plane $G_1$ and translation half-way along $a$. (Note that these symmetry elements do not occur singly; the existence of the screw axes $S_1$ automatically gives rise to $S_2$, $S_3$, and $S_4$, half-way between them; and the glide plane $G_1$ is inevitably accompanied by another, $G_2$, at a distance $\frac{1}{2}b$ from it.) Other examples will be found later in this book—notably the structure of durene, Fig. 142. The arrangement of polyethylene molecules in crystals of that substance (Fig. 136) is also worth studying. Note that not only is the twofold screw axis possessed by a single molecule retained in the crystalline arrangement, but also there are twofold screw axes relating the molecules to each other; there are three sets of such twofold screw axes, one set parallel to each unit cell axis. Perpendicular to the $b$ axis

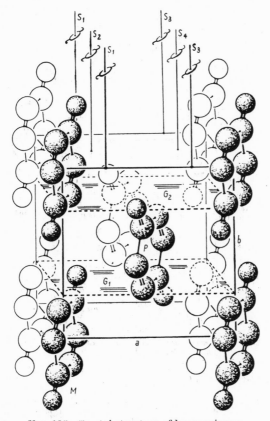

Fig. 135. Crystal structure of benzoquinone.

are glide planes, the translation being $\frac{1}{2}a$ (symbol $a$). In addition to these there is another set of glide planes perpendicular to the $a$ axis, but the translation is not simply along an axis but along the $bc$ diagonal; a special symbol $n$ is used for such glide planes involving a translation half-way along the diagonal of a cell face. There are also planes of symmetry, but not all the planes of symmetry possessed by a single molecule are retained in the crystal; those perpendicular to $c$ (the long axis of the molecule) are retained, but the plane of symmetry parallel

to the long axis of a single molecule is ignored in the crystal arrangement—in fact, formally speaking, the molecule in the crystal no longer
has a plane of symmetry parallel to its length.

A twofold screw axis has no left- or right-handed sense of helical
movement, since rotation through 180° to the left brings us to the
same place as rotation through 180° to the right. But some threefold,

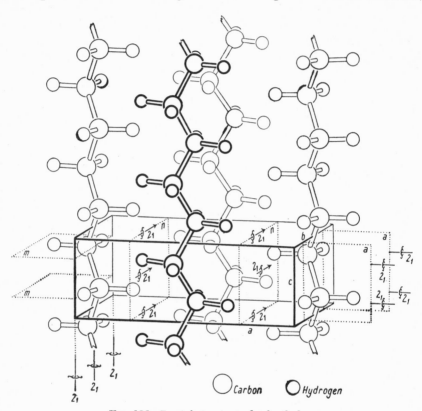

FIG. 136. Crystal structure of polyethylene.

fourfold, and sixfold screw axes may be either left- or right-handed.
This is illustrated in Figs. 137–9, which also show in a formal way the
other types of symmetry axes which may be found in trigonal, tetragonal,
and hexagonal crystals. The symbols such as $6_1$ and $4_3$ have this significance: the main figure gives the amount of rotation and the subscript
the translation. Thus, $6_1$ means a rotation of one-sixth of a turn combined with a translation of one-sixth the length of the $c$ axis, the spiral
motion being such as to give rise to a right-handed screw; $6_5$ means a
rotation of one-sixth of a turn in the same direction combined with a

translation of $5c/6$ which amounts to the same thing as $c/6$ in the opposite direction, the result being that $6_5$ is a left-handed screw, the mirror image of $6_1$. Similarly, $4_3$ is the mirror image of $4_1$, and $3_2$ the mirror image of $3_1$.

The inversion axes $\bar{3}$, $\bar{4}$, and $\bar{6}$ (also shown in Figs. 137–9) have the

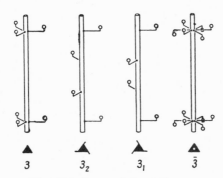

FIG. 137. Types of threefold axes.

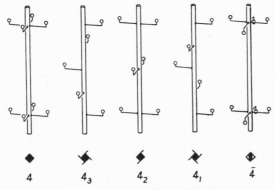

FIG. 138. Types of fourfold axes.

same significance as in morphology; thus $\bar{3}$ means rotation through one-third of a turn combined with inversion through a point.

The only other symmetry element involving translation which remains to be mentioned is the glide plane having a translation of one-quarter of a cell-face diagonal; this type of glide, symbolized $d$, is found only in a few space-groups.

**Effects of screw axes and glide planes on X-ray diffraction patterns.** The existence in a crystal of screw axes or glide planes is necessarily not revealed by the shape of the crystal, since the shape of a polyhedron cannot exhibit symmetry elements possessing translation.

Shape-symmetry may tell us that a particular crystal has a fourfold axis, but it cannot tell us whether this axis is a simple rotation axis or a screw axis. Nor is it possible by examining the shape of a crystal to distinguish between a reflection plane and a glide plane. But X-ray diffraction patterns do make such distinctions, and in a very straight-forward manner: just as it is possible to detect compound ('centred') lattices by noticing the absence of certain types of reflections (p. 233), so also it is possible to detect screw axes and glide planes, for the presence of atoms or groups of atoms related by translations which

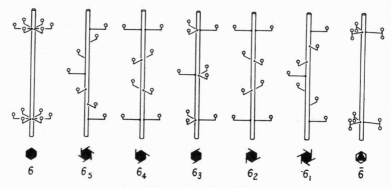

FIG. 139. Types of sixfold axes.

are simple submultiples of a unit cell edge (one-half, one-third, one-quarter, or one-sixth) necessarily causes the absence of particular types of reflections.

Consider, for instance, first of all the twofold screw axis and its effect on X-ray beams reflected by the crystal plane perpendicular to the screw axis. The first-order reflection 001 would be produced when waves from atomic plane $MM'$ (Fig. 140) are one wavelength ahead of waves from atomic plane $PP'$; but, exactly half-way between these planes is an exactly similar sheet of atoms $NN'$, waves from which would be half a wavelength ahead of those from $PP'$ and thus of exactly opposite phase (and, of course, equal amplitude). Waves from atomic planes $NN'$, $QQ'$, and so on evidently cancel out those from $MM'$, $PP'$, etc., and the resultant intensity of the 001 reflection is zero. There may be other atoms in the crystal, formally independent of those just mentioned; but since any other atoms in the crystal are also related to each other by the screw axes, the same conclusion is valid. The second-order reflection 002, however, is produced when waves from $MM'$ are two wavelengths ahead of those from $PP'$, and when this occurs, waves from $NN'$ are one wavelength ahead of those from $PP'$ and therefore in phase with them; the reflection 002 is therefore not cancelled. Similarly, all odd-order reflections from this plane are bound to be absent, while all even-order reflections may be present; in fact, the spacing along the $c$ axis appears to be halved, since if we observed only

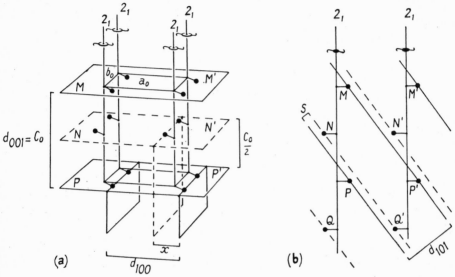

Fig. 140. Twofold screw axes. Effect on X-ray reflections.

the different orders of 00$l$, we should call the first reflection 001 and thus be led to suppose that the $c$ axis has a length half the true value which is obtained when the first reflection is given its true indices 002.

For all other crystal planes there are no simple phase relations between waves from $M$ and those from $N$, and therefore no further systematic absences. Thus, the distance $x$ of the atoms from the screw axis in the direction of the $a$ axis is not, except by accident, a submultiple of $a_0$, and therefore there are no systematic absences of $h00$ reflections. One or two of these may not appear on the photograph because the structure amplitudes happen to be very small; but the point is that there are no *systematic* absences. The same is true for all other planes—101 for instance (Fig. 140 $b$), since the distance $s$ between such a plane of atoms as $NQ'$ and the plane through $P$ is not, except by accident, a simple submultiple of the spacing $d_{101}$.

Thus the only systematic absences caused by a twofold screw axis are the odd orders of reflection from the plane perpendicular to the screw axis.

In a similar way, in a crystal exhibiting a threefold screw axis $3_1$ or $3_2$, identical atoms are repeated on planes spaced one-third the length of the axis; therefore the reflections from the plane normal to the screw axis would, by themselves, appear to indicate a repeat distance only one-third the true axial length. The first of these reflections would be the third-order reflection in reference to the true repeat distance, while the second would be actually the sixth-order reflection. In other words, a threefold screw axis $3_1$ or $3_2$ causes the absence of the first and second orders of reflection from the plane perpendicular to the screw axis, as well as the fourth and fifth and indeed all orders not divisible by 3. When a fourfold screw axis $4_1$ or $4_3$ is present, all orders not divisible by 4 are absent, while a sixfold screw axis $6_1$ or $6_5$ cancels all but the sixth, twelfth, and other orders divisible by 6. Throughout, the only crystal plane whose reflections are affected in this way is the plane perpendicular to the screw axis.

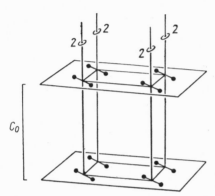

FIG. 141. Ordinary twofold axes. No systematic absences of reflections.

No such absences occur when the axes of symmetry are simple rotation axes; thus in Fig. 141 there are no subdivisions of the $c$ axis and therefore no absences of $00l$ reflections.

Glide planes are more devastating in their effects on X-ray reflections; they cause absences among a whole zone of reflections. Consider the structure of durene, 1, 2, 4, 5 tetramethylbenzene (Robertson, 1933 $b$).

$$CH_3 \quad \quad CH_3$$
$$CH_3 \quad \quad CH_3$$

The unit cell is monoclinic and contains two molecules, and the space-group is $P2_1/a$. The two molecules are related to each other by a glide plane perpendicular to the $b$ axis and having a translation of $a/2$. Consider first Fig. 142 $a$, which is a view looking straight down the $b$ axis. In this representation it can be seen that molecule $B$ is differently oriented from molecule $A$; in order to move $B$ into the position of $A$ it would be necessary to reflect it in the plane of the paper and move it half-way along the $a$ axis. But now consider Fig. 142 $b$, in which only the positions of atomic centres are shown; molecules $A$ and $B$ now look exactly the same; in fact, it looks as if the unit cell has an $a$ axis only half the true

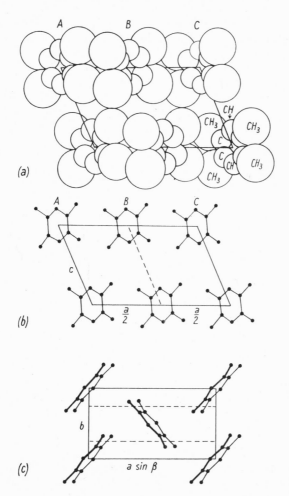

FIG. 142. Crystal structure of durene, 1, 2, 4, 5 tetramethylbenzene. ($a$) As seen when looking straight down the $b$ axis. ($b$) The same; but only the positions of atomic centres are marked. ($c$) As seen when looking straight down the $c$ axis.

length. It is the atomic coordinates in this projection which settle the intensities of the $h0l$ reflections; hence the only $h0l$ reflections present are those which would be given by the half-sized apparent unit cell—reflections for which the true $h$ is even. (Reflections having $h$ odd are those for which the phase-difference of waves from molecules $A$ and $C$

is an odd number of wavelengths; but in these circumstances the phase-difference of waves from $A$ and $B$ is an odd number of *half* wavelengths; hence waves from $B$ cancel waves from $A$. All reflections having $h$ odd are therefore absent.) From all other viewpoints, such as the $c$ projection, Fig. 142 $c$, the $a$ axis does *not* appear to be halved, and therefore there are no systematic absences in any zone other than $h0l$. The only other systematic absences are the odd orders of $0k0$, owing to the two-fold screw axis along $b$.

In some crystals there is a glide plane $n$ having a translation, not along an axis, but half-way along a face-diagonal of the cell. In fact, the same

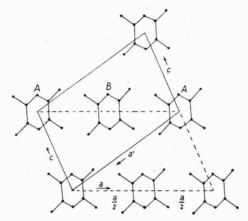

FIG. 143. Crystal structure of durene, showing alternative unit cell $a'c$ having symmetry $P2_1/n$.

crystal that we have already described as having the space-group symmetry $P2_1/a$ could alternatively be described by a different cell $a'c$ (Fig. 143) having the symmetry $P2_1/n$, one molecule being derived from the other by reflecting in the glide plane and translating half-way along the diagonal of the $a'c$ plane. If, as before, we look along the $b$ axis, we see molecule $B$ looking exactly the same as $A$ but translated half-way along the $a'c$ diagonal; in other words, the projected cell seen from this viewpoint appears to be centred, and thefore all reflections from $h0l$ planes having $h+l$ odd (for example, 100, 001, 102, 201, 302, 203, and so on) must be absent. These are the only systematic zone absences, since from all other viewpoints there is no apparent centring. These absent reflections are of course the same as in the first description of the cell; they are merely denoted by different indices, 101 of $P2_1/a$ being $20\bar{1}$ of $P2_1/n$, and $\bar{1}01$ of $P2_1/a$ being 001 of $P2_1/n$; and so on.

In a similar way a glide plane normal to the $c$ axis of a crystal having a translation of one-quarter of the $ab$ diagonal (symbolized $d$) nullifies all $hk0$ reflections except those for which $h+k$ is divisible by 4.

In some hexagonal, tetragonal, and cubic space groups there are glide planes which are not normal to cell edges; they are normal to the diagonals of cell faces. Glide planes of this type, normal to the diagonals of the 001 cell face and having a translation of $c/2$, cause all $hhl$ reflections with $l$ odd (for example 223) to be absent.

Ordinary reflection planes $m$ cannot be detected in this way because they cause no systematic absences; thus when two molecules related by a reflection plane are seen from a direction normal to the reflection plane, one molecule is exactly eclipsed by the other; there is no apparent halving of an axis or a diagonal, and therefore there are no systematic absences due to a plane of symmetry.

Thus, while screw axes and glide planes can be detected and distinguished from each other by observing which types of reflections are absent, ordinary rotation axes and reflection planes cannot be detected in this way, since neither type leads to any systematic absences of reflections.

The presence of symmetry elements having translation, together with the lattice type, can always be deduced, as in the above discussion, from first principles. The types of absences and the elements of translation causing them are summarized in Table V. The absences for all

## TABLE V

| Element of translation | Symbol | Absent reflections |
|---|---|---|
| Body-centred lattice | $I$ | $hkl$ with $h+k+l$ odd |
| Lattice centred on 001 face | $C$ | $hkl$ with $h+k$ odd |
| Face-centred lattice (all faces) | $F$ | $hkl$ with $h+k$ or $k+l$ or $l+h$ odd |
| Glide plane $\perp c$, translation $\dfrac{a}{2}$ | $a$ | $hk0$ with $h$ odd |
| ,, $\perp c$, ,, $\dfrac{a+b}{2}$ | $n$ | $hk0$ with $h+k$ odd |
| ,, $\perp c$, ,, $\dfrac{a+b}{4}$ | $d$ | $hk0$ when $h+k$ not divisible by 4 |
| ,, $\perp 110$, ,, $\dfrac{c}{2}$ | $c$ | $hhl$ when $h$ odd |
| Twofold screw axis $\parallel c$ | $2_1$ | $00l$ with $l$ odd |
| Threefold ,, ,, ,, | $3_1, 3_2$ | $00l$ when $l$ not divisible by 3 |
| Fourfold ,, ,, ,, | $4_1, 4_3$ | $00l$ when $l$ not divisible by 4 |
| ,, ,, ,, ,, | $4_2$ | $00l$ with $l$ odd |
| Sixfold ,, ,, ,, | $6_1, 6_5$ | $00l$ when $l$ not divisible by 6 |
| ,, ,, ,, ,, | $6_2, 6_4$ | $00l$ when $l$ not divisible by 3 |
| ,, ,, ,, ,, | $6_3$ | $00l$ with $l$ odd |

the space-groups are tabulated by Astbury and Yardley (1924), and also in *International Tables for X-ray Crystallography* (1952).

**Diffraction symmetry in relation to point-group symmetry.** So far, in our consideration of the intensities of X-ray reflections in the process of discovering the general arrangement in a crystal, we have dealt only with reflections of zero intensity, and we have seen that when certain types of reflections have zero intensity the presence

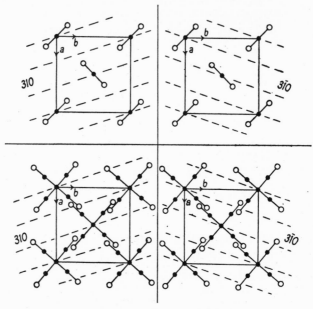

Fig. 144. Above: urea (c projection). 310 and $3\bar{1}0$ planes have the same structure amplitude. Below: penta-erythritol (c projection). 310 and $3\bar{1}0$ planes have different structure amplitudes. Note positions of atoms with respect to planes in each case.

of elements of translation in the structure may be inferred. We now consider in a general way the intensity relations between the reflections which *are* recorded on the photographs, for in certain circumstances the symmetry of the diffraction effects gives some useful information.

The nature of the relation which exists between the symmetry of diffraction effects and that of the crystal may be gathered by consideration of the $hk0$ intensities of two simple tetragonal crystals—urea ($O{=}C(NH_2)_2$), whose point-group symmetry is $\bar{4}2m$, and penta-erythritol ($C(CH_2OH)_4$), belonging to class $\bar{4}$. For urea (see Fig. 144), the intensity of 310 is the same as that of $3\bar{1}0$, as is obvious from the relation of the molecules to the traces of these planes; the equality arises from the fact that the molecular plane is at 45° to the unit cell edges. In penta-erythritol, owing to the fact that the principal molecular planes are not at 45° to the unit cell edges, the relation of the molecules to the 310 planes is quite different from their relation to the $3\bar{1}0$ planes, and therefore the intensity of 310 is very different from that of $3\bar{1}0$. The same is true for the general planes: $hkl$ and $h\bar{k}l$ intensities are the same for urea, but different for penta-erythritol.

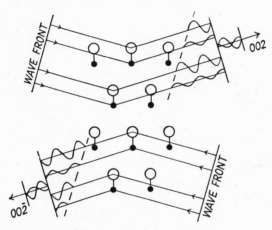

FIG. 145. Reflection of X-rays in opposite directions by a non-centrosymmetric structure. The phase-differences of waves from different atoms are, except in special circumstances, the same for 002 as for $00\bar{2}$; hence the intensities are the same. Hence the symmetry of an X-ray diffraction pattern ('Laue symmetry') is the point-group symmetry of the crystal plus a centre of symmetry.

The planes in penta-erythritol which have corresponding indices, yet give different intensities of X-ray reflections, are just those planes which, as crystal faces, have different rates of growth, since the orientation of the molecules with respect to the crystal planes determines both these properties. Therefore it might be thought that the symmetry of diffraction effects—the symmetry of the reciprocal lattice, if we think of the points of this lattice as each having a 'weight' proportional to the structure amplitude of the corresponding set of crystal planes— is the same as that of the crystal shape, or in other words the point-group symmetry. And so it is, except in one important respect: it is not possible, except in special circumstances, to decide from X-ray diffraction effects whether a crystal has a centre of symmetry or not (Friedel, 1913). In a crystal lacking a centre of symmetry (Fig. 145), the intensity of reflection by a set of crystal planes depends simply on the phase-differences between the waves from different atoms, and these phase-differences are normally just the same for reflection in one direction—002 in the diagram—as they are for reflection in the opposite direction $00\overline{2}$. Therefore the diffraction symmetry of a crystal is normally the point-group symmetry plus a centre of symmetry. Friedel's law has been shown to break down when the wavelength of the X-rays is near that of an absorption edge for some of the atoms in the crystal: there is an anomalous phase-change on diffraction which is not reversed when the direction of reflection is reversed (Coster, Knol, and Prins, 1930; see also Bragg, *The Crystalline State*, p. 93); the consequences of this effect, and the important uses to which it has been put, are discussed later, on p. 261 and p. 400. Except in these very special circumstances, 'Friedel's law' holds, and therefore the diffraction symmetry corresponds with one of the eleven different point-groups which are obtained by adding a centre of symmetry to each of the thirty-two true point-groups (see Table VI).

The diffraction symmetry is strikingly shown in Laue photographs—diffraction patterns produced by sending a beam of X-rays comprising a wide range of wavelengths ('white' X-rays) along a principal axis of a stationary crystal. ('White' X-rays are best obtained from an X-ray tube with a tungsten target, run at 60 kV. If a copper target is used, the characteristic $K$ wavelengths should be removed by an iron filter.) Each crystal plane reflects only those X-rays which have such a wavelength that the Bragg equation is obeyed. Laue photographs of ammonium chloride (cubic) and penta-erythritol (tetragonal) are shown in Plate XIII. Both these crystals have a fourfold axis of symmetry, and the X-ray beam is sent down the fourfold axis in both cases. It is immediately obvious that in ammonium chloride there are apparent planes of symmetry parallel to the fourfold axis, while in penta-erythritol there are not. The conclusions that may be drawn from these patterns are that ammonium chloride (cubic) must belong to one of the point-groups having diffraction symmetry $m3m$ (classes $\overline{4}3m$, 432, and $m3m$), while penta-erythritol must belong to one of the tetragonal classes having diffraction symmetry $4/m$ (classes $4/m$, $\overline{4}$, and 4).

Since the diffraction symmetry is shown so strikingly in Laue photographs, it is often called the 'Laue symmetry'. The information on diffraction symmetry is of course all contained in moving-crystal photographs taken by monochromatic X-rays, provided that reflections with similar indices are separated, as they are in tilted crystal photographs

PLATE XIII

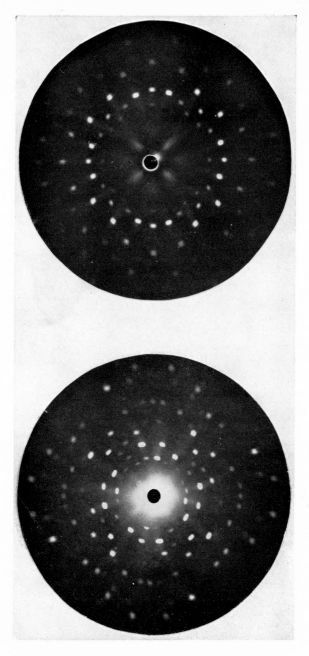

Laue photographs of ammonium chloride (above) and
penta-erythritol (below). X-ray beam along fourfold axis

and moving-film photographs; but Laue photographs show it much more obviously.†

The information obtainable from the Laue symmetry is meagre; it consists simply in the distinction between crystal classes, and then only in the more symmetrical systems—cubic, tetragonal, hexagonal, and trigonal (see Table VI). But it is useful in cases in which morphological features do not give clear evidence on this point.

TABLE VI

| Crystal classes | Laue symmetry |
|---|---|
| Triclinic: 1, $\bar{1}$ | $\bar{1}$ |
| Monoclinic: $m$, 2, $2/m$ | $2/m$ |
| Orthorhombic: $mm2$, 222, $mmm$ | $mmm$ |
| Tetragonal: (a) $\bar{4}$, 4, $4/m$ | $4/m$ |
|         (b) $\bar{4}2m$, $4mm$, 422, $4/mmm$ | $4/mmm$ |
| Trigonal and hexagonal: | |
|       (a) 3, $\bar{3}$ | $\bar{3}$ |
|       (b) $3m$, 32, $\bar{3}m$ | $\bar{3}m$ |
|       (c) $\bar{6}$, 6, $6/m$ | $6/m$ |
|       (d) $\bar{6}m2$, $6mm$, 622, $6/mmm$ | $6/mmm$ |
| Cubic: (a) 23, $m3$ | $m3$ |
|      (b) $\bar{4}3m$, 432, $m3m$ | $m3m$ |

We return now to the breakdown of 'Friedel's law' which occurs when a wavelength is used which is near that of an absorption edge for certain atoms in a non-centrosymmetric crystal. This phenomenon is due to an anomalous phase displacement of the waves scattered by the atoms in question. In normal scattering, the phase of the reflected wave in a Bragg reflection is 90° in advance of the incident wave, but when all the atoms in the crystal are the same or when the incident wavelength is far from those of the absorption edges of all the atoms, this phase-shift can be ignored because all the scattered waves are affected in exactly the same way. When, however, the incident wavelength is a little shorter than that of the absorption edge of one type of atom, the advance of the scattered wave from this atom is more than 90°. In effect, therefore, the wave scattered by the excited atom is advanced with respect to those from atoms which are scattering normally. The effect of this on the amplitude of the combined scattered

† Laue photographs were formerly much used in structure determination, especially by American workers in the years 1920–30 (for methods, see the books by Wyckoff (1931) and Davey (1934)); but the methods described here, in which monochromatic X-rays are passed through rotating crystals, have important advantages and have superseded the Laue method.

wave is illustrated in Fig. 146, which shows the waves from the same
two-atom non-centrosymmetric structure as in Fig. 145. First of all
(Fig. 146 *a*) the waves are shown as they would be if scattering were
normal for both atoms; in relation to wave *D*, wave *E* is about 120°
in advance for 002; for the opposite reflection 00$\bar{2}$, wave *E* is the same

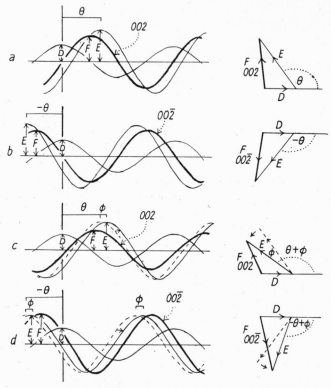

FIG: 146. Anomalous scattering in a non-centrosymmetric crystal. Effect on + and −
reflections. Left: representation of amplitudes and phases of waves. Right: corresponding vector diagrams (scale of amplitudes doubled). *a* and *b*: 002 and 00$\bar{2}$ reflections
of structure of Fig. 145, when scattering is normal for both atoms. *c* and *d*: the same
reflections when scattering is anomalous for atom giving wave *E*.

amount behind (Fig. 146 *b*), but the resulting amplitude of the combined wave (heavily marked) would be the same for both reflections.
Vector representations of the phases and amplitudes are shown on the
right to bring out the point in a different way: the resultant vector $F_{00\bar{2}}$
is the same length as $F_{002}$. In Fig. 146 *c* and *d* are corresponding diagrams when anomalous scattering occurs for *E*. Two effects occur: one
is that the scattering power for *E* is reduced, the other that the phase
of the wave is advanced. The reduction of scattering power would

reduce the intensity of both reflections equally; but the advancement of the wave affects them differently. For 002, since wave $E$ is already 120° in advance of $D$, the further advancement increases the phase-difference and weakens the reflection; but for $00\bar{2}$, since $E$ is 120° behind $D$, the advancement of $E$ brings it more nearly in phase with $D$, and so the reflection is strengthened.

The difference was first demonstrated by Coster, Knol, and Prins (1930) in zinc blende (ZnS) crystals by using the $L\alpha_1$ radiation of gold, which just excites the $K$ electrons of zinc. For a discussion of the anomalous phase displacement, which can be of the order of 10° and therefore produce very appreciable intensity changes, see James (1948), Dauben and Templeton (1955), and Pepinsky (1956).

The effect may obviously be put to good use, for if it is found that opposite reflections $hkl$ and $\bar{h}\bar{k}\bar{l}$ of any crystal are different in intensity (provided, of course, that the intensity difference is not due to trouble-some ordinary absorption effects in an awkwardly shaped crystal), it may be concluded that the crystal lacks a centre of symmetry. In other words, in these favourable circumstances the information obtainable from the symmetry of the diffraction effects is not so restricted as the earlier paragraphs in this section have stated: the diffraction pattern as a whole—the reciprocal lattice—can be non-centrosymmetric, and can thus reveal lack of centrosymmetry in the crystal structure. The application is less restricted than might be supposed, for Peterson (1955) has shown that small but appreciable intensity effects occur even for wavelengths quite far from the absorption edge. An alternative method is to use the 'white' radiation from an ordinary X-ray tube: the streak due to 'white' radiation shows, in the neighbourhood of the absorption edge, the intensity changes which have been described (Grenville-Wells and Lonsdale, 1954).

The anomalous phase-displacement method detects essentially a polar axis; this means that it can detect lack of centrosymmetry in general, for all non-centrosymmetric crystals have polar directions. For instance, although crystal class $\bar{4}$ is not usually referred to as a polar class (for its fourfold axis is not polar), nevertheless, except for the fourfold axis and all directions normal to it, all other directions are polar (see *International Tables*, 1952, p. 43), and the corresponding regions of the reciprocal lattice will therefore show the intensity differences which have been described.

It is important to notice that this method not only reveals polar directions in a crystal structure; it does much more—it determines in an absolute sense the orientation of the polar groups of atoms in the crystal, for the relative intensities of $hkl$ and $\bar{h}\bar{k}\bar{l}$ reflections settle which end of the polar group is towards the $[hkl]$ direction. In this way the investigation of Coster, Knol, and Prins (1930) settled the absolute orientation of the polar groups in zinc blende, ZnS. In this crystal there are alternate layers of zinc and sulphur atoms parallel to the {111} faces with alternate long and short layer spacings Zn.S..Zn.S..; the optically bright faces that give the stronger X-ray reflections have sulphur atoms of the closely spaced pair Zn.S facing outwards, while the dull faces that give the weaker X-ray reflections have the zinc atoms facing outwards. Some further important consequences of this power of determining absolute orientation will appear later (see p. 400).

**Intensity distribution in relation to space-group symmetry.** We have seen that information on space-group symmetry is given by a consideration of the types of absent reflections, and by a recognition of the symmetries shown by the diffraction pattern as a whole. Yet another approach based on the diffraction pattern as a whole (before we proceed to the intensities of individual reflections) is a consideration of the distribution of intensities. First of all, it should be remembered that for any unit cell containing a given set of atoms, the average value of $F^2$ is a constant, whatever the symmetry: it is equal to the sum of the squares of the diffracting powers of the atoms in the cell, $\sum_{j=1}^{n} f_j^2$ (Wilson, 1942 b). (The average value of $F^2$ is often called the 'average intensity', but this term may be misleading, since it is not the measured intensity that is in question, but the value of $F^2$ derived from it when the angle factors and temperature factor are taken out.) Although the average of all the $F^2$ values is the same for crystals of different symmetries, the distribution of magnitudes around the average does depend on the symmetry. For a centrosymmetric crystal, there is a greater proportion of weaker reflections, balanced by fewer but stronger reflections in the upper range, than for non-centrosymmetric crystals, which give a more uniform distribution. (The physical basis of this is best appreciated in terms of the concept of the molecular transform, described later, p. 421.) Quantitatively, Wilson (1949 a) showed that a consequence of this is that the average value of $F$ is greater for a non-centrosymmetric than for a centrosymmetric crystal, and that the ratio of the square of the average of all the $F$'s to the average of all the $F^2$ values is 0·785 for a non-centrosymmetric crystal but only 0·637 for a centrosymmetric crystal.

In more detail, Howells, Phillips, and Rogers (1950) worked out distribution curves for the two types of crystals, expressed as the proportions of reflections having $F^2$ values less than or equal to a given fraction of the average $F^2$; these are shown in Fig. 147: the curve for a centrosymmetric crystal lies above that for a non-centrosymmetric crystal. These curves have been used effectively in a number of structural investigations to decide whether the crystal in question had a

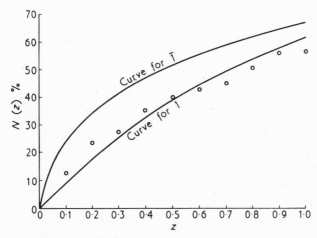

Fig. 147. Intensity distribution for meta tolidine dihydrochloride, compared with theoretical curves for 1 and $\bar{1}$ (Fowweather and Hargreaves, 1950).

centre of symmetry or not, and the results of one such test (Fowweather and Hargreaves, 1950) are shown in the diagram. It is of course essential that the number of reflections should be large enough to make statistical tests significant: the method would not work for simple structures with small unit cells giving few reflections. Moreover, the atoms should all be in general positions, and should not be too dissimilar in diffracting power (Hargreaves, 1955). The method is evidently very suitable for many crystals of organic substances; it is complementary to, and of much wider application than, the method based on anomalous scattering.

This statistical method can be applied to *zones* of reflections, provided that the number of reflections available is great enough; it is thus possible to decide whether any of the principal projections are centrosymmetric or not. It is advisable in all statistical tests to consider the reflections in groups, each for a limited range of diffraction angle, for the statistical relations do not apply to the systematic decline of intensity with increasing diffraction angle (owing to the decline of atomic scattering factors and the thermal motion factor). For an example (*bis*-hydroxydurylmethane) see Chaudhuri and Hargreaves (1956).

Wilson (1950) has also shown that other symmetry elements can be detected by statistical methods. If a crystal has a mirror plane of symmetry perpendicular to the *b* axis, the *b* projection will show atoms overlapping in pairs, and the scattering for the *h0l* reflections will be equal to that of half the number of atoms, each with twice the scattering factor. The local average $F^2$ (i.e. for a given range of diffraction angle) will therefore be, not $\sum_{j=1}^{j=n} f_j^2$, but $\sum_{j=1}^{j=n/2} (2f_j)^2$, which is twice as great ; the local average $F^2$ for the *h0l* reflections is therefore twice as great as for the general *hkl* reflections.

Similarly, a twofold axis parallel to *b*, since it fixes pairs of atoms with the same *y* coordinate, should cause the *0k0* reflections to be, on the average, twice as strong as the general *hkl* reflections. The number of reflections along a central row of the reciprocal lattice may not, however, be large enough to make the statistical method applicable. A twofold axis also makes a projection along this axis a centrosymmetric projection.

The statistical methods are valuable because they detect symmetry elements which are not revealed by a consideration of absent reflections, or by 'Laue symmetry'. In principle, it is possible to distinguish between all the crystal classes (point-groups) by statistical methods ; in fact, as Rogers (1950) has shown, it is possible by X-ray diffraction methods alone (using absent reflections as well as statistical methods) to distinguish between nearly all the space-groups (see p. 269).

Certain crystals have been found to give intensity distribution curves which do not fit either the theoretical centrosymmetric or non-centrosymmetric types. In some crystals composed of centrosymmetric molecules, the centres of symmetry of the molecules are not utilized in the crystal arrangement, but the molecules are associated in pairs related centrosymmetrically to each other. The intensity distribution curves of these crystals lie *above* the centrosymmetric curve; they have been called hypercentric. Other deviations from normal distributions may occur, and may be informative on molecular symmetry or arrangement (Lipson and Woolfson, 1952).

**Space-group symbols.** All the symmetry elements which can be discerned in all possible arrangements of atoms have now been mentioned. The number of different symmetry elements is not large ; nevertheless, as may be imagined, the number of different ways of arranging asymmetric groups of atoms by combining the various symmetry elements in different ways is considerable. The total number is in fact 230. Three different crystallographers, Schönflies, Fedorov, and Barlow, all working independently, had derived the complete list in the years 1890–4—long before the advent of X-ray methods made it possible to utilize the knowledge. Diagrams showing the symmetries of all the space-groups are to be found in *International Tables* (1952); one of them is reproduced in Fig. 155 to illustrate the conventional representation (in a projection) of the commonest symmetry elements.

In referring to any particular space-group, the symbols for the symmetry elements are put together in a way similar to that used for the point-groups. First comes a capital letter indicating whether the lattice is simple ($P$ for primitive), body-centred ($I$ for inner), side-centred ($A$, $B$, or $C$), or centred on all faces ($F$). The rhombohedral lattice is also described by a special letter $R$. Following the capital letter for the lattice type comes the symbol for the principal axis, and if there is a plane of symmetry or a glide plane perpendicular to it, the two symbols are associated thus: $P\dfrac{2}{m}$, $P\dfrac{2_1}{c}$, or, more conveniently for printing, $P2/m, P2_1/c$. Then follow symbols for the symmetries of secondary axes, and planes of symmetry or glide planes parallel to the axes. The set of symbols is often abbreviated, only such symbols as are necessary for unique characterization of the space-group being given. Thus, it is not necessary to write $P2/m\ 2/m\ 2/m$ since $Pmmm$ implies the existence of twofold axes as well as planes of symmetry. Note that $P222$ is a different space-group having no planes of symmetry.

**Procedure in deducing the space-group.** The number of possible space-groups for a crystal under investigation is, of course, limited by the knowledge (usually already possessed at this stage) of the crystal system to which it belongs. From this point it is often possible to identify the space-group unequivocally from the X-ray diffraction pattern.

In examining a list of X-ray reflections for this purpose, it is best to look first for evidence of the lattice type—whether it is simple ($P$) or compound; systematic absences throughout the whole range of reflections indicate a compound lattice, and the types of absences show whether the cell is body-centred ($I$), side-centred ($A$, $B$, or $C$), or face-centred ($F$). When this is settled, look for further absences; systematic absences throughout a zone of reflections indicate a glide plane normal to the zone axis, while systematic absences of reflections from a single principal plane indicate a screw axis normal to the plane. The result of such a survey, followed by an examination of the list of absences for all space-groups (see *International Tables*, 1952) may be to settle the space-group unequivocally. Thus orthorhombic crystals of methyl urea, $CH_3.NH.CO.NH_2$, give all types of reflections except $h00$ with $h$ odd, $0k0$ with $k$ odd, and $00l$ with $l$ odd. The lattice is evidently primitive, and there are no glide planes; but there are screw axes parallel to all three edges of the unit cell. The only possible space-group is $P2_12_12_1$ (Corey and Wyckoff, 1933).

As another example, $p$-azoxyanisole,

$$CH_3O—\bigcirc—N{=}N—\bigcirc—OCH_3$$
$$\overset{\|}{\underset{O}{}}$$

is monoclinic, and since it gives all types of general ($hkl$) reflections, its lattice is primitive; but in the $h0l$ zone, reflections for which $h+l$ is odd are absent, indicating a glide plane with a translation of $\frac{1}{2}a+\frac{1}{2}c$ (symbol $n$), and also the odd orders of $0k0$ are absent, indicating that there is a screw axis parallel to $b$. The only possible space-group is $P2_1/n$ (Bernal and Crowfoot, 1933 $a$). (This could be described alternatively, with a change of $a$ and $c$ axes, as $P2_1/a$ or $P2_1/c$.)

Our third example will be more complex. The X-ray diffraction patterns of 1,2 dimethylphenanthrene (Bernal and Crowfoot, 1935) show no $hkl$ reflections having $k+l$ odd; the lattice is therefore centred on the $a$ face (symbol $A$). In the $h0l$ zone, reflections with $l$ odd must of course be absent; since for these $k$ is 0 and $k+l$ is thus odd; but it is found that $h0l$ reflections with $h$ odd are also absent. Evidently there is, perpendicular to the $b$ axis, a glide plane with translation $a/2$. The only other zone showing additional systematic absences is $0kl$; not only are reflections having $k+l$ odd absent (owing to the $A$ face-centred lattice), but also all reflections having $k$ odd or $h$ odd are absent; it therefore appears that there is, perpendicular to the $a$ axis, a glide plane having one translation of $b/2$ and another translation of $c/2$. This appears at first sight a new sort of glide plane not previously mentioned; but actually, owing to the $A$ face-centred lattice, a glide of $b/2$ is indistinguishable from a glide of $c/2$. This is illustrated in Fig. 148, which symbolizes the projection in question. A group of atoms $M$ at the corner of the cell is repeated at the face-centre $P$; if we imagine these groups reflected in the plane of the paper and translated $b/2$, $M$ reaches $N$ and $P$ reaches $Q$. Exactly the same result would be obtained by translating $c/2$; $M$ would reach $Q'$, which is equivalent to $Q$, and $P$

would reach $N'$, which is equivalent to $N$. It therefore does not matter whether we call this a glide of $\frac{1}{2}b$ or $\frac{1}{2}c$; and the space-group may be called $Aba2$ or $Aca2$; convention calls it $Aba2$. Reference to the list of space-groups shows that $Aba2$ is the only one causing this particular combination of absences. (The verdicts on space-groups in these examples could have been arrived at mechanically, by simply noting the absent reflections and looking up the list of space-groups; but it is best to approach such problems from first principles. Reference should, however, always be made to the list of space-groups to avoid missing any possibilities.)

Other examples will be found in Chapter IX; these include rutile, the structure whose general arrangement was assumed earlier in this chapter.

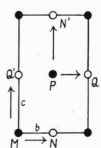

The types of absent reflections alone do not always settle the space-group uniquely. For instance, an orthorhombic crystal whose X-ray diffraction pattern exhibits no systematic absences may have either space-group symmetry $Pmmm$, or alternatively $P222$, or $Pmm2$. In such a case, intensity statistics may decide the matter; they may reveal the centre of symmetry in $Pmmm$ (which the other two space-groups do not possess), or show the three centrosymmetric projections but overall non-centrosymmetric character of $P222$, or thirdly the one centrosymmetric projection (due to a twofold axis) and the two planes of symmetry of $Pmm2$. Intensity statistics, however, are only effective for crystals having a sufficient number of atoms of similar diffracting power in general positions. If they do not give clear indications, for instance for an organic substance containing a heavy atom, the use of anomalous scattering may reveal the presence or absence of a centre of symmetry; this is only practicable, however, if X-rays of a wavelength a little shorter than that of an absorption edge of the heavy atom can be used.

Fig. 148. Lattice side-centred on 100 (symbol $A$); glide plane perpendicular to the $a$ axis (that is, in the plane of the paper).

If X-ray diffraction methods alone do not decide the space-group, the morphology or certain physical properties of the crystal may supply the desired information. Some caution is necessary in considering crystal shape-symmetry, because the shape of a crystal may have a symmetry higher or lower than that of the atomic arrangement. (See Chapter II.) If, in crystals grown from a solution or melt of high purity, there is definite evidence of enantiomorphic or polar character, the crystal class and with it the space-group are settled, but if the crystal shape has holohedral symmetry, it is by no means certain that the atomic arrangement has holohedral symmetry.

When the conditions of growth of a crystal are unknown the evidence of its shape should be regarded with reserve. There are, indeed, cases in which the shape of a crystal is inconsistent with clear X-ray evidence on atomic structure—for instance, cuprite $Cu_2O$ (Greenwood, 1924; Bragg, 1937; Miers, 1929). Possibly this is due to the presence of impurities during growth (see p. 54).

If the combination of X-ray and morphological evidence does not determine the space-group uniquely, additional information may be sought by tests for piezo-electric and pyro-electric properties, and by an optical examination for any evidence of rotation of the plane of polarization. (See Chapter VIII.) The results of such tests may settle the matter, since only certain crystal classes have these properties. Only positive results are decisive; the apparent absence of piezo-electric or pyro-electric effects may be due to feeble phenomena.

If after such tests the space-group is in doubt, there is no other course than to proceed with the next stage in the interpretation of the X-ray patterns, trying arrangements in each of the possible space-groups in turn. There may be stereochemical reasons for supposing that one arrangement is more likely than others, and this arrangement will naturally be tried first. Such possibilities cannot be discussed in general terms; they are specific for each crystal. Familiarity with the general background of crystal chemistry and molecular stereochemistry is desirable.

## Information given by a knowledge of the space-group

1. *Molecular or ionic symmetry.* If the space-group of a particular crystal has been determined unequivocally, this knowledge may make it possible to draw certain definite conclusions about the symmetry of the molecules or ions of which the crystal is composed—and this without any attempt to discover the positions of individual atoms.

Consider the space-group symmetry $P2_1/a$. A structure having this symmetry can be built by placing a group of atoms in any general position in the unit cell, and repeating this group in accordance with the demands of the complex of symmetry elements. Thus, in Fig. 149, if group $A$ (symbolized by a question mark because we do not yet know anything about the positions of individual atoms) is regarded as the reference group, the glide plane $a_1$ gives rise to group $B$; and the lower screw axis creates $C$ from $A$, as well as a second glide plane $a_2$ from $a_1$, and thence $D$ from $C$. Now the group of atoms forming the element of structure need have no symmetry at all. The symmetry $P2_1/a$ can be attained by arranging four *asymmetric* groups in the manner indicated. (All monoclinic crystals of the holohedral class with primitive lattices contain four asymmetric groups.) But if we find that a particular

crystal has this symmetry but contains only two molecules in the cell, then each molecule must have twofold symmetry of some kind. If the substance is a high polymer, each molecule may possess either a screw axis or a glide plane or a centre of symmetry, since all these twofold elements of symmetry are present in the group $P2_1/a$; but if the substance is a monomer, the molecules cannot have symmetry elements of translation, and therefore must each have a centre of symmetry. The asymmetric element of structure is half a molecule; each molecule consists of two asymmetric halves related by a centre of symmetry.

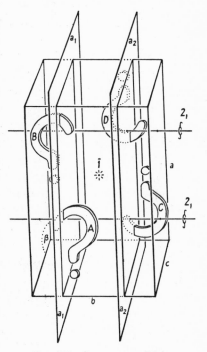

FIG. 149. Space-group $P2_1/a$.

A good example of the value of such evidence is the conclusion that the molecule of diphenyl $C_6H_5.C_6H_5$ has a centre of symmetry. The situation is exactly that just described—the space-group symmetry is $P2_1/a$ and there are only two molecules in the unit cell; hence each molecule has a centre of symmetry (Hengstenberg and Mark, 1929; Clark (G. L.) and Pickett, 1931). Assuming that the benzene ring is planar and that the connecting link also lies in the nuclear plane, the fact that in the crystal the molecule has a centre of symmetry leads at once to the important stereochemical conclusion that the two rings are coplanar—in the crystal, at any rate; any twist at the single bond would destroy the centre of symmetry (Fig. 150). Even if no assumptions are made, it is still certain that the mean planes of the two rings are parallel.

But suppose a crystal having this same symmetry $P2_1/a$ is found to contain four molecules? It would appear at first thought that each molecule is asymmetric, since it requires four asymmetric objects (two left-handed and two right-handed) to make up this symmetry. This conclusion, however, would not necessarily be correct; it embodies the assumption that the asymmetric object is to be identified with the molecule—an assumption which is not warranted. The asymmetric unit in a crystal may be, and often is, a molecule; but it is not necessarily one particular molecule—it may be half one molecule and half another, the two molecules being geometrically different and unrelated by symmetry operations. Consider an actual example. The crystal of stilbene, $C_6H_5.CH{=}CH.C_6H_5$, has the space-group symmetry $P2_1/a$, and there are four molecules in the unit cell (Robertson, Prasad, and Woodward, 1936; Robertson and Woodward, 1937). If the asymmetric object were any one particular molecule, then there would be in the unit cell two left-handed and two right-handed molecules, mirror images of each other. It turns out, however, that there are two types of unrelated molecules, both having a centre of symmetry; the asymmetric unit is half one of these molecules and half the other, the halves being obtained by mentally bisecting the molecules through their centres of symmetry (see Fig. 151). These two types of molecules are geometrically slightly different from each other; they are not stereoisomers in the ordinary sense—the difference is due to the distorting effects of the different surroundings of the two types. The differences are more marked in *trans*-azobenzene, $C_6H_5.N{=}N.C_6H_5$, which has a similar structure; half the molecules are flat, while in the rest the benzene rings are rotated 15° out of the plane of the central C—N=N—C group (Lange, Robertson, and Woodward, 1939). An example of this sort of thing in an ionic crystal is in the structure of potassium dithionate, $K_2S_2O_6$ (Stanley, 1956), in which there are two types of $O_3S.SO_3$ groups of considerably different configuration; in one, the angle between the $SO_3$ groups, projected along the S—S axis, is 23·5°, in the other 54·5°. That chemically identical molecules should arrange themselves so that the surroundings of half of them are different from those of the rest seems odd. Evidently intermolecular forces and the requirements of good packing are satisfied better by this arrangement than they would be

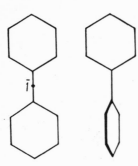

FIG. 150. Structure of diphenyl molecule (in the crystal). The two benzene rings must be coplanar (left); any twist at the connecting link (right) would destroy the centre of symmetry.

by an arrangement of crystallographically equivalent molecules; but the phenomenon does not appear to be understood in detail. These examples show that caution is necessary in forming conclusions on molecular symmetry: it is possible to conclude, from a knowledge of the space-group and the number of molecules in the unit cell, only that

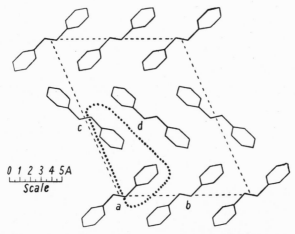

FIG. 151. Structure of stilbene. The asymmetric unit (ringed) consists of half one molecule and half another, the two types of molecules being unrelated by symmetry elements (Robertson and Woodward, 1936).

the molecule in its crystal setting has a certain minimum symmetry. In truth the molecular symmetry may be higher (if, as in the examples given, there are non-equivalent molecules), but it cannot be lower than that indicated by the sort of evidence considered here. The minimum symmetries of molecules in the various space-groups, taking into account different possible numbers of molecules in the unit cell, are given in Astbury and Yardley's tables (1924). (These symmetries do not refer to high polymer molecules.)

The above remarks refer to the symmetries of molecules in crystals. It is very important to remember that the symmetry of a molecule in its crystal setting is not necessarily the full symmetry of an isolated molecule, since, as we have seen, the full symmetries of molecules are not always utilized in forming crystalline arrangements. Suppose, for example, that X-ray and other evidence leads to the definite conclusion that certain molecules in their crystal setting have no symmetry. It does not follow that these molecules in isolation are asymmetric: it may be that in isolation they would have axes of symmetry or planes of symmetry, or even a centre of symmetry, but that these are ignored in the formation of the crystalline arrangement. An extreme example here is the monoclinic form of 1:2, 5:6 dibenzanthracene, a molecule which in itself has a plane of symmetry, a twofold axis, and a centre of symmetry; all these are ignored in the crystal arrangement, which has symmetry $P2_1$ (Robertson and White, 1956).

When the number of molecules in the unit cell is greater than the number of asymmetric units necessary to give rise to the space-group symmetry, it is certain that there are in the crystal two or more crystallographically non-equivalent types of molecules. This is so in ascorbic acid (vitamin C), for instance (Cox, 1932 $a$; Cox and Goodwin, 1936).

2. *Molecular dimensions.* In research on substances of unknown or partially known constitution, a knowledge of the shape and size of the molecules may be of great value in confirming or rejecting suggested structural formulae. It has been pointed out (p. 200) that when a unit cell contains only one molecule, the dimensions of the cell suggest possible molecular dimensions. But clearly, when there is more than one molecule in the unit cell, the shape and size of the cell merely suggest the possible dimensions of a group of molecules: the dimensions of an individual molecule cannot be deduced directly, for the cell might be divided into two or more identical volumes in an infinite variety of ways. If, however, the space-group is known, this knowledge may lead to the conclusion that the molecules are related to each other by certain symmetry operations, and this restricts the number of ways of subdividing the unit cell. Still further restrictions may be imposed if the constitution of the molecule is partly known. A knowledge of some of the physical properties, particularly the birefringence, pleochroism, or magnetic anisotropy, may lead to definite conclusions on the orientation of whole molecules or of particular atom groups (see Chapter VIII), and these conclusions may impose still further restrictions on the mode of subdivision of the unit cell, and in fact may determine definitely the overall size and shape of each molecule. This subject cannot be discussed in general terms; each substance presents its own specific problems. It is desirable in considering the possibilities to use models in which the atoms have the correct effective external radii: abstract thinking or drawing diagrams on paper may be misleading.

An outstanding example of the use of such methods is the work of Bernal (1932) on substances of the sterol group. X-ray and optical evidence led to the conclusion that these molecules have the approximate dimensions $5 \times 7 \cdot 2 \times 17$–$20$ Å, and this played an important part in the abandonment of earlier structural formulae and the elucidation of the correct constitution (Rosenheim and King, 1932).

3. *Locations of atoms in relation to symmetry elements. Equivalent positions and their multiplicities.* After gaining as much knowledge as possible on the general shape, orientation, and symmetry of the molecules or ions in a crystal, the next step is to try to locate particular atoms. This it is sometimes possible to do by reasoning of the type already used. Thus, if an atom is placed in a space-group having six-fold rotation axes, it is inevitably multiplied by 6, unless it is placed actually *on* one of the sixfold axes; therefore, if, in a space-group having sixfold rotation axes, it is found that there is only one atom of a particular kind in the unit cell, that atom must lie on a sixfold axis, for only in this position can sixfold repetition be avoided. This brings us to a general consideration of the multiplicity of different types of positions in the various space-groups.

A 'space-group' is a group of symmetry elements. If an atom is placed in a quite general position in the unit cell, it is inevitably multiplied by the symmetry elements, and thus other atoms, exactly equivalent to the first, are found at other positions which are related in a precise way to those of the first. Each space-group has its own characteristic number of equivalent general positions. Thus all primitive (that is, not centred) space-groups in the polar and holoaxial classes of the orthorhombic system (classes $mm2$ and $222$) have four equivalent general positions, while primitive holohedral space-groups (class $mmm$) have eight equivalent general positions. Thus, if in space-group $Pmm2$ an atom is placed in a general position $xyz$ (see Fig. 152, left), one plane of symmetry creates another at $\bar{x}yz$, and the second plane of symmetry creates another from each of these, at $x\bar{y}z$ and $\bar{x}\bar{y}z$ respectively. General positions in space-group $Pmm2$ are thus fourfold positions.

Suppose, however, we place an atom *on* one of the planes of symmetry, $m_2$, at position $x0z$. Plane $m_2$ does not create a second atom; it merely makes one-half of the atom the mirror image of the other half. But plane $m_1$ does create another atom, at position $\bar{x}0z$ (Fig. 152, right). Similarly, if an atom were placed on $m_1$ at position $0yz$, only one more atom would be created, at $0\bar{y}z$. Thus positions on planes of symmetry are twofold positions. It should be noted that there are also planes of symmetry half-way along $a$ and $b$ edges of the cell, and therefore $x\frac{1}{2}z$ is a twofold position (reflected by $m_1'$ as $\bar{x}\frac{1}{2}z$), as is also $\frac{1}{2}yz$ (reflected by $m_2'$ as $\frac{1}{2}\bar{y}z$).

Finally it will be evident that, if an atom is placed at any position on a twofold axis where two planes of symmetry intersect—for instance, at $00z$—it is not multiplied at all; $00z$ is thus a onefold position. Other onefold positions are $\frac{1}{2}0z$, $0\frac{1}{2}z$, and $\frac{1}{2}\frac{1}{2}z$; in other words, in this space-group any position on any one of the twofold axes is a onefold position.

If, in a crystal having this space-group symmetry $Pmm2$, there is only one atom of a particular kind, it must necessarily lie on one of the twofold axes. If there are two chemically identical atoms, some caution is necessary; they may occupy one set of twofold positions, but another possibility which cannot be excluded is that the atoms may actually

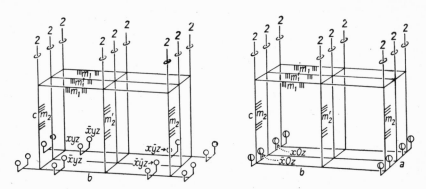

FIG. 152. Space-group $Pmm2$. Left: fourfold (general) positions.
Right: twofold positions.

occupy two of the (crystallographically non-equivalent) onefold positions. Similarly, when there are four chemically similar atoms, they may occupy the fourfold (general) positions, or two independent sets of twofold positions, or even four independent onefold positions.

In general, any position lying on a plane of symmetry, a rotation axis, an inversion axis, or a centre of symmetry (these are the symmetry elements which do not involve translation) is a special position, having fewer equivalent companions than the general positions. But note carefully that positions lying on screw axes or glide planes are *not* special positions (unless they also lie on non-translatory elements): an atom lying on a screw axis or a glide plane is multiplied just as surely as if it were lying at a distance from the symmetry element—see Fig. 153. And in space-groups exhibiting translatory symmetry elements only, all positions in the cell are general positions; this is so, for instance, in the frequently occurring space-group $P2_12_12_1$, the equivalent positions in which are illustrated in Fig. 154: every position in the cell has four-fold multiplicity.

In many space-groups some of the positions of low multiplicity are fixed positions in the cell: no variable parameters are involved. Thus in the monoclinic space-group $P2_1/c$ the twofold positions are centres of symmetry. There are four different pairs of centres of symmetry, the coordinates of which are:

(a) $000, 0\frac{1}{2}\frac{1}{2}$

(c) $00\frac{1}{2}, 0\frac{1}{2}0$

(b) $\frac{1}{2}00, \frac{1}{2}\frac{1}{2}\frac{1}{2}$

(d) $\frac{1}{2}0\frac{1}{2}, \frac{1}{2}\frac{1}{2}0$.

There are no onefold positions, and all other positions in the cell are fourfold. If in a unit cell having this symmetry there are only two atoms of a particular kind, these must lie in one pair of centres of symmetry; and we may choose which pair we like, for all give the same arrangement as far as these atoms are concerned. This is the situation in platinum phthalocyanine: the two platinum atoms in the cell lie without any doubt in a pair of symmetry centres (see p. 376).

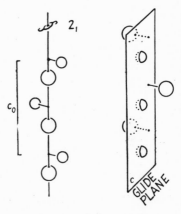

Fig. 153. Atoms lying *on* screw axes or glide planes are multiplied, no less than those at a distance.

Note, however, that if in this same space-group $P2_1/c$ there is one pair of atoms of one kind and one pair of another kind, each pair of atoms must occupy a pair of symmetry centres; but the relation between the two pairs of atoms is not uniquely defined, for the arrangement with one pair in (a) and the other in (b) is not the same as the arrangement with one pair in (a) and the other pair in (c); and the combination (a)+(d) is a third different arrangement. The correct arrangement may be found by calculating the intensities of the X-ray reflections for the different arrangements; this must be done simultaneously with the determination of the parameters of the rest of the atoms in the cell. (See next section, and also, p. 339.)

In all except very simple structures most atoms lie either in partly restricted positions, involving one or two variable parameters, or in general positions involving three variable parameters. We shall pass to the methods of determining these variable parameters in the next section; but before leaving this section there is one other very useful consideration to be mentioned. If a structure is known to have twofold axes (*not* screw axes) and certain atoms do not lie *on* the twofold axes, the distance of the centre of one of these atoms from a twofold axis cannot be less than the radius of the atom, for any smaller distance would mean that two equivalent atoms on opposite sides of the twofold axis overlap each other. Similarly, the centre of an atom must lie either *on* a plane of symmetry (a reflection plane, *not* a glide plane) or else at a distance from it not less than the atomic radius. The same is true for a centre of symmetry. For three-, four-, and sixfold rotation

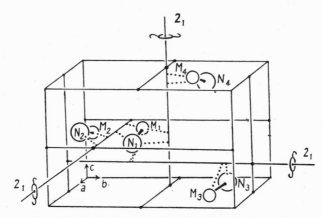

FIG. 154. Equivalent positions in space-group $P2_12_12_1$.

axes we have to imagine a ring of atoms round the axis; none of them can touch the axis, hence the smallest permissible distance is greater than the atomic radius. Such considerations have played a large part in the solution of silicate structures such as that of beryl, $Be_3Al_2Si_6O_{18}$ (Bragg, W. L., and West, 1926).

The space-groups illustrated here are simple ones having a maximum multiplicity of 4. In many space-groups, however, the multiplicity of the general positions is much higher—16, or 32, or even 96 in some of the highly symmetrical space-groups. The multiplicities and the co-ordinates of equivalent positions (both general and special) are given in *International Tables* (1952). Specimen diagrams are reproduced in Fig. 155 to show the conventional way of representing equivalent positions and the commonest symmetry elements. Some examples of the use of the tables of equivalent positions will be found in Chapter IX; attention is drawn first of all to the derivation of the structure of sodium nitrite $NaNO_2$, since the arrangement has the symmetry $Imm2$, closely related to the one ($Pmm2$) used as an example here.

The application of the theory of space-groups to crystal structure determination involves the assumption that equivalent sites in the crystal are occupied by identical atoms. Fortunately this is true for

the majority of crystals, though there are some exceptions. Consideration of the abnormal types of crystals is deferred to the end of Chapter
IX. For the present we shall continue with the account of the methods
of solving normal structures.

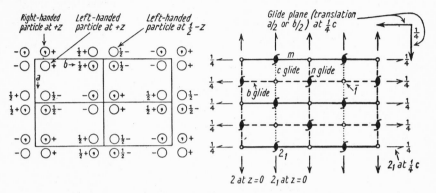

FIG. 155. Symmetry elements and equivalent positions in space-group *Cmca*.

**Determination of atomic parameters.** At this stage in the attempt
to find the positions of the atoms in the unit cell it is known that the
complete arrangement has certain symmetries. If the space-group is
$P2_12_12_1$ (Fig. 154), a particular atom $M_1$ which may be taken as the
standard of reference is repeated by the symmetry elements in other
definite positions in the cell $M_2$, $M_3$, and $M_4$; a second type of atom
$N_1$, which is formally independent of the first-mentioned, is also
repeated in other definite positions $N_2$, $N_3$, and $N_4$ by the same scheme
of symmetry elements; and so on. Each type of reference atom has
three parameters $x$, $y$, and $z$, which are the coordinates of the atom
with respect to the unit cell edges expressed as fractions of the lengths
of these edges. If the coordinates of each reference atom can be found,
the other three of each group are bound to be at $\frac{1}{2}-x$, $-y$, $\frac{1}{2}+z$, at
$\frac{1}{2}+x$, $\frac{1}{2}-y$, $-z$, and at $-x$, $\frac{1}{2}+y$, $\frac{1}{2}-z$ (if the origin of the cell is, in
accordance with convention, a point half-way between neighbouring
screw axes as in Fig. 154).

The procedure in determining the parameters will naturally vary
with circumstances, but a few general principles can be given. First,
as to the most convenient method of calculation. We have seen (p. 228)
that for any crystal plane $hkl$ the contribution of each atom (coordinates
$xyz$) to the expression for the structure amplitude consists of a cosine
term $f \cos 2\pi(hx+ky+lz)$ and a sine term $f \sin 2\pi(hx+ky+lz)$. Equivalent atoms (those related to each other by symmetry elements) have

coordinates which are related to each other in a simple way, and on this account the cosine terms for the whole group may be combined to form a single expression, the evaluation of which is usually more rapid and convenient than the process of dealing with each atom separately. Thus, the cosine terms for four equivalent atoms in space-group $P2_12_12_1$ (coordinates given above), on being expanded and combined, are found to be equal to the expression

$$A = +4f \cos 2\pi\left(hx - \frac{h-k}{4}\right)\cos 2\pi\left(ky - \frac{k-l}{4}\right)\cos 2\pi\left(lz - \frac{l-h}{4}\right).$$

The sine terms combine in a similar way to form the expression

$$B = -4f \sin 2\pi\left(hx - \frac{h-k}{4}\right)\sin 2\pi\left(ky - \frac{k-l}{4}\right)\sin 2\pi\left(lz - \frac{l-h}{4}\right).$$

If the combined expressions are used, it is only necessary to consider each reference atom in turn; the expressions take care of the rest of each group. The cosine term for each independent group is evaluated and then all the cosine terms are added together. Sine terms for all the independent groups are likewise added together. $A^2+B^2$ is then $= F^2$, which for an 'ideally imperfect' crystal is proportional to the intensity the $hkl$ reflections would have if the atoms really were in the postulated positions. The combined expression for the contribution of a set of equivalent atoms, for each space-group, is to be found in *International Tables* (1952).

When there is only one variable parameter in a crystal structure its determination is straightforward: calculation of the intensities of various reflections for a range of values of this parameter (as was done for rutile on p. 230) leads directly to the selection of the value which gives the best agreement with the observed intensities. It is usually necessary to calculate only for a small range of parameters, for it is likely to be obvious, from the strength or weakness of certain reflections, that the parameter can only be near a certain value (see again the evidence on rutile, p. 231). Usually, reflections at small angles fix it approximately, while the high-order reflections at large angles lead to a more accurate value.†

Similar methods can be used whenever a parameter can be isolated.

† This is not true in all circumstances. For instance, the diffracting power of the oxygen atom falls off with increasing angle of diffraction much more rapidly than does that of iron—so much so that in lepidocrocite ($\beta$-FeO.OH) the intensities of the high-order diffractions are determined almost entirely by the positions of the iron atoms; the parameters of the oxygen atoms must be fixed by means of some of the low-order diffractions.

This is well illustrated by the determination of the structure of ammonium hydrogen fluoride $NH_4HF_2$ by Pauling (1933). The crystals are orthorhombic, and the unit cell has the dimensions $a = 8\cdot33$ Å, $b = 8\cdot14$ Å, $c = 3\cdot68$ Å and contains four molecules. The general arrangement, which has the symmetry *Pman*, was suggested by reference to the already known structure of $KHF_2$ (Bozorth, 1923) and a consideration of the modifications brought about by the formation of hydrogen bonds between nitrogen and fluorine atoms: in this arrangement the nitrogen atoms are at $\frac{1}{4}\frac{1}{4}z_1$, $\frac{3}{4}\frac{1}{4}z_1$, $\frac{1}{4}\frac{3}{4}\bar{z}_1$, and $\frac{3}{4}\frac{3}{4}\bar{z}_1$, half the fluorine atoms at $x00$, $\bar{x}00$, $(\frac{1}{2}+x)\frac{1}{2}0$, and $(\frac{1}{2}-x)\frac{1}{2}0$, and the others at $\frac{1}{2}yz_2$, $\frac{1}{2}\bar{y}\bar{z}_2$, $0(\frac{1}{2}-y)z_2$, and $0(\frac{1}{2}+y)\bar{z}_2$.

The intensities of the $h00$ reflections depend only on the value of $x$ (this is the only parameter along the $a$ axis); hence the relative intensities of the various orders of $h00$ lead to the determination of $x$. (The results are presented in Pauling's paper in the form of curves like those for rutile in Fig. 123.) Similarly $y$ was found from the relative intensities of the $0k0$ reflections. Along the $c$ axis there are two parameters $z_1$ and $z_2$, but $z_1$ was isolated from $z_2$ by considering only those $hkl$ reflections which have $h$ odd and $k$ odd; if the expressions for the contributions of all the atoms in the cell are combined together, the complete structure amplitude for these reflections is found to be

$$F = 4f_F(\cos 2\pi hx - \cos 2\pi ky \cos 2\pi lz_2),$$

an expression which does not contain $z_1$. The already known values of $y$ and $x$ were used, and thus $z_2$, the only variable in the expression, could be determined in the same straightforward way. This left only one parameter, $z_1$, to be determined; this could have been found from the intensities of various remaining types of reflections; actually it was found from the relative intensities of $hkl$ reflections having $h$ and $k$ both even, the structure amplitude for these being

$$F = 4f_{NH_4} \cos 2\pi\left(\frac{h+k}{4}+lz\right) + 4f_F(\cos 2\pi hx + \cos 2\pi ky \cos 2\pi lz_2).$$

In the more complex structures it is usually necessary to determine a number of parameters simultaneously; in crystals of complex organic compounds, for instance, more often than not the atoms are all in general positions and there are therefore three parameters for each atom. Such problems cannot be solved by the methods described for isolated parameters. It is necessary to postulate likely positions for the atoms, to calculate the intensities which these positions would give, and to compare these calculated intensities with those observed. The prospects of success depend on whether the postulated positions are anywhere near the correct positions, giving some measure of agreement with observed intensities; if they are, the correct positions can be found by judicious small displacements of some or all the atoms from the positions first chosen.

The following discussion relates chiefly to complex crystals in which all the atoms have much the same diffracting powers—crystals such as those of many organic compounds; for it is in these circumstances that the indirect method of trial and error must often be used. For crystals containing a minority of heavy atoms together with a larger number of lighter atoms in the unit cell, the direct or semi-direct methods described in Chapter X are more appropriate.

The first step should be to gain a general idea of the distribution of the atoms. A general idea of the shape and orientation of the molecules may have been gained by reasoning based on a knowledge of the unit cell dimensions and the space-group, together with physical properties such as optical or magnetic birefringence, and whatever stereochemical knowledge is available on the type of substance in question. If so, this will lead to the postulation of approximate atomic coordinates.

Failing this, a direct attack on the problem of the interpretation of the intensities of the X-ray reflections may be made. In any case, this is the next stage. The only X-ray intensities so far considered quantitatively (in discovering the space-group) have been zero intensities; the next to be considered are those of maximum intensity, since these may indicate the whereabouts of the greatest concentrations of atoms. The strongest reflections are usually those at small angles. If one of these is much stronger than any others, it may be that all the atoms lie on or near the lattice planes responsible for this outstandingly strong reflection. If absolute (not merely relative) intensities are available, this idea can be checked directly; if the intensity is about the maximum possible by co-operation of diffracted waves from all the atoms in the cell (taking into account all angle factors), then all the atoms must lie on or near the reflecting planes. Even if absolute intensities are not available, it is still possible to check the idea, though in a less direct way: if all the atoms lie on particular crystal planes, then the structure amplitudes for all orders of reflection from these planes must be equal and therefore the actual intensities of the different orders diminish regularly from one to the next, owing to the effect of the angle factors. This argument has been much used; for an example, see the structure of sodium nitrite, p. 334. If a decline is maintained only for two or three orders, the higher ones being apparently erratic, or if the decline is greater or smaller than the normal decline due to angle factors, then the atoms must be somewhat dispersed from the planes in question. As an example, in the determination of the structure of benzoquinone (Robertson, 1935 $a$) the great strength of the $20\bar{1}$ reflection and the rapid decline of the intensities of the second and third orders ($40\bar{2}$ and $60\bar{3}$) were used as evidence that the flat molecules lie nearly, but not quite, along the $20\bar{1}$ planes (see Fig. 156); and the final result of the analysis showed that this is correct. In crystals containing atoms of widely different diffracting powers, such evidence may mean that the more strongly diffracting atoms lie on the planes in question, with the more weakly diffracting ones somewhere in between.

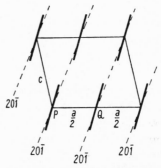

If two or three reflections in the same principal zone are much stronger than all the others, the atoms lie approximately along lines parallel to this zone axis. Fibres of crystalline chain polymers, for instance, often give two or three very strong reflections from planes parallel to the fibre axis; this shows that in the crystalline regions the chain molecules are

FIG. 156. Orientation of molecules in the crystal of benzoquinone. Since the space-group is $P2_1/a$, there are molecules at $P$ and $Q$; the great strength of $20\bar{1}$ shows that the flat molecules lie nearly along the $20\bar{1}$ planes.

fairly well extended (not meandering) and parallel to the fibre axis: if we look along the chain axis (usually called $c$), we see the $ab$ projection, and in this projection the chains, seen end-on, appear to be compact groups of atoms. Thus, in polyethylene (Bunn, 1939) and some of the polyesters (Fuller, 1940) the $ab$ projection of the unit cell is rectangular (Fig. 157) and two chain molecules run through it; the 200 and 110 reflections are far stronger than any others, and this shows that the atoms appear from this viewpoint to be in compact groups at the corners and centres of the projected cells. In poly*iso*butene the 200 and 110 planes have the same spacing (Fuller, Frosch, and Pape, 1940), and in the fibre photograph (Plate X) these reflections are superimposed, forming a spot of very great intensity. If the projected cell is not rectangular, there may be three very strong reflections, from planes such as those in Fig. 158.

Such considerations, applied to the low-order (small-angle) reflections, give a general idea of the distribution of the atoms, if these happen to be in sheets or in strings. In the case of molecular crystals they indicate the general orientations of sheet or chain molecules. The occurrence in these crystals of the atomic centres in compact groups is due partly to the chain or sheet structure of the molecules, and partly to the fact that the effective external radii of atoms (which govern the distances between molecules) are much greater than the distances between atoms linked by primary bonds.

Any outstandingly strong reflections at large angles may give similar

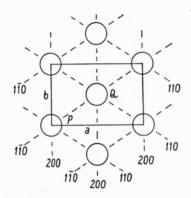

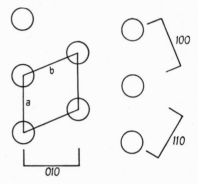

FIG. 157. Packing of chain molecules in polyethylene and some of the polyesters. The chains, seen end-on, appear to be compact groups of atoms at *P* and *Q*.

FIG. 158. High polymers whose unit cells projected along the fibre axis are not rectangular may give three very strong reflections. If the fibre axis is *c*, these reflections may be 100, 010, and 1$\bar{1}$0.

information about the distribution of the atoms within the molecules. For instance, the crystal of chrysene (monoclinic, $a = 8\cdot34$ Å, $b = 6\cdot18$ Å, $c = 25\cdot0$ Å, $\beta = 115\cdot8°$, space-group $I2/c$) gives a very strong 0.3.17 reflection, and this suggests that the atoms lie on planes of this type. But it is not known whether the phase of the reflection (the sign of the structure amplitude) is positive with respect to the centre of symmetry at the origin—which would mean that the atoms lie on the 'positive' planes in Fig. 159 *b*—or negative, as it would be if the atoms lay on the planes in Fig. 159 *a*. However, the chemical structure and probable dimensions of the molecule are known, and if such a molecule is placed in the cell oriented as in Fig. 159 *b* (an orientation suggested by the cell dimensions), the atoms do lie on the 'positive' 0.3.17 planes; and this postulated orientation is confirmed by the fact that the 060 reflection is also strong—Fig. 159 *b* shows that the atoms lie on 'negative' 060 planes (Iball, 1934).

Another example of the use of this type of evidence is to be found in the determination of the structure of crystalline rubber (Bunn, 1942 *a*). First of all it must be mentioned that the chain molecules, seen end-on,

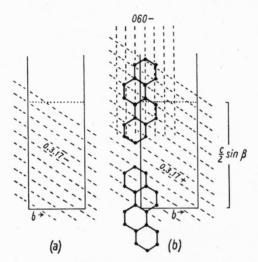

FIG. 159. Structure of chrysene.

lie as in Fig. 160. (The great strength of the 200 and 120 reflections, coupled with the fact that there are four molecules passing through the unit cell, gives this information.) A strong hint of the distribution of the atoms is given by the fact that the 10.0.0 reflection is recorded; it is weak, but the fact that it is there at all (considering the large angle of reflection) must mean that the structure amplitude for this reflection is large. Again, the atoms may lie on 'positive' planes, as in Fig. 160 *a*, or 'negative' planes, as in Fig. 160 *b*; but the probable configuration of the chain molecules, derived from reasoning based on the repeat distance of the molecules (the length of the *c* axis of the cell) is such that the first of these alternatives is evidently the correct one. Considerations of this sort were also used effectively by Dunitz (1949) in solving the crystal structure of tetraphenyl cyclobutane.

This is as far as it is possible to go by simple inspection; the discovery of the positions of individual atoms, and the determination of the parameters with as much accuracy as the experimental evidence allows, must rest on detailed calculations. When atomic positions have been postulated as the result of considerations such as those just given, it is usually best to concentrate on one principal projection of the structure; the projection chosen should be the one expected to give the clearest resolution of the different atoms, and calculations should first of all be carried out for the zone of reflections relevant to this projection. (The $hk0$ reflections yield the $x$ and $y$ coordinates of the atoms—that is, they give a picture of the structure projected along the $c$ axis; and so on.) Following this (assuming that the intensities of this first zone of reflec-

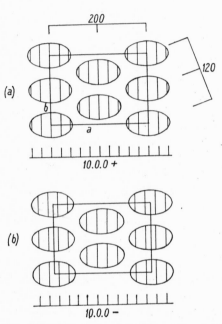

FIG. 160. Structure of rubber. The great strength of 200 and 120 shows that the four chain molecules, seen end-on, lie in the positions shown. The large structure amplitude of 10.0.0 shows that there are concentrations of atoms either on the 10.0.0+ planes (above) or the 10.0.0− planes (below).

tions are successfully accounted for and a reasonable projected structure is obtained), the other principal projections may be considered; and finally the whole structure is checked by calculations of all the $hkl$ intensities.

In the attempt to obtain correct calculated intensities the following problem arises: suppose a particular set of atomic coordinates gives some measure of agreement of calculated with observed intensities for one projection, but nevertheless there are still considerable discrepancies, especially among the higher order reflections—a situation which probably means that the postulated atomic coordinates are roughly correct, but need adjustment. Which atoms should be moved, and by how much?

It should be remembered that when a reference atom is moved, all the atoms related to it by symmetry elements move also in a manner determined by the symmetry elements; and the problem is to know, for any particular reflection, the direction in which to move the reference atom so that the contribution of the whole group of related atoms either increases or decreases. This problem is best solved by the use of charts which show at a glance the magnitude of the structure amplitude for such a group of atoms for all coordinates of the reference atom.

**Graphical methods and machines for evaluating structure amplitudes.** The evaluation of the structure amplitudes for a large number of reflections (it may run into hundreds) is a task of such magnitude that methods of shortening it are very welcome. For any principal zone (*hk0*, *h0l*, or *0kl*) only two coordinates of each atom are concerned in the structure amplitude, and therefore a graphical method may be used : charts showing the values of such functions as

$$\cos 2\pi(hx+ky) \quad \text{or} \quad \cos 2\pi hx \cos 2\pi ky$$

may be constructed (Bragg and Lipson, 1936), and on them the contribution of a group of related atoms may be read. Great accuracy is not required in structure amplitude calculations in the early stages of an investigation, and the $\pm 1$ per cent. or so obtainable by such graphical methods is adequate. Such charts have, in addition, the very great advantage that they show at a glance what movements of atoms are required to increase or decrease the calculated intensity for any reflection.

Projected arrangements may be described as 'plane-groups', for which a nomenclature conforming to that of the space-groups is used ; the most frequently encountered plane-groups are illustrated in Fig. 161. A pair of atoms having coordinates $xy$ and $\bar{x}\bar{y}$ (that is, related by an apparent two-fold axis at the origin) form plane-group $p2$ ; the contribution of this pair to the structure amplitude is

$$2f \cos 2\pi(hx+ky).$$

For the 230 reflection a chart showing $\cos 2\pi(2x+3y)$ for all values of $x$ and $y$ is required ; such a chart is shown in Fig. 162. It is made square for convenience ; the real shape of the projected cell does not matter, since structure amplitudes do not depend on the shape of the cell but only on atomic coordinates expressed as fractions of the unit cell edges.

A complete chart would show contours at intervals of 0·1 filling all the spaces between the nodes ; but it is unnecessary to draw anything but the

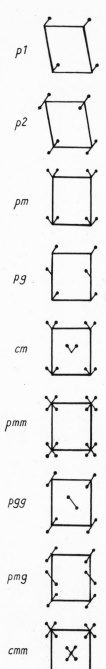

*p1*

*p2*

*pm*

*pg*

*cm*

*pmm*

*pgg*

*pmg*

*cmm*

Fig. 161. Some of the plane-groups.

nodes, since the value at any point can be readily found by using a 'master key' which is fitted between the nodes in the way shown in the diagram: the structure amplitude at the point $P$ is obviously $-0.73$. If the chart is made on transparent material (tracing cloth is durable material for this purpose), atomic positions can be plotted, as fractions of unit cell edges, on white paper; for crystal plane 230 the chart show-

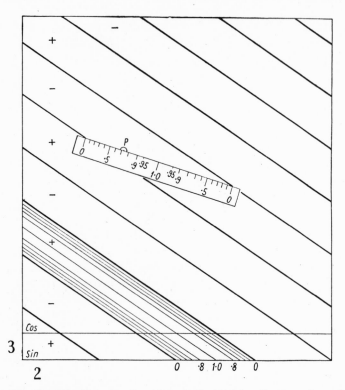

FIG. 162. Chart for the estimation of $\cos 2\pi(2x+3y)$ for all values of $x$ and $y$.

ing $\cos 2\pi(2x+3y)$ is laid on the plot of atomic coordinates and the contribution of each atom is read off. Note that this same chart can be used not only for plane 230, but also for $\bar{2}30$, 320, and $\bar{3}20$ by turning it over or reversing the axes. But a different chart is required for each different pair of numerical values of $h$ and $k$. In order to serve for sine as well as cosine terms each chart is extended in one direction, the origins for sine and cosine terms being $\pi/2$ apart.

Four atoms having coordinates $xy$, $\bar{x}\bar{y}$, $(\frac{1}{2}+x)(\frac{1}{2}-y)$, and $(\frac{1}{2}-x)(\frac{1}{2}+y)$ form plane-group $pgg$ (see Fig. 161). The combined structure amplitude for such a group of atoms is $4 \cos 2\pi hx \cos 2\pi ky$ when $h+k$ is even, and $4 \sin 2\pi hx \sin 2\pi ky$ when $h+k$ is odd.

Charts showing these functions are divided by the nodes into rectangular sections filled by curved contours (Fig. 163). Here it is even more desirable to construct skeleton charts with a set of 'master keys' to fit the differently shaped rectangular sections. The same chart can be used either for the two functions already mentioned or for

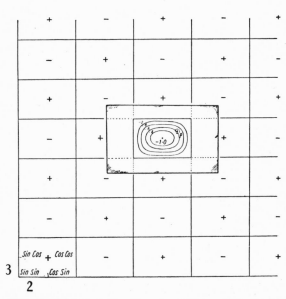

FIG. 163. Chart for the estimation of $\cos 2\pi 2x \cos 2\pi 3y$ (and other similar functions) for all values of $x$ and $y$.

$\sin 2\pi hx \cos 2\pi ky$ or $\cos 2\pi hx \sin 2\pi ky$ (which are required for some plane-groups) by appropriate placing of the origin.

A set of charts for the functions already mentioned suffices for graphical evaluation of the structure amplitudes for the principal zones ($hk0$, $h0l$, $0kl$) of all triclinic, monoclinic, and orthorhombic crystals; since, in Barker's words, this group is the centre of gravity of the crystal kingdom (a large proportion of known substances—including nearly all organic substances—crystallize in these systems), such a set of charts has a very wide range of usefulness. It should be noted that for certain projections of space-groups containing glide planes the projected plane unit cell area appears to have one or both axes subdivided; in other words, the unit cell dimensions of the 'plane-group' are submultiples of those of the corresponding 'space-group'; in such circumstances it is necessary to remember to multiply the atomic coordinates and divide the indices of the reflections to make them appropriate to the plane-group in question.

For basal plane projections ($hk0$) of hexagonal and tetragonal crystals, and for projections of cubic crystals (for which $hk0$, $h0l$, and $0kl$ are all equivalent), the charts showing the combined contributions from a set of crystallographically equivalent atoms have a more complex form. Charts for these and all possible 'plane-groups' are illustrated in the paper by Bragg and Lipson. For some of the more highly symmetrical space groups, it is not possible to represent the contributions of a complete set of equivalent atoms by one point on a plane chart. Chrobak (1937) pointed out that, if there are symmetry elements inclined obliquely to the plane of the projection, all three parameters $x$, $y$, and $z$ may be involved in the coordinates of each atom, and three parameters cannot be represented by a point with two-coordinates. For instance, the threefold axes of the cubic system (along the cube body diagonals) produce equivalent points with coordinates such as $xyz$, $yzx$, and $zxy$, and on a plane chart these would be represented by the three points $xy$, $yz$, and $zx$. For this reason, the structure amplitude graphs for principal projections of some of the cubic space groups are not those for the basal projection of the tetragonal system; for instance, the graph for a principal projection of space group $P23$ is that for plane group $pmm$.

Figures for hexagonal plane-groups have been evaluated by Beevers and Lipson (1938). It should be noted that if charts for the hexagonal and square plane-groups are not available (the labour of constructing them is considerable), sets of equivalent atoms may be divided into subgroups whose contributions may be separately read off on the charts for the less symmetrical plane-groups. Thus, for any pair of atoms related by a (projected) centre of symmetry (plane-group $p2$), the contribution is given by $2 \cos 2\pi(hx+ky)$; any four atoms related in the projection by two apparent planes of symmetry at right angles (plane-group $pmm$) contribute $4 \cos 2\pi hx \cos 2\pi ky$ to the structure amplitude; and so on.

The value of these charts, in showing what adjustments of atomic parameters will increase or decrease the structure amplitude, has already been mentioned. To this little need be added except a suggestion on procedure in dealing with several independent reference atoms simultaneously. This is best explained by an actual example. In attempting to find the $x$ and $y$ coordinates of the atoms in the $hk0$ projection of polychloroprene (Bunn, 1942 $a$) a particular set of postulated coordinates gave roughly correct intensities for the $hk0$ reflections, but there were still some discrepancies, the most serious of which were that the calculated structure amplitude of 240 was too small and that of 420 too great. By using the charts it was readily seen that the movements of atoms which could rectify these discrepancies are as follows:

$$
\begin{array}{cccccc}
 & C_1 & C_2 & C_3 & C_4 & Cl \\
\text{To increase 240} & \nearrow & \uparrow & \searrow & \nearrow & \rightarrow \\
\text{To decrease 420} & \rightarrow & \uparrow & \nearrow & \searrow & \rightarrow
\end{array}
$$

$\left(\begin{smallmatrix} b \\ \uparrow \rightarrow a \end{smallmatrix}\right)$

These verdicts are fairly consistent; in particular, it appears that a movement of $C_2$ upwards or Cl to the right would have the desired effect. Since the diffracting power of Cl is much greater than that of C, a movement of Cl would be much more effective than a similar movement of C. But if Cl is moved, it is found that the intensities of some of the other reflections are adversely affected; in particular, 410 becomes too strong. The movements now required to weaken 410 are as follows:

$$
\begin{array}{cccccc}
 & C_1 & C_2 & C_3 & C_4 & Cl \\
\text{To weaken 410} & \uparrow & \rightarrow & \uparrow & \searrow & \leftarrow
\end{array}
$$

It is not now desired to shift Cl; and of the other atoms it is not desirable to move $C_4$ downwards, as this would weaken 240 again; therefore it seems that the correct thing to do is to move $C_1$ and $C_3$ upwards; in this way, not only is 410 weakened, but 240 is strengthened further. The magnitudes of the movements required were found by trial.†

It will be evident that these methods can only be used *after* approximately correct atomic positions have been postulated. If the positions postulated are not approximately correct, the calculated intensities are nothing like those observed, and it is not possible to decide what movements are necessary to put matters right. Everything therefore depends on whether the preliminary reasoning leads to an approximately correct structure. This is the great limitation of the method of trial.

Three-dimensional charts are not practicable, but for many space-groups the plane charts just described can be utilized for general $(hkl)$ reflections in the following way. For space-group $P2_12_12_1$ the structure amplitude is $\sqrt{(A^2+B^2)}$, where

$$
A = \sum 4f \cos 2\pi\left(hx - \frac{h-k}{4}\right)\cos 2\pi\left(ky - \frac{k-l}{4}\right)\cos 2\pi\left(lz - \frac{l-h}{4}\right)
$$

and

$$
B = -\sum 4f \sin 2\pi\left(hx - \frac{h-k}{4}\right)\sin 2\pi\left(ky - \frac{k-l}{4}\right)\sin 2\pi\left(lz - \frac{l-h}{4}\right).
$$

† A numerical 'least squares' method of adjusting parameters is described by Hughes (1941).

The $xy$ positions of the atoms are plotted on a transparent square chart in the manner already described; the $z$ positions are plotted on a separate strip. To find $A$, the product of the first two cosine terms is read off on a chart giving $\cos 2\pi hx \cos 2\pi ky$ by suitably displacing the origin; for instance, for plane 231, $2\pi\left(\dfrac{h-k}{4}\right)$ is $-90°$ and $2\pi\left(\dfrac{k-l}{4}\right)$ is $+180°$; using the 23 chart, the origin of the atomic position chart is shifted 90° backwards along the $x$ axis and 180° forwards along the $y$ axis. The last cosine term is read off on the strip, using a one-dimensional chart giving $2\pi lz$; for plane 231, $2\pi\left(\dfrac{l-h}{4}\right)$ is $-90°$, and the origin of the strip must therefore be displaced backwards 90°. The only calculation is then the multiplication of the two graphically estimated figures and $f$, the diffracting power of the atom. Sine terms are obtained in a similar way from the same charts.

The procedure is of course longer than for planes of type $hk0$, etc., but it is very much shorter than straightforward calculation of $hkl$ structure amplitudes.

As another example, the structure amplitude for space-group $P2_1/a$ is given by

$$A = 4\cos 2\pi\left(hx+lz+\frac{h+k}{4}\right)\cos 2\pi\left(ky-\frac{h+k}{4}\right); \qquad (B = 0).$$

The $x$ and $z$ positions of the atoms are plotted on a square chart, and the first cosine terms read off on the Bragg and Lipson chart for plane-group $p2$, the origin being displaced by $2\pi\left(\dfrac{h+k}{4}\right)$; the $y$ positions are plotted on a strip as in the previous example, and the second term read off, again after the appropriate displacement of the origin; the two terms are then multiplied.

For the general planes of triclinic crystals the structure amplitude is given by

$$[\textstyle\sum f \cos 2\pi(hx+ky+lz)]^2 + [\textstyle\sum f \sin 2\pi(hx+ky+lz)]^2.$$

The Bragg and Lipson charts cannot be used for these expressions. The following method uses slide-rule technique and has been found to save much time and effort. A strip $A$ is prepared (Fig. 164) on which phase angles and the corresponding cosine and sine values are marked. For a particular atom in the structure the postulated coordinates are marked on a separate strip of paper $B$. The phase angle for any crystal plane $hkl$ is found by placing the two strips together, first of all with their origins opposite to each other (Fig. 164 $a$) and then displacing strip $B$ in the following way. For crystal plane 111, for instance, a pointer (a needle point or a sharp pencil point) is placed at $x$, and strip $B$ is moved along so that its origin comes opposite the pointer (Fig. 164 $b$); the pointer is now moved to $y$ (Fig. 164 $c$), the origin shifted to the pointer, and so on. For 121 two '$y$' displacements would be made. For $2\bar{3}1$ two $x$ displacements, three *negative* $y$ displacements, and one $z$ displacement would

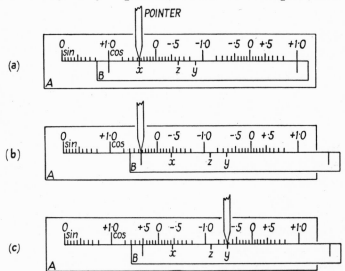

Fig. 164. Slide-rule method for determination of cos (or sin) $2\pi(hx+ky+lz)$.

be made. The value of the cosine (or sine) for the final phase angle is read off, and only needs multiplying by $f$ to give the contribution of the atom in question. A separate paper strip should be prepared for each independent atom in the structure. If the phase angle becomes so large that it is outside the range of strip $A$, it must be transferred back by shifting the pointer $2\pi$. This disadvantage of a slide rule could be remedied by making $A$ and $B$ circles or disks.

Graphical methods give sufficient accuracy for the earlier stages of a structural investigation, when the problem is to find the approximate positions of the atoms; but later, when refinement is attempted, either by the trial methods already described or by the direct methods based on the calculation of the electron density distribution described in Chapter X, more accurate calculations of structure amplitudes are required. The magnitude of the task, for a large number of reflections, especially when there are many atoms in the structural unit, is so great that mechanical aids over and above the usual desk calculating machines are almost essential. Several different types of machines have been devised specifically for structure amplitude calculations, based either on the principle of the planimeter (Evans and Peiser, 1942; Booth, 1947) or on that of the Kelvin tide predictor (Booth, 1948; Vand, 1949, 1950). Pepinsky (1952) has an electronic analogue computer, S-FAC (structure factor analogue computer), which permits one to put in atomic coordinates, shift them at will, and instantaneously observe the effect on the structure amplitudes and phases. Finally, the general purpose electronic digital computers are now widely used for sets of structure amplitude calculations.

**Optical diffraction methods.** 1. *The 'fly's eye' method.* W. L. Bragg (1944) has suggested a method of avoiding the calculation of structure amplitudes altogether, at any rate in the early stages of structure determination. This method consists in making, on a scale small enough to give optical interference effects, a plane pattern corresponding to the postulated crystal structure as seen from one particular direction (usually a unit cell axis); the diffraction pattern produced when monochromatic light passes through this imitation crystal corresponds to the X-ray diffraction pattern produced by the real crystal—that is to say, the relative intensities of the optical diffraction spots correspond with those of the X-ray diffraction spots for the particular zone selected. Thus, suppose the $c$ projection of a crystal is being considered; $x$ and $y$ coordinates for all the atoms are postulated and a picture is made, on a very small scale, showing many repetitions of the projected unit cell; this is done by a photographic reduction method (described below). The diffraction pattern may be observed by looking through a telescope at a point-source of monochromatic light several feet away; when the pattern which represents the crystal structure is placed between the source and the telescope, many images of the source are seen; the relative intensities of these images should correspond with those of the $hk0$ X-ray reflections, if the postulated structure is correct. Another simple method of observing the diffracted beams is to set up a microscopic objective lens (of, say, 2 inches focal length) to produce an image of a monochromatic point-source several feet away, and to examine this image by means of a microscope; when the pattern representing the crystal structure is placed between the source and the 2-inch lens, many images are seen; the 2-inch lens may conveniently be screwed into the substage of the microscope. That this method does give correct intensities is shown by Plate XIV, in which the upper photograph shows part of a pattern representing the $b$ projection of the phthalocyanine crystal (actually 676 repetitions were made), and the lower photograph shows the diffraction pattern given by it. The actual structure amplitudes obtained from the $h0l$ X-ray reflections (Robertson, 1935 c, 1936 a) are given in Table VII, and it can be seen that there is a close correspondence between the optical and X-ray intensities; there are some discrepancies among the weaker spots, but the agreement is on the whole very good—quite good enough to show that the method can be used for the purpose of finding approximate atomic positions.

## TABLE VII

*Structure amplitudes for the phthalocyanine crystal*

| $l$ | | | | | | | | |
|---|---|---|---|---|---|---|---|---|
| 7 | +24 | 0 | −13 | +26 | 0 | −25 | 0 | 0 |
| 6 | −50 | −72 | −67 | −33 | +21 | 0 | +16 | 0 |
| 5 | −60 | +10 | 0 | −76 | 0 | +12 | +13 | 0 |
| 4 | +17 | −13 | 0 | −37 | 0 | +62 | 0 | −30 |
| 3 | −39 | +6 | −13 | +38 | +20 | +20 | −13 | −10 |
| 2 | −85 | −92 | −46 | −40 | 0 | +28 | +52 | +11 |
| 1 | +78 | 0 | +80 | −55 | +15 | +13 | +12 | +16 |
| 0 | | +97 | −85 | −31 | 0 | −14 | −41 | +9 |
| $\bar{1}$ | +78 | +17 | −74 | 0 | −13 | +27 | −31 | −22 |
| $\bar{2}$ | −85 | +68 | −48 | −16 | 0 | 0 | −42 | −37 |
| $\bar{3}$ | −39 | −61 | +38 | +31 | −15 | −46 | −13 | 0 |
| $\bar{4}$ | +17 | +36 | 0 | +31 | +42 | +15 | +10 | 0 |
| $\bar{5}$ | −60 | 0 | +43 | +17 | +44 | 0 | 0 | 0 |
| $\bar{6}$ | −50 | +22 | +59 | −22 | −15 | 0 | +9 | 0 |
| $\bar{7}$ | +24 | 0 | +13 | 0 | −38 | −13 | 0 | 0 |
| | 0 | 1 | 2 | 3 | 4 | 5 | 6 | 7 | $h$ |

The multiple pattern is made in the following way (see Fig. 165). The atoms in one projected unit cell are represented by illuminated holes in an opaque screen. (A square coordinate system is used for convenience, just as square charts are used in the graphical methods.) A multiple photograph of this one unit cell is taken by means of a multiple pinhole camera known as 'the fly's eye' (Fig. 165 a) which consists of 676 pinholes in an area 5 mm square (made by drawing a large pattern of black dots on white card and taking a small photograph on a fine-grained plate). The distances between the illuminated holes and the pinholes, and between pinholes and photographic plate, must be such that the images are properly contiguous, to preserve correct coordinates in the unit cell. Atoms of different diffracting power may be represented either by holes of different sizes, or else, if the holes are all the same size, by covering those holes representing the lighter atoms during part of the exposure.

Another method of making patterns by means of the multiple pinhole camera is to use a single small light-source (such as a car headlamp bulb) which is photographed in various positions, each of which represents the position of an atom in the projected unit cell. Atoms of different diffracting powers are represented by exposures of different lengths.

The multiple patterns made by these methods consist of black 'atoms' on a transparent ground; but the pattern in the upper part of Plate XIV is a reversed pattern (clear 'atoms' on a black ground) made by printing the primary pattern on another plate; both give the same diffraction

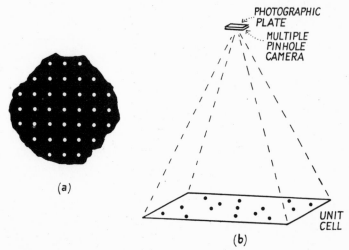

FIG. 165. The 'fly's eye' method. *a*. Part of multiple pinhole camera. *b*. Arrangement for making repeating patterns by the multiple pinhole camera. Atoms in the unit cell are represented by points of light.

pattern except that the central (zero-order) spot is much brighter for the 'black on white' pattern; for this reason the reversed 'white on black' pattern is better for reproduction, because the central spot is less bright and does not swamp the centre of the diffraction pattern.

The glass of which photographic plates are made is not optically flat, but over a small area 5 mm square it is so nearly flat that the diffraction pattern is not seriously affected. Imperfections in the gelatin coating could give trouble, but this can be avoided by putting on the surface a drop of liquid having the same refractive index as gelatin (1·50) and covering with another glass plate (a microscope slide or cover-glass); this is in any case essential when the multiple pattern contains 'atoms' of different diffracting power, because, owing to the removal of different amounts of silver salts from the gelatin, the thickness of gelatin is not the same at all atoms, and the resulting phase displacements of the light

PLATE XIV

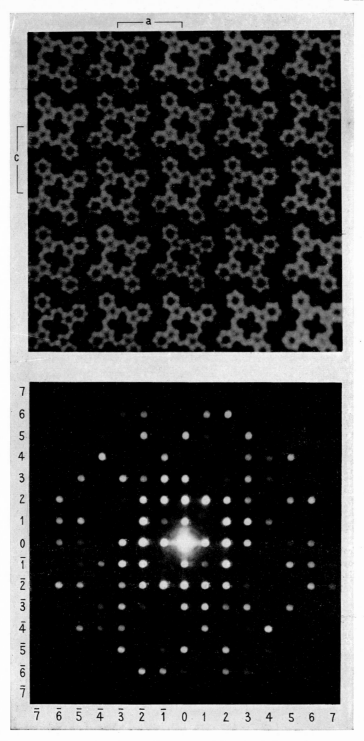

Above: pattern representing the *b* projection of the phthalocyanine structure.
Below: optical diffraction pattern given by it

PLATE XV

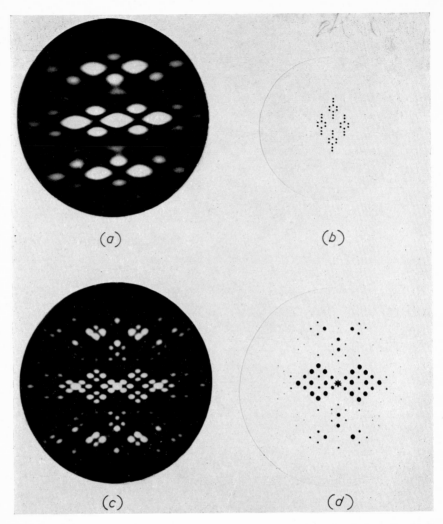

(a) Diffraction pattern of a mask representing (001) projection of a single unit cell of
p-di-isocyanobenzene, CN.C$_6$H$_4$.NC. (b) Mask representing projection of four adjacent
unit cells. (c) Diffraction pattern of (b). (d) Weighted reciprocal lattice—areas of spots
proportional to structure amplitudes. (Hanson and Lipson, 1952)

would seriously affect the diffraction pattern; the immersion liquid, having the same refractive index as gelatin, restores uniformity of optical path-length.

The great advantage of the 'fly's eye' method is its rapidity: a pattern representing the projection of a crystal of the complexity of phthalocyanine or penicillin can be made in one hour—and this time includes the plotting of atomic positions, the successive exposures of a lamp at each of the atomic positions, and the photographic processing (with final washing in methyl alcohol for the sake of rapid drying). Visual inspection of the diffraction pattern shows at once how far the relative intensities of the spots correspond with the X-ray intensities, and examination of the plotted atomic positions on the Bragg and Lipson structure amplitude charts can then be made to decide what adjustments will improve the agreement. This was the method used in the early stages of the work on sodium benzylpenicillin; about twenty successive trials (in as many days) led to a rough structure which was then refined by other methods (Crowfoot, Bunn, Rogers-Low, and Turner-Jones, 1949).

The sign of each structure amplitude can also be determined by the 'fly's eye' method: a second pattern is made with an extra 'atom' at the centre of symmetry, which necessarily adds a positive contribution; spots that are strengthened must be positive, while those that are weakened are negative.

**Optical diffraction methods.** 2. *The transform method.* It is not absolutely necessary to make a multiple pattern of many repetitions of the unit cell projection: it is possible to obtain the desired information (the relative intensities of the diffracted beams corresponding to X-ray reflections) from the diffraction pattern given by a group of points representing the atoms in one unit cell. The possibility of doing this is indicated by the following consideration.

A group of points representing the atoms in the projection of one unit cell give a diffraction pattern which is not limited to particular directions: it gives a continuous distribution of diffraction intensity, not a spot pattern corresponding to the reciprocal lattice. (The continuous distribution of diffracting power of a single unit corresponds to what is called the 'transform' in the same way as the spot diffraction pattern of an array of units corresponds to a reciprocal lattice whose points are weighted according to structure amplitudes.) If now we place alongside this one unit a number of others accurately arranged as in the crystal, each of these units would by itself give the same continuous diffraction pattern; but the diffracted light from the various units is annulled by destructive interference except in certain directions such that the wave from one unit is in phase with the wave from the next—either exactly one wavelength or a whole number of wavelengths in advance or behind. The diffracted light intensity in any one diffraction spot from a repeating pattern evidently corresponds to that given by one unit in that same direction; the difference is that one unit gives a continuous diffraction pattern, whereas an extended repeating pattern of many units gives only spot samples of this continuous diffraction pattern. The diffraction spots given by a repeating pattern represent the continuous diffraction pattern of a single unit *sampled at the reciprocal lattice points.* It follows that if the continuous diffraction pattern of a single unit is photographed, and a transparent grid representing the reciprocal lattice is placed on it, the relative intensities at the reciprocal lattice points give the required information.

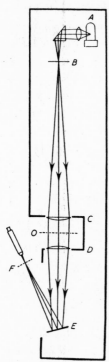

To obtain sufficient light intensity from a group of diffracting centres representing the atoms in one unit cell, it is necessary to work on a bigger scale than in the 'fly's eye' method; the sizes of the 'atoms' and the distances must be larger, and therefore the diffraction pattern will be smaller, unless a lens of longer focal length is used. Taylor, Hinde, and Lipson (1951) describe the optical diffractometer illustrated in Fig. 166, in which two lenses of long focal length are used, the pattern which represents the atoms of one unit cell being placed in the parallel beam between the two lenses. The pattern, consisting of holes punched in an opaque card screen, is made by plotting atomic positions on a larger scale, and using a pantograph punch to make holes on the required small scale. An example of an 'optical transform' is shown in Plate XV.

Fig. 166. An optical diffractometer. *A*, light source; *B*, pinhole; *C* and *D*, lenses; *E*, optically flat mirror; the diffraction pattern of an object placed at *O* is seen in plane *F*. (Taylor, Hinde, and Lipson, 1951.)

The required information can be obtained from the diffraction pattern of one unit cell by superimposing on it a grid representing the reciprocal lattice, accurately oriented. This can be avoided if, instead of one unit cell, four contiguous unit cells are represented; the diffraction pattern (Plate XV) is then crossed by two sets of dark fringes that divide it up at the correct reciprocal lattice intervals, giving a pattern that looks like a diffuse 'fly's eye' pattern (Hanson and Lipson, 1952). This would appear to be the most convenient alternative to the original 'fly's eye' method, over which it has the advantage that it is not tied to a fixed (normally square) coordinate system as the 'fly's eye' method is; a true coordinate system can always be used. On the other hand, it is not so easy to represent atoms of different diffracting powers; however, it can be used for many organic substances. The diffuseness of the diffraction pattern is no real disadvantage: the intensity at the centre of each patch corresponds to the intensity of the corresponding spot in a 'fly's eye' pattern. It is certainly much easier to appreciate relative intensities at the reciprocal lattice positions in these four-unit patterns than in one-unit patterns with superimposed grids; in addition, the four-unit patterns do not have to be photographed and printed—they can be inspected in the diffractometer and conclusions drawn at once.

**Concluding remarks on the method of trial and error.** The general procedure in structure determination by trial has been described. It remains to mention certain experimental and theoretical devices which are of less general application but which are valuable in special circumstances.

*a.* In some diffraction patterns certain types of reflections—the types which if absent altogether would indicate the presence of glide planes or screw axes—are consistently very weak, suggesting the existence of pseudo glide planes or pseudo screw axes. For instance, if all $h0l$ reflections with $h$ odd are very weak, this means that in the $b$ projection there are, about half-way along the $a$ edges of the cell, groups of atoms (molecules, perhaps) looking much the same as, but not identical with, groups of atoms at the cell corners. (See the structure of ascorbic acid, p. 346.) Similarly, it is not uncommon to see in a rotation photograph that the odd layer lines are much weaker than the even ones; this means that there is a pseudo unit cell with one edge (the edge parallel to the axis of rotation) half the true length: one half the unit cell is similar to, but not identical with, the other.

*b.* Two isomorphous crystals in which atoms of different diffracting powers occupy corresponding sites give diffraction patterns in which corresponding reflections have different intensities. The differences of structure amplitudes may be used to locate these atoms: the differences may be regarded as the structure amplitudes which would be given by a hypothetical crystal consisting only of hypothetical atoms having a diffracting power equal to the difference between the diffracting powers of the replaceable atoms in the real crystals. By solving the structure of the hypothetical crystal, using the differences of structure amplitudes, the positions of the replaceable atoms can be found independently of the remaining atoms in the real cell. (The assumption on which this method rests is true only for the stronger reflections: for the weaker reflections, the replacement of one atom by another may cause a change of sign of the structure amplitude, in which case the difference in magnitude of the structure amplitudes does not correspond with the required arithmetical difference. The stronger reflections may, however, provide sufficient evidence for successful location of the atoms in question.)

c. In crystals containing atoms of very similar atomic numbers (copper and manganese, for instance) it may not be possible by normal methods to distinguish between the two species of atom because their diffracting powers are very similar for most X-ray wavelengths. But if an X-ray wavelength lying between the absorption edges of the atoms concerned is used, the difference between the diffracting powers is enhanced, so that distinction is possible (Bradley and Rodgers, 1934).

One final remark. Adjustment of postulated atomic positions by trial need be carried only so far as to settle the phases of the majority of the reflections; from that point the direct method described in Chapter X can be used.

**The background of crystal chemistry.** Ideally, crystal structures should be deduced from the X-ray diffraction patterns of crystals (together with such physical properties as are rigorously determined by internal symmetry) without making any stereochemical assumptions. Most of the simple structures, and some of the more complex ones, have been determined in this way. In the early days of the use of X-ray methods for the determination of crystal structures it was necessary that structures should be deduced by rigorous reasoning from physical data, so that the foundations of crystal chemistry should be well and truly laid. In some of the more complex structures, however, it would be difficult to determine all the atomic positions by such methods alone; and in these circumstances the obvious course is to make use of the wealth of information contained in the large number of crystal structures already established, as well as stereochemical information obtained by other methods, and those physical properties which have been shown by experience to give reliable structural information. There is no reason why the fullest possible use should not be made of the generalizations resulting from previous studies, providing one retains an open mind with regard to the possibilities of deviations from or exceptions to these generalizations. After all, such considerations are only used to indicate approximate atomic positions which, it is hoped, will give approximately correct X-ray intensities; the atoms are then moved about independently until the best possible agreement between the calculated and observed intensities of X-ray reflections from a wide range of planes is obtained. The proof of the correctness of the structure is this agreement, and it does not matter how it is attained—whether by rigid deduction from the X-ray diffraction pattern alone or by reasonable induction from general principles arising from a survey of previously determined structures.

The danger of using the non-rigorous methods is that the possibility of there being more than one arrangement of atoms satisfying the X-ray intensities may be overlooked; there is a danger that the arrangement first selected, if it gives good agreement between observed and calculated intensities, may be accepted without further question. The only remedy here is ruthless self-criticism on the part of the investigator. The chance that two or more arrangements of atoms are equally compatible with the X-ray results is small. It is only in crystals containing both heavy and light atoms that there is an appreciable chance of ambiguity; the heavy atoms may usually be placed with certainty, but lighter atoms, since they contribute comparatively little to the X-ray intensities, may be moved appreciably from selected sites or even to quite different sites without altering radically the calculated intensities. Wyckoff (*The Structure of Crystals*) draws attention to some cases in which alternative structures have been proposed; potassium dithionate (Helwig, 1932; Huggins, 1933) may be cited as an example. Such ambiguities have usually been resolved by subsequent investigations more precise in technique and critical in approach.

In crystals in which different atoms have much the same diffracting power (many organic crystals, for instance) the interchange of different atoms such as nitrogen, oxygen, and carbon will have little effect on the calculated intensities; but usually in such circumstances chemical evidence indicates that all combinations but one are definitely ruled out or wildly improbable. Granted that there is only one possible chemical grouping of atoms in the molecule, the fact that the diffracting powers of all the atoms are similar is actually an advantage, for the chance that two different crystal structures give approximately the same calculated intensities is in these circumstances very small.

It is not within the scope of this book to describe the principles of crystal chemistry and molecular stereochemistry which have so far emerged. The reader is referred for an account of the former subject to Evans's *Crystal Chemistry* (1939) and Pauling's *Nature of the Chemical Bond* (1940), and for the latter to textbooks of organic chemistry such as Freudenberg's *Stereochemie* (1932–4) and the volumes on *Progress in Stereochemistry* edited by Klyne and de la Mare (1954, 1958). It must suffice to observe here (in broadest outline) that the mode of packing of atoms, ions, or molecules in crystals may be regarded as controlled by two principles—the principle of close packing (the closest packing obtainable in view of the shapes and sizes of the building units), and, where ions are concerned, the tendency for an electrically charged unit to surround itself with units of opposite charge. Some of the silicate mineral structures may be regarded as close-packed arrangements of the comparatively large spherical oxygen ions, with the positive ions fitting into the spaces between them; and the use of this generalization played an important part in the solution of some of these structures (Bragg, 1930). Pauling (1929) went farther and formulated a set of rules based on the principle of local satisfaction of electrostatic forces. In molecules and complex ions atoms are joined by the comparatively short, strong, and precisely directed covalent bonds; the covalent radii in such units are only about half the external radii of the atoms, and a molecule or complex ion may thus be regarded as an assemblage of partly merged spheres; Fig. 134 illustrates this. The configurations of aliphatic organic molecules are determined first of all by the tetrahedral disposition of the four bonds of a carbon atom; in double- and triple-bonded groupings the joining of atoms by pairs or triplets of bonds results in a planar configuration of atomic centres in the group

$$\underset{b}{\overset{a}{\diagdown}}C=C\underset{c}{\overset{d}{\diagup}}$$

and a linear configuration of a—C≡C—b. In chain molecules comparatively free rotation round single bonds as axes leads to molecular flexibility; nevertheless certain configurations—those in which the single bonds of covalently linked atoms are staggered (see Fig. 198, p. 356)—are more stable than others, and these configurations are found in crystals (Bunn, 1942 *b*). Aromatic ring molecules, including fused-ring structures like anthracene and chrysene, are flat (J. M. Robertson, 1953). There are exceptions to these last two generalizations of molecular stereochemistry, in molecules in which overcrowding of non-bonded atoms forces the molecules into configurations different from the ones favoured by the bond structures; the accumulation of information on these overcrowded molecules is providing valuable knowledge of the sometimes opposing internal forces that determine molecular configurations (Bunn and Holmes, 1958; Klyne, 1954; Klyne and de la Mare, 1958).

As for the physical properties of crystals, some account of crystal morphology and optics has been given in Chapters II and III, where, however, these subjects were developed only as far as was necessary for identification purposes. For structure determination further consideration of both these subjects, as well as others such as the magnetic, pyro-electric, and piezo-electric properties of crystals, is desirable; this will be found in Chapter VIII.

Examples of the use of stereochemical generalizations and physical properties in structure determination will be found in Chapter IX.

The present chapter on the methods of structure determination would not be complete without some mention of the fact that two structural principles which have so far been tacitly assumed are not always obeyed. The first of these principles is that atoms in crystals occupy precise positions, about which they merely vibrate to a degree depending on the temperature; when the atoms are the constituents of molecules or polyatomic ions this means that the molecules or ions have precisely defined orientations as well as precise mean positions. The second principle is implied in the application of the theory of space-groups to structure determination: it is assumed that the members of a set of crystallographically equivalent positions are all occupied, and that they are occupied by identical atoms. In the majority of crystals these principles are obeyed, but there are some in which one or the other of them is violated: in some crystals, at certain temperatures, whole molecules or ions rotate; in others equivalent positions are occupied indiscriminately by two or more different kinds of atoms; in still others some members of a set of equivalent positions are empty, the gaps being randomly distributed. This subject will not be pursued farther at present; some account of it will be found towards the end of Chapter IX, where examples of different types of abnormal structures are given. Here, in this chapter on the general principles of structure determination, it is only necessary to point out that, in setting out to determine the structure of any crystal, it is obviously necessary to bear in mind the possibility of abnormalities of this sort.

# VIII

# EVIDENCE ON CRYSTAL STRUCTURE
# FROM PHYSICAL PROPERTIES

A STUDY of the physical properties of a crystal—its shape and cleavages, its optical and magnetic characteristics, or piezo- and pyro-electric behaviour—cannot lead to a detailed knowledge of its structure, but it can give valuable information on the general features of the structure; it may lead to a partial knowledge of the internal symmetry, to definite conclusions on the general shape and orientation of molecules or polyatomic ions in the crystal, or to a general idea of the arrangement of the molecules or the distribution of forces.

**Shape and cleavage.** The general shape of a crystal gives an indication of the relative rates of growth of the structure in different directions. Crystals which are roughly equi-dimensional have much the same rate of growth on all the faces which have developed, but those which are markedly plate-like or rod-like have very unequal rates of growth in different directions, and this anisotropy of rate of growth is due either to the effect of the shape and arrangement of the molecules, or to the particular distribution of forces in the crystal, or to both these factors.

In molecular crystals held together by weak undirected van der Waals forces the shape and arrangement of the molecules appear to decide the relative rates of growth. Long molecules tend to pack parallel to each other, forming plate-like crystals in which the long molecules are perpendicular or nearly perpendicular to the plane of the plate (Fig. 167 a). It is apparently easier to add a molecule to an existing layer than to start a new one. Flat molecules sometimes form needle-like crystals in which the planes of the molecules are approximately perpendicular to the needle axis (Fig. 167 b); it is easier to add a flat molecule to an existing pile than to start a new pile alongside the first. On the other hand, either long or flat molecules may form arrangements in which the molecules are not all parallel, giving approximately equi-dimensional crystals. It is evident that when the general shape of a molecule is known through chemical evidence, the shape of the crystals may indicate the general arrangement. Molecules which are roughly spherical, such as hexamethylene tetramine, form roughly equi-dimensional crystals.

In many crystals it is not possible to distinguish individual molecules;

in silicates, for instance, there may be continuous one-, two-, or three-dimensional networks. In plate-like crystals such as mica and the clay minerals, as well as the simpler 'layer lattices' such as $CdI_2$ and $MoS_2$, there are sheets of atoms extending through the whole crystal; in any one sheet the atoms are held together by strong ionic forces, but between neighbouring sheets the forces are much weaker. The cleavage, as well as the anisotropy of rate of growth, is due to this distribution of forces. In other crystals, such as chrysotile, $3MgO.2SiO_2.2H_2O$ ('asbestos'), there are continuous strings of atoms held together by strong ionic forces, the strings being held together by weaker forces; the result is a needle-like or fibrous habit and easy cleavages parallel to the fibre axis.

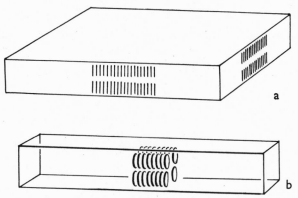

Fig. 167. (a) Long molecules, packed parallel, give plate-like crystals, while (b) flat molecules, packed parallel, give needle-like crystals.

In molecular crystals held together by ionic forces (for instance, salts of organic acids) or polar forces such as 'hydrogen bonds' (for instance, alcohols and amides), the two influences, shape and distribution of forces, may not co-operate, and it is difficult to form any definite conclusions on the structure from crystal shape and cleavage, though it is well to keep these properties in mind during structure determination, for any suggested structure should account for them.

The above remarks refer only to the relative dimensions of crystals. A consideration of the indices of the principal bounding faces may lead to further conclusions, at any rate for molecular crystals. The bounding faces on crystals are apparently those planes having the greatest reticular density of atoms or molecules; the indices of the bounding faces may therefore indicate the general arrangement of the molecules. For instance, when a crystal is found to be bounded entirely or mainly by faces of 110 type (110, 011, 101, etc.) it is likely that there are molecules at the corners and centres of the unit cells, since this is the arrangement that gives greatest reticular density on these planes. For instance, crystals of hexamethylene tetramine $(CH_2)_6N_4$ are rhombic dodecahedra, all the bounding faces of which are of type 110, and the molecular arrangement is body-centred (Dickinson and Raymond, 1923). For similar reasons, in crystals bounded entirely by 111 faces the molecules are likely to be arranged in a face-centred manner, and in prismatic crystals bounded by faces of 110 type a base-centred arrangement is probable. It should be noted, however, that the arrangements need not be centred in the strict (space-lattice) sense; the molecules present at cell-centres or face-centres need not be oriented in the same way as those at the corners of the cell. Benzene crystals, for instance, grow as orthorhombic bipyramids bounded by {111} faces, but the molecular arrangement is not strictly face-centred; there are molecules at the corners and face-centres of the unit cell, but they are not all oriented in the same way (Cox, 1928, 1932 b).

When ionic or polar forces play an important part in binding atoms or molecules together in a crystal, matters are more complex, since the rates of growth of crystal faces appear to be influenced by the distribution of electric charges as well as the reticular density (Kossel, 1927). The subject has not so far received much attention, and it is unwise to attempt to formulate generalizations.

A more detailed consideration of the types of faces present on a crystal may lead to definite conclusions on the point-group symmetry of the atomic or molecular arrangement. This subject has been discussed in Chapter II; the necessity for caution in accepting morphological evidence on internal symmetry should be remembered. According to Donnay (1939), it is possible to go farther, and to deduce (from the relative 'importance' of the different faces) the presence or absence of glide planes and screw axes and in fact the whole space-group symmetry. But although the correct space-group symmetry of some crystals has been deduced from morphological evidence, it would be unwise to place too much reliance on such considerations, for there are some striking exceptions to 'Donnay's law'. (See Donnay and Harker, 1937.) In any case, where X-ray methods are used it is unnecessary to attempt to use morphological evidence to this extent.

**Refractive indices.** The relations between the refractive indices of crystals and their atomic structures were first pointed out by W. L. Bragg (1924 b), who succeeded not only in correlating birefringence with structure in a general way but even in calculating, from the known structures of several crystals (first of all calcite and aragonite), the actual values of the refractive indices and getting them approximately correct. Here we are concerned, for the moment, with the reverse process—the use of refractive indices to provide clues to the atomic arrangements in crystals.

Bragg's theory is roughly this: consider (to take the simplest situation) the effect of a diatomic molecule or ion on light passing through it, first of all when the electric vector of the light waves lies along the line joining the atoms—or, as we usually say, the vibration direction of the light is parallel to the line joining the atoms (Fig. 168 a). Each atom becomes polarized— that is, positive and negative parts suffer a relative displacement in the direction of the electric vector, to an extent which depends on the strength of the

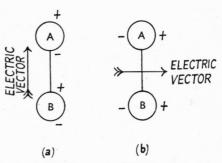

(a)          (b)

FIG. 168. Illustrating Bragg's theory of the refractive indices of crystals.

electric field and the 'polarizability' of the atom. But the two atoms will also affect each other; the presence of dipole $A$ increases (by induction) the polarization of $B$, and the presence of $B$ increases the polarization of $A$. Each atom is thus polarized more than it would be if the other were absent. If, however, the electric vector of the light waves is perpendicular to the line joining the atoms, as in Fig. 168 b, the induction effect of dipole $A$ is to decrease the polarization of $B$, and similarly the presence of $B$ decreases the polarization of $A$. The effective dielectric constant is therefore much greater for situation $a$ than for situation $b$, and since the refractive index is proportional to the square root of the dielectric constant,† the refractive index is much higher when the electric vector lies along the line joining the atoms than when it is perpendicular to this direction.

In a similar way it is easy to show that a flat molecule or polyatomic ion (such as $CO_3^{--}$ ion, in which all the atoms lie in a plane and the oxygen atoms form an equilateral triangle round the carbon atom) has a higher refractive index when the electric vector lies in the plane of the group of atoms than when it is perpendicular to this plane.

In crystals, the molecules or polyatomic ions are surrounded by others, the presence of which complicates matters; but the distances between

† See for instance Richtmeyer, 1928, p. 111.

atoms in neighbouring molecules or polyatomic ions are much greater than those between atoms linked by primary bonds, and since the induction effect is very sensitive to distance (inversely proportional to the cube of the distance), the induction effects of neighbouring molecules or polyatomic ions are small. The main factor controlling the bire-fringence of crystals containing strongly birefringent molecules or poly-atomic ions is the relative orientation of these units. Where they are all parallel, as in most carbonates and some nitrates, the refractivities of the crystal are approximately those of the individual polyatomic ions; where the birefringent units are inclined to each other their individual effects are partially, or in cubic crystals completely, cancelled out.

The effect of interatomic distance is strikingly illustrated by the fact that the birefringence of nitrates in which the nitrate ions are all parallel is much greater than that of carbonates of similar structure, though the interatomic distances in the nitrate ion are only slightly less than those in the carbonate ion:

| | | $\alpha$ | $\beta$ | $\gamma$ | Distances | |
|---|---|---|---|---|---|---|
| | | | | | O—O | N(or C)—O |
| KNO$_3$ . . . . | | 1·335 | 1·506 | 1·506 ⎱ | 2·10 | 1·21 |
| NaNO$_3$ . . . | | 1·336 | 1·586 | (= $\beta$) ⎰ | | |
| CaCO$_3$ (calcite) . . | | 1·486 | 1·658 | (= $\beta$) ⎱ | 2·18 | 1·26 |
| ,, (aragonite) . . | | 1·530 | 1·681 | 1·686 ⎰ | | |

In view of this, it is not surprising that neighbouring ions have only minor effects, since the distances between oxygen atoms in neighbour-ing ions are 2·7 Å. Nor is it surprising that in crystals in organic sub-stances, where the distances between linked carbon atoms are 1·3–1·5 Å and the distances between carbon atoms in neighbouring molecules 3·5–4·2 Å, the refractive indices depend almost entirely on the refrac-tivities of individual molecules and the relative orientations of these molecules in the crystals.

The examples in Table VIII (in addition to those already quoted) will gives some idea of the birefringence to be expected for various groups. (See also Wooster, 1931.)

Organic substances containing double bonds have higher average refractive indices than singly-linked compounds, and the refractive index for light vibrating along the double bond is higher than for other directions; this is due, partly at any rate, to the fact that the distance between carbon atoms joined by a double bond (1·33 Å) is considerably less than that between singly-linked carbon atoms (1·53 Å). A succession of conjugated double bonds along a chain gives an extremely high refractive index for light vibrating along the chain; a good example is methyl bixin

$$CH_3O—CO—CH=\{CH—C(CH_3)=CH—CH=\}_4CH—CO—OCH_3$$

which has a refractive index of 2·6 for the chain direction, the other principal indices being 1·47 and 1·65 (Waldmann and Brandenberger, 1932). Aromatic compounds, if the rings are all parallel to each other in the crystal, have very high refractive indices for vibration directions in the plane of the rings and a low index normal to the ring; they are thus strongly negatively birefringent.

TABLE VIII

| | | $\alpha$ | $\beta$ | $\gamma$ | Sign | $\gamma-\alpha$ | Reference |
|---|---|---|---|---|---|---|---|
| Linear | NaN$_3$ | .. | .. | .. | + | Very large | Wooster, 1938. |
| | Ca(OCl)$_2$.3H$_2$O | (= $\beta$) | 1·535 | 1·63 | + | 0·095 | Bunn,Clark,andClifford,1935. |
| Obtuse V-shaped | NaNO$_2$ | 1·340 | 1·425 | 1·655 | + | 0·315 | Bunn, not published elsewhere. |
| Low pyramid | KClO$_3$ | 1·410 | 1·517 | 1·524 | − | 0·114 | Zachariasen, 1929. |
| Flat with planes parallel | PbCO$_3$ | 1·804 | 2·076 | 2·078 | − | 0·274 | Larsen and Berman, 1934. |
| | NaHCO$_3$ | 1·380 | 1·500 | 1·586 | − | 0·206 | Winchell, 1931. |
| | C$_6$(CH$_3$)$_6$ | 1·481 | 1·680 | 1·720 | − | 0·239 | Winchell, 1954. |
| | C$_6$H$_3$(C$_6$H$_5$)$_3$ | 1·524 | 1·867 | 1·873 | − | 0·349 | Orelkin and Lonsdale, 1934. |
| | C$_{10}$H$_8$ (naphthalene) | 1·442 | 1·775 | 1·932 | − | 0·490 | Bhagavantam, 1929. |

When flat molecules have their planes inclined at a large angle to each other but all parallel to a line, the refractive index for light vibrating along this line is high, but in all directions perpendicular to this line the refractive index is moderately low (corresponding to an average value for the other two principal directions in the molecule); the birefringence is thus positive, not negative. Thus in the tetragonal crystal of urea $O=C(NH_2)_2$, the planes of the Y-shaped molecules are perpendicular to each other but parallel to a line (the $c$ axis); consequently this crystal is uniaxial positive ($\omega = 1·481$, $\epsilon = 1·602$).

It will be evident that the birefringence and the orientation of the indicatrix may be used in a semi-quantitative manner as evidence of the orientation of strongly birefringent groups of atoms in crystals. When a crystal containing flat molecules or ions is found to have strong negative birefringence it can be assumed that the flat groups are all roughly parallel to each other and perpendicular to the direction of lowest index; and when a crystal containing chain molecules or ions is found to have strong positive birefringence it can be assumed that the chains are all roughly parallel to each other and to the direction of highest index. Some idea of the birefringence to be expected for a particular group can often be obtained from the properties of crystals of already known structure. Evidence of this type is, in general, all that is required in structure determination; the details—the precise orientation of the groups and the atomic positions—must be settled by the interpretation of X-ray diffraction patterns; the conclusions from optical properties merely provide the starting-point for trial structures.

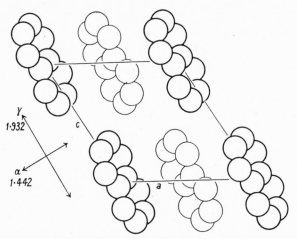

Fig. 169. Structure of naphthalene.

A few examples will show the value of such considerations. Naphthalene (monoclinic, $a = 8.29$ Å, $b = 5.97$ Å, $c = 8.68$ Å, $\beta = 122° 42'$) has refractive indices 1.442, 1.775, and 1.932. The birefringence is so strong that we should not be far wrong in assuming that the planes of the two molecules in the cell are roughly parallel; and if we associate the three indices with the three vibration directions of the molecule itself, we are led to suppose that the longest axis of the molecule lies parallel to the vibration direction of $\gamma$ (that is, nearly parallel to $c$), and the intermediate axis along $b$ (the $\beta$ vibration direction).

The complete structure, determined by Robertson (1933 c), shows that this is substantially correct; the two molecules have their longest axes almost exactly parallel to the direction of highest index, and their intermediate axes tilted (one in one direction and the other in the opposite direction) 29° to the $b$ axis (Fig. 169).

In a crystal of hexamethylbenzene (triclinic, with one molecule in the unit cell) the vibration direction for the lowest refractive index is almost exactly normal to the 001 plane (Bhagavantam, 1930), indicating that the plane of the molecule is almost exactly parallel to 001; and again this is correct (Lonsdale, 1929).

Potassium chlorate is monoclinic; it has strong negative birefringence, and the vibration direction for the lowest refractive index lies in the $ac$ plane, making an angle of 56° with the $c$ axis. The conclusion that the low pyramidal (that is, more or less flat) chlorate ions have their oxygen triangles normal to this direction of least refractive index is correct within 1° (Zachariasen, 1929).

Turn now to crystals whose structures are as yet unknown. The substance $C_6H_5$—CH=CH—CO—$C_6H_4$—$CH_3$, the molecules of which are expected to be elongated in shape, forms orthorhombic crystals having the refractive indices and vibration directions $\alpha = 1\cdot607$, $\parallel a$, $\beta = 1\cdot634$, $\parallel c$, $\gamma = 1\cdot881$, $\parallel b$ (Groth, 1906–19). The strong positive birefringence shows that all the molecules in the crystal have their long axes roughly parallel to each other, and to the vibration direction having the highest refractive index, that is, the $b$ axis. Also, the fact that the two low indices are so similar indicates that the planes of the benzene rings in the crystal are not all parallel to each other.

Vaterite, or $\mu$-$CaCO_3$, which grows in the form of hexagonal plates, is interesting, because it has fairly strong positive birefringence ($\omega = 1\cdot550$, $\epsilon = 1\cdot650$), in contrast to calcite and aragonite, which are strongly negative. The strong positive birefringence shows that the negative carbonate ions cannot be parallel to the plane of the crystal plate; the planes of the flat carbonate ions must be roughly perpendicular to the plane of the crystal plate. An arrangement in which the planes of the carbonate ions are parallel to the apparent sixfold axis but not parallel to each other would give $\epsilon$ similar to the highest index of calcite or aragonite (actually a little lower because the density of $\mu$-$CaCO_3$ is low), and the indices for vibrations in the plane of the plate definitely higher than the low indices of calcite and aragonite. The reported indices of $\mu$-$CaCO_3$ (Winchell, 1931) are indeed of this order. These considerations also lead to a further conclusion of structural significance. The unit cell is stated to contain two molecules (Olshausen, 1925). Now in a carbonate ion the only symmetry axes in the plane of the atoms are twofold axes. Trigonal or hexagonal symmetry cannot be achieved by any arrangement of two carbonate ions oriented as the optical properties demand. Hence, if the cell really contains two molecules, its symmetry cannot be trigonal or hexagonal; or alternatively, if the symmetry is trigonal or hexagonal, the true unit cell must be larger than that reported.

Quantitative calculations of the refractive indices by means of the Bragg theory can give more precise indications of molecular orientation; this was done for oxalic acid and some of its salts by Hendricks and Deming (1935). There is, however, an alternative method that lends itself more readily to the calculation of directional properties of molecules and crystals than the Bragg theory; this is based on the concept of bond polarizability in place of the atom polarizability used in the Bragg theory. For average (not directional) polarizabilities, it was shown by Denbigh (1940) that an empirical additive scheme of bond polarizabilities, in which each different type of chemical bond is associated with its own polarizability contribution, and the contributions of the various bonds are simply added together, can give the refractive index of an organic liquid, or the average refractive index of a crystal, just as accurately as the older scheme of atom polarizabilities. For directional properties in anisotropic crystals it is necessary to use, not an average polarizability for each bond, but an ellipsoid of polarizability; to each bond is assigned one longitudinal and one transverse polarizability (the ellipsoid of polarizability being assumed to be an ellipsoid of revolution).

For a polyatomic molecule the polarizability $P$ in a principal direction of the polarizability ellipsoid of the molecule is given by

$$P = \sum p_L \cos^2\theta + \sum p_T \sin^2\theta \quad \text{(summed for all the bonds),}$$

where $\theta$ is the angle between a bond and the direction in question, $p_L$ is the longitudinal polarizability (along the bond), and $p_T$ the transverse polarizability (across the bond). Values of the longitudinal polarizability and the transverse polarizability for a number of individual bonds have been obtained from experimental measurements of the Kerr effect (birefringence due to orientation of molecules by an electric field) and of the state of polarization of light scattered by gas molecules of simple chemical structure: by combining information from several substances and solving simultaneous equations, individual bond polarizabilities have been obtained (Wang, 1939; Denbigh, 1940; Le Fèvre and Le Fèvre, 1955).

For a crystal, the polarizability for a principal direction of the ellipsoid is calculated by using the same expression; the refractive index $n$ for that direction is taken to be related to the polarizability by the Lorenz–Lorentz expression,

$$\frac{n^2-1}{n^2+2} \cdot \frac{M}{d} = \frac{4}{3}\pi NP.$$

The crystal is thus treated as an assemblage of molecules which contribute independently, without influencing each other; since distances between atoms in neighbouring molecules (usually 2·5–4·0 Å) are much greater than those between bonded atoms within a molecule, little error is to be expected through neglecting molecular interaction. A more serious possible source of error is the neglect of interaction between neighbouring bonds within the molecule; such errors are minimized by using values of individual bond polarizabilities derived from molecules similar in local structure to those in the crystal under consideration; for instance, for aliphatic chain compounds the value for C—C deduced from the refractive indices of chain hydrocarbon crystals should be used (Bunn and Daubeny, 1954).

Some values of polarizabilities for the more common types of bonds are given in Table IX. It is found that the refractive indices of strongly

TABLE IX

*Bond polarizabilities*

|  | $p_L \times 10^{25}\ cm^3$ | $p_T \times 10^{25}\ cm^3$ | Ref. |
|---|---|---|---|
| C—C | 9·7 | 2·5 | 1 |
| C=C | 29·0 | 10·7 | 2 |
| C≡C | 35·4 | 12·7 | 2 |
| C—C aromatic | 22·5 | 4·8 | 2 |
| C(arom.)—C(aliph.) | 14·0 | 3·0 | 3 |
| C—N | 13·8 | 2·2 | 3 |
| C—O | 14·6 | 1·7 | 3 |
| C=O | 20·0 | 10·0 | 3 |
| C—H | 8·2 | 6·0 | 1 |
| N—H | 5·8 | 8·4 | 2 |
| O—H | 4·8 | 8·0 | 3 |
| C—F | 15·0 | 4·0 | 4 |
| C—Cl | 36·7 | 20·8 | 2 |
| C—Br | 50·4 | 28·8 | 2 |

*References*: 1, Bunn and Daubeny, 1954; 2, Denbigh, 1940; 3, Bunn and Daubeny, not previously published; these are empirical values used to obtain reasonable agreement for the crystals in Table X; 4, Le Fèvre and Le Fèvre, 1955. See also H. A. Stuart, 1955, p. 449; Le Fèvre and Le Fèvre, 1954, 1958.

birefringent crystals, especially of aromatic compounds, calculated from the figures given, agree approximately with the measured values; some examples are given in Table X. The refractive indices are naturally calculated for the extinction directions of the crystals. The angles made by all the bonds in the unit cell with the principal optical directions must be calculated; for highly symmetrical molecules it may be permissible to calculate polarizabilities for principal directions in the molecule first, and then to calculate for the principal optical directions in the crystal; but in general it is best to work straight from the bond directions to the principal optical directions.

Good agreement is not to be expected for weakly birefringent crystals, in which the contributions of differently directed bonds largely neutralize each other. Perhaps the best indication of the degree of approxima-

## TABLE X

### Refractive indices of crystals

(For each crystal, the upper figure gives the observed refractive index for the sodium $D$ line (Winchell, 1954), the lower figure that calculated from the bond polarizabilities of Table IX.)

| Crystal | Symmetry | | $\alpha$ | $\beta$ | $\gamma$ |
|---|---|---|---|---|---|
| $C_{38}H_{78}$ | Orthorhombic | obs. | 1·518 | 1·523 | 1·588 |
| | | calc. | 1·513 | 1·546 | 1·587 |
| Oxalic acid | Orthorhombic | obs. | 1·445 | 1·540 | 1·635 |
| | | calc. | 1·395 | 1·543 | 1·625 |
| Pentaerythritol | Tetragonal | obs. | 1·548 ($\epsilon$) | 1·559 ($\omega$) | |
| | | calc. | | 1·533 ($\omega$) | 1·545 ($\epsilon$) |
| ,, tetra-acetate | Tetragonal | obs. | | 1·433 ($\omega$) | 1·483 ($\epsilon$) |
| | | calc. | | 1·439 ($\omega$) | 1·517 ($\epsilon$) |
| Resorcinol | Orthorhombic | obs. | 1·578 | 1·620 | 1·627 |
| | | calc. | 1·552 | 1·620 | 1·622 |
| Hexamethylbenzene | Triclinic | obs. | 1·481 | 1·680 | 1·720 |
| | | calc. | 1·473 | 1·720 | 1·720 |
| Diphenyl | Monoclinic | obs. | 1·560 | 1·654 | 1·945 |
| | | calc. | 1·515 | 1·733 | 1·937 |
| Terphenyl | Monoclinic | obs. | 1·584 | 1·687 | 2·004 |
| | | calc. | 1·533 | 1·738 | 1·993 |
| Dibenzyl | Monoclinic | obs. | 1·529 | 1·629 | 1·757 |
| | | calc. | 1·490 | 1·660 | 1·756 |
| Benzil | Trigonal | obs. | | 1·659 ($\omega$) | 1·678 ($\epsilon$) |
| | | calc. | | 1·609 ($\omega$) | 1·689 ($\epsilon$) |
| Fluorene | Orthorhombic | obs. | 1·578 | 1·663 | 1·919 |
| | | calc. | 1·536 | 1·725 | 1·913 |
| Naphthalene | Monoclinic | obs. | 1·442 | 1·775 | 1·932 |
| | | calc. | 1·487 | 1·772 | 1·964 |
| Anthracene | Monoclinic | obs. | 1·556 | 1·786 | 1·959 |
| | | calc. | 1·509 | 1·812 | 2·105 |
| Chrysene | Monoclinic | obs. | 1·585 | 1·787 | 2·068 |
| | | calc. | 1·541 | 1·842 | 2·078 |

tion to be expected is given by hexamethylbenzene; the molecules themselves have hexagonal symmetry, and, being all parallel to each other in the crystal, would be expected to give uniaxial negative optics, with $\beta = \gamma$ and $\alpha$ much lower; although this is roughly true, it is found that $\beta = 1·680$ and $\gamma = 1·720$; this difference is due either to molecular interaction in the optical sense (that is, to the deficiencies of the bond polarizability scheme), or to some distortions of the molecules (due to the triclinic packing) which have not been detected in the X-ray diffraction studies.

The bond polarizability scheme gives a better appreciation of the optical characteristics of molecules than the simple ideas of molecular shape used in earlier pages. For instance, if shape in itself were the dominant factor, aliphatic saturated chain molecules would be expected to be very strongly positively birefringent; in fact, unbranched chain hydrocarbon molecules have only moderate positive birefringence (see Table X), because the carbon-carbon bonds are not parallel to the chain axis but form a zigzag. Side substituents reduce the birefringence, because the bonds joining them to the chain are perpendicular to the chain axis; thus poly*iso*butene $(-CH_2-C(CH_3)_2-)_p$ and polyvinyl chloride $(-CH_2-CHCl-)_p$ are only weakly positively birefringent. The double bonds perpendicular to the chain in the $C{=}O$ groups of nylon 66 $(-NH(CH_2)_6NH.CO(CH_2)_4CO-)_p$ bring the $\beta$ refractive index nearly up to $\gamma$ (Bunn and Garner, 1947).

The bond polarizability scheme has been used by Treloar (1954, 1958) and Saunders (1956, 1957) in studies of the birefringence of stretched rubberlike substances; by combining stress birefringence values with rubber elasticity theory, they have calculated the apparent size of the rigid chain unit (the chain being regarded as a string of freely jointed rigid units); in actual fact such chains are semi-flexible, and comparison of the sizes of the apparent rigid units of different polymers gives some idea of the relative flexibilities of the chains; the $CH_2$ chain is stiffer than the polyisoprenes rubber and gutta-percha. The scheme has also been used to calculate the refractive indices of polymer crystals, which cannot be measured experimentally because the crystals cannot be obtained free from amorphous material or as single crystals of sufficient size; from the measured birefringence of oriented sheets, the calculated indices, together with X-ray diffraction measurements of crystal orientation, have been used to estimate the degree of molecular orientation of amorphous material (Holmes and Palmer, 1958; Stein, 1958).

**Absorption of light.** Observation of the absorption of light in different vibration directions may also be useful. Not very much work has yet been done on this subject, but it seems that for molecules containing chromophoric groups such as a polyene chain $(-CH{=}CH-)_n$, or quinonoid

$$=C\!\!\bigg\langle\begin{array}{c}C{=}C\\[2pt]C{=}C\end{array}\bigg\rangle C=$$

or azo $-N{=}N-$ groups, the absorption is largely confined to the vibration direction parallel to the double bonds. Thus, in a crystal of methyl bixin, the vibration direction along the polyene chain is characterized not only by a very high refractive index as we have already seen, but also by very high absorption; it is practically black for this direction, and red or yellow for other directions. For other examples of the use of such evidence see Bernal and Crowfoot, 1933 a (azoxy compounds), W. H. Taylor, 1936 (rubrene, etc.), and Perutz, 1939, 1953 (parallelism of the four chromophoric groups in molecules of methaemoglobin and oxyhaemoglobin, and deduction of molecular orientation in other protein crystals). In crystals of the complex substances used as dyestuffs the colours (that is, the positions of the absorption bands) for the principal vibration directions are often very different from each other; a study of these absorptions in relation to the chemical constitution of the molecules and their orientation in the crystals should throw much light on the problem of the relation of colour to chemical constitution; and this knowledge, in turn, will be useful in the determination of crystal structures of new substances.

The dichroism of infra-red absorption bands can be used in a similar way; indeed the information obtained may be more specific, for some bands are known to be associated with simple vibrations of specific groups of atoms. Suppose an absorption band at a particular frequency is known to be due to a stretching mode of a diatomic group such as C—H, N—H, O—H, or C=O; the direction of dipole moment change ('transition moment') during the vibration is along the bond, and consequently absorption is strongest when the vibration direction of the polarizer is parallel to the bond direction. For a crystal in which all the bonds of this type are parallel to each other, the strength of the band will be greatest when the vibration direction of the polarizer is parallel to this direction, and least when it is perpendicular to this direction; consequently, when it is found that the dichroism is strong for such an absorption band (by taking spectra for several angular settings of the polarizer), it can be concluded that all bonds of the type in question are nearly parallel to the vibration direction in which the greatest absorption is observed. For simple bending modes the transition moment is perpendicular to the bond, and the sign of the dichroism is therefore opposite to that of the stretching modes. Such effects have been used by Crooks (1947) and Brown and Corbridge (1948, 1954) to indicate the orientation of C=O, N—H, and N—$C_6H_5$ groups in the crystal of acetanilide. For such studies it is necessary to grow thin plate crystals; this is done by cooling a thin film of the melted substance between rock-salt plates and starting crystallization at one end by touching with a seed crystal. ·

This method is of greatest value only when all the bonds of one type in the unit cell are roughly parallel to each other, so that strong dichroism results : an observation of weak dichroism may rule out certain arrangements, but cannot give positive information. Some caution is necessary in drawing quantitative conclusions, at any rate for certain bonds, for it has been shown by single-crystal studies on substances of known structure that the transition moment of the $C=O$ bond in amide groups is inclined at about $20°$ to the bond direction (Abbott and Elliott, 1955; Sandeman, 1955). This is probably largely an intramolecular effect, but there are also intermolecular effects which give rise, in certain structures, to striking polarization effects : in orthorhombic crystals of unbranched paraffin hydrocarbons (from $C_{20}$ to polythene), the absorption band due to the $CH_2$ rocking vibration, which normally occurs at 725 cm$^{-1}$, is split into a doublet at 720 and 730 cm$^{-1}$, of which the 720 cm$^{-1}$ component is completely polarized along the $a$ axis while the 730 cm$^{-1}$ component is completely polarized along $b$ (Krimm, 1954). The reason is that there are two differently oriented molecules in the unit cell (see Fig. 136, p. 250), and the vibrations of the $CH_2$ groups in these neighbouring molecules combine when they are in phase to give the higher frequency vibration at 730 cm$^{-1}$ polarized along $b$, while when they are opposite in phase they combine to give the 720 cm$^{-1}$ vibration polarized along $a$ (Stein, 1955; Keller and Sandeman, 1955; Krimm, Liang, and Sutherland, 1956). Such splitting does not occur in crystals of chain compounds in which the molecular planes are all parallel, as in the triclinic forms of these substances, and the observation of the singlet or doublet character of this $CH_2$ rocking band can therefore be used, in preliminary considerations of structure, to indicate the type of molecular packing. This band is also a singlet (as would be expected) in hexagonal forms in which the chain molecules are rotating (Chapman, 1957).

Infra-red dichroism has been used in studies of polymer specimens in which the chain molecules are parallel to each other, to give evidence on the orientation of particular atomic groups. In nylon and polyvinyl alcohol (Ambrose, Elliott, and Temple, 1949), 'Terylene' (Miller and Willis, 1953), and polytetrafluoroethylene (Liang and Krimm, 1956) the results are consistent with structures already established by X-ray methods. Turning to more complex structures not yet solved in detail by X-ray methods, infra-red dichroism has indicated that in cellulose the O—H bonds are predominantly parallel to the chain axis (Mann and Marrinan, 1956, 1958); in synthetic polypeptides it serves to distinguish between $\beta$ configurations, in which the N—H and C$=$O bonds are perpendicular to the chain axis, and $\alpha$ (helical) configurations, in which these bonds are roughly parallel to the chain axis (Bamford, Elliott, and Hanby, 1956).

**Rotation of the plane of polarization.** One other optical character which may sometimes contribute information useful in structure determination is the rotation of the plane of polarization. In cases where the shape or the X-ray diffraction pattern or other properties do not yield unequivocal evidence on point-group symmetry, a positive observation of the phenomenon may settle the question. (For experimental method, see Chapter III.)

A question which may sometimes be asked is this: 'If an enantiomorphous crystal—that is, one possessing neither planes, nor inversion axes, nor a centre of symmetry—is dissolved in a solvent, does the solution necessarily rotate the plane of polarization of light?' The answer to this question is, 'Not necessarily'. If the molecules or ions of which the crystal is composed are themselves enantiomorphous, then the solution *will* be optically active. But it must be remembered that enantiomorphous crystals may be built from non-centrosymmetric molecules which in isolation possess planes of symmetry—these planes of symmetry being ignored in the crystal structure; such molecules in solution would not rotate the plane of polarization of light. (A molecule of this type, in isolation, may rotate the plane of polarization of light (see p. 91), but the mass of randomly oriented molecules in a solution would show no net rotation.) An example is sodium chlorate $NaClO_3$; the crystals are enantiomorphous and optically active, but the solution of the salt is inactive because the pyramidal chlorate ions (see Fig. 131) possess planes of symmetry.

**Magnetic properties.** Anisotropy of diamagnetic susceptibility has been used, in much the same way as optical anisotropy, as evidence of molecular orientation in crystals.

All substances composed of ions, atoms, or molecules having no resultant orbital or spin moment (this includes organic substances and inorganic salts, except those containing transition elements like iron and platinum) are diamagnetic. This means that when placed near a magnet they are repelled; or, more precisely, when placed in a non-uniform magnetic field they tend to move to a weaker part of the field. Evidently a piece of a diamagnetic substance when placed in a magnetic field becomes (by induction) a magnet in opposition to the inducing field—behaviour opposite to that of ferromagnetic and paramagnetic substances. The force of repulsion is exceedingly minute, but can be measured if a powerful magnet and delicate suspensions are used. The ratio of the induced magnetism to the field strength is known as the diamagnetic susceptibility.

Crystals, except those belonging to the cubic system, are anisotropic in this respect; the force of repulsion varies with the orientation of the crystal with respect to the direction of the field. The graph representing vectorially the diamagnetic susceptibility in all directions in a crystal is an ellipsoid, whose orientation with respect to the unit cell is restricted by symmetry in exactly the same way as that of the optical indicatrix. Thus, for uniaxial crystals the magnetic ellipsoid is an ellipsoid of revolution whose unique axis coincides with the threefold, fourfold, or sixfold axis of the crystal; for orthorhombic crystals the ellipsoid has three unequal axes which necessarily coincide with the three axes of the crystal; for monoclinic crystals the only restriction is that one of the principal axes of the magnetic ellipsoid must coincide with the $b$ axis of the crystal; while for triclinic crystals the orientation of the ellipsoid is not restricted in any way.

The available methods for the determination of diamagnetic susceptibilities in crystals will not be described here. Papers by Rabi (1927), Krishnan and his collaborators (1933, 1934, 1935), and the excellent review of the whole subject by Lonsdale (1937 a) should be consulted. See also Wooster (1957).

For many aromatic molecules, and for the flat nitrate and carbonate ions, the relative dimensions of the magnetic ellipsoid are opposite to those of the refractive index ellipsoid: the susceptibility is numerically much greater in the direction normal to the plane of the molecule or ion than in directions lying *in* the plane. This is partly a matter of relative electron density in the different directions; but for aromatic substances, with their large conjugated ring systems, it seems that the large orbits of the resonance electrons play an important part. (Pauling, 1936; London, 1937; Lonsdale, 1937 b.)

Crystals in which the molecules are all parallel to each other have the same characteristics as the individual molecules. But when there are two or more differently oriented molecules in the unit cell, the magnetic anisotropies of the individual molecules are to some extent neutralized. The magnetic properties of a crystal are, very precisely, the vectorial sum of those of the constituent molecules. (For equations, see Lonsdale,

1937 *a*.) The effects of neighbouring molecules on each other are negligible, the reason being that induced magnetic effects are exceedingly feeble. Magnetic properties therefore have, at any rate theoretically, some advantage over optical properties for the determination of molecular orientation, since molecular interaction does play a small part in determining refractive indices. However, in structure determination, physical properties are needed only to indicate approximate molecular orientations, and for this purpose optical properties are quite satisfactory, and usually much easier to measure than magnetic properties. The precise details of the structure are settled by X-ray analysis. Magnetic properties are likely to be most valuable in circumstances in which refractive indices are not easily measured. For instance, crystals of many substances used as dyes are so strongly coloured that even minute crystals are almost opaque, so that it is scarcely possible to measure refractive indices.

The magnetic ellipsoid of a crystal or a molecule is not always the inverse of the refractive index ellipsoid. This is shown by the properties of potassium chlorate, $KClO_3$. Optically, the chlorate ion is strongly negative like the nitrate and carbonate ions; but magnetically it is also negative, in contrast to the nitrate and carbonate ions which are positive. (Krishnan, Guha, and Banerjee, 1933.) The reason, no doubt, lies in the pyramidal form of the chlorate ion (Fig. 131). The refractive indices are determined largely by the triangle of oxygen atoms forming the base of the pyramid; the chlorine atom at the apex has little effect, because $Cl^{+5}$ is less polarizable than $O^{-2}$. Magnetic properties are determined by quite different factors, electron density being important —and for this reason the comparatively heavy and dense chlorine atom and its position outside the plane of the oxygen atoms plays a very important part. The effect does not appear to have been quantitatively explained, and the facts prompt caution in interpreting magnetic properties except for molecules or complex ions of well-established characteristics.

Crystals composed of aliphatic chain molecules provide further examples of special effects which give rise to diamagnetic characteristics different from those which might have been expected. The susceptibilities of several such crystals have been shown to be numerically greater along the chain molecules than across them; thus the magnetic characteristics of these chain molecules (one large susceptibility and two smaller ones) are the same as those of flat aromatic molecules, not inverse as might have been expected.

The magnetic properties of crystals composed of aromatic polynuclear molecules may give information on the relative orientations of the benzene rings to each other. Thus, Clews and Lonsdale (1937) concluded from the magnetic anisotropy of crystals of o-diphenylbenzene that the planes of the o-phenyl groups are inclined at 50° to the plane of the main ring.

The relations between paramagnetic and ferromagnetic properties and structure are less simple than in the case of diamagnetic substances, and will not be dealt with here; the reader is referred to the review by Lonsdale (1937 a).

**Pyro-electric and piezo-electric tests.** When a crystal belonging to one of the non-centrosymmetric classes is heated or cooled, it develops electric charges and becomes positive at one end and negative at the other end of each polar axis. Therefore, if a crystal is found to be pyro-electric, it must belong to one of the classes which lack a centre of symmetry. Various qualitative tests for pyro-electric character have been used. The three most suitable for small crystals are the following:

(a) Crystals are placed on a metal plate or spoon and dipped in liquid air. When the grains have cooled, the plate is tilted until it becomes vertical; pyro-electric crystals stick to the metal, others fall off. (Martin, 1931.)

(b) Small crystals are attached to fine silk threads, and two or more are dipped in liquid air; pyro-electric crystals tend to stick to each other, others do not. (Robertson, 1935 c.)

(c) A crystal is heated; the charges formed on it are then dissipated by passing it through a flame. It is then allowed to cool in a bell jar full of magnesium oxide smoke (made by burning magnesium in it); the charges developed on cooling cause fine filaments of magnesium oxide to grow out from the crystal along the lines of force, forming a pattern like that of iron filings round a magnet. (Maurice, 1930.)

Only positive results are significant: feeble pyro-electricity may escape detection by these tests.

Piezo-electricity is the property, possessed by some crystals, of developing electric charges when compressed or extended in particular directions. Conversely, when a potential difference is applied to suitable points on such a crystal, it expands or contracts. Piezo-electric properties can occur in all crystals lacking a centre of symmetry, except those belonging to the cubic class 432 (Wooster, 1938). A test for such properties, suitable for small crystals or even powders, is the following.

The crystals are placed between the plates of a condenser which forms part of an oscillating circuit. An audio-frequency amplifier, with headphones or speaker, is connected to the oscillator. When the frequency of the oscillator is changed continuously by means of a variable condenser in the circuit, clicks (or, for a large number of small crystals, rustling noises) are heard. The reason is that whenever the frequency of the oscillator happens to coincide with a natural frequency of one of the crystals, there is a sudden change of current through the condenser and consequently an impulse which is amplified by the audio-frequency amplifier. For a suitable circuit see Wooster (1957).

**Other physical properties.** Anisotropy of thermal and electrical conductivity, coefficient of thermal expansion, elasticity, and dielectric constant may also provide information on internal structure. These properties, however, have so far been little used in structure determination, because they are less easily measured than those already considered; consequently not very much experimental evidence is available for the purpose of generalizing on the relations between such properties and structural features. For further information on these subjects, see Wooster (1938), Nye (1957).

A sudden change in average dielectric constant (measured by using powdered material) when a substance is heated has been taken as evidence of the onset of molecular rotation at the temperature of the sudden change. (White and Bishop, 1940; White, Biggs, and Morgan, 1940; Turkevitch and Smyth, 1940.) A sudden narrowing of a nuclear magnetic resonance absorption band is also an indication of the onset of molecular rotation; see for instance Andrew and Eades (1953). Specific heat anomalies also accompany the onset of molecular rotation. (Fowler, 1935; Eucken, 1939.)

# IX

## SOME EXAMPLES OF CRYSTAL STRUCTURE DETERMINATION BY TRIAL

THE principles of the methods by which atomic positions are deduced from X-ray diffraction patterns have been described in Chapters VI and VII; and examples of the separate stages (determination of unit cell dimensions, deduction of space-group, calculation of structure amplitudes, and so on) have been given. It is now intended, in this chapter, to describe the complete process of structure determination in several examples. The structures described are all relatively simple ones; they have been chosen on the ground that they display the utilization of the essential principles in relatively simple circumstances. In some of the examples the help given by physical properties (the subject of Chapter VIII) is an important feature. (The train of reasoning by which each structure is deduced does not, in all cases, coincide with that followed in the original investigations.) Many structures of far greater complexity than these have been worked out completely; but success in such cases has usually been possible through the application of stereochemical principles derived from simpler structures; the principles of interpretation of the X-ray patterns and the physical properties are essentially the same. The use of stereochemical principles is brought out in some of the later examples. The chapter ends with a section on abnormal structures in which the crystallographic ideals embodied in the application of the theory of space-groups are not followed.

In setting out to discover the relative positions of the atoms in a crystal, it is best, when the unit cell dimensions have been determined and the intensities of the reflections measured, to calculate $F$ for each reflection. (See Chapter VII.) Absolute values of $F$, derived from intensities in relation to that of the primary beam, form the ideal experimental material, though very many structures have been determined from a set of relative $F$'s. The reliability of the set of figures depends on the success with which the corrections for thermal vibrations, absorption, and extinction effects have been estimated.

Some of the simplest structures of all are those of many metallic elements, in which there is one atom to each lattice point. These need not detain us long; for clearly, as soon as the lattice type has been deduced (by inspection of the indices of the reflections), the whole structure is completely determined. Thus aluminium has a cubic unit cell containing four atoms and gives only reflections having all even or all odd indices; hence the lattice is face-centred, and there is one atom to each lattice point. The structure presents no further problems. Similarly, molybdenum has a cubic unit cell containing two atoms and gives only reflections having $h+k+l$ even; hence the lattice is body-centred, there is only one atom to each lattice point, and the whole structure is settled.

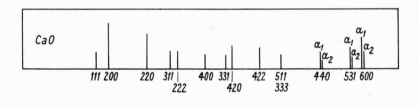

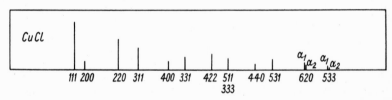

FIG. 170. Diagram representing powder photographs of calcium oxide and cuprous chloride. Abscissae represent distances of arcs along the film; ordinates represent relative intensities (estimated visually).

Many binary salts, oxides, and sulphides are a little more complex, two atoms being associated with each lattice point; it is necessary to discover the relative positions of the two atoms. This can be done by mere inspection of the set of structure amplitudes, and confirmed by a very moderate amount of calculation. Two examples will be given—calcium oxide and cuprous chloride.

**Calcium oxide, CaO,** is cubic, and the unit cell ($a = 4.80$ Å) contains four molecules of CaO. The only reflections present (Fig. 170) are those having all even or all odd indices; the lattice is therefore face-centred. If the origin of the unit cell is taken as the centre of a calcium atom, then there are also calcium atoms at the centres of the cell faces (Fig. 171 a). It is now necessary to place the oxygen atoms. Note first of all that the oxygen atoms by themselves also form a face-centred lattice (an oxygen atom might have been chosen as the origin of the cell—the two sorts of atoms obviously have equal rights in this respect); the only problem therefore is the relation of the oxygen lattice to the calcium lattice. Inspection of the powder photograph shows that reflections with odd indices, such as 111 and 531, are weaker than those with even indices at about the same angle. (With one exception—the pair 311 and 222, which are about equally strong; but, since the number of equivalent reflections is 24 for 311 and only 8 for 222, it is evident that $F$ for 311 is much smaller than that for 222.) Consider the placing of one oxygen atom. To weaken 111 the oxygen must be somewhere on or near the plane $ABC$ (marked 111− in Fig. 171 $a$). Since 200 is strong, it must be somewhere on or near the planes marked 200+; and since 220 is strong, it must be on or near the planes marked 220+. Its position is evidently somewhere near where these three types of planes intersect, that is, at $A$ or $B$, or the similar positions $D$, $E$, $F$, etc. There is no need to choose between these positions, for if we place an atom at any one of them, say $A$, identical atoms immediately spring into being at $B$, $C$, $D$, etc., forming a face-centred lattice; and it should be noted that, to preserve the symmetries of the cubic system, they must be *exactly* half-way along the edges and in the centre of the cell (Fig. 171 $b$). In confirmation, it is found that structure amplitudes calculated for this arrangement agree with those experimentally determined, and the structure, which is analogous to that of sodium chloride (see p. 237), is established. Note that in this arrangement (a very common one among binary compounds) every atom is equidistant from six of the other kind of atom.

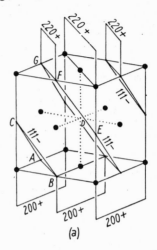

(a)

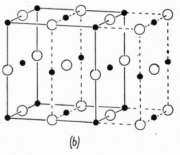

(b)

FIG. 171. Structure of calcium oxide, CaO.

**Cuprous chloride, CuCl,** is also cubic ($a = 5\cdot41$ Å) with four molecules in the unit cell. Since the only reflections present on the powder photograph (Fig. 170) are those with all even or all odd indices, the lattice is, like that of calcium oxide, face-centred. It is, however, immediately obvious from the photograph that the arrangement must be different from that of calcium oxide, since the 111 reflection of cuprous chloride is much stronger than 200; in the calcium oxide pattern the opposite is true. It is evident that the face-centred chlorine lattice must be placed in such a way with respect to the face-centred copper lattice that for 111 the chlorine atoms lie on or near the same planes as

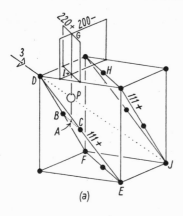

(a)

copper atoms, while for 200, chlorine planes interleave copper planes. Note also that 220 is strong, and thus all the atoms, both copper and chlorine, lie on or near 220 planes. Taking the centre of a copper atom as the origin of the cell (Fig. 172 a) and focusing attention on the placing of one chlorine atom (the rest will follow inevitably from the first), the position A seems a possible site, since at this point the planes marked 111+, 200−, and 220+ intersect. This will not do, however; if the other reflections on the photograph are examined, it will be found that 222 is absent; if the chlorine were at A, which lies on the plane DCEF, then 222 would be strong—its F would be as great as that of 111. (There are other reasons why position A will not do, but this one will suffice.) To account for the absence of 222, the chlorine must be moved out of the 111+ plane—but not too far, in view of the strength of 111.

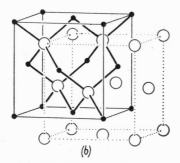

(b)

Fig. 172. Structure of cuprous chloride, CuCl.

The absence of 222 can be accounted for by moving the chlorine away from plane DEF by a distance equal to half the spacing of 222, since at this position waves from the chlorine will oppose those from the copper atoms (and the same will be true for all the other chlorine atoms); actually the intensity should not be zero, but evidently this reflection is too weak to show on the photograph. Half the spacing of 222 is one-quarter the spacing of 111, and therefore the intensity of 111 will not be adversely affected to any serious extent. The chlorine atom, in moving away from plane DEF, must keep to the line AG, to preserve the correct intensities for 200 and 220. The position necessary to account for all the intensities so far considered is thus P, half-way between $A$ and $I$. It is also to be noted that $P$ is equidistant from copper atoms $B$, $C$, $D$, and $H$, and, moreover, when the other chlorine atoms are placed so that they all form a face-centred arrangement (Fig. 172 $b$) the essential symmetries of the cubic system (the diagonally disposed threefold axes) are preserved. $P$, for instance, lies on the diagonal $DJ$. The symmetry is not holosymmetric but tetrahedral; the crystal class (point-group) is $\overline{4}3m$ and the space-group $F\ \overline{4}3m$. Calculation of the remaining structure amplitudes and comparison with those experimentally determined show that this arrangement is indeed correct. This arrangement, in which each chlorine atom is tetrahedrally surrounded by four copper atoms (in contrast to CaO, with its octahedral six-coordination), is found in many of the less polar binary solids. In diamond the same arrangement, but with all the atoms identical, is found, and reflections which are weak for CuCl are absent altogether for diamond.† In view of the preferred tetrahedral configuration of carbon bonds this arrangement in diamond is not surprising.

**Titanium dioxide, TiO$_2$ (rutile).** In the structures so far considered, all the atoms have occupied very special positions in the unit cell; there were no continuously variable parameters to be determined. The structure of rutile, now to be considered, is a simple example of a structure in which there is one parameter. This structure has been described on p. 226, where it was introduced in connexion with the calculation of structure amplitudes. The general arrangement of the atoms was assumed, and the effect of the variation of the oxygen parameter on the structure amplitudes of the reflections was demonstrated (Fig. 123). Here we shall consider the evidence which leads to a knowledge of the general arrangement of the atoms.

The tetragonal unit cell, the dimensions of which ($a = 4\cdot58$ Å, $c = 2\cdot98$ Å) can be calculated from either powder or single-crystal photographs, contains two titanium and four oxygen atoms. A survey of the indices of the reflections (see the powder photograph in Plate XI) shows that there are no systematic absences among those of the general ($hkl$) type; hence the lattice is primitive. For the principal zones‡ the only systematic absences are $h0l$ reflections having $h+l$ odd (together with the equivalent type $0kl$ with $k+l$ odd); hence there are glide planes

† Except that diamond gives a very weak 222 reflection. This is taken as an indication that the electron cloud of the carbon atom is not spherical, but has tetrahedral symmetry. (Bragg, W. H., 1921; Brill, 1950.)

‡ It should be remembered that in the cubic, tetragonal, and hexagonal systems there may be glide planes perpendicular to the diagonals of the basal plane; hence the set of $hhl$ reflections constitutes a 'principal zone'; absence of $hhl$ reflections having $l$ odd indicates the existence of such a glide plane.

$n$ having diagonal translation perpendicular to both $a$ and $b$ axes. If the list of tetragonal space-groups is consulted, it will be found that the only possible space-groups are $P4_2nm$ and $P4_2/mnm$. (Remember that the latter means $P\dfrac{4_2}{m}nm$.)

The shapes of rutile crystals give no hint of polar character, hence the holohedral space-group $P4_2/mnm$ is the more likely to be correct. It will be considered first.

Consider the positions of the titanium atoms. There are only two of these in the unit cell; if one is placed at the corner of the unit cell, then the other can only be at the centre of the cell: the glide planes having diagonal translation demand it.†

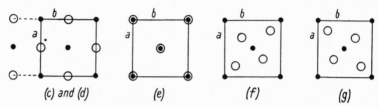

(c) and (d)       (e)       (f)       (g)

Fig. 173. Fourfold positions in space-group $P4_2/mnm$.

The positions of the four oxygen atoms can best be deduced by referring to the lists of equivalent positions in *International Tables* (1952). There are five sets of fourfold positions in space-group $P4_2/mnm$:

(c)  $0\frac{1}{2}0$; $\frac{1}{2}00$; $0\frac{1}{2}\frac{1}{2}$; $\frac{1}{2}0\frac{1}{2}$.

(d)  $0\frac{1}{2}\frac{1}{4}$; $\frac{1}{2}0\frac{1}{4}$; $0\frac{1}{2}\frac{3}{4}$; $\frac{1}{2}0\frac{3}{4}$.

(e)  $00z$; $00\bar{z}$; $\frac{1}{2}, \frac{1}{2}, \frac{1}{2}+z$; $\frac{1}{2}, \frac{1}{2}, \frac{1}{2}-z$.

(f)  $xx0$; $\bar{x}\bar{x}0$; $\frac{1}{2}+x, \frac{1}{2}-x, \frac{1}{2}$; $\frac{1}{2}-x, \frac{1}{2}+x, \frac{1}{2}$.

(g)  $x\bar{x}0$; $\bar{x}x0$; $\frac{1}{2}+x, \frac{1}{2}+x, \frac{1}{2}$; $\frac{1}{2}-x, \frac{1}{2}-x. \frac{1}{2}$.

All except the last two of these sets can be dismissed very simply by the following consideration: the $x$ and $y$ coordinates of (c) and (d) are $\frac{1}{2}0$ and $0\frac{1}{2}$, and the $c$ projection looks like Fig. 173. This projected arrangement is centred, and if it were correct, all $hk0$ reflections having $h+k$ odd would be absent. Actually, such reflections are present—for example, 210. Hence these arrangements can be dismissed. Similarly the (e) arrangement in projection appears centred, and can likewise be dismissed. It is therefore certain that the oxygen atoms occupy either the (f) or the (g) set of fourfold positions. Since (f) and (g) are equiva-

† In *International Tables* (1952) a second set of twofold positions is given: $00\frac{1}{2}$ and $\frac{1}{2}\frac{1}{2}0$. This set, however, represents the same arrangement as the first set 000, $\frac{1}{2}\frac{1}{2}\frac{1}{2}$.

lent—that is, they give rise to exactly the same complete arrangement (see Figs. 173 and 174)—we can use either.

The general arrangement is thus settled, and it remains only to determine the value of the single variable parameter $x$; the weakness of 200 indicates that it is not far from $0.25$; its precise magnitude is found by calculating the intensities of a number of reflections for a range of positions around this value. The best agreement between calculated and observed intensities is obtained for $x = 0.31$.

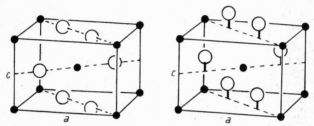

FIG. 174. Structure of rutile, $TiO_2$. Arrangements in $P4_2/mnm$ (left) and $P4_2nm$ (right).

Since the whole X-ray diffraction pattern is accounted for by this arrangement whose space-group symmetry is $P4_2/mnm$, this appears to be the correct structure. It is, however, necessary to consider whether any arrangement in the other possible space-group $P4_2nm$ would account for the intensities equally well. In this space-group the titanium atoms are in the same positions as before, but the oxygen atoms occupy the following set of fourfold positions:

(c)  $(xxz)$, $(\bar{x}\bar{x}z)$, $(\frac{1}{2}+x, \frac{1}{2}-x, \frac{1}{2}+z)$, $(\frac{1}{2}-x, \frac{1}{2}+x, \frac{1}{2}+z)$,

giving the arrangement illustrated in Fig. 174. It differs from the $P4_2/mnm$ arrangement in that the oxygen atoms are all shifted along the $c$ axis by a distance $z$. The $x$ parameter must be either $0.31$ or $0.19$, to account for the $hk0$ intensities (see Fig. 123). The $z$ parameter is given by the intensities of the other reflections; we need go no farther than the consideration of 002, the intensity of which is such that $z$ can only be about zero: any value far from zero would give 002 too weak in comparison with the $hk0$ intensities. Other intensities involving $z$ establish that its value is exactly zero. (At the same time, $x$ is established as $0.31$, not $0.19$.) But this arrangement with $z$ zero is none other than the $P4_2/mnm$ arrangement we have already considered; this structure is therefore established as correct beyond doubt.

**Urea, $O{=}C(NH_2)_2$.** Crystals of urea are tetragonal, and their distinctive habit (Fig. 175) places them without any doubt in class $\bar{4}2m$ (tetragonal scalenohedral in Groth's nomenclature, ditetragonal alternating in Miers's). The unit cell dimensions are $a = 5\cdot67$ Å, $c = 4\cdot73$ Å, and these figures, together with the known density of $1\cdot335$ g/cm³, lead to the conclusion that this unit cell comprises two molecules of urea. There are no systematic absences among the $hkl$ reflections, hence the lattice is primitive ($P$). There are no systematic absences among $hk0$, $0kl$, or $h0l$ reflections, hence there are no glide planes. In fact, the only systematic absences are $h00$ reflections for which $h$ is odd (and, of course, $0k0$ reflections for which $k$ is odd, since the $a$ and $b$ axes are equivalent); the only symmetry elements involving translation are therefore screw axes $(2_1)$ parallel to $a$ and $b$. If the list of tetragonal space-groups and their systematic absences is consulted, it will be found that the only possible space-group is $P\bar{4}2_1m$.

In considering the positions of the atoms in the unit cell we are entitled to assume that the atoms are linked together in molecules in the manner established by chemical evidence:

$$\begin{array}{ccc} H_2N & & NH_2 \\ & \diagdown \diagup & \\ & C & \\ & \| & \\ & O & \end{array}$$

This means that we may consider first of all (in order to attain a general idea of the atomic positions) the symmetry of the molecule, and the relation of the two molecules in the cell to the symmetry elements of space-group $P\bar{4}2_1m$, the c projection of which is shown in Fig. 175.

Consider the axes of symmetry in the crystal. There are fourfold inversion axes, twofold axes, and twofold screw axes. Now a molecule having the chemical structure $O{=}C(NH_2)_2$ cannot have a fourfold inversion axis; neither can it have a screw axis (since it is a finite molecule). Hence the molecules cannot lie on these crystal axes; the two molecules must be related to each other by these axes. On the other hand, a molecule of this structure may well possess a twofold axis passing through the C and O atoms; consequently the twofold axes ($A$ in Fig. 175) are likely sites for molecules. Furthermore, it is to be noted that each twofold axis stands at the intersection of two mutually perpendicular planes of symmetry—and these also are likely to be possessed by a molecule of urea (see Fig. 131). Further consideration shows that all other positions are impossible; for instance, if we put a molecule at $B$, it is inevitably repeated at $B'$, $B''$, and $B'''$; this is out of the question, since we know there are only two molecules in the unit cell, not four. It is therefore certain that each molecule lies on a twofold axis, and thus the C and O atoms of the molecule lie, one above the other, on this twofold axis. Moreover, the nitrogen atoms must lie on the symmetry planes; for, suppose them displaced from the symmetry planes, as at $C$

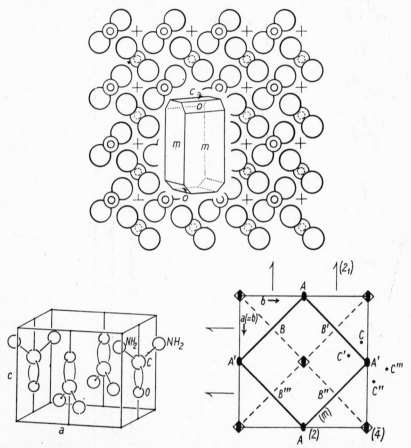

FIG. 175. Structure of urea. Above: habit of urea crystals, with arrangement of molecules as seen along $c$ axis. Below, left: arrangement of molecules, general view. Below, right: symmetry elements of space-group $P\bar{4}2_1m$ ($c$ projection).

in Fig. 175; multiplication would inevitably occur, and there would be four nitrogen atoms to each molecule, which we know is incorrect.

It is thus certain that the molecules are arranged as in Fig. 175, with the carbon and oxygen atoms on twofold axes and the nitrogen atoms on the diagonally placed planes of symmetry.

An alternative argument will now be given, which arrives at the same conclusion as that already given, but takes a different course; it starts with a consideration of the equivalent positions in the space-group $P\bar{4}2_1m$, and only introduces the concept of molecular structure at the end. Both arguments are included here, because it is often useful to think in both ways; consideration of the placing of molecules of known chemical structure is often more appropriate for organic crystals, while the argument from equivalent positions is more likely to be useful for ionic structures.

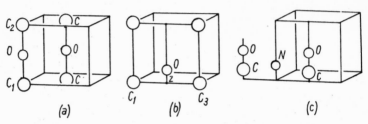

FIG. 176. Consideration of possible atomic positions in urea. Left: C atoms at ($a$), O atoms at ($b$). Centre: C atoms at ($a$), O atoms at ($c$). Right: C and O atoms at ($c$), N atoms at ($d$).

In the unit cell of urea we have to place two carbon, two oxygen, and four nitrogen atoms. Consider first the carbon and oxygen atoms. The twofold positions in space-group $P\bar{4}2_1m$ are

($a$) $000$; $\tfrac{1}{2}\tfrac{1}{2}0$;

($b$) $00\tfrac{1}{2}$; $\tfrac{1}{2}\tfrac{1}{2}\tfrac{1}{2}$;

($c$) $0\tfrac{1}{2}z$; $\tfrac{1}{2}0z$.

Suppose we put the carbons at ($a$) and the oxygens at ($b$). In this case an oxygen atom would be equidistant from $C_1$ and $C_2$ (Fig. 176 $a$); in other words its distance from the carbon atom in its own molecule would be the same as its distance from a carbon atom in a different molecule, which is very unlikely. Suppose now we put carbons at ($a$) and oxygens at ($c$); the same situation develops—an oxygen would be equidistant from $C_1$ and $C_3$ (Fig. 176 $b$). Only by putting both carbons and oxygens at two sets of ($c$) positions, with different values of $z$ (Fig. 176 $c$), can we keep the intramolecular and intermolecular carbon-oxygen distances different from each other.

For the nitrogens consider the fourfold positions

($d$) $00z$, $00\bar{z}$; $\tfrac{1}{2}\tfrac{1}{2}z$; $\tfrac{1}{2}\tfrac{1}{2}\bar{z}$;

($e$) $x$, $\tfrac{1}{2}+x$, $z$; $\bar{x}$, $\tfrac{1}{2}-x$, $z$; $\tfrac{1}{2}+x$, $\bar{x}$, $\bar{z}$; $\tfrac{1}{2}-x$, $x$, $\bar{z}$.

Suppose we put them at ($d$) positions. Remembering that carbons and oxygens are at ($c$), it is evident that a nitrogen is equidistant from two carbon atoms (Fig. 176 $c$); the ($d$) positions can therefore be rejected for the same reason as before. We are left only with the ($e$) positions, and are thus brought to the same conclusions as in the previous form of argument—that is, that the structure is as shown in Fig. 175, a structure in which there are four independently variable parameters to be determined, $x_N$, $z_N$, $z_C$, and $z_O$.

The best experimental determinations of the structure amplitudes for the various reflections are those of Wyckoff (1930, 1932) and Wyckoff and Corey (1934), who measured the intensities of the reflections from a pressed cake of powder and from a single crystal in the form of a

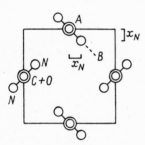

FIG. 177. Urea. View along
c axis.

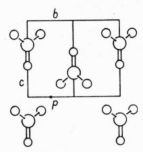

FIG. 178. Urea. View along a axis.
Plane-group pmg.

cylindrical rod, using the ionization spectrometer. The powder data were used to indicate the corrections for secondary extinction to be applied to the single crystal data (see p. 224).

It is best to determine $x_N$ first, by considering the $hk0$ intensities; for this projection $x_N$ is the only variable, since carbon and oxygen atoms are fixed (one underneath the other) as in Fig. 177. It is simply a question of calculating the $hk0$ intensities for a range of positions along the diagonal line $AB$ in Fig. 177. This is done most rapidly by Bragg and Lipson's graphical method (Fig. 163), the chart for plane-group $pgg$ being used. It is important to remember to use the 'cos cos' origin for reflections having $h+k$ even and the 'sin sin' origin for those having $h+k$ odd. It is also important to use the correct scattering powers; the $NH_2$ group may be regarded as a single scattering unit containing nine electrons, consequently scattering powers in the ratios $6:8:9$ are appropriate for C, O, and $NH_2$ respectively. The value of $x_N$ giving the best overall agreement between calculated and observed $F$'s is $0.145$ (Wyckoff, 1932).

The three $z$ parameters must all be determined together; it is simplest to consider first the $0kl$ intensities, which will give positions in the $a$

projection, Fig. 178. To use the graphical method, shift the origin to $P$ in Fig. 178, and on the chart use the 'cos cos' origin for reflections having $k$ even and the 'sin sin' origin for those having $k$ odd, these being the appropriate expressions for this plane-group $pmg$. It is important to remember that there are two $NH_2$ groups and only one carbon and one oxygen in the structure. It would not be profitable to describe in detail the procedure in shifting the atoms about in the attempt to obtain correct $F$'s. But two remarks may be made. The first is that, in order to limit the possible atomic positions, it is justifiable to assume, as Hendricks (1928 a) did in the earliest work, that the distance C—O is somewhere between 1·0 and 1·7 Å, while C—N is 1·0–1·5 Å. (In working out organic structures nowadays it would be justifiable to assume much narrower limits, owing to the accumulation of knowledge since that time.) The second is that when a particular set of atomic positions gives a set of structure amplitudes some of which are seriously wrong, inspection of the charts shows in which direction each atom should be moved in order to increase or diminish the structure amplitude for a given reflection (see p. 290).

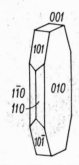

FIG. 179. Habit of sodium nitrite, $NaNO_2$.

The whole structure should be checked by calculations of $hkl$ intensities. The appropriate expression will be found in the *International Tables* (1952). It is possible to use the Bragg and Lipson charts to shorten such calculations (see p. 291). The final parameters were found by Wyckoff and Corey to be $z_C = 0·335$, $z_O = 0·60$, $x_N = 0·145$, $z_N = 0·18$.

Sodium nitrite, $NaNO_2$, forms orthorhombic crystals of the shape of Fig. 179. This shape has holohedral symmetry $mmm$; the internal symmetry might, however, be lower than this (see p. 269), and therefore atomic arrangements in all three classes of the orthorhombic system ($mmm$, 222, and $mm2$) may be considered.

The unit cell has the dimensions

$$a = 3·55 \text{ Å},$$
$$b = 5·56 \text{ Å},$$
$$c = 5·38 \text{ Å},$$

and contains two molecules of $NaNO_2$ (Ziegler, 1931). All reflections for which $h+k+l$ is odd are absent, hence the lattice is body-centred ($I$). There is evidently only one molecule of $NaNO_2$ associated with each lattice point; the problem of structure determination is simply to group the atoms of one molecule of $NaNO_2$ at one corner of the cell; the other molecule is arranged in exactly the same way at the centre of the cell.

There are no further systematic absences; the absences of odd orders of $h00$, $0k0$, and $00l$ are included in the general statement that reflections having $h+k+l$ odd are absent. This means that, for a body-centred lattice, we cannot tell (from the systematic absences) whether twofold screw axes are present or not. The possible space-groups are

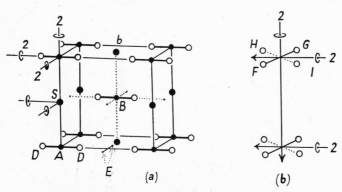

FIG. 180. Sodium nitrite. Consideration of arrangement *Immm*.

therefore *Immm* in the holohedral class, *I*222 and *I*$2_1 2_1 2_1$ in the enantiomorphic class, and *Imm*2 in the polar class. Of these, *I*$2_1 2_1 2_1$ can be ruled out at once because there are no twofold positions in this space-group.

Consider now *I*222, which has several sets of twofold positions. Put a nitrogen atom $A$ at the origin (its companion $B$ will necessarily be at the centre of the cell). At the centres of edges and faces (as well as at the corners of the cell) three twofold axes intersect (Fig. 180 $a$), and a sodium atom, to avoid multiplication, must lie at one of these points, that is, either exactly half-way along the $c$ axis (at $S$) as in the diagram, or else at one of the other points mentioned. For the two oxygen atoms of the reference molecule the positions available are along the edges of the cell, either at $D$ or in similar positions such as $E$. (For, suppose we put them *off* one of the twofold axes as in Fig. 180 $b$; $F$ and $G$ would be inevitably repeated at $H$ and $I$.) We may assume that the two oxygen atoms of the nitrite ion are closely associated with the nitrogen atom, hence if we have our reference nitrogen atom at the origin, the two oxygen atoms belonging to it will be found along one of the axes. In Fig. 180 $a$ they are shown on $b$, but they might equally well be on $a$ or $c$.

It is now necessary to note that this sort of arrangement has planes as well as axes of symmetry; in other words, we cannot place $2NaNO_2$ in an orthorhombic cell to give symmetry $I222$; the attempt to do so leads inevitably to symmetry $Immm$.

We now consider the structure amplitudes which this highly symmetrical type of arrangement would give, beginning with the various orders of $h00$, $0k0$, and $00l$. Only the even orders are present (the lattice being body-centred). If the $NO_2$ groups are as in Fig. 180 $a$, the oxygen atoms lie *on* both 200 and 002 planes; hence all the orders of 200 and 002 would have the same $F$'s, or in other words, the successive orders of both 200 and 002 should show a normal decline of actual intensity. Similarly, if we put the oxygens along $a$, the successive orders of 020 and 002 should show a normal decline; or, if we put them along $c$, the orders of 200 and 020 should decline regularly: in each case the successive orders of *two* principal planes should decline normally. In actual fact, the decline of intensities for the orders of both 002 and 020 is not regular (002 vw, 004 w; 020 vs, 040 w). Hence the actual arrangement in the sodium nitrite crystal is not one of those so far considered: the correct space-group cannot be $Immm$.

(There is also another quite different reason for dismissing such arrangements: they would be unstable. For instance, the forces between the ions in Fig. 180 $a$ (assuming the orientations of the ions were maintained) would make the $a$ and $c$ axes equal and the symmetry tetragonal with $b$ as the fourfold axis.)

We are thus driven to try arrangements having the lower symmetry $Imm2$. This space-group has twofold axes parallel to only one (we do not know which) of the cell edges, with planes of symmetry intersecting on each twofold axis. This means that, if we put a reference nitrogen atom at the origin as before, the oxygen atoms must lie on one face of the cell, but need not form a straight line with the nitrogen atom; the $NO_2$ ion may be V-shaped as in Fig. 181 $a$. Further, the sodium atoms must lie on the twofold axes, but need not be exactly half-way along the cell edges; this point is also illustrated in the diagrams.

The plane of the nitrite ion can be defined: it must lie in the only principal plane showing a normal decline of intensities—that is, 200. The nitrite ions must therefore lie as in Fig. 181 $a$ (with $c$ as the polar twofold axis) or as in Fig. 181 $b$ (with $b$ as the polar twofold axis).

Before trying to decide which orientation of nitrite ions is correct, consider the positions of the sodium ions. The outstanding fact bearing on this is that 101 is very strong. With nitrite ions at the corners of the cell, the only way of ensuring this is to put sodium atoms on or near the $b$ edges of the cell; others will fall near the centres of the $ac$ faces as in Fig. 181 $c$. Putting in the nitrite ions in the two possible orientations $a$ and $b$, we get the two complete arrangements $d$ and $e$. In trying to choose the more likely of these, consider the fact that 020 is very strong while 002 is very weak. For arrangement $d$, in which sodium atoms are exactly half-way along $b$, the only way of ensuring that 020 shall be strong and 002 weak is to put the oxygens fairly near

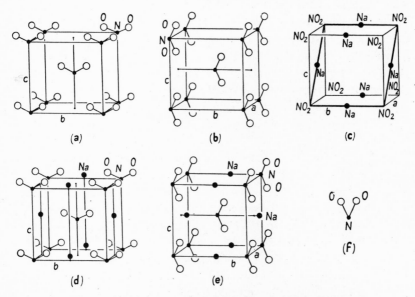

(a)                    (b)                    (c)

(d)                    (e)                    (F)

FIG. 181. Sodium nitrite. Arrangements having symmetry *Imm*2.

the $c$ axis and well away from the $b$ axis (about a quarter of the way up $c$). This would give an acute-angled nitrite ion as in $f$, where $y < z$. This seems improbable. In arrangement $e$, on the other hand, the intensities mentioned can be satisfied by an obtuse-angled ion; this therefore appears to be the more probable arrangement. Calculations of structure amplitudes, in the first instance for $0kl$ planes† and finally for all planes, confirm that this is correct, and give the precise positions of the atoms. The parameters were found by Ziegler (1931) to be (taking the nitrogen atom as the origin) $y_{Na} = 0\cdot50$, $y_O = 0\cdot083$, $z_O = 0\cdot194$. In later work in which the electron density methods of Chapter X were used, these parameters were modified a little (Carpenter, 1952, 1955; Truter, 1954). Note that since it turns out that the polar axis is $b$, it is desirable to

† Best done graphically, using Bragg and Lipson's charts. The plane-group for this projection is $cm$.

alter the nomenclature and interchange $b$ and $c$, to conform with the convention that the polar axis should be called $c$.

The optical properties of the sodium nitrite crystal are fully consistent with this arrangement. The birefringence (largely due to the nitrite ion) is very strong and positive, as would be expected for a crystal containing roughly linear ions packed parallel: $\alpha$ 1·340, ‖ $a$, $\beta$ 1·425, ‖ $b$, $\gamma$ 1·655, ‖ $c$.† The plane of the V-shaped ions is normal to $a$, the vibration direction of lowest index, while the longest dimension of the ion lies along $c$, the vibration direction of highest index. These facts might indeed have been used in deducing the orientation of the nitrite ions in the crystal. The derivation from X-ray intensities alone has been given, however, as it forms a good example of the use of such evidence.

**Sodium bicarbonate, $NaHCO_3$.** The structure of sodium bicarbonate is more complex than that of sodium nitrite, and it would be rather difficult to solve it by the use of X-ray data alone. The optical properties, however, provide valuable evidence, and the solution of the complete structure by Zachariasen (1933) forms a very good example of the combined use of optical and X-ray evidence.

The dimensions of the monoclinic unit cell ($a = 7\cdot51$ Å, $b = 9\cdot70$ Å, $c = 3\cdot53$ Å, $\beta = 93°$ 19') were found by using the rotation and oscillation photographs of a single crystal. These dimensions, together with the known density of 2·20 $g/cm^3$, lead to the conclusion that there are four molecules of $NaHCO_3$ in the unit cell. Absent reflections are those in the $h0l$ zone for which $h+l$ is odd—indicating a glide plane $n$ perpendicular to $b$—and also the odd $0k0$ reflections, indicating that there are twofold screw axes parallel to $b$. The space-group is evidently $P2_1/n$. (This is equivalent to $P2_1/a$, with a change of $a$ and $c$ axes—see p. 256. $P2_1/a$ is the normal set-up given in *International Tables*, 1952.)

In this space-group the general positions have fourfold multiplicity. (Coordinates‡ $xyz$, $\bar{x}\bar{y}\bar{z}$, $(\frac{1}{2}+x)(\frac{1}{2}-y)(\frac{1}{2}+z)$, $(\frac{1}{2}-x)(\frac{1}{2}+y)(\frac{1}{2}-z)$.) The only special positions have twofold multiplicity; these are pairs of symmetry centres. There are four such pairs :§ (a) $000$, $\frac{1}{2}\frac{1}{2}\frac{1}{2}$; (b) $\frac{1}{2}00$, $0\frac{1}{2}\frac{1}{2}$; (c) $00\frac{1}{2}$, $\frac{1}{2}\frac{1}{2}0$; (d) $\frac{1}{2}0\frac{1}{2}$, $0\frac{1}{2}0$. We have to assign 4Na, 4H, and 4CO$_3$ to appropriate sets of equivalent positions. Hydrogen atoms will be ignored for the present: their positions were not found directly by X-ray methods.

We are entitled to assume that in this crystal there are carbonate

---

† Measurements by the author.

‡ Usually expressed more briefly as $\pm xyz$, $\pm(\frac{1}{2}+x)(\frac{1}{2}-y)(\frac{1}{2}+z)$.

§ The symmetry centres are incorrectly paired in the original paper.

groups having the same shape and dimensions as in other carbonate crystals—that is, equilateral triangles of oxygen atoms with carbon atoms at the centres (see Fig. 131). Now the carbonate ion does not possess a centre of symmetry; therefore neither the carbon atoms nor any of the oxygen atoms lie at the centres of symmetry; they lie in general positions.

No such argument applies to the sodium atoms, which can be assumed confidently to be independent ions; they may well lie at centres of symmetry. It is of course not certain that they do: they may either occupy two pairs of symmetry centres or alternatively one set of general positions.

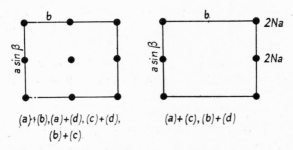

$(a)+(b),(a)+(d),(c)+(d),$
$(b)+(c)$

$(a)+(c),(b)+(d)$

FIG. 182. Sodium carbonate, c projection. Sodium atoms in pairs of symmetry centres.

Assume first of all that the sodium ions do occupy two sets of symmetry centres, and consider the c projection only. Although in space there are four different combinations of two pairs of symmetry centres, there are only two different projected arrangements, which are illustrated in Fig. 182. Other combinations are equivalent to these: thus $(a)+(b)$ is equivalent to $(a)+(d)$, when seen from this viewpoint.

The orientation of the carbonate groups may be inferred from the optical properties of the crystals. The birefringence is very strong ($\alpha$ 1·378, $\beta$ 1·500, $\gamma$ 1·580), and $\alpha$ is so low that it may be assumed that the planes of the carbonate ions are all perpendicular to the vibration direction for this refractive index; this direction lies in the $ac$ plane, making an angle of $27\frac{1}{2}°$ with the $c$ axis. Zachariasen accepted this, and also the dimensions of the carbonate ion as found in other crystals; and attempted to find, by trial, positions in the $c$ projections which would satisfy the observed $hk0$ intensities. This involved moving one reference carbonate ion about, and also rotating it in its own plane, for each of the sodium arrangements shown in Fig. 182. The other three carbonate ions are of course related to the reference ion by the symmetries of $P2_1/n$.

Positions giving correct relative intensities for the $hk0$ reflections could not be found, and Zachariasen therefore concluded that the sodium ions do not lie in symmetry centres but in general positions. He then moved the sodium ions (or rather, in practice, one reference ion) about in this same projection. (Carbonate contributions for various positions and orientations of the carbonate ions were already known as a result of the first set of calculations.) A set of positions satisfying the $hk0$ intensities was found; the arrangement is shown in Fig. 183.

The only coordinates remaining to be found were then those along the $c$ axis; these involve only two variable parameters, one for the sodium and one for the carbonate ion. The values of these parameters were found without much difficulty from the relative intensities of some of the other reflections; the principle was to compare structure amplitudes for reflections at similar angles. Finally the structure was checked by calculations of the intensities of all reflections within a wide angular range.

Although only visual estimates of intensities were used, the number of reflections for which calculations were made is so large that the parameters may be accepted with considerable confidence. A view of the structure seen along the $b$ axis is shown in Fig. 183.

In the calculations hydrogen atoms were ignored; but their positions are indicated by the fact that one oxygen–oxygen distance is abnormally low (2·55 Å)—a fact which is taken as evidence for the existence of a 'hydrogen bond' between these oxygen atoms. (See Pauling, 1940.) The principal result of chemical interest which came from this investigation was the proof of a striking example of hydrogen bond formation, at a time when the existence of this type of bond had not long been realized and was exciting considerable interest.

Zachariasen rounded off this work by calculating the three principal refractive indices of the crystal on the basis of his structure, accepting Bragg's theory (1924). The calculated values are close to the known indices of the crystal.

$p$-**Diphenylbenzene, $C_6H_5 . C_6H_4 . C_6H_5$, and dibenzyl, $C_6H_5 . CH_2 . CH_2 . C_6H_5$.** The crystal structures of these two substances present very similar problems and will be considered together. In both crystals the unit cell is monoclinic and contains two molecules, and in both crystals the space-group symmetry is $P2_1/a$. (Absent reflections: $h0l$ with $h$ odd, indicating the existence of glide planes perpendicular to the $b$ axis with a translation of $a/2$, and $0k0$ with $k$ odd, indicating the existence of twofold screw axes parallel to $b$.)

These facts lead at once to a valuable stereochemical conclusion, as

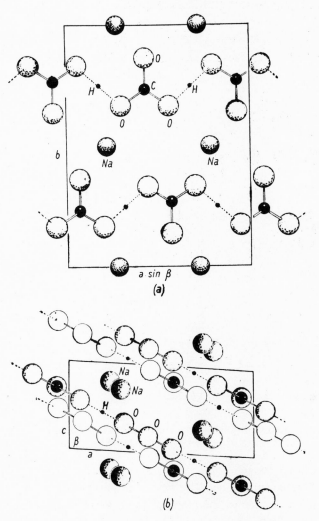

FIG. 183. Structure of sodium bicarbonate, $NaHCO_3$.
Above, *c* projection; below, *b* projection.

in the case of diphenyl discussed on p. 271. It takes four asymmetric units to give the symmetry $P2_1/a$, and therefore, since there are only two molecules in the unit cell, each molecule must possess twofold symmetry; and since finite molecules cannot possess either a screw axis or a glide plane, they must possess the only other symmetry element in the cell—a centre of symmetry.

From this point we shall consider the substances separately. The centre of symmetry in *p*-diphenylbenzene obviously lies in the middle

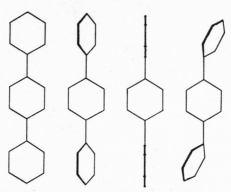

FIG. 184. *p*-Diphenylbenzene. Centrosymmetric configurations.

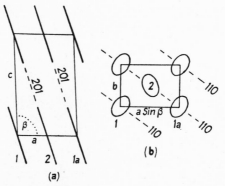

FIG. 185. *p*-Diphenylbenzene. Approximate orientation of molecules in unit cell.

of the central benzene ring; and the existence of it means that the planes of the terminal benzene rings are parallel to each other. They may be at any angle to the plane of the central benzene ring, but they *must* be parallel to each other (Fig. 184).

Consider now the approximate orientation of the molecules in the unit cell. The dimensions of the cell ($a = 8.08$ Å, $b = 5.60$ Å, $c = 13.59$ Å, $\beta = 91° 55'$) suggest that the long molecules lie very roughly parallel to the long $c$ axis; and the fact that the 201 reflection is very strong suggests that the long molecules lie along the traces of these planes, as in Fig. 185 *a*. If this is true, and we look along the $c$ axis, we should see the long molecules more or less end-on; the strength of 110 confirms this (see Fig. 185 *b*).

It remains to define the orientation of the molecules more precisely

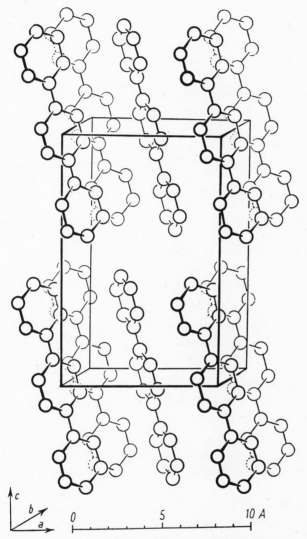

Fɪɢ. 186. Structure of *p*-diphenylbenzene. (*Strukturbericht*, 1933–5, p. 681.)

and to fix the positions of all the carbon atoms. There is no further help to be gained from symmetry considerations—all the atoms are in general positions, as in most organic crystals; atomic positions are found by the laborious process of trial. The carbon atoms in the asymmetric unit

$$CH\begin{matrix} CH-CH \\ CH-CH \end{matrix}C-C\begin{matrix} CH- \\ CH- \end{matrix}$$

must be moved about until the calculated intensities agree with those actually observed. Pickett, who worked out the structure in 1933, assumed that the benzene ring is a flat regular hexagon, that the C—C distance is 1·42 Å as in hexamethylbenzene, and that the C—C link lies in the planes of both rings. The problem therefore was to rotate the

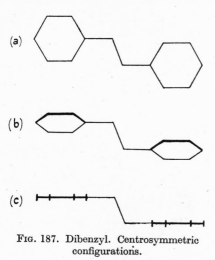

terminal ring with respect to the central ring, and to alter the orientation of the whole molecule to find which position (if any) satisfies the intensities of the re-flections. The procedure followed was to attempt first to satisfy the intensities of the small-angle reflections, and then to work out-wards, the atomic coordinates being defined more and more closely as this went on. It was found that molecules having all three rings coplanar, oriented as in Fig. 186, give correct intensities for all the reflections. Note that the long axes of the molecules lie almost precisely along the 201 planes, in accordance with our preliminary expectation; and, moreover, they are parallel to the *ac* face of the cell, which makes the structure easy to visualize.

Fig. 187. Dibenzyl. Centrosymmetric configurations.

The structure of dibenzyl $C_6H_5.CH_2.CH_2.C_6H_5$ is formally similar to that of *p*-diphenylbenzene, but its elucidation (accomplished by J. M. Robertson, 1934 *a*) was a rather more complex problem. We may note first of all that a greater variety of molecular configurations might be assumed by rotation round the three single bonds. However, thanks to the existence of the centre of symmetry in the molecule (which must be half-way between the $CH_2$ groups), some of these can be imme-diately rejected: it is certain that the three single bonds form a plane zigzag as in the paraffin hydrocarbons, since this is the only configura-tion of the three bonds which has a centre of symmetry. It is also certain that the planes of the benzene rings are parallel to each other; they may be twisted at any angle to the central zigzag (Fig. 187) but they *must* be parallel to each other.

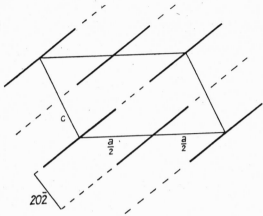

FIG. 188. Dibenzyl. Approximate orientation of molecules in unit cell.

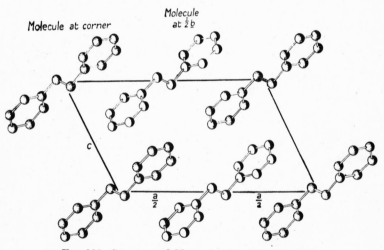

FIG. 189. Structure of dibenzyl, $C_6H_5.CH_2.CH_2.C_6H_5$.

A rough idea of the orientation of the molecules in the unit cell (dimensions $a = 12·77$ Å, $b = 6·12$ Å, $c = 7·70$ Å, $\beta = 116°$) is given by the fact that the highest structure amplitude is that of $20\bar{2}$; the long molecules therefore lie approximately along these planes (Fig. 188). The atoms must, however, be somewhat dispersed from these planes, since the absolute value of the structure amplitude falls considerably short of the maximum possible (70 out of 113).

In attempting to find the atomic coordinates Robertson considered first the more symmetrical molecular configurations $a$ and $c$ of Fig. 187, and calculated structure amplitudes for various orientations of both models. Starting with the inner (small-angle) reflections and working outwards as usual, he found that agreement between calculated and observed intensities over the whole range of reflections could not be achieved by type $a$, whatever the orientation of the molecules, but that good agreement could be obtained for a particular orientation of molecules of type $c$. The latter therefore appears to be correct: it was not necessary to consider intermediate configurations such as $b$. The complete structure ($b$ projection) is illustrated in Fig. 189. (It was subsequently confirmed by calculations of the distribution of electron density in the crystal in the way described in the next chapter—Robertson, 1935 $b$.)

**Ascorbic acid ('Vitamin C').** The crystal structure of this substance cannot be said to be established with the certainty and precision we associate with those already described; nevertheless, there is no reason to doubt that the structure suggested by Cox and Goodwin (1936) on the basis of a limited study of the X-ray reflections is essentially correct. The work is described here because this crystal structure presents some very interesting and instructive features. It is also historically interesting because a preliminary study by optical and X-ray methods played a part in the elucidation of the chemical structure of this biologically important substance. (Cox, 1932$a$; Cox, Hirst, and Reynolds, 1932; Cox and Hirst, 1933.)

The crystals have monoclinic sphenoidal symmetry (class 2) and grow as almost square tablets having 100 as the principal face. They have very strong negative birefringence ($\gamma$ 1·476, $\beta$ 1·594, $\sigma$ 1·750), the vibration direction of $\alpha$ being parallel to the $b$ axis. This suggests that the molecules are flat, with the plane perpendicular to the $b$ axis; indeed, the birefringence is so strong that the molecule may have a flat ring structure containing double bonds.

The X-ray results lead to the same general conclusion. The unit cell dimensions are found to be $a = 16·95$ Å, $b = 6·32$ Å, $c = 6·38$ Å, $\beta = 102\frac{1}{2}°$, and the unit cell contains four molecules. The 020 reflection is very strong, and the regular decline of the intensities of subsequent orders (040, 060) indicates that most of the atoms lie on or near the 020 planes; in other words, the molecules are flat and lie with their planes perpendicular to $b$.

The X-ray results also lead to a knowledge of the approximate molecular dimensions. It is first necessary to note that the only systematic absences are the odd orders of $0k0$; hence the space-group is either $P2_1$ or $P2_1/m$. The shape of the crystals indicates that $P2_1$ is correct. In addition, it is worth noting that $P2_1/m$ is ruled out by the fact that the substance in solution rotates the plane of polarized light; hence the molecules are asymmetric, and there cannot be equal numbers

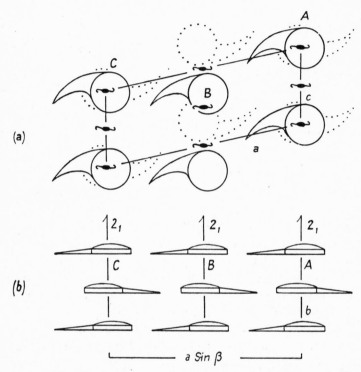

(a)

(b)

Fig. 190. Ascorbic acid. Arrangement of asymmetric molecules (represented by formal shapes) consistent with X-ray data. (a) Seen along $b$ axis. (b) Seen along $c$ axis.

of $d$ and $l$ molecules in the crystal, as would be required for $P2_1/m$; therefore the space-group must be $P2_1$. This space-group, however, requires only two asymmetric units; the unit cell actually contains four molecules, hence a group of two molecules constitutes the asymmetric unit of structure; these two molecules may be grouped in any manner whatsoever.

This seems to complicate the problem hopelessly. But the situation is not as bad as it seems; for it is found that all $hk0$ reflections for which $h$ is odd are extremely weak, and this suggests very strongly that if we look along the $c$ axis (Fig. 190 $b$) there is a molecule $B$ almost exactly half-way between molecules $A$ and $C$ and oriented in almost exactly the same way, so that from this viewpoint $B$ looks almost exactly the same as $A$ and $C$ and halves the apparent length of the $a$ axis. The packing of the nearly flat molecules is of the form shown in Fig. 190 $a$, in which $A$ and $B$ are differently related to the screw axes; there is no question of halving for the $b$ projection, since all types of $h0l$ reflections are present.

The dimensions of the molecules are therefore likely to be about $\frac{a}{2} \times c \times \frac{b}{2}$, that is, $8\cdot5 \times 6\cdot4 \times 3\cdot1$ Å. These dimensions ruled out some suggested constitutions, and played a part in suggesting the following constitution which was eventually established chemically by Herbert, Hirst, Percival, Reynolds, and Smith (1933):

The relative positions of the molecules in the unit cell were after-wards found by calculating some of the structure amplitudes for various positions. The arrangement in one sheet of molecules is shown in Fig. 191. (In the published account (Cox and Goodwin, 1936) use is made of the conception of a pseudo plane of symmetry perpendicular to the plane of the molecule and perpendicular to the $c$ axis; actually the apparent halving of $a$ in the $c$ projection does not demand any such pseudo plane of symmetry in the molecule, but can be produced with completely asymmetric molecules, as Fig. 190 shows. However, as it turns out, the configuration and arrangement of the molecules which accounts for the intensities of the principal reflections does show a pseudo plane of symmetry in the position mentioned.)

**Long-chain polymers.** To conclude this series of examples of structure determination by trial, accounts will be given of the elucida-tion of the structures of two long-chain polymers. Substances of this type are of increasing practical importance, and moreover their molecules are very interesting stereochemically. The experimental data available for the study of their crystal structures is more scanty than in the case of crystals composed of small molecules: there is no morpho-logical evidence on crystal symmetry, and only limited optical evidence

on molecular arrangement, while on account of the imperfect orientation and often small crystal size in fibre specimens, the X-ray reflections
are less sharp than those of single crystals (see Plate X), with the
result that the weakest reflections tend to be lost in the general background of the photographs. Another limitation is that, owing to the
overlapping of different reflections, only their combined intensities are
known; and there is often doubt about systematic absences. Nevertheless, to offset these disadvantages there are some compensating features

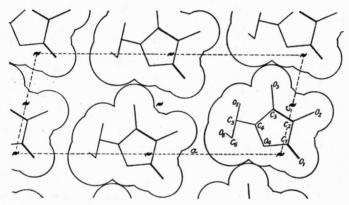

FIG. 191. Structure of ascorbic acid ($b$ projection). Only one
sheet of molecules is shown. (Cox and Goodwin, 1936.)

which make the study of chain-polymer structures less difficult and
uncertain than might be supposed. The principal advantage is that in
fibre specimens the molecules run parallel to the fibre axis (molecular
orientation being therefore partially defined from the start), and moreover the length of the unit cell edge which lies parallel to the fibre axis
is a distance *within* the molecule—a feature which has far-reaching
consequences, as we have seen in Chapter VI. There are also other
advantages; for on account of the special character of the molecules,
special arguments can sometimes be used to limit the possible arrangements in the crystal. The two examples to be described ($\beta$ gutta-percha
($-CH_2-C(CH_3)=CH-CH_2-)_n$—a naturally occurring polymer of isoprene—and rubber hydrochloride ($-CH_2-C(CH_3)Cl-CH_2-CH_2-)_n$)
are also instructive for another reason: they exhibit pseudo symmetries,
which may cause confusion if the possibility of their occurrence is not
realized.

1. *β Gutta-percha.* Interpretation of fibre photographs shows that the
unit cell of $\beta$ gutta-percha is rectangular (and therefore probably orthorhombic in symmetry), with the dimensions $a = 7.78$ Å, $b = 11.78$ Å,

$c = 4.72$ Å ($c$ being the fibre axis). Cold-rolled sheets provide confirmatory evidence, for in them the crystals tend to be oriented, not only with their $c$ axes along the direction of rolling, but also with their 010 planes in the plane of the sheet; photographs of such specimens set at particular angles to the X-ray beam can be treated as crude oscillation photographs of single crystals, the indices of the various reflections being thus checked. Four chain molecules run through the cell.

In interpreting chain-polymer photographs it is best to consider first the length of the unit cell edge which is parallel to the fibre axis, for this length is also the repeat distance of the molecules themselves; the magnitude of this repeat distance often gives valuable information on molecular configuration. Gutta-percha forms a striking example here. Its repeat distance (4.72 Å) is so short that it is probable from the start that there is only one chemical unit

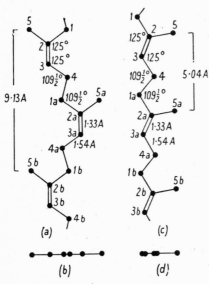

Fig. 192. Planar poly-isoprene molecules. (a) *Cis* chain. (b) End view of (a). (c) *Trans* chain. (d) End view of (c).

$$(-CH_2-C(CH_3)=CH-CH_2-)$$

in this length. With regard to *cis* and *trans* positions of chain bonds with regard to the double bond, it is evident from Fig. 192 that only the *trans* form of chain is likely to have one chemical unit in the repeat distance (the *cis* form having two). Now a *trans* chain with all its carbon atom centres in a plane would be expected to have a repeat distance of 5.04 Å, if bond lengths and angles are normal; this figure is considerably in excess of the observed repeat distance. The only way of shortening such a chain without serious and improbable alterations of bond lengths and angles is to make it non-planar: in other words, starting from a planar chain, we make rotations round the bonds. Rotations round the double bond are unlikely: all the atoms attached to the double-bonded pair of carbon atoms are likely to be in a plane. We must therefore rotate round single bonds. The only possibility is to move bond 4—1a (Fig. 192) out of plane 12345 by rotation round bond

3—4; at the same time, in order to keep unit 1a 2a 3a 4a 5a strictly parallel to unit 12345 so that the two remain crystallographically equivalent, it is necessary to rotate bond 1a—4 round bond 1a—2a. Thus one chemical unit has been moved towards the other along the chain axis while maintaining the correct distance between atoms 4 and 1a and

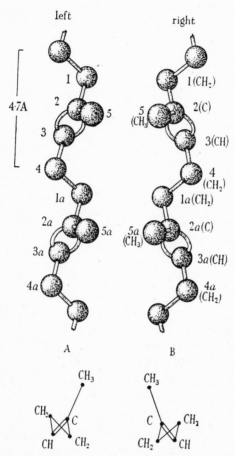

FIG. 193. Molecular models assuming planar isoprene units (*trans*) and repeat distance of 4·7 Å. Left- and right-handed molecules.

maintaining the angles 341a and 41a 2a at 109½°. In this shortening movement bond 4—1a can be rotated either clockwise or anti-clockwise, giving the two types of asymmetric molecule shown in Fig. 193; they are mirror images of each other.

The next step in the interpretation of chain-polymer photographs is usually the consideration of the projection of the structure along the fibre axis, to deduce the side-by-side arrangement of the molecules. The intensities of the equatorial reflections on the normal fibre photograph are the experimental material for this purpose. A survey of the indices of these reflections on the $\beta$ gutta-percha pattern shows that all reflections having $k$ odd are absent. It looks as if there is a glide plane normal to $c$ with a translation of $b/2$; but some caution is necessary in this particular case, for it will be observed in Fig. 193 that left- and right-handed molecules, seen along the fibre axis from either end, look almost identical as far as the positions of atomic centres are concerned; pseudo symmetries are obviously possible. Whatever the truth on this point, however, the cell as seen along $c$ apparently has its $b$ axis halved, and we can certainly work on the half-size projected cell, which has only two chain molecules passing through it.

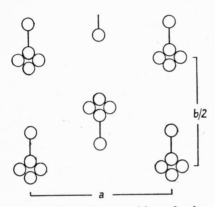

FIG. 194. Approximate positions of carbon atoms in the $c$ projection of $\beta$ gutta-percha, deduced from intensities of $hk0$ reflections.

Calculations of the intensities of the $hk0$ reflections for various positions and orientations of two molecules lead to the conclusion that they are disposed approximately as in Fig. 194. It can also be shown that no arrangement of planar molecules can possibly satisfy these intensities. (In the original investigation the interpretation of these intensities was considered before the question of chain-shortening; and an unprejudiced consideration of what atomic positions could possibly satisfy these intensities led to the arrangement of Fig. 194, implying non-planar chains; consequently, when the question of chain-shortening (to satisfy the repeat distance of the molecule) was then considered, the attainment of a non-planar molecular configuration having almost exactly the same end-view was most striking and encouraging.)

It is now possible to consider the space-group symmetry of the structure as a whole. The evidence of absent reflections will not be considered yet, for reasons already given. Instead, the known approximate arrangement in the $c$ projection will be the starting-point for a consideration of the possible complete arrangements. First, a further limitation can be imposed by the following reasoning. $\beta$ gutta-percha is made by cooling amorphous ('melted') material rapidly. 'Melted' gutta-percha is not a liquid but a rubber-like 'solid'. In such material the molecules probably do not move about relative to each other to any great extent; if they did, the material would be fluid. Neither can the enormously long molecules turn round to reverse their ends. Hence, on crystallization, the molecules settle down in an orderly manner while remaining more or less where they happen to be. Crystals form where sections of molecules happen to lie in favourable positions. Since in any such group there are likely to be equal numbers of molecules pointing both ways, we expect to find in a crystal equal numbers of molecules pointing both ways; we may admit the possibility of minor movements of sections of molecules sufficient to convert a random arrangement into an ordered crystalline arrangement, without admitting the wholesale migrations which would mean fluidity. Thus, of the four molecules passing through the unit cell, two are likely to be upside-down with respect to the others—an 'up' molecule being defined as one with its methyl groups above the double bonds and a 'down' molecule the reverse.

When all possible arrangements allowed by these limitations are considered, it is found that there are only five with orthorhombic symmetry (Fig. 195). The indices of the unambiguous reflections definitely present on the photographs do not allow us to rule any of these out, though the symmetry $P2_12_12_1$ seems more likely than $P2_12_12$ in view of the absence of 001 and 003 from photographs taken with the fibre axis oscillating with respect to the X-ray beam.

The $B$ forms of $P2_12_12_1$ and $P2_12_12$ can be ruled out by a simple consideration: the 011 reflection is fairly strong. Since the chain atoms can contribute little to its intensity, the side methyl groups must be as in Fig. 196. The choice between the remaining arrangements can only be made by detailed calculations of intensities for a range of molecular positions in each case. It would not be profitable to describe this rather laborious process here. It must suffice to observe that correct relative intensities were only obtained for the $P2_12_12_1$ arrangement. The best carbon positions are those shown in Fig. 197. (Slightly different atomic coordinates were subsequently suggested by Jeffrey (1944). The two sets of coordinates give about equally good agreement between observed and calculated intensities. Comparison of the two sets of coordinates will give some idea of the degree of precision to be expected in this work.) Hydrogen atoms are usually ignored in the earlier stages of work on organic substances; but it is noteworthy that in the work on $\beta$ gutta-percha was found necessary (in order to improve the agreement between observed and calculated intensities) to assume that the diffracting powers of C, CH, $CH_2$, and $CH_3$ groups are in the ratios $6:7:8:9$—these being the numbers of electrons in the groups. Since that time it has

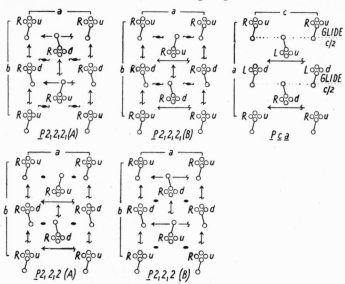

FIG. 195. Possible arrangements of molecules in $\beta$ gutta-percha. Note that for $Pca$ the axial nomenclature is changed; this is done to attain the conventional orientation of symmetry elements in this space-group. (One symmetry element in this arrangement is not shown: there is a glide plane parallel to the paper, having translation $a/2$.) $R$ = right, $L$ = left, $u$ = up, $d$ = down.

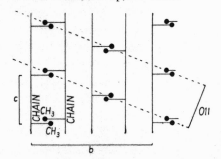

FIG. 196. Approximate positions of $CH_3$ groups in the $a$ projection of $\beta$ gutta-percha.

been found, in work on many structures, that the best agreement with observed intensities is obtained by putting in contributions of individual hydrogen atoms, placed at the sites expected on stereochemical grounds; in other words, the electron density of the hydrogen atom is not, as was at one time believed, lost in that of the carbon or other atom to which it is attached, but is for the most part spherically distributed round the proton. The contributions of the hydrogen atoms may have a considerable effect on the calculated intensities of certain reflections, if most of the hydrogen atoms give scattered waves in phase with each other.

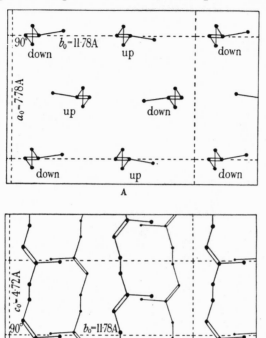

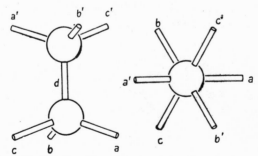

Fig. 197. Structure of right-handed $\beta$ gutta-percha crystal, seen ($A$) along the $c$ axis, ($B$) along the $a$ axis.

Fig. 198. Bond positions in saturated carbon compounds.

The results of stereochemical interest which came out of this work may be indicated (Bunn, 1942 $a$–$c$). It paved the way to a solution of the crystal structure of rubber itself (the *cis* isomer of polyisoprene) and of the synthetic rubber-like substance polychloroprene

$(—CH_2—CCl{=}CH—CH_2—)_n$; it led to suggestions on the molecular basis of rubber-like properties and to stereochemical explanations of the differences between the physical properties of the substances mentioned; and finally it led to a general consideration of the stereochemistry of chain polymers and to a new generalization on the configurations of aliphatic molecules. (See next section.)

2. *Rubber hydrochloride*

$$(—CH_2—C(CH_3)Cl—CH_2—CH_2—)_n.$$

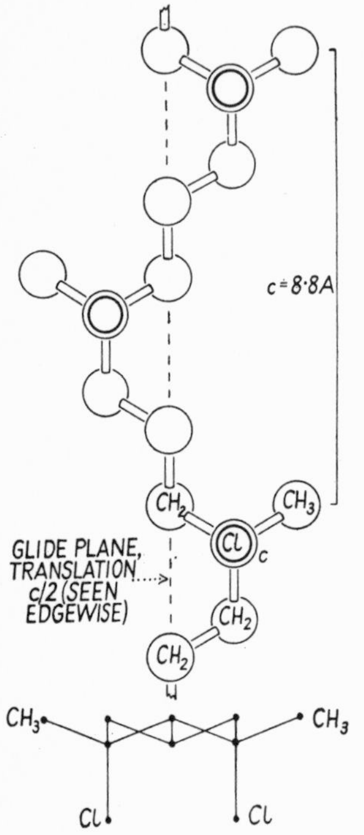

FIG. 199. Rubber hydrochloride. Molecular configuration suggested by the repeat distance and the principle of staggered bonds. (Hydrogen atoms omitted.)

This Cellophane-like substance is made by the action of hydrochloric acid on rubber. X-ray diffraction patterns show that it is crystalline (Gehman, Field, and Dinsmore, 1938), and interpretation of the patterns given by drawn fibres and sheets (Bunn and Garner, 1942) yields the information that the unit cell is rectangular, with the dimensions $a = 5.83$ Å, $b = 10.38$ Å, $c = 8.95$ Å, the last being the fibre axis. There are four chemical units in this cell.

The length of the repeat distance along the molecule suggests that it comprises two chemical units. The question of the chain configuration is obviously more complex than in the case of gutta-percha: by rotation round single bonds to various degrees, all sorts of configurations, all having the correct repeat distance, could be obtained. But although rotation round single bonds occurs in liquids and gases, certain configurations are more stable than others, and when crystallization occurs, molecules settle down in these preferred configurations. In all the well-established crystal structures containing such molecules the bonds of singly-linked carbon atoms are found to be staggered (Fig. 198). Various types of chain may be constructed by using various sequences of the three possible bond-configurations. *a'da*, *a'db*, and *a'dc*, which will be referred to as *A*, *B*, and *C* respectively. Now the only chain with an 8-atom period which has a repeat distance of about 8·95 Å is the chain *AAABAAAC*, shown in Fig. 199. This is therefore likely to be the configuration of the rubber hydrochloride molecule. This chain, more-over, seems probable from other points of view; one would expect the —$CH_2$—$CH_2$—$CH_2$— portions to be plane zigzags as in polyethylene ($A$ sequences), while a different bond-configuration at every fourth carbon atom (those which carry substituents) is an obvious possibility. The chlorine and methyl substituents may be either as in Fig. 199 or reversed; their positions, and the arrangement of the molecules, must be discovered from the intensities of the X-ray reflections.

There are only two molecules passing through the unit cell; if the symmetry is orthorhombic (as one would suppose, from the rectangular character of the cell), four asymmetric units are required; therefore each molecule must have twofold symmetry of some kind. Now the molecule in Fig. 199 has a glide plane as its only element of symmetry; therefore this must be used in the crystal structure. A survey of the reflections shows that $h0l$ reflections having $l$ odd are absent, indicating that there is, normal to $b$, a glide plane having a translation of $c/2$. Our expectations are thus confirmed, so far; and the orientation of the molecule in the cell is settled: it has its glide plane normal to $b$.

Assuming still that the symmetry is orthorhombic, the two molecules must be related to each other by a symmetry element; and this can only be either a plane of symmetry or a glide plane, perpendicular to the glide plane already mentioned, giving an arrangement in the polar class $mm2$. (Arrangements in the holosymmetric class $mmm$ would require eight asymmetric units; arrangements using axial symmetry—where this does not imply an extra plane or glide plane—have mono-clinic symmetry.) Molecules are not usually related by planes of sym-metry (see p. 248); moreover, the $a$ axis (normal to which the plane would be) is so short (5·83 Å) that there is not room for two molecules along it. Therefore we look for a glide plane normal to either $a$ or $c$. In the $hk0$ zone there is certainly no glide plane. In the $0kl$ zone the presence of a fairly strong 013 reflection rules out glide planes with $b$ or $c$ translation. (This reflection, from its position, might be 003 or 013 or both; but in view of the structure of the molecules, 003 is bound to be absent.) There remains the possibility of an $n$ glide. The great strength of the spot indexed as 021+111 (one of the strongest on the photograph) suggests that 021 is present, which would rule out an $n$ glide; but we cannot be quite certain of this. However, the arrange-ment with an $n$ glide (Fig. 200) can be ruled out, because it would give a strong 011 reflection; 011 is actually absent.

It appears, therefore, that the symmetry cannot be orthorhombic.

It may be monoclinic with the angle $\beta$ equal to 90°. In this case the $c$ glide plane possessed by the molecules themselves need not necessarily be used in the crystal structure; however, the existence of a $c$ glide in the crystal structure suggests that it *is* used. In looking for other symmetry elements (for the relation of the two molecules to each other), we find evidence (in the absence of odd $0k0$ reflections) of a screw

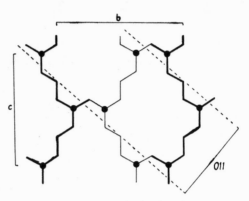

FIG. 200. Rubber hydrochloride. Projection along $a$. Consideration of arrangement with $n$ glide plane parallel to the paper.

axis along $b$, pointing to the space-group $P2_1/c$, the arrangement being as in Fig. 201.

The test of this structure is begun, as usual, by considering the $c$ projection. It can be shown that the arrangement of Fig. 201 gives approximately correct intensities for the $hk0$ reflections, if the chlorine atoms are placed on $p$ bonds and the methyl groups on $q$ bonds. The positions of the molecules along the $c$ axis are found by calculating intensities, first for $h0l$ and $0kl$ reflections and finally for the general $(hkl)$ reflections. It is found that satisfactory agreement between calculated and observed intensities is obtained for the positions shown in Figs. 201–3; this is evidently the structure of rubber hydrochloride.

The mode of packing of the molecules shows clearly the reason why the angle $\beta$ is 90°. The chlorine atom of one molecule (Cl' in Fig. 203) fits into the hollow formed by groups $CH_3$, $CH_2(2)$, and $CH_2(3)$ attached to carbon atom C of the molecule in front (that is, the next molecule along the $a$ axis). This packing ensures that the $z$ coordinate of Cl' is about the same as that of C, and since the carbon–chlorine bond is at right angles to the chain axis, the angle $\beta$ must necessarily be approximately 90°.

The coordinates of atoms in chain-polymer crystals cannot be determined with the precision attained in single-crystal work, on account of the smaller number of reflections available and the overlapping of some of them. But the amount of evidence available is sufficient (for polymers of the degree of complexity of those considered here) to leave little

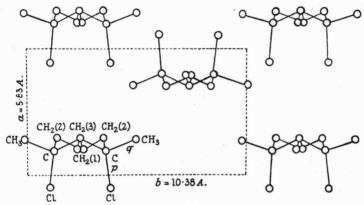

FIG. 201. Structure of rubber hydrochloride. $c$ projection.

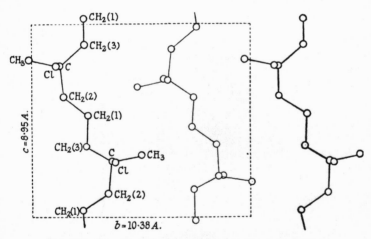

FIG. 202. Structure of rubber hydrochloride. $a$ projection.

doubt of the general arrangement, as well as the approximate coordinates of the atoms.

The principal interest of the rubber hydrochloride structure (apart from its bearing on the theory of the relation between the physical properties and the molecular structure of polymers) is that it formed the first test of validity and usefulness of the principle of staggered bonds.

**Abnormal structures.** In all the structures considered so far two structural principles have been obeyed: firstly, atoms have occupied precisely defined positions, and secondly, positions which are equivalent according to the theory of space-groups have been occupied by identical atoms. It has already been mentioned (at the end of Chapter VII) that there are some crystals in which one or the other of these principles is violated; and it is now intended to pursue this subject by giving a few examples.

Crystals which are abnormal in this way are in a minority; but they are important in their bearing on our understanding of the physical

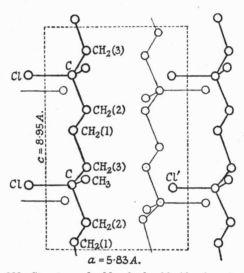

FIG. 203. Structure of rubber hydrochloride. $b$ projection.

properties of crystals and the relations between the crystalline and liquid states; and, moreover, if in attempting to determine the structure of any crystal it is found impossible to account for the intensities of the X-ray reflections by any structure based on the acceptance of the two principles mentioned, it must be considered whether any structure in which these principles are ignored can account for the X-ray pattern.

**Molecular rotation.** In a normal crystal every atom occupies a precise mean position, about which it vibrates to a degree depending on the temperature; molecules or polyatomic ions have precisely defined orientations as well as precise mean positions. When such a crystal is heated, the amplitude of the thermal vibrations of the atoms increases with the temperature until a point is reached at which the regular structure breaks down, that is, the crystal melts. But in a few types of crystal it appears that rotation of molecules or polyatomic ions sets in below the melting-point; in other words, rotation does not disturb the arrangement sufficiently to disorganize it entirely. Molecules which behave in this way are either roughly cylindrical, so that they may rotate about a particular axis without unduly disturbing their neighbours, or else roughly spherical and rotate about more than one axis. (White and Bishop, 1940; White, Biggs, and Morgan, 1940.) Evidently, when the molecules start rotating, the forces between them are still sufficient to ensure three-dimensional regularity until at a higher temperature the links between the molecules are broken by additional thermal vibrations, and the crystal melts. The onset of molecular rotation is often, but not always, accompanied by a change of symmetry.

In some crystals such rotation occurs at room temperature. One of the simplest examples is potassium cyanide, KCN; the structure is of the sodium chloride type (Fig. 127), and this can only mean that the $CN^-$ ion is rotating; it does not necessarily mean that all orientations are equally probable, but it does mean that frequent changes of orientation occur, such that the effective symmetry of the ion is the highest possible in the cubic system; neither carbon nor nitrogen atoms occupy specific positions in the structure but are in effect 'spread over' a number of positions.

Long molecules sometimes rotate about their long axes, and disk-shaped molecules or ions like $NO_3^-$ may spin in the plane of the disk. The history of the study of the long-chain primary alkyl-ammonium halides such as $C_5H_{11}NH_3Cl$ is interesting and instructive. These substances form tetragonal crystals with two molecules in the unit cell. It appeared at first (Hendricks, 1928 b) that the carbon chain in these substances is linear, with a C—C distance of 1·25 Å. Yet in other long-chain molecules the carbon chain is a zigzag, with a C—C distance of 1·54 Å and bond angles of about 110°; this form of chain is quite incompatible with the tetragonal symmetry of the alkyl-ammonium halide crystals. The dilemma was resolved by the suggestion that rotation of the chain about its long axis occurs, since in this way the zigzag chain may attain, in effect, tetragonal symmetry (Fig. 204); the spacing of 1·25 Å is the projection on the chain axis of a bond 1·54 Å in length inclined at 35° to the axis. It was then found that at low temperatures the structure changes (Hendricks, 1930); probably in this low-temperature form the molecules are not rotating.

Crystals in which molecules rotate still have three-dimensional regularity; they must not be confused with 'liquid crystals', in which there is only two-dimensional or one-dimensional regularity (see Bernal and Wooster, 1932; Randall, 1934; G. and E. Friedel and others, 1931; Oseen and others, 1933).

Evidence of molecular rotation may be given by non-crystallographic evidence; the transition from a rotating to a non-rotating state is accompanied by sudden changes in specific heat, in dielectric constant, and in width of nuclear magnetic resonance bands (see Chapter VIII).

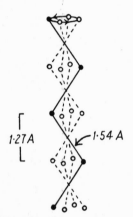

Since molecular rotation does occur in certain crystals, it is necessary, when attempting to determine the structure of any crystal, to consider this possibility. If there appears to be a conflict between the symmetry of a molecule in the crystal and the expectation based on stereo-chemical principles, or if it is found impossible to obtain correct calculated intensities on the assumption that the molecules are fixed, it should be considered whether the hypothesis of molecular rotation provides an explanation.

Fig. 204. The zigzag hydro-carbon chain in $C_5H_{11}NH_3Cl$ attains, by rotation, tetragonal symmetry.

**Mixed crystals and 'defect' structures.**
Certain substances which, by themselves, form crystals of the same structural type are able to crystallize together in the form of a 'mixed crystal', in which equivalent sites are occupied indiscriminately by different atoms. The example of $K_2SO_4$ and $(NH_4)_2SO_4$ has already been mentioned in Chapter II; there is nothing surprising in the formation of mixed crystals of these substances, since the structures of the pure substances are entirely analogous and the potassium and ammonium ions are similar both in chemical character and size. (Radii: $K^+$, 1·33 Å; $NH_4^+$, 1·43 Å.) Still simpler examples are found in some alloy systems; for instance, copper and gold, which by themselves form face-centred cubic crystals, are able to form mixed crystals containing any proportions of the two elements. Here again, similarity of chemical character and size of the two types of atoms is the underlying cause. (Radii: Cu 1·28 Å, Au 1·44 Å.) The proof that in these alloys crystallographically equivalent sites are occupied indiscriminately by the two different types of atoms is very simple. The alloy crystals are face-centred cubic, with four atoms to the unit cell, that is, one atom to each lattice point; it therefore appears, from the X-ray evidence, that the atoms in the crystal are all identical; it is, however, known that two different types of atom are present.

The only way out of this dilemma is the conclusion that the equivalent lattice points are occupied indiscriminately by the two types of atom. (A large number of unit cells is concerned in the formation of an X-ray reflection; local irregular variations of composition are not detected.) In agreement with this conclusion is the fact that the length of the unit cell edge of such an alloy lies between those of the pure components— indeed, the relation between unit cell size and composition is almost exactly linear.

The difference between a mixed crystal and a compound is well brought out by other phenomena which occur in the copper–gold system. The mixed-crystal alloys mentioned in the last paragraph are only obtained by quenching from high temperatures. If these mixed crystals are cooled slowly, or annealed at a suitable temperature, the atoms sort themselves out and form a more regular arrangement. The type of arrangement depends on the composition. Thus, an alloy of composition $Cu_3Au$, when annealed, gives an X-ray diffraction pattern containing many more reflections than that of the quenched specimen.

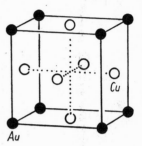

FIG. 205. Structure of $Cu_3Au$.

The reflections fit a cubic unit cell of about the same size as that of the quenched specimen, but the pattern exhibits no systematic absences; in fact the lattice is primitive, not face-centred. Detailed analysis shows that the arrangement of the atoms is that of Fig. 205, a properly ordered arrangement in which equivalent sites are occupied by identical atoms. This is a very simple and clear example of the effect of ordered and disordered arrangements on X-ray diffraction patterns; ordered arrangements, which are stable at low temperatures, give patterns containing more reflections than the disordered arrangements which are stable at higher temperatures. (In alloy systems the ordered structures obtained from mixed crystals by annealing are called 'superlattices'.)

Mixed crystals are mentioned here chiefly as an introduction to the idea that sites equivalent according to space-group theory may in some circumstances be occupied by different atoms. As far as structure determination is concerned, we need not be detained by further consideration of mixed crystals; nobody is likely to attempt to determine the structure of a mixed crystal without first knowing the structures of the pure constituents. The function of X-ray analysis here is to determine, as in the example of $Cu_3Au$, whether a substance thought to be

a mixed crystal is really a true mixed crystal or a 'compound' characterized by a superlattice; the latter is amenable to the normal methods of
structure analysis based on space-group theory, and likewise need not
detain us further.

More surprising than the formation of mixed crystals is the occurrence
of substances which are apparently compounds of fixed composition,
yet in which different atoms are scattered indiscriminately among
crystallographically equivalent sites ('defect structures'). Crystals of
lithium ferrite $LiFeO_2$, for instance, give an X-ray diffraction pattern
which indicates the sodium chloride type of structure, with an oxygen
in place of each chlorine atom and, to all appearances, $\frac{1}{2}Li^+ + \frac{1}{2}Fe^{3+}$
in place of each sodium—a result which can only mean that lithium
and ferric ions (which have the same radius, 0·67 Å) are scattered
indiscriminately over the positive sites (Posnjak and Barth, 1931).
The constancy of composition is due to the fact that the interchange-
able ions have different charges; any variation of the proportions
of $Li^+$ and $Fe^{3+}$ would mean that the whole crystal would not be
electrically neutral. $Li_2TiO_3$ has a similar structure (Kordes, 1935 b).
More complex examples of the same sort of thing occur among substances having the spinel type of structure, an arrangement common to
many mixed oxides having the formula $AB_2O_4$. In a normal spinel like
$ZnAl_2O_4$ the cubic unit cell contains eight 'molecules'; the space-group
is $Fd3m$, oxygen ions occupy a 32-fold set of positions, zinc ions an 8-fold
set of positions in which each is surrounded tetrahedrally by four
oxygens, and aluminium ions a 16-fold set of positions in which each
is surrounded octahedrally by six oxygens. But in some spinels such
as $MgFe_2O_4$, the positive ions are distributed differently over the same
pattern of sites. In the example given, half the ferric ions occupy the
8-fold positions, while the other half, together with all the magnesium
ions, are distributed at random over the 16-fold positions. (Barth and
Posnjak, 1932.) The evidence for this arrangement is of course provided
by the intensities of the X-ray reflections. This example serves to
remind us that, if satisfactory agreement between observed and calculated intensities cannot be achieved on the basis of the assumption that
equivalent sites are occupied by identical atoms, then arrangements
ignoring this principle should be tried.

Still more surprising are certain crystals in which a set of equivalent
positions is only partially occupied, some sites here and there at random
being empty. The spinel group also provides examples of this type of
structure. The cubic ($\gamma$) form of $Fe_2O_3$, for instance, gives an X-ray

diffraction pattern very similar to that of $Fe_3O_4$, which is a normal spinel $Fe^{2+}Fe_2^{3+}O_4$. In fact it appears that in the unit cell of $\gamma$-$Fe_2O_3$ there are 32 oxygen ions arranged in the same way as in $Fe_3O_4$; this leads to the surprising conclusion that there are, on the average, $21\frac{1}{3}$ iron atoms in the unit cell, these being scattered indiscriminately over the positive ion sites—and the intensities of the reflections confirm this (Verwey, 1935; Hägg, 1935 $b$). The structure of $\gamma$-$Al_2O_3$ is of the same type (Kordes, 1935 $a$; Hägg and Söderholm, 1935).

A simpler example is the iron sulphide pyrrhotite, the composition of which is roughly FeS but which always contains rather too little iron. The X-ray pattern indicates the sodium chloride type of structure, and it appears that while the negative ion positions are fully occupied by sulphur, there is a deficiency of iron atoms in the positive ion sites. (Laves, 1930; Hägg and Sucksdorff, 1933.)

The zeolite group of minerals provides further examples of defect structures. These are complex aluminosilicates, the crystals of which have a rigid framework of Al, Si, and O atoms in which there are continuous channels; water molecules may enter or leave the crystals by way of these channels, the amount of water in the crystals being variable (W. H. Taylor, 1930, 1934). (In normal hydrates the structure collapses when water is removed, a new structure being formed.) A simple substance in which the same thing occurs is calcium sulphate subhydrate $CaSO_4 . 0-\frac{2}{3}H_2O$ (Bunn, 1941).

An extreme type of defect structure is the $\alpha$ form of AgI, which is stable above 146° C. In this crystal the iodine atoms form a cubic body-centred arrangement, but the silver atoms apparently have no fixed positions at all; they wander freely through the iodine lattice (Strock, 1934, 1935).

In crystals of organic compounds, a type of disorder sometimes occurs which is akin to the mixed crystal type: for instance, in the crystal of 2-amino-4-methyl-6-chloro-pyrimidine

the molecules occur indiscriminately in two orientations in which the methyl group and the chlorine atom are interchanged (Clews and Cochran, 1947); this is possible without much strain because a methyl group and a chlorine atom are similar in size. For a similar reason 1,2 dichloro-tetramethyl benzene molecules

occur indiscriminately in six different orientations in the crystal; since the space-group symmetry is $P2_1/c$ and the unit cell contains two molecules, this crystal would appear to contain centrosymmetric molecules; it is known, however, that the molecules are not centrosymmetric; the apparent centrosymmetry is due to the disorder. This crystal is also interesting for another reason, for it is one of those in which the molecules rotate at room temperature; the rotation, however, is not continuous, but consists of jumps from one of the six orientations to another (Tulinsky and White, 1958). A third example, in which again this type of disorder leads to apparent centrosymmetry in a molecule known to be non-centrosymmetric, is the structure of the crystal of azulene

in which two different molecular orientations (with the 5- and 7-atom rings interchanged), occur indiscriminately (J. M. Robertson, Shearer, Sim, and Watson, 1958).

Disorders of the mixed crystal type can also occur in the crystalline regions of high polymer specimens. Polyvinyl alcohol,

$$(-CH_2-CHOH-)_p,$$

which was at one time thought to be regular in structure, with all OH groups in corresponding positions, has been found to be irregular, with the OH groups indiscriminately in left- and right-hand positions (Bunn, 1948); yet it crystallizes well—it is an exception to the general rule that polymers of irregular structure do not crystallize. The reason why it is able to crystallize is that the OH groups, though larger than hydrogen atoms, are not large enough to disrupt the structure; moreover, strong hydrogen bonds between many of the OH groups neutralize any strains due to the bad packing inevitable in a disordered structure.

The evidence for the various types of defect structures is (it is hardly necessary to repeat) provided by X-ray diffraction patterns. The unit cell dimensions, the chemical analysis, and the density settle the composition of the unit cell, and the intensities of the reflections settle the positions of the atoms. Those who studied these structures were forced to the rather surprising conclusions by this evidence. The moral of this tale is that the implications of X-ray diffraction patterns (in conjunction with reliable chemical analyses and densities) should be accepted boldly, even if they conflict with geometrical ideals (the application of the theory of space-groups) or with stereochemical preconceptions. Only in this way is new knowledge and a deeper comprehension of the crystalline state attained.

# X

# DIRECT AND SEMI-DIRECT METHODS

In the method of trial, crystal structures are determined by considering what atomic positions will account for the intensities of the diffracted X-ray beams. This method is not only very laborious (except for very simple structures) but also has all the disadvantages of an indirect method: so much depends on the chances of postulating an approximately correct structure. The opposite method is to record and measure the diffraction pattern, and then combine the results by suitable mathematical or experimental operations to give a picture of the crystal structure.

The reason why it is not usually possible to employ this direct method for the solution of crystal structures has already been indicated at the beginning of Chapter VII: it is that we do not usually know, and cannot determine experimentally, the phases of the various diffracted beams with respect to a chosen point in the unit of pattern. However, for certain crystals we can from the start be reasonably certain of the phase relations of the diffracted beams, or can deduce them from crystallographic evidence, and in these circumstances we can proceed at once to combine the information, either mathematically or by experimental methods in which light waves are used in place of X-rays. Otherwise, it is necessary to find approximate positions by trial, the approximation being taken as far as is necessary to be certain of the phases of a considerable number of reflections; as soon as the phases are known, the direct method can be used.

**Image synthesis.** The subject may be approached most simply by considering the process of image formation in the microscope, and in particular the formation of an image of the patterned line-grating shown in Plate VI. The simple geometrical representation of the formation of the image of a large object by a simple lens, in which light waves from different points on the object travel independently through the lens and are brought to a focus at different points, is not adequate for objects bearing fine detail commensurate with the wavelength of light, since in these circumstances, waves from neighbouring points interfere with each other. For the small patterned line-grating shown in the lower half of Plate VI, it cannot be said that an image of each line is produced independently of the images of its neighbours; owing to interference between waves from neighbouring lines, a set of diffracted beams is produced, *each of them coming from the pattern as a whole*. The formation of two of them—the first and third orders—is illustrated in Fig. 114. Thus, from the pattern of the grating, a very different pattern of diffracted beams is produced. Yet an image of the original grating *is* formed by the lens, and this image must evidently be built up by the interaction of the diffracted beams after passing through the lens. An idea of the part played by each diffracted beam may be gained in the following way.

Suppose first that, in addition to the direct (zero-order) beam, only

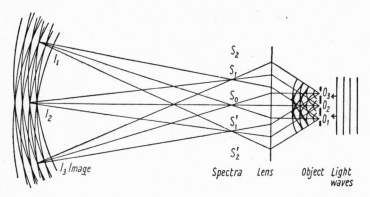

FIG. 206. Formation of the image of a diffraction grating. Paths of light rays (Bragg, 1929 *b*).

the first-order diffracted beams (one on each side of the primary beam) pass through the lens. The paths of the light rays are shown in Fig. 206, for the special case of a small distant monochromatic light-source. The parallel direct rays give an image of the source at $S_0$; the two sets of first-order diffracted rays give additional images on either side of the central image. There is thus in this plane a diffraction pattern in the form of a set of images of the source. Continuing on their way, the first-order rays reach the image plane, where they interact, producing an ordinary set of interference fringes in which there is a sinusoidal distribution of light intensity. (See top of Fig. 207.) In other words, the image given by the first-order diffracted beams alone is an extremely diffuse one; it merely shows diffuse lines (the spacing of which corresponds to the repeat distance of the pattern) without any of the details.

The second-order diffracted beams by themselves would produce a set of interference fringes having half the spacing of those of the first order, and an intensity proportional to that of the diffracted beams

B b

concerned. If this set is added to the first-order set, as in the second stage of Fig. 207, the image is modified, the resultant distribution of light intensity being that shown by the full line, obtained by adding the ordinates of the constituent (dotted) curves. In this particular case the second orders make little difference because their intensity is small; but with the addition of the third orders (also shown in Fig. 207) the

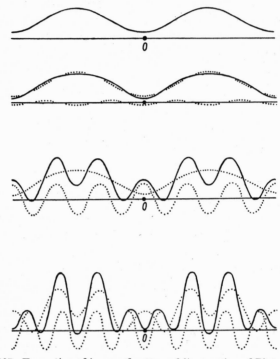

Fig. 207. Formation of image of patterned line-grating of Plate VI by superposition of different sets of interference fringes, each set being produced by a pair of diffracted beams.

details of the pattern (the pair of lines constituting the pattern-unit) begin to appear, and become sharper when the fourth orders are added. It is by the co-operation of all the orders passing through the lens that the image is built up; one may imagine all the sets of interference fringes, each with its own spacing and intensity, superposed. The larger the number of orders of diffraction taking part, the more faithful the image. This is the reason why the resolving power of a microscope objective lens combination depends on the numerical aperture, which is a measure of the angular range of diffracted beams collected by the lens.

If it were not possible to obtain an image of the pattern experimentally, it would be possible to obtain it mathematically; but in order to do so it would be necessary to know not only the positions and intensities of the diffracted beams but also their phase angles, for it is these phase angles which place the various sets of interference fringes in correct register: for the patterned line-grating which we are using as example, the first, second, and fourth orders have negative phase with respect to the origin $O$, while the third order is positive. Thus, given the position, intensity, and phase angle of every diffracted beam produced by a unidimensional pattern, we can calculate the actual density distribution along that pattern. We effect by numerical computation what is shown graphically in Fig. 207: the resultant amplitude of light vibrations at any point whose distance from the origin is $X$ (expressed as a fraction of the repeat distance) is given by the Fourier series

$$A_0 + A_1 \cos 2\pi(X - \alpha_1) + A_2 \cos 2\pi(2X - \alpha_2) + A_3 \cos 2\pi(3X - \alpha_3) + \dots$$
$$= A_0 + \sum A_n \cos 2\pi(nX - \alpha_n),$$

where each term represents the contribution of one order, the coefficients $A_1$, $A_2$, etc., being the amplitudes of the waves (the square roots of the intensities of the diffraction spots), and $\alpha_1$, $\alpha_2$, etc., the phase displacements. ($A_0$ is the amplitude of the zero-order diffraction.) For a centrosymmetric pattern, such as the one we are considering, the phase displacements are all either 0 or $\frac{1}{2}$ (in degrees, $0°$ or $180°$) with respect to the centre of symmetry, and therefore the expression

$$A_0 + \sum A_n \cos 2\pi nX$$

may be used, each coefficient $A_1$, $A_2$, etc., being given the appropriate sign, positive for a phase angle of $0°$, negative for a phase angle of $180°$.

This is a simple example of the synthesis of an image from a diffraction pattern by calculation. The synthesis of an image of a crystal structure from its X-ray diffraction pattern is more complex (because a three-dimensional diffraction grating is involved), but similar in principle, because the X-ray diffraction spots produced by an atomic pattern are absolutely analogous to the diffracted light beams formed by a pattern whose repeat distance is comparable with the wavelength of light.

**Electron density maps.** We have seen that a diffracted X-ray beam may be regarded as a reflection from a set of parallel planes of lattice points, and that the intensities of the different orders of reflection from this set of planes depend on the distribution of atoms between one plane and the next. Consequently a synthesis of all the orders of reflection from one set of planes leads to a knowledge of the distribution of scattering matter between one plane and the next, just as the synthesis of all the orders of optical diffraction from a line-grating yields a curve showing the distribution of scattering points along the grating. The scattering matter in a crystal consists of the electron 'atmospheres' of the atoms, hence a synthesis on the lines indicated yields a curve showing the distribution of electron density between one lattice plane and the next. The orders of $00l$ reflections, for instance, yield the distribution of electron density between one 001 plane and the next. The expression used for the synthesis is entirely analogous to the one for the line-grating:

Diffracting power at any level $Z$

$$= F_{000} + F_{001} \cos 2\pi(Z - \alpha_{001}) +$$
$$+ F_{002} \cos 2\pi(2Z - \alpha_{002}) + F_{003} \cos 2\pi(3Z - \alpha_{003}) + \ldots$$
$$= F_{000} + \sum F_{00l} \cos 2\pi(lZ - \alpha_{00l}).$$

$F_{001}$, $F_{002}$, and so on are the structure amplitudes for these reflections, calculated from the intensities in the way described earlier in this book. If the projection has a real or apparent centre of symmetry, the phase angles with respect to this centre of symmetry are all either 0° or 180°.

The scattering material in a crystal consists of electrons, and if we wish to calculate the absolute electron density at any level, we must use absolute structure amplitudes in the expression

$$\rho_Z \, d_{001} = F_{000} + \sum F_{00l} \cos 2\pi(lZ - \alpha_{00l}),$$

in which $\rho_Z$ is the absolute electron density at a level $Z$, $d_{001}$ is the spacing of the 001 planes, and $F_{000}$ (the structure amplitude for the zero-order diffraction) is the number of electrons in the unit cell. If only relative $F$'s are available, the constant term $F_{000}$ is not known in relation to the set of relative $F$'s; nevertheless, electron densities in relation to an arbitrary level can be calculated.

A one-dimensional Fourier synthesis can be used for the direct determination of atomic parameters along any crystal axis, provided that the phase angles $\alpha$ for the various orders of reflection are known. For an example, consider the structure of sodium nitrite, already described in Chapter IX. It is body-centred, hence only even orders of $00l$ appear; their structure amplitudes are 8, 15, 10, 2, and 7 for 002, 004, etc., respectively.

Both sodium and nitrogen atoms lie at $z = 0$ (the origin for the electron density calculations), but the parameter of the oxygen atoms is a variable one. The electron density distribution along $c$ is centro-symmetric, hence the phase angles of all reflections must be either $0°$ or $180°$. Since the combined diffracting powers of sodium and nitrogen are much higher than that of oxygen, it may be assumed that the wave at the origin ($\alpha = 0°$) is strong enough to determine the phases of all the $00l$ reflections: the waves from the oxygen atoms reduce the structure amplitudes for some reflections, but are not likely to change the phase from $0°$ to $180°$. A Fourier synthesis, assuming that all the phases are $0°$, gives an electron density distribution showing, in addition to the strong peak at the origin due to sodium plus nitrogen, a smaller peak at $z = 0\cdot20c$. This method of finding the parameter is more direct than the trial method, but can only be used if the phase angles are known. The result is rough if, as in the above example, only five orders of reflection are used; the number available can usually be increased by using a shorter X-ray wavelength.

Turn now to the calculation of an image of a crystal structure as seen along a zone axis. This is obtained by a synthesis of all the reflections from planes parallel to this zone axis. Thus, the $h0l$ reflections give an image of the structure as seen along the $b$ axis, an image in which the highlights are the points of maximum projected electron density—the atomic centres.

One way of approach to this is to consider a two-dimensional pattern on the optical scale and the formation of an image of it by a microscope lens. A two-dimensional pattern such as that in Plate XIV, when illuminated by parallel monochromatic light, gives a two-dimensional diffraction pattern (shown in the lower half of this figure) in which each diffracted beam is characterized by two order numbers. The diffracted beams, after passing through the objective lens and reaching the image plane, form the image by interference; we may imagine many sets of interference fringes, one set from each pair of diffracted beams $h0l$ and $\bar{h}0\bar{l}$, crossing each other in all directions, and by their super-position building up the image. Returning to the X-ray reflections from a crystal, we may treat the $h0l$ set of reflections as if they were diffracted beams from a two-dimensional pattern which is the $b$ projection of the crystal structure, and combine them by calculation to form an image of this pattern. The two order numbers, $h$ and $l$, for each reflection, enter into the expression in this way: $\rho_{xz}$ (projected electron density at a point $XZ$) $\times A$ (area of projected unit cell) $= F_{000} + \sum \sum F_{h0l} \cos 2\pi(hX + lZ - \alpha_{h0l})$ (Bragg, 1929 $a$). To obtain the complete image it is necessary to calculate the projected electron density at a large number of points $XZ$ all over the projected cell; for each point a large number of terms (one for each $h0l$ reflection) must be added to the constant term $F_{000}$.

Finally, synthesis of all the reflections gives the electron density at any point $xyz$ in the unit cell. The expression for this three-dimensional synthesis is $\rho_{xyz}$ (electron density at a point $XYZ$) $\times V$ (volume of unit cell) $= F_{000} + \sum \sum \sum F_{hkl} \cos 2\pi(hX+kY+lZ-\alpha_{hkl})$.

The labour involved in a three-dimensional synthesis is very great, except for the simplest structures; for this reason (and others which will appear later), the two-dimensional synthesis, giving a view of a projection of the structure, is most often used in crystal structure determination. No synthesis can be carried out, however, unless the phase angles of the reflections with respect to a reference point in the structure are known. We now consider under what circumstances it is possible to be sure of the phase angles from the start, or to deduce them from crystallographic evidence.

For a much more detailed discussion of Fourier series methods, see Robertson (1937) and Lipson and Cochran (1953).

**Direct structure determination.** In some crystal projections the phase angles of the reflections relevant to the projection are all the same (with respect to a reference point). In such circumstances the image of the structure can be calculated directly from the intensities of the reflections. The circumstances in which we can be certain that this is so are unfortunately rare. Three conditions must be fulfilled. The first is that the projection must possess apparent centres of symmetry; not necessarily true centres of symmetry in the crystal, but apparent centres of symmetry such as occur when there are twofold axes of symmetry parallel to the zone axis of the projection. With respect to any apparent centre of symmetry, the phase angles of all reflections are necessarily either $0°$ or $180°$.

The second condition is that there must be, at the centre of symmetry, an atom whose diffracting power is very much greater than that of any of the other atoms in the cell. The third is that there must be only one such atom per lattice point in the projected unit cell;[†] this atom is conveniently taken as the origin of the projected cell. In these circumstances, it is certain that the phase angles of all the reflections with respect to the origin are $0°$, since the wave from the heavy atom at

---

† Note that for certain views of some space-groups the unit cell of the projection contains fewer molecules than the real cell; see p. 255. Also, that where two heavy atoms have the same coordinates in a projection, they may be regarded as a single strong scattering for the present purposes.

the origin has a phase angle of 0° and is so strong that it overrides the effects of all the waves from the remaining atoms; the latter, if in opposition to those from the heavy atom (that is, have, in combination, a phase angle of 180°), reduce its intensity but cannot reverse its phase sign.

The necessity for the third condition may be appreciated by consideration of Fig. 208, in which there are two molecules or atom groups in the projected unit cell. Each molecule contains a heavy atom, and both heavy atoms are at centres of symmetry, but the orientation of the molecule in the centre of the projected cell is different from that

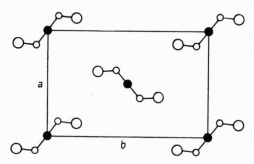

Fig. 208. For this projected structure, in which the black circles represent heavy atoms, all reflections having $h+k$ even have a phase angle of 0°, but those having $h+k$ odd may have phase angles of 0° or 180°. Therefore direct structure determination is not possible.

of the molecule at the corner. As far as the heavy atoms alone are concerned, the projected cell is centred; this means that for all reflections having $h+k$ odd, the contribution of the heavy atoms is zero, since the wave from the centre atom opposes the wave from the corner atom. But with regard to the rest of the molecule, the projection is not centred, and therefore reflections having $h+k$ odd are produced; they are due entirely to the parts of the molecules other than the heavy atoms, and their phases may be either 0° or 180°. Thus, while it is true that reflections having $h+k$ even all have a phase angle of 0° owing to the overriding effect of the heavy atoms, reflections having $h+k$ odd may have phase angles of either 0° or 180°, and there is nothing to tell us which is correct for each reflection. (For a truly face-centred cell, this difficulty does not arise; there are no reflections with $h+k$ odd, and the phase angle for all the reflections with $h+k$ even is 0°.)

The three necessary conditions are fulfilled in the $b$ projection of the platinum phthalocyanine crystal. (Robertson and Woodward, 1940.)

The unit cell is monoclinic (space-group $P2_1/a$), and contains two molecules of $PtC_{32}H_{16}N_8$. Since there are only two platinum atoms in the cell, and the only twofold positions in this space-group lie at centres of symmetry, each platinum atom lies at a centre of symmetry. In the $b$ projection the $a$ axis appears to be halved owing to the existence of the glide plane; in other words, this projection has a one-molecule cell with the heavy platinum atom at a centre of symmetry. The other atoms in the molecule of $PtC_{32}H_{16}N_8$ all have diffracting powers very much smaller than that of platinum, and therefore the phase angles will be those of the platinum atom, that is, $0°$ for every reflection. This is not true for the $a$ and $c$ projections. The direct method can therefore only be used for the $b$ projection; fortunately this is by far the most informative on the details of the molecular structure.

When electron densities are calculated for this projection by the expression already given, the map shown in Fig. 209 is obtained. Contours are drawn at intervals of one electron, except round the platinum atom, where the interval is 20 electrons. The detail shown in this striking view of the structure is remarkable; every atom is clearly resolved, and the positions of atomic centres can be read off with considerable precision. It should be noted that the flat molecule is inclined at $26·5°$ to the plane of the paper, and is therefore somewhat foreshortened in one direction.

The swamping effect of the heavy atom is of extreme value in that it enables us to assume the phases of all the reflections; but it should be noted that the intensities of the reflections must be determined with as much precision as possible, since the swamping effect tends to make the intensities more nearly equal than they would be in absence of the heavy atom.

It follows from the foregoing discussion that three-dimensional determinations by this direct method (giving the electron densities at *points* in the unit cell) are only possible when the unit cell contains only one heavy atom, which must lie at a centre of symmetry; this situation is rare.

**Phase angles from experimental evidence.** There is another set of circumstances in which the signs of the terms can be deduced from experimental evidence. This has been done for phthalocyanine itself. It so happens that the unit cell dimensions and space-group of the parent substance and the nickel derivative are identical, and it can be assumed that the orientations of the molecules are the same in both crystals. The centre of symmetry of the cell is occupied by hydrogen in the former and nickel in the latter; the contribution of hydrogen is quite negligible, hence it can be assumed that the centre of symmetry is effectively empty in the parent substance. Now the phase for the

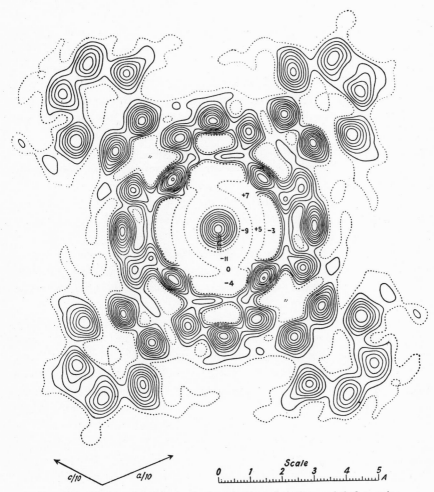

Fig. 209. Electron densities in the $b$ projection of platinum phthalocyanine. (Robertson and Woodward, 1940.)

parent substance is positive for some planes and negative for others; and it is reasonably assumed that for any particular crystal plane the contribution of the organic part of the nickel derivative has the same sign as for the corresponding plane of the parent substance. The nickel atom, however, being at the centre of symmetry, gives a positive contribution for every reflection. Therefore if, in the nickel derivative, the organic part of the molecule gives, for a particular plane, a negative contribution, this will be in opposition to that of the nickel atom, and the reflection will therefore be weaker than the corresponding reflection of the parent substance. But for some planes the organic part of the molecule will give a positive contribution, and this, co-operating with that of the nickel atom, will result in reflections stronger than those from corresponding planes of the parent substance. The procedure is therefore to measure the intensities of the reflections from both parent substance and nickel derivative, and compare the absolute intensities for corresponding planes. When the intensity for the nickel derivative is higher than that for the parent substance, it is assumed that the structure amplitude for the latter is positive; when the reverse is true, it is assumed that the structure amplitude for the parent substance is negative. In this way the signs of all the structure amplitudes for the parent substance are found. The way is thus opened for a direct Fourier synthesis. This was done by J. M. Robertson (1936 a); the phthalocyanine structure was indeed the first to be determined completely by the direct method. The electron density map so produced is very similar to that of the platinum derivative, except that the molecule is more tilted with regard to the plane of projection, and therefore appears more foreshortened. The angle of tilt is 44°. It should be noted that no assumptions of a stereochemical nature were made; the only assumptions were those based on the observed isomorphism of the crystals. (Likewise, in the case of the platinum derivative, the only assumption was that the phases are all the same.)

The work on phthalocyanine and its nickel derivative is an extreme example of the 'isomorphous replacement' method, which has been widely used. It is not often that hydrogen and heavy atom derivatives of the same molecule form isomorphous crystals, for the sizes of these ions are too different; but it is not uncommon for potassium and rubidium salts to be isomorphous, because the sizes of the potassium and rubidium ions are similar, and although the difference of diffracting power between potassium and rubidium is less than between hydrogen and nickel, it is adequate for the purpose of deducing phase angles for quite complex substances. Magnesium and zinc salts have been used in a similar way. If these replaceable atoms are at centres of symmetry, and provided that all of them have identical surroundings (identical in orientation as well as in other respects), phase angles can be deduced by comparing the absolute intensities of corresponding reflections. In three-dimensional work the replaceable atoms must be at true centres of symmetry; for projections, the replaceable atoms must be at apparent centres of symmetry, due, for instance, to twofold axes or twofold screw axes normal to the projection plane.

It is not essential to measure the absolute intensities experimentally; Hargreaves (see Lipson and Cochran, 1953) pointed out that by making use of the knowledge that the difference between the absolute structure amplitudes of corresponding reflections of the two crystals must be constant (and equal to the difference between the diffracting powers of the two ions), two sets of relative structure amplitudes can be put on the same scale. We know that the relations between absolute structure amplitudes must be as on the left-hand side of Fig. 210, where the

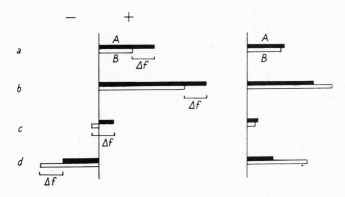

FIG. 210. Isomorphous replacement in centrosymmetric crystals. Left—Absolute structure amplitudes of corresponding reflections differ by a constant $\Delta f$. Right—Example of experimental relative amplitudes.

differences between the $F$'s of corresponding reflections of crystals $A$ and $B$ must be equal to $\Delta f$, the difference between the diffracting powers of the replaceable ions. If the relative $F$'s of the two crystals are as on the right-hand side, it is evident that by multiplying the $F$'s of crystal $A$ by about 1·5, the $\Delta f$'s of reflections $a$ and $b$ become equal. Reflection $d$ obviously has a negative $F$ in both crystals, because $F$ for $A$ is so much smaller than for $B$; and again the factor of 1·5 makes $\Delta f$ the same as in the other reflections. Reflection $c$ must be negative in crystal $B$ and positive in crystal $A$, to satisfy the condition that the algebraic difference of $F$'s must be constant. The correction factors necessary to put both sets of $F$'s on an absolute scale can also be calculated, for the constant difference between $F$'s must be equal to the difference of absolute diffracting powers of the two ions. Comparisons such as those in Fig. 210 should only be made for groups of reflections at about the same

Bragg angle, for of course the $f$'s decline with increasing angle. For further details see Hargreaves's papers (1957), in which the direct determination of the structure of magnesium and zinc paratoluene sulphonates by this method is described. In practice, a graph of $F_A$ against $F_B$ shows clearly both the signs and the scaling factors.

It is found all too often that in a heavy atom derivative or a pair of isomorphous salts the 'marker' atoms do not lie in centres of symmetry, or that the other conditions necessary for direct structure determination are not fulfilled. Pepinsky (1956) advocates the use of derivatives containing complex ions such as ferrocyanide $[Fe(CN)_6]^{-4}$, ferricyanide $[Fe(CN)_6]^{-3}$, reineckate $[Cr(NCS)_4(NH_3)_2]^{-1}$, hexa urea chromium $[Cr(NH_2.CO.NH_2)_6]^{+3}$, nitroprusside $[Fe(CN)_5NO]^{-2}$, and the like. These large ions play an important part in settling the arrangement and may form a framework in which organic molecules fit; the heavy atoms are quite likely to lie in centres of symmetry.

Another useful suggestion is to use a single substance, instead of a pair of isomorphous crystals, and to take X-ray diffraction patterns with two different wavelengths, one of which is near the absorption edge of the 'marker' atom; one of the effects of anomalous scattering in these circumstances is that the scattering power of the 'marker' atom is altered; in most circumstances it is reduced, often by several electron units. Comparison of the absolute intensities of corresponding reflections given by the two radiations gives, in principle, the same information as for an isomorphous pair of centrosymmetric crystals examined with the same radiation. This method has one advantage: it is equivalent to perfect isomorphism, whereas in an isomorphous pair of substances all the atoms may be in slightly different positions, with consequent effects on the intensities. Its disadvantage is that the change of diffracting power in anomalous scattering is not very great, and high accuracy of measurement of intensities of reflections and correction for absorption is necessary (Lipson and Cochran, 1953; Pepinsky, 1956). With increasing precision of experimental measurements, this method may well prove valuable. It should be remembered that if the wavelength used is slightly *shorter* than that of the absorption edge, the phase-shift of the wave from the anomalously scattering atom should be taken into account as well as the change of diffracting power; if the wavelength used is slightly longer than that of the absorption edge, there is no phase-shift, only a reduction of scattering power. (See Fig. 221, p. 409.) For scattering powers in anomalous scattering conditions, see James (1948), Dauben and Templeton (1955).

**Refinement of approximate structures by image synthesis.**
Most crystal structures must still be solved, or partially solved, by
indirect methods. But the indirect methods—the method of trial, or
the vector methods mentioned later in this chapter—need be carried
only as far as the correct placing of such atoms as constitute the greater
part of the scattering material. As soon as the approximate positions
of these atoms have been found by trial, or by vector methods, the
phases of some of the reflections are known; the phases for some of the
weakest reflections may be wrong, but those of the strong reflections
are bound to be correct, and with this information a preliminary Fourier
synthesis can be carried out. The electron density map so obtained
indicates atomic positions with a little more precision than at first, and
may reveal the approximate positions of atoms which were not taken
into account in the calculations leading to the assignment of phases.
The new positions can be used to check the phases of the weaker
reflections; there will be a few changes, and a second synthesis can then
be carried out. An alternative procedure is to include in the first
synthesis only those terms whose signs are bound to be correct—that
is, those reflections which are strong in the photographs and also have
large calculated structure amplitudes. In the next synthesis more terms
are included, and so on. This process constitutes a direct method of
adjusting atomic coordinates towards more probable values; naturally
it is most successful for projections in which the atoms are seen clearly
resolved from each other. The first effective use of this method to locate
atoms whose positions were at the time quite unknown appears to have
been in the work of Beevers and Lipson (1934) on the structure of
copper sulphate pentahydrate, $CuSO_4.5H_2O$; the copper atoms lie in
two centres of symmetry, but do not in themselves determine a sufficient
number of phases; but when the sulphur atoms were located, and phases
due to the contributions of both copper and sulphur atoms were calculated and used in a Fourier synthesis, the resulting map revealed the
approximate positions of the oxygen atoms.

The process of refinement by electron density calculation is now the
standard method. Early examples were, among inorganic substances,
diopside $CaMg(SiO_3)_2$ determined by W. L. Bragg (1929 *b*), and among
organic substances stilbene $C_6H_5$—CH=CH—$C_6H_5$ determined by
Robertson and Woodward (1937). They are both illustrated, in Figs.
211 and 212 respectively.

A common situation is that, in a crystal of a heavy atom derivative,
the heavy atoms are not in centres of symmetry, though the crystal

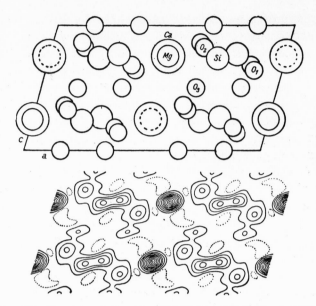

FIG. 211. Structure of diopside, $CaMg(SiO_3)_2$. (W. L. Bragg, 1929 $b$.)

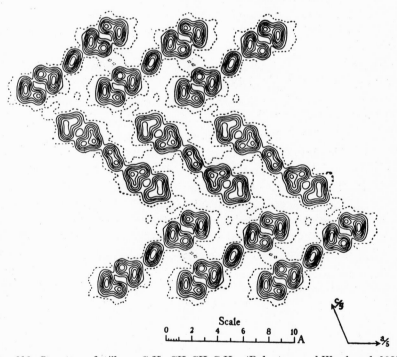

Scale

0    2    4    6    8    10
|....|....|....|....|....|A

FIG. 212. Structure of stilbene, $C_6H_5.CH:CH.C_6H_5.$ (Robertson and Woodward, 1937.)

symmetry is centrosymmetric, at any rate in one or more projections. In these circumstances the combined wave from the two or more heavy atoms may have a phase of either 0° or 180° with respect to the centre of symmetry used as the origin, and moreover varies greatly in magnitude from one reflection to another. If the diffracting power of the heavy atoms is great enough in relation to that of the rest of the structure, it is possible to locate them without much difficulty, either by trial or by the interatomic vector methods described later in this chapter. It may then be assumed that the phase angle of the wave due to heavy atoms alone is also that of the complete structure; this will certainly be true for the stronger reflections; for some of the weaker ones, the heavy atom contribution may be small and the rest of the structure may reverse the sign; consequently an image synthesis based on most of the reflections will give an approximate structure, which can then be refined by successive syntheses incorporating more terms and correcting the signs of some of the weaker ones. An early example is the solution of the structure of picryl iodide by Huse and Powell (1940), which is described in more detail later. The use of heavy atom derivatives in this way has become very widespread, and is an extremely powerful method. Most of the major successes of the X-ray diffraction method of crystal structure analysis of complex organic compounds have been achieved in this way. The most impressive up to the time of writing (1959) is the solution of the structure of vitamin $B_{12}$ (a molecule of about 100 atoms excluding hydrogens) by D. C. Hodgkin and her collaborators. The molecule contains a cobalt atom, which was located by the Patterson interatomic vector synthesis described later; although the cobalt atom is not really heavy enough to dominate the phases, nevertheless the first three-dimensional electron density synthesis based on the cobalt phases did reveal, in a rough fashion, recognizable groups of atoms surrounding the cobalt atoms. With the help of a selenium atom deliberately introduced as an SeCN group, and with the addition of more and more contributions to correct the phases of more and more reflections, detail was gradually filled in to give the complete structure of derivatives and eventually of the $B_{12}$ molecule itself (Hodgkin, Kamper, Lindsey, MacKay, Pickworth, Robertson (J. H.), Shoemaker, White, Prosen, and Trueblood, 1957). The method has even been used effectively for sign determination in protein crystals having centrosymmetric projections; different heavy atom derivatives of haemoglobin, with the heavy atoms in different sites, gave consistent verdicts for signs (Green, Ingram, and Perutz, 1954).

Difficulties may arise if the heavy atoms are found to be in special positions, related to each other by symmetry elements which the complete structure does not possess. For example, in rubidium benzyl penicillin $(P2_12_12_1)$ the rubidium atoms were found to have $z = 0$, and for this reason make no contribution to many reflections; a synthesis in which the indeterminate reflections were omitted had too high a symmetry; however, the probable position of the sulphur atom was indicated, and the inclusion of contributions by sulphur atoms improved matters, but not to the point where refinement could proceed effectively. This structure was ultimately solved by using a variety of methods, including a comparison of a rough electron density map with that of sodium benzyl penicillin, which was based on phase angles obtained not by heavy atom methods (for none of the atoms in the molecule are heavy enough) but by trial (p. 297). See Crowfoot, Bunn, Rogers-Low, and Turner-Jones (1949).

**Phase angles in non-centrosymmetric crystals.** Difficulties of another sort arise in non-centrosymmetric projections, for in these the phase angles may have any values: it is no longer a question of deciding between $0°$ and $180°$ for each reflection. Nevertheless, heavy atom methods have been used successfully, in conjunction with stereochemical assumptions. Cholesteryl iodide has the non-centrosymmetric symmetry $P2_1$; for the $b$ projection, which is centrosymmetric, a straightforward synthesis based on the phases of iodine contributions gave a rough solution, which was successfully refined. The other projections are non-centrosymmetric, but the two iodine atoms related by the twofold screw axis are centrosymmetrically related in the projections; the point midway between them was taken as origin, and a synthesis based on iodine contributions naturally gave a centrosymmetric map. This map consists of two structures superimposed—the correct one, and another related to it by a centre of symmetry. Fortunately it was possible, with the aid of the already solved $b$ projection and stereochemical considerations based on the chemical structure and normal bond lengths and angles, to disentangle the two structures, and further refinement based on calculated phase angles for one structure led ultimately to an undoubtedly correct solution (Carlisle and Crowfoot, 1945).

If two isomorphous derivatives in which the replaceable atoms have considerably different diffracting powers are available, an improved form of this method can be used. Strychnine sulphate pentahydrate and the corresponding selenate form isomorphous monoclinic crystals of space group $C2$; Bokhoven, Schoone, and Bijvoet (1951) solved the centrosymmetric $b$ projection by the straightforward method first used by J. M. Robertson for phthalocyanine, but for the non-centrosymmetric projections they made use of the differences between the structure amplitudes of corresponding sulphate and selenate reflections to give

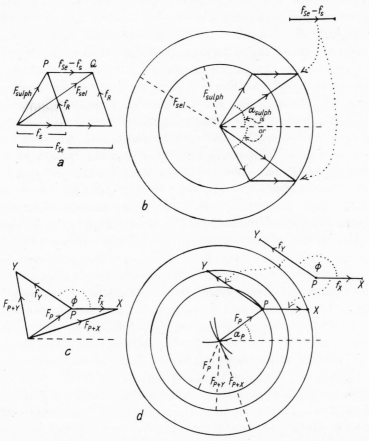

FIG. 213. Determination of phase angles in non-centrosymmetric crystals. *a*. Amplitudes and phases for corresponding reflections in isomorphous sulphate and selenate of strychnine. *b*. Knowledge of $F_{sulph}$, $F_{sel}$, and $(f_{Se}-f_S)$ gives magnitude but not sign of $\alpha$. *c*. Amplitudes and phases for a protein and two isomorphous derivatives with heavy atoms at different sites. *d*. Knowledge of $F_P$, $F_{P+X}$, $F_{P+Y}$, $f_X$, $f_Y$ and $\phi$ gives unique solution for $\alpha_P$.

phase angles in the following way. The structure amplitude $F$ of a particular sulphate reflection is the resultant of the diffracting power of the sulphur atom $f_S$ at the origin (Fig. 213 *a*), and that of the rest of the molecule $f_R$ at a phase angle $\phi$; for the corresponding selenate reflection, $f_{Se}$ is considerably greater than $f_S$, but at the same phase angle (zero), while $f_R$ has the same magnitude and phase angle as in the sulphate. The length $PQ$ is thus equal to $f_{Se}-f_S$, which is a known quantity. In practice, experimental measurements give $F_{\text{sulph}}$ and $F_{\text{sel}}$ (they must be in absolute units); if these are represented by circles having these radii (Fig. 213 $b$), the problem is simply to fit a horizontal line of length $(f_{Se}-f_S)$ so that it touches both circles, with its right-hand end touching the $F_{\text{sel}}$ circle. It fits in two places, as shown in the diagram; the phase angles for $F_{\text{sulph}}$ and $F_{\text{sel}}$ are thus determined in magnitude but not in sign. Bokhoven, Schoone, and Bijvoet used, for each reflection, both positive and negative phase angles together to produce, for the sulphate, a centrosymmetric electron density map representing superimposed mirror-image structures; it was interpreted with the aid of stereochemical considerations, just as in the case of cholesteryl iodide. This method is better than the cholesteryl iodide method, in that it uses correct magnitudes for the phase angles, but of course it is still imperfect, owing to the ambiguity of sign. The structure for strychnine found in this work (after further refinement) agrees well with that found in strychnine hydrobromide $(P2_12_12_1)$ by J. H. Robertson and Beevers (1951), who, having found the bromine atoms in vector maps, then performed a three-dimensional calculation of electron densities based on the phase angles of the bromine contributions alone.

The solutions of these crystal structures of enantiomorphous substances of natural origin give the complete stereochemistry of the molecules concerned, except for one piece of information: the normal X-ray methods do not reveal which of the two mirror-image structures is the correct one. There are, however, special X-ray methods that do give this information; these are described in a later section.

Three isomorphous crystals in which replacement takes place at the same site do not give any additional information; but three isomorphous crystals in which replacement takes place at two different sites can be used to deduce phase angles fully defined as to sign as well as magnitude, provided that the relative positions of the two sites are known (Bokhoven, Schoone, and Bijvoet, 1951; Harker, 1956). The method is being used for proteins, to which groups containing different heavy atoms can be attached at different sites, giving isomorphous crystals; and it is simplest to illustrate the principle for the situation in which the three isomorphous crystals are those of the untouched protein and two heavy atom derivatives having the heavy atoms at different sites; it is also assumed, again for the sake of simplicity, that the unit cell is triclinic and contains only one molecule.

The site of the first heavy atom $X$ is taken as the origin. If we knew the structure, we could represent the structure amplitude for a particular reflection of the protein itself $(P)$ by the line $F_P$ (in Fig. 213 $c$), the phase angle with respect to the origin being $\alpha_P$. For the $P+X$ derivative there is an additional contribution for this same reflection, of magnitude $f_X$ (the scattering power of atom $X$) and phase angle zero— so the line $f_X$ is horizontal. The resultant amplitude is $F_{P+X}$. For the other heavy atom derivative $P+Y$ there is a contribution $f_Y$, at a phase angle $\phi$, giving a resultant amplitude $F_{P+Y}$. In practice we know $F_P$, $F_{P+X}$, and $F_{P+Y}$ from the measured intensities (they must be absolute values); we also know $f_X$ and $f_Y$, the scattering powers of the heavy atoms, and the angle $\phi$, because the relative positions of $X$ and $Y$ in the unit cell are known; the problem is to find $\alpha_P$. If $F_P$, $F_{P+X}$, and $F_{P+Y}$ are represented by three concentric circles having these radii (Fig. 213 $d$), the problem is solved by fitting the triangle $PXY$ so that $P$ touches circle $F_P$, $X$ touches circle $F_{P+X}$, and $Y$ touches circle $F_{P+Y}$; if we set $PX$ horizontal because we are using $X$ as origin, there is only one place where the triangle fits the circles, and this determines $\alpha_P$. A convenient construction to use in practice is to draw the triangle $PXY$ and construct circles with radii $F_P$, $F_{P+X}$, and $F_{P+Y}$, using $P$, $X$, and $Y$ respectively as centres; the point of intersection of all three gives the solution. (For any two circles, there are two solutions, but for three circles there is only one solution, apart from accidental coincidences.)]

The phase angles for other reflections are found in the same way. In this problem, it is essential that the phase angles for all reflections refer to the same enantiomorph: the ambiguity of sign in strychnine sulphate must be avoided. This is ensured in the present method by a knowledge of the relative positions of the two heavy atoms: polarity is inserted in the calculations by keeping one heavy atom, so to speak, always on the same side of the other, so that the resulting phase angles always refer to, say, an erect left-hand molecule and not an inverted right-hand molecule. (This does not mean that the absolute configuration is determined; it only means that all the calculations refer to the same enantiomorph.)

The crux of the method is that the relative positions of the heavy atoms in the two different crystals must be known. When nothing detailed is known of the molecular structure, it is not easy to obtain this information. Perutz (1956) devised methods based on Fourier syntheses of the Patterson type referred to in a later section, which give interatomic vector maps; the combined data for the two heavy-atom derivatives, in special correlation functions, give the relative positions of the heavy atoms. These and other methods led to the determination of the phase angles in myoglobin and thence to a solution of the structure showing for the first time the twists and turns of the chain in this globular protein molecule (Kendrew, Bodo, Dintzis, Parrish, and Wyckoff, 1958).

**Correction of incorrect structures by the error synthesis.** This is a method which combines some of the characteristics of the trial and error method with the quantitative procedure of Fourier series methods. If a set of atomic coordinates has been arrived at which gives calculated structure factors showing some measure of agreement with the experimental values, and yet the structure will not refine by the straightforward electron density method described on p. 381, it may be that a majority of atoms are correctly placed, but others are in totally incorrect positions. The problem is to discover which are the incorrectly placed ones. The discrepancies between observed and calculated structure amplitudes are the clues to the solution of the problem, and the principle of the error synthesis is to use these discrepancies in a quantitative manner to reveal what is wrong with the structure. Yet not all the discrepancies can be used in this direct way, for the all too familiar reason that the phase angles to be used in the calculations are not all known. Nevertheless, *some* of the required phase angles (signs of the structure amplitudes in a centrosymmetric structure) are certain: if a particular reflection is observed to be weak, but the calculated structure amplitude is large and positive, it is certain that some scattering matter must be taken away from positive regions in the structure amplitude chart and put in negative regions. If a moderate negative calculated structure amplitude is found for a reflection absent from the photographs, it is certain that some matter must be moved from negative to positive regions in the appropriate structure amplitude chart. The direct quantitative way of using these discrepancies is to combine them by Fourier synthesis—to use values of $F_{obs}-F_{calc}$ as coefficients in a synthesis which will give a map of the errors, with negative densities in regions from which atoms should be removed and positive densities showing where these atoms should be re-sited.

For reflections of this type (weak or absent in the observed diffraction pattern, medium or strong in the calculations), there is no doubt about the sign of the discrepancy, and only a small uncertainty in its magnitude, arising from a doubt whether the weak reflection should have the same sign as the calculated value or not: however, if the calculated $F$ is $+29$ and the observed $F$ is $\pm 3$, the discrepancy $F_{obs}-F_{calc}$ is either

$+3-29 = -26$, or else $-3-29 = -32$. There is no great difference between these figures; either could be used, but in view of the doubt, it is best to use simply the value of $-F_{calc}$, that is, $-29$. On the other hand, for a reflection observed to be strong but calculated to be weak, the sign of the discrepancy is unknown, since the sign of $F_{calc}$ might be wrong; it should therefore be omitted. Since it is possible to use only part of the discrepancy information, the resulting map of errors will contain some spurious features; nevertheless, the outstanding features are likely to be significant. A strong negative region at the position of one atom would show that it should be removed, and a strong positive region elsewhere would suggest where it should be re-sited. If an atom is on a steep slope, this would suggest that it should be moved towards the positive region.

The relation between the error synthesis method and the standard refinement method of p. 381 is that while the normal refinement method uses in a quantitative way the intensities of the reflections which *are* present (or, rather, those among them whose phase angles are thought to be certain), the error synthesis, on the other hand, uses the information that certain reflections are *not* present or are very weak. However, although this is the essential distinction between the two methods, it is advisable, in the error synthesis, to include every available discrepancy of reasonably certain sign, including the magnitudes of the discrepancies in the structure factors of those strong reflections whose phase angles are considered certain and whose calculated structure factors, though of the right order of magnitude, are not exactly correct; for reflections of this type, it does not matter whether the calculated structure factor is greater or less than the observed value. By using as much discrepancy information as possible, the chances of discovering what is wrong with the structure are increased.

The error synthesis method was first used in helping to solve the structure of sodium benzyl penicillin (Crowfoot, Bunn, Rogers-Low, and Turner-Jones, 1949). The chemical structure of the molecule was incompletely known, and at the time when the error synthesis was tried, the general configuration was in doubt. Trial and error methods (including the 'fly's eye'), followed by electron density calculations for one projection, had given a possible rough structure (Fig. 214 $a$), but the normal procedure of successive electron density calculations did not lead to further refinement. The work so far had been based on an extended configuration of a molecule consisting of a chain of three rings, and in casting about for the basis of a drastic modification, it seemed that the

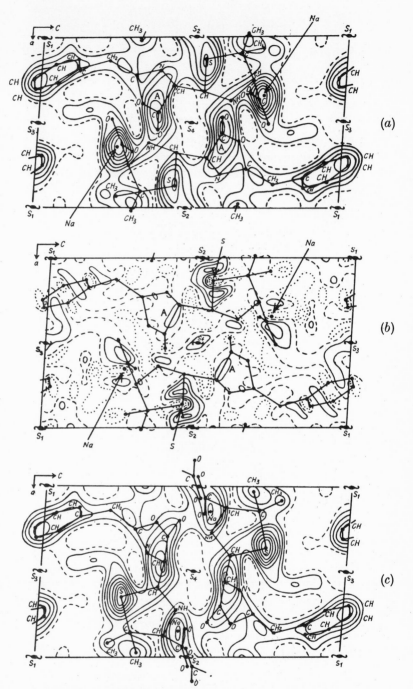

FIG. 214. Sodium benzyl penicillin. (a) Approximate electron density map, b projection, with atomic coordinates appropriate to extended molecular configuration. (b) Error synthesis map. (c) The same electron density map as (a), with atomic coordinates appropriate to a curled configuration of the same molecule.

molecule might be curled into a horse-shoe shape; comparison of the rough electron density maps of the two different crystal structures of the sodium and rubidium salts, and a critical examination of one of the vector maps of the sodium salt, suggested this curled configuration. The error synthesis map left little doubt that the curled configuration was correct, for it showed, as its outstanding feature (Fig. 214 b), a strongly negative region just where a sulphur atom had been placed, flanked by two strong positive regions, indicating that instead of a single scattering centre, two scattering centres were required; the extended configuration could not give this feature, but, as Fig. 214 c shows, the curled configuration could have a sodium atom and a carboxyl group at this position. The curled configuration was therefore adopted, and from this point refinement followed rapidly, and led to the establishment of the final structure in both crystals. The final details of the chemical structure (which turned out to have, in the central part of the molecule, a different ring system from that initially assumed) only appeared in the later refinement by the standard method, but the error synthesis played an important part in leading to the correct configuration of the molecule in place of the wrong one that had been assumed initially; the main indication of the error synthesis was certainly correct.

A more precise though less adventurous application of the error synthesis is to the location of hydrogen atoms in the final stages of a structural investigation, and the detection of minor deviations of the structure from the idealized model used for the structure factor calculations. The diffracting power of hydrogen atoms is small, and for this reason they are not usually included in structure factor calculations made in the course of solving the structural problem; nevertheless, they do make an appreciable contribution to the magnitude of the structure amplitude, and their presence is one of the reasons why calculated structure amplitudes do not agree accurately with the experimental values. The contributions of hydrogen atoms are too small to affect the phase angles of all but the weakest reflections, and consequently the use of the calculated phase angles with the experimental structure amplitudes in electron density calculations should reveal the hydrogen atoms in the resulting electron density distribution. Indeed it does, provided that the experimental structure amplitudes are sufficiently accurately determined; but these atoms are not well defined, for the electron density even at the centre is small, and hydrogen atoms therefore appear as weak bulges on the sides of other atoms, often without even a weak maximum of electron density to mark the centre. An error synthesis (or difference synthesis, as it is sometimes called) reveals them much more definitely, as was shown by Cochran (1951) in his work on the structure of adenine hydrochloride. (For another good example, mono-ethylamine hydrobromide, see Jellinek, 1958.) Even under these circumstances, however, they are less well defined than the heavier atoms —their contours tend to be distorted, and their centres cannot be determined with the precision attained for other atoms.

The reason for the distortions is, of course, that the error synthesis brings out all the other deviations from the idealized model used for the structure amplitude calculations, which usually assumes perfectly spherical atoms; experimental errors in the determination of the structure amplitudes (due to extinction or absorption effects) will also make their mark on the results of the error synthesis. A procedure for distinguishing between experimental errors and other effects is given by Jellinek (1958). Apart from experimental errors, the principal contributors to the error synthesis map, other than hydrogen atoms, are slightly incorrect coordinates for the principal atoms, and anisotropic thermal motions which produce apparently non-spherical atoms. The contributions of hydrogen atoms can be removed by including them in the structure amplitude calculations; the resulting error synthesis map will show the other effects, which can usually be recognized. If an atom is seen to be on a slope, it should be moved slightly in the direction of positive density by an amount that can be calculated from the slope (Cochran, 1951); if it has slight positive regions on two opposite sides, it is probably vibrating predominantly in the direction indicated. One other possible contributor is a real deviation from a spherical distribution of electrons round each atom, due for instance to a slightly increased electron density along covalent bonds; evidence for this, however, is not likely to be clear unless the other effects have been adequately accounted for. The search for such evidence should be based on diffraction data obtained at very low temperatures to minimize thermal movements. For a more detailed discussion of these matters, see Lipson and Cochran (1953).

The work of Cox, Cruickshank, and Smith (1958) on the crystal structure of benzene at $-3°$ C (a little below the melting-point) illustrates well this sort of application of the error synthesis. Fig. 215 shows the error synthesis (or difference synthesis) map in the plane of the benzene ring after a series of refinements in which only carbon atoms were included in the structure amplitude calculations, and thermal vibrations were assumed to be isotropic with a temperature factor $B = 6 \cdot 0$ Å$^2$.

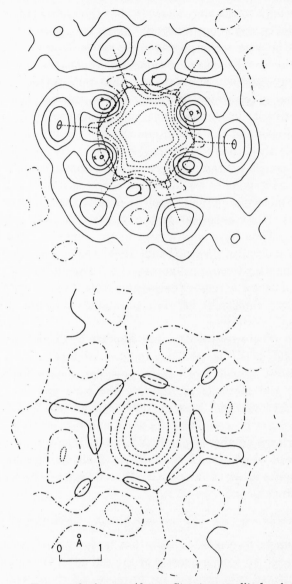

Fig. 215. Benzene. Error synthesis maps. Above—Structure amplitude calculations based on carbon atoms only, and on isotropic thermal motions. Below—After hydrogen atoms and anisotropic thermal motions were included in calculations. (Cox, Cruickshank and Smith, 1958.)

The map shows the hydrogen atoms quite clearly, but they are all drawn out tangentially to the ring, showing that the molecule is indulging in rotatory oscillations about its sixfold axis. This motion is also responsible for the positive regions between the carbon atoms: spherical atoms were used in the calculations of structure amplitudes, but the rotation makes them effectively elliptical and thus puts rather more electron density between the atoms. The other noteworthy feature is a deficiency of electron density inside the carbon ring. Subsequent work in which the hydrogen atoms and the anisotropic thermal motion were included in the structure amplitude calculations removed nearly everything from the error map except for the negative region within the ring, which thus appears to correspond to a real feature of the electron density distribution in this molecule—a lower electron density than would be expected from a ring of six spherical carbon atoms. Electron deficiencies of similar magnitude have been found in the rings of naphthalene and anthracene molecules (Cruickshank, 1956, 1957); qualitatively this is in agreement with theoretical expectation. The ultimate aim of X-ray analysis is of course to remove everything from the error map, by attaining very close agreement between calculated and observed structure amplitudes.

**Methods of computation.** The number of reflections in a single zone ($hk0$, $h0l$, or $0kl$) is not likely to be so large as to make the labour of computation prohibitive. It is, however, a task of considerable magnitude, and methods of reducing the time and effort are very desirable. Beevers and Lipson (1936) convert $\cos 2\pi(hX+kY)$ into $\cos 2\pi hX \cos 2\pi kY - \sin 2\pi hX \sin 2\pi kY$ and for the addition of these terms for a large number of points $XY$, use a large set of prepared card strips, each of which gives $F\cos 2\pi hX$ (or $F\sin 2\pi hX$) for given values of $F$ and $h$ and a range of values of $X$; thus, a typical strip for $F = +23$, $h = 3$, gives values of

$$23\cos(2\pi\times 3\times\tfrac{0}{60}), \quad 23\cos(2\pi\times 3\times\tfrac{1}{60}), \quad 23\cos(2\pi\times 3\times\tfrac{2}{60}),$$

and so on up to $23\cos(2\pi\times 3\times\tfrac{15}{60})$, that is, for points separated by $\tfrac{1}{60}$ of the cell edge up to one-quarter of the cell edge. The various reflections are divided into groups; for instance, all those with $h = 3$ are grouped together, since it is necessary to add up $F_{310}\cos 2\pi 3X \cos 2\pi Y$, $F_{320}\cos 2\pi 3X \cos 2\pi 2Y$, $F_{330}\cos 2\pi 3X \cos 2\pi 3Y$, and so on—or in other words $\cos 2\pi 3X(F_{310}\cos 2\pi Y+F_{320}\cos 2\pi 2Y+F_{330}\cos 2\pi 3Y+...)$. The terms in the brackets are added up (for the various values of $Y$) by taking out the appropriate strips and adding up the numbers on them. This provides a new coefficient $F'$ for each value of $Y$; so we have

$$F' \cos 2\pi 3X.$$

Similar operations for other groups of reflections give (for this same value of $Y$) $F' \cos 2\pi X$, $F' \cos 2\pi 2X$, and so on. Strips for these expressions are now taken out, and the numbers on them are added up, giving the electron densities at the range of points $X$. For positions of $X$ and $Y$ beyond one-quarter of the cell edge the anti-symmetry of $\cos \theta$ about $\theta = 90°$, and the symmetry of $\sin \theta$ about the same point, are used. A somewhat different method, using three-figure coefficients, is described by Robertson (1936 b).

Before starting a synthesis, it is necessary to remember the multiplicities of different types of reflections. Thus, a principal projection of an orthorhombic crystal—for instance, the $c$ projection—corresponds to a principal plane of the reciprocal lattice, in which there is one point 000 at the origin, two equivalent points $h00$ and $\bar{h}00$ (and likewise $0k0$, $0\bar{k}0$), and four equivalent points $hk0$, $h\bar{k}0$, $\bar{h}k0$, and $\bar{h}\bar{k}0$; in the synthesis, therefore, $F_{000}$ occurs once only, $F_{h00}$ and $F_{0k0}$ are doubled, and $F_{hk0}$ are multiplied by four. For plane-group $p2$ (the $b$ projection of a monoclinic crystal, for instance), $F_{h0l}$ is different from $F_{\bar{h}0l}$, and all $F_{h0l}$ (including $F_{h00}$ and $F_{00l}$) are doubled; it will be found that

$$\sum F \cos 2\pi(hX + lZ)$$

$$= \sum \{(F_{h0l} + F_{\bar{h}0l})\cos 2\pi hX \cos 2\pi lZ - (F_{h0l} - F_{\bar{h}0l})\sin 2\pi hX \sin 2\pi lZ\}$$

and it is best to compile tables of $(F_{h0l} + F_{\bar{h}0l})$ and $(F_{h0l} - F_{\bar{h}0l})$ before starting the synthesis.

For structures lacking a centre of symmetry, the phase angle $\alpha$ must be taken into account. For calculation purposes, the expression for electron density in terms of $F$ and $\alpha$ is converted into one in terms of $A$ and $B$, where

$$A = F \cos 2\pi\alpha \quad \text{and} \quad B = F \sin 2\pi\alpha.$$

For example, for a projection having plane-group symmetry $pg$, the expression for the electron density becomes

$\rho \times$ area of unit cell projection

$$= F_{00} + \sum \cos 2\pi hX(A_{hk} \cos 2\pi kY + B_{hk} \sin 2\pi kY) \quad \text{(for even } k)$$

$$+ \sum \sin 2\pi hX(A_{hk} \sin 2\pi kY - B_{hk} \cos 2\pi kY) \quad \text{(for odd } k),$$

$A$ and $B$ being the same as in the structure amplitude expression on p. 228, where $F = \sqrt{(A^2 + B^2)}$. If the experimental value $F_{obs}$ for a particular reflection is different from $F_{calc}$ $(= \sqrt{(A^2_{calc} + B^2_{calc})})$, the procedure is to multiply $A_{calc}$ and $B_{calc}$ by the ratio $F_{obs}/F_{calc}$, giving $A_{obs}$ and $B_{obs}$ appropriate to the value of $F_{obs}$. For further details on procedure, see Lipson and Cochran (1953), and for the expressions for different space-groups see *International Tables* (1952).

In most crystal structure determinations in which image synthesis methods have been used, two-dimensional syntheses have been made for one, two, or three principal zones. A three-dimensional synthesis giving the distribution of electron density throughout the unit cell is in principle the ideal culmination of a crystal structure investigation, but the labour involved when ordinary desk methods are used is so great that a full three-dimensional synthesis is not usually attempted. Limited three-dimensional syntheses, for a particular region or on a particular plane, are practicable by desk methods; early examples were for penta-erythritol tetra-acetate (Goodwin and Hardy, 1938 *a, b*) and for poly-ethylene (Bunn, 1939). A projection of the contents of a slice of the unit cell (from, say, $z = 0$ to $z = \frac{1}{4}$) is sometimes useful, to avoid the overlapping that may occur in a full projection; expressions for this type of synthesis are given by Booth (1945).

The limitations mentioned do not apply if the work can be done on a machine; various types of mechanical and electrical analogue machines for Fourier synthesis have been described (see Lipson and Cochran, 1953), culminating in Pepinsky's XRAC (X-ray analogue computer), in which structure amplitudes and phases for a two-dimensional synthesis are put in on an array of dials, and the electron density map appears at once on a cathode ray tube (Pepinsky, 1952). An increasing propor-tion of Fourier syntheses (and indeed crystallographic calculations of all types) is done on electronic digital computers.

**Optical synthesis.** We have seen that the formation, by a lens, of the image of a microscopic pattern may be regarded as occurring in two stages: first, diffracted beams are formed by interference; secondly, when the diffracted beams are reunited in the image plane, interference again occurs, and the formation of the image may be regarded as the result of the superposition of many sets of interference fringes, one set from each pair of diffracted beams. The calculation of an image of a crystal structure from an X-ray diffraction pattern is simply the mathematical equivalent of the second stage: in summing the Fourier series we are simply adding up the contributions of the various sets of interference fringes.

The use of optical methods in place of calculations was suggested by W. L. Bragg. His first method consists in photographically printing sets of imitation interference fringes. For each pair of reflections $h0l$ and $\bar{h}0\bar{l}$, a set of light and dark bands, having the same distribution of intensity as a set of interference fringes and a spacing and orientation appropriate to the reflections in question, is printed, the exposure being proportional to the structure amplitude. The superposed bands, crossing in many directions, build an image of the projected crystal structure. For examples, see *The Crystalline State*, by W. L. Bragg, pp. 231–4; W. L. Bragg, 1929 *b*; Huggins, 1941, 1944.

Bragg's second method is much more elegant; real optical interference effects are produced. Beams of light, one for each X-ray reflection in a chosen zone, are arranged so as to produce, by interference, an image of the projected crystal structure. The apparatus used consists essentially of two lenses, each of about 6 feet focal length, placed a few inches apart. At the principal focus of one lens is a pinhole source of monochromatic light. Between the lenses, therefore, the light is parallel, and if there were no obstruction in the path of the light, an image of the pinhole source of light would be formed at the principal focus of the second lens. If, however, an opaque plate drilled with a pattern of holes is put between the lenses, multiple images of the point-source are formed at the principal focus of the second lens: the diffraction pattern of the original pattern of holes is produced. If the holes are arranged like the points in the reciprocal lattice of a crystal zone, and the area of each hole is proportional to the structure amplitude for the reciprocal lattice point, the diffraction pattern is a representation of the arrangement of atoms in the crystal as seen along the zone axis, provided that the phases of all the X-ray reflections concerned are the same. The image is of course very small, and must be viewed or photographed by means of a microscope. We may regard the formation of this image in the following way. The first stage in image formation—the production of diffracted beams—is accomplished by X-rays, since these have an appropriate wavelength for the purpose; then, for each diffracted X-ray beam, a beam of visible light is substituted, so that the second stage of image formation—the recombination of the diffracted beams—is accomplished in the medium of visible light. This view of the process must not be taken too literally: it must be remembered that, on account of the three-dimensional character of the atomic arrangement, the crystal must be moved in relation to the X-ray beam in order to give diffracted beams. It is perhaps truer to say that one zone of three-dimensional X-ray diffractions is treated as a set of two-dimensional diffractions produced by a flat pattern which is the projection of the actual crystal structure; the recombination of these diffracted beams yields an image of this flat pattern. Bragg (1939) showed that a substantially correct image of the *b* projection of the diopside crystal is formed by this method.

To introduce phase-differences, small mica plates have been used. Buerger (1951) cut small plates from the same uniform cleavage sheet, and placed one over each hole, suitably tilted to give the appropriate increase in optical path-length. Hanson, Taylor, and Lipson (1951) used mica plates to control both amplitude and phase: the reciprocal lattice was represented by an array of equal holes, and placed between crossed polarizers; a mica plate over each hole was rotated to some position between the two extinction positions to give the correct amplitude; different signs were obtained by rotating the plate either clockwise or anti-clockwise.

The optical method is interesting not so much for any practical use in solving structures or performing Fourier synthesis as for its educative and demonstrative value: it makes clear the physical principles of image formation.

**Resolving power; and other general matters.** Just as the resolving power of a microscopic objective lens depends on the angular range of diffracted beams collected by it, so the resolution in a calculated image of a crystal structure depends on the number of diffracted beams used in the synthesis. It can be shown (W. L. Bragg and West, 1930) that peaks cannot be distinguished if the distance between them is less than $0.61d_0$, where $d_0$ is the lower limit of the spacings of the crystal planes whose $F$'s are used in the synthesis. If reflections are recorded up to a Bragg angle of nearly 90°, $d_0$ ($= \lambda/2 \sin \theta$) is about $\lambda/2$, which, for the much-used copper $K\alpha$ radiation, is $0.75$ Å; therefore peaks are resolved only if they are more than about $0.5$ Å apart. Since atoms in crystals are always 1 Å or more apart, resolution could always be achieved by three-dimensional synthesis; but for the more usual (because more practicable) two-dimensional synthesis, projected distances are often less than $0.5$ Å, and therefore the desirability of using short waves, giving a lower limit of $d_0$, a larger number of reflections, and thus better convergence of the Fourier series, is indicated (Cox, 1938).

There is another important point. If a Fourier series is cut off sharply when the terms are still appreciable, false detail will appear in the electron density map. To avoid this, for crystals giving strong reflections at large angles, an artificial temperature factor may be applied to the intensities, to make the $F$'s fade off gradually instead of stopping abruptly. (The intensities are multiplied by $e^{-2B\left(\frac{\sin\theta}{\lambda}\right)^2}$, where $B$ is a constant.) For examples, see W. A. Wooster (1936) and Wells (1938).

Even when this is done, electron density maps usually show, in the regions of low density, irregularities which do not appear to have any significance; they are probably due to inaccuracies in the measurement of the intensities of the reflections, or to approximations in calculation. The positions of the atomic centres, however, are not in doubt.

When some of the atoms are imperfectly resolved in electron density maps (this frequently happens in two-dimensional work, and it may happen even in three-dimensional work if the angular range of re- corded reflections is limited), the overlapping displaces the electron density maxima from the correct positions of the atomic centres, or may even merge neighbouring atoms into a ridge without distinct peaks. Atomic coordinates must then be adjusted to obtain the best agree- ment between calculated and observed structure amplitudes. This is best done by the numerical procedure introduced by Hughes (1941), in which the sum of the squares of the errors $\sum(|F_{obs}|-|F_{calc}|)^2$ is mini- mized; the solution of a set of simultaneous equations involving the coordinates of a number of atoms is practicable by machine methods. This 'least squares' method is indeed often used instead of the Fourier synthesis of errors as a refinement method involving all the atoms.

If the absolute intensities of the X-ray reflections are not available— but only relative intensities—the value of the constant term (the equivalent of $F_{000}$ in the equations given previously) in relation to the other terms of the Fourier series (which are in this case in arbitrary units) is not known; the figures for the electron density obtained by calculation, omitting the constant term, will all be wrong by this amount; but for the purpose of locating atomic centres, this is of no consequence: the image formed by the electron density contours is of precisely the same form.

It is worth noting that although, in using Fourier series methods, it is desirable to measure the intensities of X-ray reflections as accurately as possible, nevertheless surprisingly good approximations to correct atomic positions can be obtained by using mere visual estimates of intensities. This is well illustrated by two independent determinations of the structure of cyanuric triazide, one (Hughes, 1935) based on visual estimates of intensities, and the other (Knaggs, 1935) on accurate measurements. There is not a great deal of difference in the results, though the latter are naturally to be preferred. This comparison is a good illustration of the statement already made (Chapter VII), that the intensities of X-ray reflections are very sensitively related to atomic positions: small changes of atomic positions mean large changes of the relative intensities of different reflections.

**The absolute configuration of enantiomorphic molecules.** X-ray diffraction patterns intended for crystal structure determination are usually obtained under such conditions that 'Friedel's law' is obeyed: the X-ray wavelength used is nowhere near the absorption edge of any of the atoms in the crystal, so that phase-shifts on scattering are the same for all atoms, and even in crystals with polar axes, reflections in opposite directions from the same set of planes ($hkl$ and $\bar{h}\bar{k}\bar{l}$ reflections) have the same intensities. In consequence, a non-centrosymmetric crystal composed of enantiomorphic molecules all of the same hand gives a centrosymmetric diffraction pattern (reciprocal lattice). This does not mean that a false structure containing a centre of symmetry is obtained as the solution of the structural problem; it is usually known from optical and morphological evidence that the crystal lacks a centre of symmetry, and this information is inserted during the course of the work, and leads to a non-centrosymmetric structure as the solution. Indeed, only a non-centrosymmetric structure could give correct calculated intensities. For instance, in cholesteryl iodide (Carlisle and Crowfoot, 1945), a derivative of an asymmetric molecule of natural origin, an electron distribution obtained by direct methods from the diffraction pattern (location of the iodine atoms by Patterson synthesis, followed by use of the iodine phase angles, as in picryl iodide, p. 412) was a superposition of two structures, an approximation to the correct one and another related to it by a centre of symmetry. It was found possible to disentangle these by using the known chemical constitution of the molecule together with the known bond lengths and angles, and after refinement the final solution showed asymmetric molecules arranged according to space-group $P2_1$.

One piece of information is still missing, however: which of the two structures is the correct one? Which stereochemical configuration corresponds with the naturally occurring molecule and rotates the plane of polarized light in the correct direction? The normal X-ray diffraction pattern cannot give this information; and, in fact, until 1949 no method of determining the absolute configuration of an asymmetric molecule had been found. There was a convention for tartaric acid, chosen arbitrarily by Fischer (Fig. 216), but it could equally well have been right or wrong. Bijvoet (1949) realized that X-ray diffraction patterns obtained under such conditions that 'Friedel's law' is not obeyed could give the desired information. We have seen on p. 263 that in a polar crystal containing atoms of different atomic number, the use of an X-ray wavelength a little shorter than the absorption edge of one type of atom reveals the absolute orientation of polar groups in the crystal; Bijvoet realized that the application of the same method to a crystal composed of asymmetric molecules all of the same hand can reveal the absolute configuration of the asymmetric molecules.

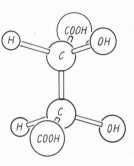

FIG. 216. The Fischer convention for natural dextro-rotating tartaric acid, now known to be correct.

For the appreciation of the essential principle, the simplest example would be a triclinic crystal of space-group $P1$, with one asymmetric molecule to the unit cell. Normal X-ray methods do not tell us whether the correct structure is that of Fig. 217 (i), or the corresponding structure related to it by a centre of symmetry, Fig. 217 (ii). But notice that the choice is between what we will call an erect left-hand molecular configuration (Fig. 217 (i)) and an inverted right-hand configuration (Fig. 217 (ii)); there is no question of an erect right-hand configuration (Fig. 217 (iii)) or an inverted left-hand configuration (Fig. 217 (iv)), for in these the atoms are quite differently related to the unit cell, would not satisfy the observed intensities of the reflections, and indeed would not even fit in geometrically. Since the choice is between an erect left-hand configuration and an inverted right-hand configuration, a decision whether the molecule is erect or inverted settles at the same time whether it is left-handed or right-handed. The determination of absolute orientation—the decision whether a molecule is erect or inverted—is precisely what can be achieved by making use of an anomalous phase-shift.

If the molecule contains one suitable moderately heavy atom—the shaded atom in Fig. 217—(the rest being carbon, oxygen, and the like), and an X-ray wavelength a little shorter than the absorption edge of the heavy atom is used, the anomalous phase-shift on scattering by the heavy atom has the effect of advancing the wave from it in relation to the waves from the rest of the atoms. The scattering by the rest of the molecule can be represented by a single combined wave $E$ in Fig. 218, and it can be seen that for the 001 reflection of the erect configuration, the wave $D$ from the heavy atom, which is in front of $E$, is still further

D d

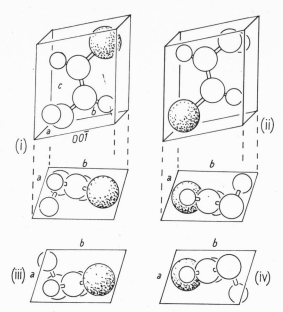

Fig. 217. Normal diffraction does not distinguish between a left-hand erect molecule (i) and a right-hand inverted molecule (ii). It does exclude right-hand erect and left-hand inverted molecules, seen in $c$ projection in the same unit cell in (iii) and (iv), because atomic coordinates in the unit cell are quite different from those in (i) and (ii).

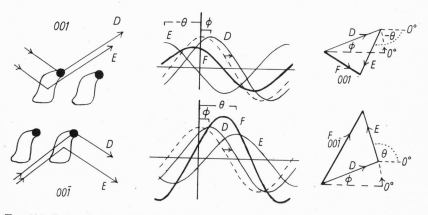

Fig. 218. Determination of the absolute configuration of a non-centrosymmetric structure by using anomalous scattering. Left—Scattering by anomalously scattering atom $D$, and by the rest of the molecule, $E$. Centre—Representation of amplitudes and phases of waves. Right—Corresponding vector representation (scale of amplitudes doubled).

advanced by the anomalous phase-shift, and so is more out of phase with $E$, thus decreasing the resultant amplitude $F$ of the reflection (obtained by adding the ordinates of $D$ and $E$ waves in the centre diagrams, or by vector addition of their amplitudes in the right-hand diagrams). For $00\bar{1}$, on the other hand, wave $D$, which is behind wave $E$, is advanced by the anomalous phase-shift and so is more nearly in phase with $E$, the result being an increased net amplitude $F$. The opposite would be true for the inverted configuration—001 would be stronger than $00\bar{1}$. The phase relations for any reflection in normal scattering can be calculated from the atomic coordinates already settled by the standard structure determination, and it is therefore a simple matter to decide which reflection, $hkl$ or $\bar{h}\bar{k}\bar{l}$, is strengthened and which weakened by the anomalous phase-shift, for both erect and inverted structures. A single observation of any pair of reflections exhibiting differences would settle the matter; but, of course, some would show larger differences than others, depending on the phase relations of $D$ and $E$ waves, and in any case it is advisable to observe several pairs to make sure that the verdicts are consistent.

The crystal first studied in this way by Bijvoet and his colleagues was sodium rubidium tartrate tetrahydrate, $NaRbC_4H_4O_6 . 4H_2O$, a member of the very series of isomorphous double tartrates used by Pasteur a century earlier in the historic investigation which led to the first recognition of the existence of left- and right-handed molecules. These crystals are orthorhombic, and the arrangement of the molecules in them (four to the unit cell) has symmetry $P2_12_12$; the structure is somewhat more complicated than in the triclinic one-molecule crystal already discussed, nevertheless the situation at the end of a normal structure determination is essentially the same. Two molecules related by a screw axis are necessarily the same way up, and the choice is between a pair of what we will call erect left-hand molecules and a pair of inverted right-hand molecules; just as in the one-molecule triclinic cell, there is no question of erect right-hand or inverted left-hand molecules, which would be differently related to the unit cell and would give quite different intensities from those actually observed. The structure of one of this series of double tartrates —the sodium potassium salt (Rochelle salt) had already been worked out by Beevers and Hughes (1941), and all Bijvoet and his colleagues had to do was to take X-ray diffraction patterns of crystals of the sodium rubidium salt with zirconium $K\alpha$ radiation (which excites the rubidium atoms), to calculate the phase angles for certain pairs of reflections and the effect of the anomalous phase-shift on the intensities, and to observe which of each pair of reflections was the stronger. The pairs of reflections compared were, as a matter of convenience, not $hkl$ and $\bar{h}k\bar{l}$, but $hkl$ and $h\bar{k}l$, the latter being equivalent to $\bar{h}k\bar{l}$; several pairs gave consistent verdicts and led to the conclusion that natural dextro tartaric acid which rotates the plane of polarization of light to the right has the configuration shown in Fig. 216, while the configuration of the laevo acid is the mirror image of this. The convention chosen arbitrarily by Fischer is, as it happens, correct. This first discovery of the absolute configuration of an asymmetric molecule by Peerdeman, van Bommel, and Bijvoet (1951) was achieved almost exactly a century after Pasteur's original discovery of the existence of left- and right-handed tartaric acids, and the work was done, appropriately enough, in the laboratory which bears another name famous in the history of stereochemistry—the van 't Hoff laboratory in Utrecht.

Although the anomalous phase shifts and the differences of intensity between $hkl$ and $\bar{h}k\bar{l}$ reflections are greatest when an X-ray wavelength only slightly shorter than the absorption edge of one type of atom is used, the calculations of Hönl (1933; see also James, 1948) show that the effects are appreciable even when much shorter X-rays are used; and Peterson (1955) has confirmed this experimentally, by detecting intensity differences averaging 8 per cent. in the diffraction patterns of tyrosine hydrochloride and hydrobromide produced by monochromatic copper $K\alpha$ radiation. It is therefore possible to use this method of determining absolute configurations without resorting to the less common radiations; it is, however, necessary to measure intensities with as much accuracy as possible, by Geiger counter methods and by using cylindrical specimens to avoid absorption errors. Peterson's work was soon followed by the determination of the absolute configuration in sodium chlorate crystals by Ramachandran and Chandrasekaran (1957), who used copper $K\alpha$ radiation, and in $\alpha$ quartz by de Vries (1958), who used chromium $K\alpha$ radiation, and established that in laevo $\alpha$ quartz the space-group is $P3_12$, not $P3_22$. ($P3_12$ has right-hand screw axes, the rotation being clockwise as one travels forwards; the rotation of the plane of polarized light, which is left-handed (anti-clockwise) in the usual convention in which one is looking into an approaching light beam, has a right-hand screw sense if one travels with the beam, and thus the rotation of the plane of polarized light, as it happens, is in the same sense as the silica helices in the crystal. There is, however, no necessary simple relation between the sense of optical rotation and the

atomic arrangement; the magnitudes of the rotations are vastly different, and in some crystals may be opposite in sense.)

The determination of absolute configurations in these investigations
was based on a qualitative use of the anomalous scattering effects—on
simple observations of which of two opposite reflections, $hkl$ or $\bar{h}\bar{k}\bar{l}$, was
the stronger. It is, however, possible in principle to make quantitative
use of the differences between $F_{hkl}$ and $F_{\bar{h}\bar{k}\bar{l}}$ to determine phase angles
directly. The difference between $F_{hkl}$ and $F_{\bar{h}\bar{k}\bar{l}}$ depends on the phase
relations of the waves from the anomalously scattering atom and from
the rest of the molecule: when these two waves are nearly in phase,

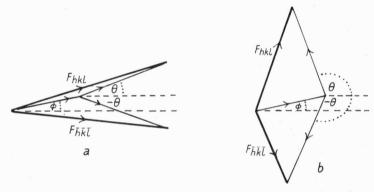

FIG. 219. $a$. The difference between $F_{hkl}$ and $F_{\bar{h}\bar{k}\bar{l}}$ is small when waves from the anomalously scattering atom and the rest of the molecule are nearly in phase. $b$. The difference
is greater when the two components are at about 90° to each other.

there is little difference in magnitude between the resultant $F_{hkl}$ and $F_{\bar{h}\bar{k}\bar{l}}$
(see Fig. 219 $a$); much greater differences of $F$ result when these two
waves are at about 90° to each other (Fig. 219 $b$). It should therefore
be possible to use the magnitude of the difference between $F_{hkl}$ and
$F_{\bar{h}\bar{k}\bar{l}}$ to calculate the phase angles.

There is a difficulty, however: there is not a unique solution, but an
ambiguity which is illustrated in Fig. 220. First let us assume that we
know the structure, and that there is one anomalously scattering atom
in the unit cell at the origin. The phase relations for $hkl$ and $\bar{h}\bar{k}\bar{l}$ reflections are shown together in Fig. 220 $a$; wave $OL$ from the anomalously
scattering atom is advanced (for both reflections) by an angle $\phi$, while
wave $LP$ from the rest of the molecule is at $+\theta$ for $hkl$ but $-\theta$ for $\bar{h}\bar{k}\bar{l}$;
the advancement $\phi$ is responsible for the difference between $F_{hkl}$ ($= OP$)
and $F_{\bar{h}\bar{k}\bar{l}}$ ($= OP'$). Draw circles of radii equal to $F_{hkl}$ and $F_{\bar{h}\bar{k}\bar{l}}$ and join
$PP'$; $PP'$ is evidently perpendicular to $OX$, and $PQ = 2LM$ (see legend
to Fig. 220). Now consider the problem as it arises in practice. $F_{hkl}$

and $F_{\bar{h}\bar{k}\bar{l}}$ are known (they are calculated from the measured intensities), and we can therefore draw the two circles as in Fig. 220 $b$; $PQ$ is also known, for it is $2LM$, that is, twice the so-called 'imaginary' part $\Delta f''$ of the scattering power of the anomalously scattering atom—a known magnitude (see below, p. 408). The problem is to fit the vertical line $PQ$ so that it touches both circles, with $P$ touching the $F_{hkl}$ circle. Unfortunately, it fits in two places, giving two possible values for the phase angle of $F_{hkl}$, either $\alpha$ or $180°-\alpha$. (The other two positions below the horizontal origin line are not possible; $P$ (the upper end of $PQ$)

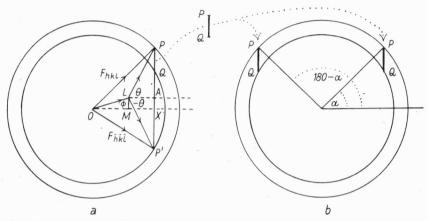

Fig. 220. Ambiguity in the determination of phase angle from $F_{hkl}$ and $F_{\bar{h}\bar{k}\bar{l}}$. Note that
$$PQ = PP'-QP' = 2AP'-2XP' = 2(AP'-XP') = 2AX = 2LM = 2\Delta f''.$$

must touch the $F_{hkl}$ circle, which in this example is the larger; if $F_{hkl}$ had been smaller than $F_{\bar{h}\bar{k}\bar{l}}$, the correct pair of positions would have been below the horizontal origin line.) For an analytical formulation of the problem, see Okaya and Pepinsky (1956).

Notice that the ambiguity here is a horizontal one, giving a choice between $\alpha$ and $180°-\alpha$; in the method given earlier for finding the magnitudes of phase angles—the isomorphous replacement method used by Bokhoven, Schoone, and Bijvoet (1951) for strychnine sulphate and selenate—the ambiguity was a vertical one, giving a choice between $\alpha$ and $-\alpha$. Evidently a complete solution can be obtained by combining the two (Bijvoet, 1952): if two isomorphous crystals containing replaceable atoms of different diffracting power are available, and a wavelength giving anomalous scattering by the marker atom is used for one of them, phase angles can be determined in both magnitude and sign, and the whole structure, including the absolute configuration, can be solved directly without any initial stereochemical assumptions. For instance, for the present example (Fig. 220 b), if an isomorphous crystal is available which contains, in place of the anomalously scattering atom, a different atom of greater scattering power, the value of $F_{hkl}$ given by this crystal (in absolute units) gives the required information. A longer vector for the atom at the origin pushes $P$ to the right, which means, if $\alpha$ is less than 90°, a larger circle (a larger value of $F'_{hkl}$), while if $\alpha$ is greater than 90°, it means a smaller circle. It is therefore sufficient to observe whether $F'_{hkl}$ for the crystal containing the heavier atom is greater or less than $\frac{1}{2}(F_{hkl}+F_{\bar{h}\bar{k}\bar{l}})$ for the crystal containing the lighter, anomalously scattering atom; if $F'_{hkl}$ is the greater, $\alpha$ is the correct solution, while if $F'_{hkl}$ is the smaller, $180°-\alpha$ is the correct solution.

It may not be necessary to have an isomorphous pair: it may be sufficient to obtain diffraction patterns for one crystal only for a wavelength giving normal scattering in addition to those for anomalous scattering; the scattering power of the marker atom is usually rather greater in normal scattering than in anomalous scattering, and the difference may be great enough to give the information required. The structure amplitudes must, however, be known in absolute units; it is not easy to obtain this information with sufficient accuracy. A possible way of checking the absolute structure amplitudes would be to make use of reflections for which $F_{hkl}$ and $F_{\bar{h}\bar{k}\bar{l}}$ in the anomalously scattering crystal are nearly equal; this would mean that $\alpha$ is either near 0° or near 180°. Under these circumstances, the difference

$$F'_{hkl}-\tfrac{1}{2}(F_{hkl}+F_{\bar{h}\bar{k}\bar{l}})$$

must be equal to the known difference between the diffracting power in normal scattering and that in anomalous scattering; in other words, Hargreaves's (1946) method of deducing absolute from relative intensities (p. 379) is applicable.

An alternative procedure would be to use the isomorphous replacement method for the quantitative aspect, giving the magnitude of $\alpha$, the anomalous scattering method being used qualitatively to decide whether $\alpha$ or $-\alpha$ is the correct solution for the $hkl$ reflection: if $F_{hkl}$ is larger than $F_{\bar{h}\bar{k}\bar{l}}$, then $\alpha$ is the correct solution. The available evidence in fact, gives two independent determinations of magnitude as well as a discrimination between the ambiguities inherent in either method alone. In practice, it may be better to use the isomorphous replacement method for the quantitative aspect; the reason is that anomalous scattering by the lighter atoms may not be negligible (see Blow, 1958), and may thus lead to appreciable error in the phase angle determined by the anomalous scattering method. Whether this error is serious in comparison with other sources of error is not yet clear; up to the time of writing (1959), the quantitative use of anomalous scattering to determine phase angles has not been adequately explored.

In using the results to produce electron density maps, it would be as well to work, not with values of $F_{hkl}$ and $F_{\bar{h}\bar{k}\bar{l}}$ (which include the contributions of the anomalously scattering atom), but with $LP$ and $LP'$ (together with phase angles $\theta$ and $-\theta$) of Fig. 220 a—the structure amplitudes of the structure *minus the anomalously scattering atom*; the phase-shift at the anomalously scattering atom would give some curious effects in an electron density map. Alternatively, such effects can be avoided by using the values of $F'_{hkl}$ from the diffraction pattern in normal scattering conditions (with, of course, phase angles deduced from the combination of evidence); the resulting electron density map would include the marker atom without any curious phase-shift effects.

The principles of this method have been illustrated for the simplest situation—a unit cell with one anomalously scattering atom; but similar methods can be used when there are two or more anomalously scattering atoms, as soon as the positions of these are known.

The treatment of anomalous scattering given here has been in terms of a scattering power $f$ and a phase-shift angle $\phi$. Information on anomalous scattering is often given in other terms (for instance in James, 1948, and Dauben and Templeton, 1955), which are explained in Fig. 221 a. The difference between the normal scattering power $f_0$ and the so-called 'real' part of $f$ is called $\Delta f'$, and this is usually negative so that $f_0 + \Delta f'$ is smaller than $f_0$. The so-called 'imaginary' part of $f$ is called $\Delta f''$, and is always positive. The angle $\phi$ is given by $\tan \phi = \Delta f'' / (f_0 + \Delta f')$, and $f^2 = (f_0 + \Delta f')^2 + (\Delta f'')^2$. $PQ$ in Fig. 220 is equal to $2\Delta f''$. The way in which $\Delta f'$ and $\Delta f''$ depend on the incident wavelength (in relation to the absorption edge) is illustrated in Fig. 221 b and c. According to James (1948), $\Delta f'$ and $\Delta f''$ are independent of the angle of diffraction, at any rate for $K$ absorption edges; this would be expected, because the anomalous effects are due to the innermost $(K)$ electrons. Since the normal diffracting power of an atom declines with increasing $(\sin \theta)/\lambda$ (Fig. 121), the anomalous scattering effects are relatively much greater for the higher order reflections at larger angles than for the low order reflections; thus, for the iron atom the normal diffracting power at small angles is near 26 (the atomic number), and for Cu$K\alpha$ radiation this is reduced by only $1\frac{1}{2}$ units, but at $(\sin \theta)/\lambda = 1$ the normal diffracting power is 6·3, so that for Cu$K\alpha$

radiation it becomes $6\cdot3 - 1\cdot5 = 4\cdot8$, the reduction being nearly 25 per cent. Since $\Delta f''$ for $CuK\alpha$ is about 3 units (Fig. 221 c), $\phi$ is $7°$ for small angle reflections but over $30°$ for $(\sin\theta)/\lambda = 1$ (Fig. 221 d). It is not clear whether $\Delta f'$ and $\Delta f''$ are independent of the reflection angle for $L$ and $M$ absorption edges; there may be some variation with $\theta$, since

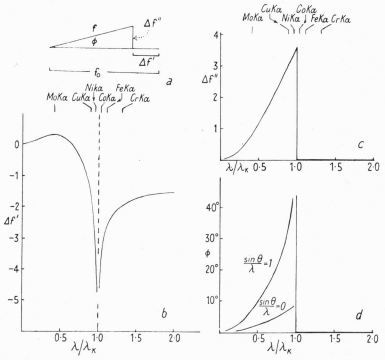

Fig. 221. Anomalous scattering of X-rays of wavelength near that of an absorption edge. Iron atom, $K$ absorption edge. a. Definitions. b, c and d. $\Delta f'$, $\Delta f''$, and $\phi$ in relation to $\lambda/\lambda_K$ (the ratio of incident wavelength to that of the $K$ absorption edge of the iron atom).

$L$ and $M$ electrons are farther from the centre of the atom than $K$ electrons.

**Interatomic vectors.** Although, in the absence of knowledge of the signs of the Fourier terms, it is not possible to deduce directly the actual positions of the atoms in the cell, it is theoretically possible to deduce interatomic vectors, that is, the lengths and directions of lines joining atomic centres. Patterson (1934, 1935 a) showed that a Fourier synthesis employing values of $F^2$ (which are of course all positive) yields this information. The Patterson function

$$P_{XYZ} = \sum\sum\sum |F_{hkl}|^2 \cos 2\pi(hX + kY + lZ)$$

exhibits peaks at vector distances from the origin equal to vector distances between pairs of maxima in the electron density. Thus, if (Fig. 222 left) there are atoms at positions $A$, $B$, and $C$ in the unit cell, the function $P_{XYZ}$ obtained by the above three-dimensional synthesis would show maxima at $A'$, $B'$, and $C'$ in Fig. 222 (right), where $OA' = AB$, $OB' = BC$, and $OC' = AC$. A two-dimensional synthesis of all the $hk0$ intensities $(P_{XY} = \sum \sum |F_{hk0}|^2 \cos 2\pi(hX+kY))$ would give these peaks projected on to the $ab$ face of the vector cell—that is, at $D$, $E$, and $F$ in Fig. 222. The height of each peak is proportional to the product of the scattering powers of the two atoms concerned.

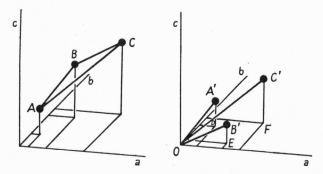

FIG. 222. Left: atoms in unit cell. Right: corresponding vectors.

Calculations of the Patterson function may be carried out in exactly the same way as those of electron densities. Bragg's optical method may also be used; indeed, in general it may be applied more readily to the formation of vector maps, since (the signs of the $F^2$ coefficients being all positive) the question of phase adjustment does not arise. The optical method has been shown to give a correct vector map for the $b$ projection of haemoglobin.

A straightforward $F^2$ synthesis gives a large peak at the origin, which expresses the fact that any atom is at zero distance from itself. If necessary, this origin peak can be removed; the method for doing this, as well as a procedure for sharpening other peaks, are given in Patterson's 1935 paper.

The usefulness of the $F^2$ synthesis is subject to the inherent limitation of a vector diagram: vectors are all erected from a single point. The vector diagram, when obtained, must be interpreted in terms of actual atomic coordinates. (For the relations between peak positions on vector maps and the equivalent points in the 17 plane-groups, see Patterson, 1935 $b$.) For simple structures this presents little difficulty, but for more complex structures it may be almost as difficult to interpret the vector diagram as it would be to solve the structure by trial. This is due, not only to the nature of vector diagrams, but also to the fact that, for unit cells containing many atoms (especially those of organic substances, where interatomic distances do not differ much from each other), some of the vectors are very likely to lie close together so that the individual peaks are not resolved. This is so even in a three-dimensional vector model; for instance, in Fig. 222 (right), $A'$ and $B'$ would be rather close together, since the vectors $AB$ and $BC$ in the cell are similar in length and orientation, and might not be resolved. In a projection the chances of overlapping are obviously greater still. Further, the number of peaks in a vector map rises rapidly with the number of atoms in the cell: if there are $N$ atoms in the cell ($N$ peaks in an electron density map), there are $N(N-1)$ peaks in a vector map.

This is a pity, for it is precisely for the more complex structures that some help by a direct method is most needed. However, if some of the atoms in the cell have much greater diffracting powers than the others, the vectors between the heavy atoms will stand out, and the information thus gained may lead to a knowledge of the coordinates of these atoms. The positions of the iodine atoms in picryl iodide were found in this way, and the knowledge paved the way to a subsequent $F$ synthesis which gave an image of the projected structure (Huse and Powell, 1940); and in the determination of the structure of $NiSO_4 . 7H_2O$, an $F^2$ synthesis threw considerable light on the positions of the Ni and S atoms (Beevers and Schwartz, 1935).

The results for picryl iodide are particularly clear and simple. Crystals of this substance are tetragonal, with unit cell dimensions $a = 7\cdot03$ Å and $c = 19\cdot8$ Å; and the absent reflections indicate the enantiomorphous pair of space-groups $P4_12_1$ and $P4_32_1$. (In agreement with this conclusion, the crystals rotate the plane of polarization of light.) There are four molecules in the unit cell, and therefore, since the general position is eightfold, each molecule must possess twofold symmetry; this can only be the twofold axis lying perpendicular to the $c$ axis and along the $ab$ diagonal of the cell. These twofold axes necessarily pass through the iodine atoms, which lie in the only fourfold positions in the cell:

$$x, x, 0; \quad \bar{x}, \bar{x}, \tfrac{1}{2}; \quad \tfrac{1}{2}-x, \tfrac{1}{2}+x, \tfrac{1}{4}; \quad \tfrac{1}{2}+x, \tfrac{1}{2}-x, \tfrac{3}{4}.$$

From the fact that 110 and 220 are both strong, it appears that the iodine atoms are not far from the corners and centres of the cells—that is, $x$ is small. For the determination of $x$ by the $F^2$ synthesis the 110 projection appears to be the most suitable; from this viewpoint the iodine atoms appear as in Fig. 223 $a$; the vectors $V_1$ and $V_4$ are exactly equivalent and will amalgamate to a single peak at $\frac{1}{4}c$ (Fig. 223 $b$); so will $V_2$ and $V_3$; and $V_5$ and $V_6$ will give a single peak at $\frac{1}{2}c$. For the 100 projection there would not be this amalgamation, and the larger number of peaks might lead to confusion, at any rate for some values of $x$. The result of Huse and Powell's synthesis of the $hhl$ reflections is shown in Fig. 224. The vector marked with an arrow is $V_2+V_3$, and the distance

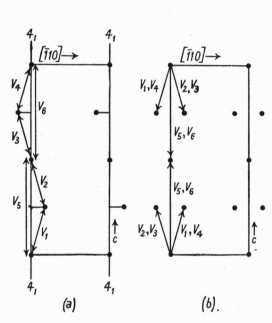

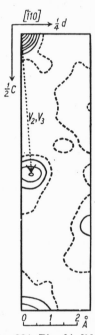

Fig. 223. Fourfold positions in space-group $P4_12_1$. $a$. View along 110. $b$. Corresponding vector diagram.

Fig. 224. Picryl iodide. Vector map, 110 projection. (Huse and Powell, 1940.)

of the peak from the cell edge is 0·045 of the $ab$ diagonal—which means that $x$ is also 0·045. The 001 vector map (Fig. 225), obtained by a synthesis of the $hk0$ reflections, confirms this; the peaks near the origin are not resolved, and are thus useless for the purpose, but the two peaks near $\frac{1}{2}\frac{1}{2}$ give the information required. (Corresponding vectors are marked in the diagrams.)

With this information, the signs of the $F$'s for iodine atoms alone were calculated, and an $F$ synthesis performed for the 110 projection.

The resulting electron density map indicated approximate positions for the lighter atoms, and doubtful signs were then recalculated, using this information. (It is interesting that there were only two changes of sign.) Using the altered signs, a second $F$ synthesis was performed, giving the electron density map shown in Fig. 226; the vectors in this diagram are marked to correspond with the peaks in the vector map, Fig. 224. Owing to the fact that the lighter atoms are not well resolved (this is a consequence of the swamping effect of the iodine atoms),

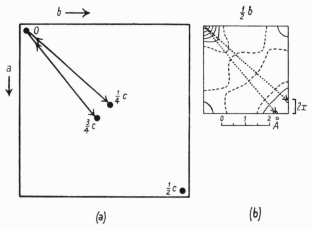

Fig. 225.  Picryl iodide.  $a$. Fourfold positions, 001 projection.
$b$. Vector map. (Huse and Powell, 1940.)

final adjustments were made by trial, to get the best possible fit of calculated to observed intensities.

The presence of comparatively heavy atoms may in some circumstances confer a further advantage. Suppose there is one heavy atom in a projected cell, and this atom is at a centre of symmetry. We have already seen that if the atom is heavy enough, the signs of all the $F$'s will be positive with respect to the heavy atom, and projected electron densities may be calculated directly. If, however, the atom is not heavy enough to determine all the signs of the $F$'s, this method cannot be used. (For instance, a copper atom in a large organic molecule would not determine all the phases as platinum does in platinum phthalocyanine.) The next best thing is to carry out an $F^2$ synthesis, producing a vector map. The strongest peaks will be at the corners of the projected vector cell, and they naturally present vectors between heavy atoms. The next strongest peaks will represent vectors between a heavy atom and the lighter atoms; since the heavy atom is at the origin, these peaks represent the actual coordinates of the lighter atoms. It is true that theoretically there should be subsidiary peaks representing vectors between light atoms, and these might be expected to confuse the picture; but in practice (since the height of a peak is proportional to the product of the atomic numbers of the atoms concerned) confusion from this source is not likely to be appreciable.

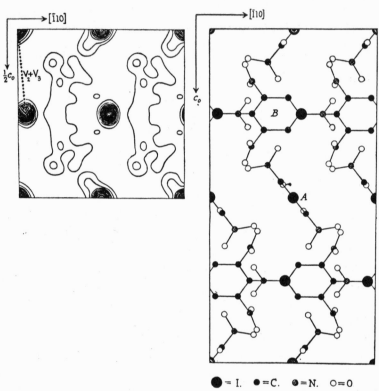

$\bullet$ = I.   $\bullet$ = C.   $\circledcirc$ = N.   $\circ$ = O

FIG. 226. Picryl iodide. Electron density map, 110 projection. (Huse and Powell, 1940.)

Many ingenious applications of vector maps have been suggested and used. For instance, pairs of isomorphous crystals are often used for difficult structures, and if the replaceable atoms are not at symmetry centres, it is necessary to find their parameters. If the replaceable atoms are heavy enough, they may be located readily as in picryl iodide; if not, the vector maps of the two isomorphous crystals may be compared; the differences indicate which peaks are due to the replaceable atoms. Alternatively, a Patterson synthesis may be computed in which the differences between structure amplitudes of corresponding reflections of the two crystals are used ('difference Patterson'); the resulting vector map shows only the peaks due to the replaceable atoms.

Similar in principle to this is the use of two different X-ray wavelengths on the same crystal, one near to and the other far from the absorption edge of a marker atom, to give different diffracting powers; this is the 'ideal isomorphism' method advocated by Lipson and Cochran (1953) and Pepinsky (1956). A comparison of the vector maps for the two wavelengths, or a vector map based on the differences of structure amplitudes for corresponding reflections for the two wavelengths, indicates which peaks are due to the marker atoms.

Special problems arise when two different heavy atom derivatives, with the heavy atoms in different sites, are used for the purpose of determining phase angles in non-centrosymmetric crystals (see p. 387): it is essential to know the relative positions of the two heavy atoms. Perutz (1956) found that a sort of 'combination difference Patterson synthesis'—a Fourier synthesis in which the coefficients are

$$(|F_{H_1}|^2 - |F|^2)(|F_{H_2}|^2 - |F|^2)$$

—reveals the relative positions of the heavy atoms; in this expression $F_{H_1}$ and $F_{H_2}$ are the structure amplitudes for the two heavy atom crystals and $F$ that of the heavy atom-free crystal, all for the same reflection. Another function giving this information is a Fourier synthesis using as coefficients the products $A_1 A_2$, where $A_1$ and $A_2$ are the so-called 'real' parts of the structure factors of the heavy atom-free compound, referred to the different heavy atom positions, or the centres between them, as origins.

**Vectors between symmetry-related atoms.** A three-dimensional $F^2$ synthesis over the whole unit cell would involve a large amount of labour, but a three-dimensional $F^2$ synthesis of limited scope, giving the Patterson function over a particular plane or along a particular line, is more practicable, since the labour of computation involved is that of a two-dimensional or one-dimensional Fourier synthesis. Moreover, as Harker pointed out (1936), provided the crystal has planes or axes of symmetry (or screw axes or glide planes), it is easy to specify on which plane or along which line of the vector cell the most useful information will be found; the synthesis can therefore be restricted to the appropriate plane or line. If the crystal has axes or screw axes of symmetry, vectorial distances of atoms from these axes can be obtained, the labour involved being that of a two-dimensional synthesis although the whole of the reflections are used. If the crystal has planes or glide planes of symmetry, the labour of a one-dimensional synthesis (but again using the whole of the reflections) yields the distances of the atoms from these planes. This procedure can be followed for all but triclinic crystals, the only ones which have no axes or planes of symmetry.

To specify which plane or line of the vector cell contains the desired information, consider the equivalent positions of the atoms in relation to the symmetry element. Suppose the crystal in question has a two-fold axis parallel to $b$. If there is an atom at $x$, $y$, $z$, there is an equivalent atom at $\bar{x}$, $y$, $\bar{z}$ (Fig. 227 $a$). The vector between these (Fig. 227 $b$)

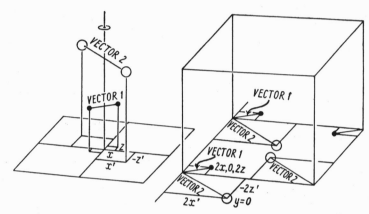

FIG. 227. $a$. Twofold axis, real cell. $b$. Corresponding vector cell.

lies on the $ac$ face of the vector cell ($y = 0$), and there will be a maximum in the Patterson function $P_{XYZ}$ at the point $2x$, $0$, $2z$. On this $ac$ face of the cell there will be a maximum for each crystallographically different kind of atom; by halving the coordinates the distances of the atoms from the twofold axis are obtained. It is therefore necessary to evaluate the Patterson function only on the $ac$ face of the cell, that is, for points $x$, $0$, $z$.

In working out the values of

$$\sum_{h=-\infty}^{h=+\infty} \sum_{k=-\infty}^{k=+\infty} \sum_{l=-\infty}^{l=+\infty} |F_{hkl}|^2 \cos 2\pi(hX+kY+lZ)$$

for all points $x$, $0$, $z$, note that for all planes having the same $h$ and $l$—for example 201, 211, 221, 231, $2\bar{1}1$, $2\bar{2}1$, etc.—the cosine term is the same, since $kY = 0$. Hence, before starting the calculations, add up the $F^2$'s for all those planes; and likewise for other sets of planes having the same $h$ and $l$. Thus the expression simplifies to

$$P_{X0Z} = \sum_{h=-\infty}^{h=+\infty} \sum_{l=-\infty}^{l=+\infty} \left[ \left\{ \sum_{k=-\infty}^{k=+\infty} F_{hkl}^2 \right\} \cos 2\pi(hX+lZ) \right].$$

For all crystals with axes of symmetry, whether two-, three-, four- or sixfold, the vectors between equivalent atoms are parallel to a face of the real unit cell; the maxima in $P_{XYZ}$ therefore lie on a face of the vector cell, and their positions can be found by evaluating $P_{X0Z}$ (or $P_{0YZ}$ or $P_{XY0}$, as the case may be).

When a crystal has a twofold screw axis parallel to $b$, there are equivalent atoms at $x$, $y$, $z$, and $\bar{x}$, $y+\frac{1}{2}$, $\bar{z}$ (Fig. 228 $a$). The vector between these has components $2x$, $\frac{1}{2}$, $2z$, and there will therefore be a maximum in the Patterson function at the point $2x$, $\frac{1}{2}$, $2z$ (Fig. 228 $b$).

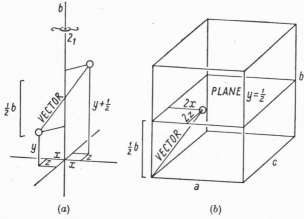

FIG. 228. $a$. Twofold screw axis, real cell. $b$. Corresponding vector cell.

For every pair of atoms related by the screw axis there will be a maximum somewhere on the plane $y = \frac{1}{2}$, and it is therefore only necessary to evaluate $P$ all over this plane, that is, $P_{X\frac{1}{2}Z}$, to determine the vector distances of the atoms from the screw axis.

In a similar way, it can be shown that if a crystal has a plane of symmetry perpendicular to its $b$ axis, the Patterson function has maxima along the $b$ axis of the cell (the line $0$, $y$, $0$, in Fig. 229) which indicate the distance of atoms from the plane of symmetry. For a glide plane perpendicular to $b$, with a translation $c/2$, the distance of atoms from this plane are indicated by maxima along the line $0$, $y$, $\frac{1}{2}$.

There are other circumstances in which some of the atomic coordinates in a crystal can be discovered by evaluation of the Patterson function over a particular plane or along a particular line. For instance, it may be known, from a consideration of the space-group and the equivalent positions in the unit cell, that there is one particular atom at the origin of the cell and others somewhere on the plane $y = \frac{1}{2}$. The

E e

Patterson function will show maxima on this plane at positions which give immediately the actual coordinates of these atoms. Similar considerations were used in the determination of the structure of potassium sulphamate $NH_2SO_3K$ (Brown and Cox, 1940); it was known that the $y$ coordinates of the potassium ions are 0 and $\frac{1}{2}$, while those of the sulphur atoms are $\frac{1}{4}$ and $\frac{3}{4}$; consequently, the Patterson function on the plane $y = \frac{1}{4}$ shows maxima at positions corresponding to K-S vectors. Atomic positions are not given directly, but can be derived from the positions of Patterson peaks by a consideration of the equivalent positions in the space-group.

Although such considerations have been useful in solving certain

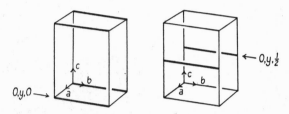

Fig. 229. Left: When a crystal has a plane of symmetry normal to $b$, the distances of atoms from this plane are given by maxima along the line $0y0$ of the vector cell. Right: When there is a glide plane perpendicular to $b$, with translation $c/2$, the distances of atoms from this plane are given by maxima along the line $0y\frac{1}{2}$ of the vector cell.

structures, it is found all too often that there are serious difficulties and ambiguities of interpretation. For instance, we have seen that in a crystal with a twofold axis of symmetry along $b$, information about distances of atoms from the twofold axis is to be found on the $b$ face of the vector cell (Fig. 227). If, however, there is a pair of atoms with about the same $y$ coordinate but not related by the twofold axis, a peak for this pair will also appear, and moreover the height of such a peak between atoms unrelated by symmetry but by chance having about the same coordinate is double that of the symmetry-related pairs, for there are twice as many 'accidental' vectors. Furthermore, it can be shown that a peak at $2x$, 0, $2z$, though it may be due to an atom at $x, y, z$ (and a symmetry-related one at $\bar{x}, y, \bar{z}$), can also be due to an atom at $x, y, z+\frac{1}{2}$, or $x+\frac{1}{2}, y, z$, or $x+\frac{1}{2}, y, z+\frac{1}{2}$. Such ambiguities severely limit the usefulness of Patterson–Harker vector maps for the more complex structures. (See Buerger, 1946; Lipson and Cochran, 1953.)

**Unravelling vector maps.** Many attempts have been made to devise systematic methods of deducing the actual atomic arrangement from the vector map. It was shown by Wrinch (1939) that a vector set of *points* can always be unravelled to reveal the original set of points; the method, and variants of it suggested by others, are described by Lipson and Cochran (1953). In practice, we have to deal with the result of a Patterson synthesis, which is not a set of points but a continuous function showing a confusing distribution of peaks and ridges, for the most part not resolved into individual interatomic peaks; if there is a minority of heavy atoms in the structure, the peaks due to these stand out, and serve to locate the heavy atoms—there is little difficulty in unravelling as far as this, as we have seen in the case of picryl iodide; but further progress may be difficult. For molecular crystals Beevers (1952) has emphasized the special significance of the region 1 to 2·5 Å from the origin of the vector cell, which must contain only vectors between chemically linked or next-but-one atoms within the molecule, because vectors between atoms in different molecules are always longer than this; a three-dimensional map of this region, if it shows well-marked atomic peaks, may reveal the orientation of bonds, especially for molecules which by virtue of their symmetry or regularity contain two or more parallel bonds and therefore coincident vectors; effective use has been made of such features in work on the sugars (Beevers, 1952; McDonald and Beevers, 1952) and salicylic acid (Cochran, 1951 b), which contain six-atom rings. When there are two or more differently oriented molecules in the unit cell, the vectors in all of them of course appear; nevertheless, provided that well-defined peaks are present (it is advisable to use a procedure for obtaining sharpened peaks), it may be possible to recognize the features expected for a particular type of molecule. Success cannot be expected for very complex molecules unless they have some regularly repeated groups giving coincident vectors.

Another procedure, introduced by Beevers and Robertson (J. H.) (1950), makes it possible, when there are several molecules in the unit cell, to locate the lighter atoms, if the one heavy atom in each molecule has already been located by the methods already mentioned. Suppose there are four molecules in the unit cell, and consider one of the lighter atoms in one of the molecules. There is a vector from this light atom to each of the four heavy atoms in the cell; somewhere in the array of peaks in the vector map are four peaks all due to this one light atom, but which are the four having this common origin? The way to find out (and thereby to locate the light atom) is to place a vector map with its origin at the position of one of the heavy atoms, and superimpose on it other copies of the vector map with their origins on the positions of the other three heavy atoms; where four peaks, one from each of the vector maps, coincide is the position of one of the light atoms. Even when individual vector maps do not show well-resolved peaks, the method should be useful, because only at the sites of atoms will the intensity in the superimposed set build up to a significant peak. The process has been described as if vector map projections were used; but it is of course possible to carry out the numerical equivalent three-dimensionally—and this is the most effective procedure. It has been used successfully by Robertson (J. H.) and Beevers (1951) in solving the structure of strychnine hydrobromide, which has four molecules arranged according to space group $P2_12_12_1$; the approximate positions of the 27 carbon, nitrogen, and oxygen atoms in the molecule were revealed by this 'vector convergence' method.

**Vectors in non-centrosymmetric crystals.** The ordinary Patterson synthesis of the X-ray data of a non-centrosymmetric crystal gives a centrosymmetric vector distribution; and even if the X-ray data obtained under anomalous scattering conditions are used (it will be remembered that the diffraction pattern is non-centrosymmetric under these conditions), the vector distribution obtained is still centrosymmetric because the cosine function has this symmetry. It has been shown by Okaya, Saito, and Pepinsky (1955) that a synthesis of the Patterson type, but using sines instead of cosines,

$$P_s(XYZ) = \sum \sum \sum |F_{hkl}|^2 \sin 2\pi(hX+kY+lZ),$$

gives, for a diffraction pattern taken under anomalous scattering conditions, the distribution of vectors between anomalous scatterers and normal scatterers, *including the absolute direction of the vectors*; peaks representing vectors from anomalous scatterers to normal scatterers are positive, those from normal to anomalous scatterers are negative. In other words, it gives the non-centrosymmetric vector distribution in the crystal, and if the $P_s$ map of an enantiomorphous crystal can be unravelled to give the actual atomic positions, the absolute configuration is revealed. The unravelling is less difficult than that of an ordinary Patterson synthesis, because the $P_s$ map shows only vectors involving the anomalously scattering atoms; vectors between normal scatterers do not appear; the map in fact gives the distribution of normal scatterers about anomalous scatterers, in an absolute sense.

This important development does for non-centrosymmetric crystals what the Patterson synthesis does for centrosymmetric crystals; it has been used successfully in solving the structure and absolute configuration of $d$-2[Co(NH$_2$.CH$_2$.CH$_2$.NH$_2$)$_3$]Cl$_3$.NaCl.6H$_2$O. For further information, see Pepinsky and Okaya (1956), Pepinsky (1956). On the relative merits of this approach and the methods of phase angle determination described on pp. 405–8, see Ramachandran and Raman (1956), Pepinsky and Okaya (1957).

**Molecular transforms.** The transform of a molecule or a non-repeating group of atoms such as the contents of one unit cell has been mentioned earlier (p. 297) in connexion with optical analogue methods of representing the relative structure amplitudes of crystal reflections. The transform is the reciprocal of a single unit, in the same way as the reciprocal lattice is the reciprocal of a repeating pattern of many units. Imagine a reciprocal lattice with each point carrying a weight proportional to the structure amplitude of the corresponding crystal reflection; this weighted reciprocal lattice is a representation of the distribution of diffracting power of the crystal. The corresponding reciprocal representation of the distribution of diffracting power of a single unit is called the transform of the unit; unlike the reciprocal lattice, it is a continuous function, and the reciprocal lattice of a repeating pattern may be regarded as a set of spot samples of the transform of one unit. If we imagine the three-dimensional transform with the reciprocal lattice superimposed on it (with origins coincident), the amplitude of the transform at any reciprocal lattice point is the same as the structure amplitude of the crystal reflection corresponding to that reciprocal lattice point.

One way of solving the structure of a crystal composed of molecules of known configuration, one to the unit cell, is to calculate the molecular transform and then to consider what orientation of the transform with respect to the reciprocal lattice gives correct structure amplitudes at the reciprocal lattice points. One of the limitations of this method is that the calculation of transforms in sufficient detail to be useful is very laborious. The amplitude $G$ of the transform is given by essentially the same expression as that for the structure amplitude $F$ of a crystal reflection:

$$G = \sum f_n \cos 2\pi(hx_n + ky_n + lz_n) \text{ for a centrosymmetric group,}$$

where $x_n$, $y_n$, and $z_n$ are the coordinates of the $n$th atom and $h$, $k$, and $l$ are no longer restricted to integral values. Alternatively, for convenience of calculation, $x_n$, $y_n$, and $z_n$ can be expressed in relation to an artificial large unit cell, and $h$, $k$, and $l$ can then be given integral values. (It is simply a question of calculating the transform at points on a sufficiently finely meshed lattice.) For a non-centrosymmetric group $G = \sqrt{(A^2+B^2)}$, where

$$A = \sum f_n \cos 2\pi(hx_n+ky_n+lz_n)$$

and
$$B = \sum f_n \sin 2\pi(hx_n+ky_n+lz_n).$$

If the problem is restricted to two dimensions (for a projection of the structure), calculations are practicable, or, better still, can be avoided altogether by using the optical analogue method (Lipson and Taylor, 1951, 1958); moreover, for a flat molecule the transform need only be obtained for the plane of the molecule. The effect of tilting the molecule with respect to the projection plane so that it is foreshortened in a particular direction is simply to lengthen the transform in that direction.

Structures with one flat molecule in the unit cell (or at any rate in a projection of the unit cell) are, however, not common, and in any case could be solved by other methods. The principal value of the studies of the transforms of such molecules that have been made is that they have brought out the relation between the outstanding features of molecular structure and the outstanding features of the transform. Aromatic condensed-ring molecules, for instance, having hexagonal rings of carbon atoms (C—C distance 1·4 Å), give transforms showing strong regions arranged in hexagonal form round the origin at a distance of 0·8 Å$^{-1}$ determined by the size of the benzene ring (Lipson and Taylor, 1951); in a weighted reciprocal lattice—a diagram in which each reciprocal spot is given an area proportional to the structure amplitude —these regions show up as groups of strong reciprocal lattice points arranged in the form of a hexagon; if the plane of the molecule is in the plane of the projection, the hexagon is a regular one, each region being at 0·8 Å$^{-1}$ from the origin. The six strong regions are due to the parallel lines of atoms in the benzene ring (Fig. 230), which are spaced 1·2 Å apart and therefore give strong regions in the transform at $1/1·2 = 0·8$ Å$^{-1}$ from the origin; and the reciprocal lattice points in these regions are the strong high-order reflections which have been much used in the structure amplitude approach, illustrated for chrysene in Fig. 159, p. 285; the six strong regions of the benzene ring transform lie in this structure on the reciprocal lattice points 0.3.17, 0$\bar{6}$0, 0.3 $\overline{17}$, 0.$\bar{3}$.$\overline{17}$, 0$\bar{6}$0, and 0.$\bar{3}$.17. If the molecule is imagined to rotate in the unit cell, these reflections would become weak and the intensity would appear in a different set of reciprocal lattice points. In fused-ring aromatic molecules the different rings co-operate, because they are all

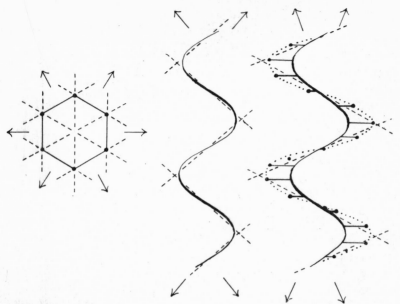

Fig. 230. Left—Atoms of the benzene ring lie on the sets of parallel broken lines; these lead to strong regions of the transform in the directions of the arrows. Centre—A helix gives strong regions in the transform in directions perpendicular to the broken lines. Right—The effect of side chains is to move strong regions nearer to the axis.

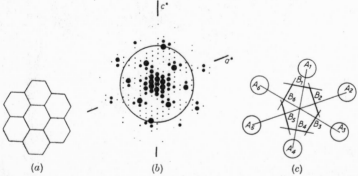

Fig. 231. Coronene. (a) Form of the molecule. (b) $h0l$ section of the weighted reciprocal lattice (areas of spots proportional to structure amplitudes). (c) Derivation of foreshortening of tilted molecule from peaks in reciprocal space. $A_1$, $A_2$, etc., are the positions of the benzene peaks derived from (b); perpendiculars to the $A$ vectors are drawn at $B_1$, $B_2$, etc., at distances from the origin equal to reciprocals of $A$ vectors; these lines give the projected shape of the benzene ring.

oriented in the same way. If the hexagonal group of strong regions in the weighted reciprocal lattice is elongated in one direction, as for coronene, Fig. 231, this means that the molecule is tilted so that it is foreshortened in this direction, and the degree of foreshortening (and thus the angle of tilt) can be calculated, as in Fig. 231 c (Hanson, Lipson, and Taylor, 1953).

Most crystal structures, even in projection, have two or more molecules in the unit cell. The transform of a group of two or more differently oriented molecules may be very different from the transform of a single molecule, but the difference can only be a weakening of certain regions where the transforms of the differently oriented molecules are out of phase; the strong regions of the transform of the group *must* be strong regions of the transform of the single molecule. Fortunately, it is often possible to recognize in the weighted reciprocal lattice strong regions which reveal the orientations of two or more molecules: for instance, two sets of six peaks revealing two orientations of the benzene ring (Taylor, 1952). Furthermore, different features in the same molecule, such as a ring and a chain, may make contributions to the transform which can be recognized independently so that the orientation of each of them can be deduced (Kenyon and Taylor, 1953; Crowder, Morley, and Taylor, 1957). It may also be possible, when the orientations of the molecules are settled, to draw some conclusions about their relative positions, by examining parts of the weighted reciprocal lattice that are weak in places where the transform of a single molecule is strong; this can only mean interference between waves from the different molecules, and the positions of the weak regions may indicate the separation distance (Taylor, 1954).

Only molecules with well-marked features of symmetry or regularity can be expected to produce plainly recognizable features in the transform. This is the reason why the transform concept has been used successfully in studies of the structures of crystals of aromatic substances. Another type of molecule that lends itself readily to the transform approach is the helical chain type of molecule that is found in some important high polymers, both natural and synthetic, and in this field the transform approach is particularly valuable because it is not always possible to be certain of the unit cell or space-group symmetry for these substances: the transform approach makes it possible to draw valuable conclusions about the molecular structure from the general characteristics of the diffraction pattern, without necessarily knowing the indices of the reflections. A helix, seen from a direction at right angles to its axis, looks like a sine wave (Fig. 230), and no matter how the atoms are placed along it (provided that they are not far from the sine-wave line), will give a strong diffracted intensity in the directions indicated, because the majority of atoms lie near the planes marked; the transform will have maxima in these directions, at a distance from the origin equal to the reciprocal of the spacing of these planes. Moreover, the transform must have approximately cylindrical symmetry, because the helix looks much the same from all directions at right angles to its axis (the deviations from precise cylindrical symmetry depend on the placing of the atoms); the transform, in fact, has strong regions in rings centred on the axis, and some reciprocal lattice points are certain to lie on these rings.

The synthetic polypeptides poly-L-alanine $(—NH.CH(CH_3).CO—)_p$ ($\alpha$ form) and poly-$\gamma$-methyl-L-glutamate

$$(—NH.CH(CH_2.CH_2.COOCH_3).CO—)_p$$

illustrate this point. Diffraction patterns of fibres of these substances show very strong reflections with a Bragg spacing of about 4·4 Å at an angle of 30–40° to the fibre axis (Bamford, Brown, Elliott, Hanby, and Trotter, 1952); this is consistent with the helical chain configuration proposed by Pauling, Corey, and Branson (1951), which has a pitch of 5·4 Å and a diameter of about 4 Å. If the helix is a large-scale one, more than one 'order' of this reflection may be seen on the diffraction pattern, giving lines of reflections radiating from the centre at the characteristic angle to the meridian, the slope of the helical winding being at right angles to the line of reflections; some of the nucleic acids give patterns of this type, showing an X-shaped arrangement of strong reflections (Wilkins, Stokes, and Wilson, 1953; Franklin and Gosling, 1953), and the positions of the strong reflections are consistent with the helical configuration suggested by Watson and Crick (1953), which has a pitch of 34 Å and a diameter of 20 Å. (The regions between the widely spaced strands of the helix are of course not empty, but are occupied by side-chains, the atoms of which would lie on other helices of different diameter; however, the greatest concentrations of atoms, including the more strongly diffracting phosphorus atoms, lie along the strand of the main helix. In addition, the Watson–Crick model contains two intertwined helices, but this feature does not destroy the outstanding features of a typical helical diffraction pattern.) If there are side-chains standing out from the main-chain helix, as in poly-$\gamma$-methyl-L-glutamate, the side-chain atoms lie on helices of the same pitch but greater diameter (Fig. 230); this has the effect of bringing the strong regions of the transform nearer to the axis, so that strong reflections lie nearer the meridian than for an unbranched helical chain.

Chain molecules often coil in such a way that one turn of the helix does not comprise a whole number of chemical chain units; for instance, in polyisobutene ($-CH_2-C(CH_3)_2-)_p$ there are 1·6 chemical units per turn, so that exact geometrical repetition occurs only after 8 chemical units and 5 turns of the helix (Bunn, 1947; Bunn and Holmes, 1958). Cochran, Crick, and Vand (1952) discovered a remarkably neat mathematical approach to problems of diffraction by such molecules; they found that if $S$ is the number of structural units and $T$ the number of turns of the helix in the geometrical repeat unit, the intensity on the $l$th layer line is given by an expression containing Bessel functions whose order $n$ is given by integral solutions of $n = (l-Sm)/T$, where $m$ is any whole number. For each layer line there is a series of values of $n$, but since the numerical value of a Bessel function declines rapidly with increasing value of $n$, only the low order terms need be taken into account; moreover, strong reflections will only be found on layer lines associated with low values of $n$. For polyisobutene, $S = 8$ and $T = 5$, and substitution of these in the simple expression above shows that Bessel functions of order 0 or 1 occur only for layer lines 0, 3, 5, 8, 11, 13, and 16, so that the strongest reflections should be found on these layer lines; this is indeed true—the diffraction pattern in Plate X shows strong reflections on the equator and the 3rd, 5th, and 8th layer lines, and the others are seen on tilted fibre photographs. The configuration of this molecule had been deduced earlier by structure amplitude considerations, but it could have been arrived at, or at any rate suggested, much more easily by the Cochran, Crick, and Vand equation. Another example is that given by the authors just mentioned: in poly-γ-methyl-L-glutamate the repeat distance along the chain is 27 Å, and in this length the Pauling helix takes 5 turns and comprises 18 chemical chain units. The Cochran, Crick, and Vand equation shows that the lowest order Bessel functions, and therefore the strongest reflections, occur on layer lines 0, 5, 8, 10, 13, and 18; the diffraction patterns do indeed show the strongest reflections on these layer lines (the very strong 4·4 Å reflection mentioned earlier is on the 5th layer line) and this gives strong support to the Pauling configuration (Cochran and Crick, 1952). (The exact repeat may be 43·2 Å, with 8 turns and 29 chemical units, or 103 Å, with 19 turns and 69 chemical units (Brown and Trotter, 1956), but these configurations differ only very slightly from that first mentioned; the same layer lines, but labelled with different order numbers, would be indicated by the equation.) Methods of calculating the distribution of intensity along the layer lines of the transform by using Bessel functions have also been devised by Cochran, Crick, and Vand (1952). The optical analogue method has been used effectively by Elliott and Malcolm (1959) for investigating the effects of alternative side-chain positions on the intensities along the layer lines for these substances; intensities in the optical transform were measured photometrically.

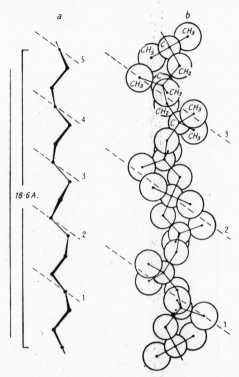

FIG. 232. Configuration of poly*iso*butene molecule ($-CH_2-C(CH_3)_2-)_p$.
(*a*) Chain alone. (*b*) Chain with methyl groups.

The poly*iso*butene molecule illustrates a point made earlier—that the contributions of different features of the same molecule to the transform can often be recognized independently. In a side-view of the molecule (Fig. 232), the main chain shows five 'crinkles' owing to the five turns of the helix, and the majority of the atoms lie near the five planes marked in the left-hand diagram; this is the origin of the strong reflections on the fifth layer line; the side methyl groups make little contribution to these. On the other hand, the methyl groups lie for the most part near the three planes marked in the right-hand diagram; this is the origin of the strong reflection on the third layer line, to which the main chain atoms make little contribution.

An important application of the transform concept led to great progress in the study of the structure of haemoglobin, the red protein of blood. In describing this, it is first necessary to make the point that the transform of a centrosymmetric projection consists of alternate regions of positive and negative sign (phase angles of 0 or $\pi$), separated by nodes where the intensity is zero. This is illustrated by the optical representation of the transform of the durene molecule in Plate XVI, due to Lipson and Taylor (1951); this plate also illustrates how the sign in an optical transform can be determined quite simply by making another pattern with an extra diffracting unit at the centre of symmetry which necessarily makes a positive contribution; positive regions in the original transform are strengthened while negative regions are weakened by this extra unit (Pinnock and Taylor, 1955). For crystals with large unit cells, and thus small-meshed reciprocal lattices, each region of the transform is likely to include several reciprocal lattice points, and thus the reciprocal lattice exhibits groups of points having the same sign. In an unsolved structure, however, it is not known which reciprocal lattice points belong to each group: the positions of the zero intensity lines in the transform are not known. Perutz found that the shape of the unit cell of horse methaemoglobin changes with degree of hydration; the reciprocal lattice points therefore move through the transform as hydration changes. By observing the changes of intensity of corresponding reflections in the centrosymmetric $b$ projection with degree of hydration, it was possible to deduce whereabouts in the transform the sign changes occur, because reflections that decline in intensity and then increase again probably change sign in passing through a node of zero intensity (Boyes-Watson, Davidson, and Perutz, 1947; Bragg, Howells, and Perutz, 1952; Perutz, 1954). The signs were subsequently checked by the heavy atom isomorphous replacement method and found to be correct (Green, Ingram, and Perutz, 1954). This work has led to the calculation of an electron density map of the haemoglobin crystal (Bragg and Perutz, 1954). It will not often be possible to use this method, because the unit cells of most crystals do not change shape in this way.

The transform concept has been illuminating in many ways. One more example will be mentioned. In the transform of a centrosymmetric group of atoms, the phase angle is necessarily either 0 or $\pi$, and regions of opposite sign are separated by nodal lines of zero intensity; in the transform of a non-centrosymmetric group there is no such limitation of phase angles, so that the intensity does not have to go

PLATE XVI

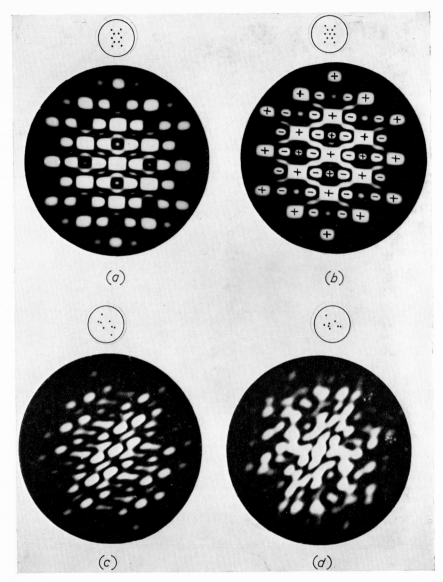

Above: diffraction patterns of (a) mask representing molecule of durene, 1,2,4,5 tetra-methyl benzene, (b) the same mask with an extra hole at the centre; positive regions are strengthened, negative regions weakened. (Lipson and Cochran, 1953.) Below: diffraction patterns of (c) the centrosymmetric arrangement of holes shown inset, and (d) the non-centrosymmetric arrangement of holes shown inset (C. A. Taylor, 1952)

through zero between regions of very different phase angle—strong regions of phase angle near 0 and $\pi$ can be connected by a continuous strong region of gradually changing phase angle; consequently, the transform of a non-centrosymmetric group is not crossed by dark lines (Plate XVI). This observation links up with the intensity statistics of Wilson (1949 a) mentioned earlier (p. 264): for non-centrosymmetric crystals the intensities of the reflections tend to be more uniform than for centrosymmetric crystals, which give a greater range of intensities, with a greater number of weak values.

**Relations between phases and amplitudes of different reflections.** Experience has shown that a crystal structure is correct if the calculated intensities of all the reflections, for a certain set of positions of the atoms which are known to be present in the unit cell, agree with the observed intensities, within reasonable limits of error. It seems that all the information for the solution of the structural problem is contained in the set of observed intensities, together with the known scattering powers of the atoms; this means that it ought to be possible to calculate the structure by solving equations containing the moduli of the structure amplitudes and the atomic scattering powers, without any experimental evidence on the phase relations. Up to the time of writing, however, no methods of solving the equations, except in the simplest cases, have been found. Nevertheless, some progress has been made along a line suggested by the thought that, if all the necessary information is contained in the moduli of the structure amplitudes, the phase relations are somehow implied by the relative magnitudes of the structure amplitudes; if the phase relations could be deduced, the image synthesis methods already described would lead to the solution of the structural problem.

The first important step in this direction was taken by Harker and Kasper (1948), who derived relations between pairs or small groups of reflections in a centrosymmetric structure in the form of inequality expressions. The simplest of these says that if $U_{hkl}$ is the 'unitary structure amplitude'—the structure amplitude expressed as a fraction of what it would be if the waves from all atoms were exactly in phase with each other†—then

$$U_{hkl}^2 \leqslant \tfrac{1}{2} + \tfrac{1}{2} U_{2h,2k,2l}.$$

If $U_{hkl}^2 > \tfrac{1}{2}$ (that is, $U_{hkl} > 0.71$), then the second-order reflection

† $U_{hkl} = F_{hkl}/\Sigma f$, where $f$ is the scattering power of each atom at the value of $(\sin\theta)/\lambda$ appropriate for the $hkl$ reflection.

$2h$, $2k$, $2l$ must be positive. If both $U^2_{hkl}$ and $U^2_{2h,2k,2l}$ are $> \frac{1}{4}$ (that is, $|U_{hkl}|$ and $|U_{2h,2k,2l}|$ are both $> \frac{1}{2}$), then again the second-order reflection is positive. (But the sign of the first-order reflection is not settled.) This says no more than can be gathered by inspecting the Bragg and Lipson structure amplitude charts, but many other inequality relations have been derived that are not so obvious. For instance, if the structure has a twofold axis, $U^2_{hkl} \leqslant \frac{1}{2} + \frac{1}{2} U_{2h,0,2l}$, and if there is a twofold screw axis, $U^2_{hkl} \leqslant \frac{1}{2} + \frac{1}{2}(-1)^k U_{2h,0,2l}$. These expressions only give information about the phases of reflections with even indices; but others deal with odd indices, for instance

$$|U_{hkl} + U_{h'k'l'}|^2 \leqslant (1 + U_{h+h',k+k',l+l'})(1 + U_{h-h',k-k',l-l'}),$$

and a similar expression with negative instead of positive signs before the $U$'s; these give relations between, for instance, $30\bar{9}$ and $202$ on the left-hand side and $50\bar{7}$ and $1.0.\overline{11}$ on the right-hand side. The various expressions appropriate to the different space-groups are collected together in *International Tables* (1952).

The Harker–Kasper inequalities only give information on signs when the unitary structure amplitudes are large; the larger the $U$'s, the better the chances of obtaining useful information. Very often the information obtained is a relation between signs, not an absolute sign determination; nevertheless the accumulation of information often gives valuable results. According to Zachariasen (1952), the method of inequalities will only lead to a structure determination if 20 per cent. or more of the $U$'s are greater than 0·3. This is likely to be so only for structures with a small number of atoms in the asymmetric unit. The method played an important part in the solution of the structure of decaborane, $B_{10}H_{14}$, by Kasper, Lucht, and Harker (1950), in which the number of boron atoms in the asymmetric unit is 5; but in general the more complex the structure, the fewer are the strong reflections. Nevertheless, even when the method will not determine a structure completely, it may provide a few signs to supplement the results of other methods.

Sayre (1952) discovered an equality relation between all the structure amplitudes, or between all those in one zone, for a structure of equal atoms, well resolved from each other. In itself it is not easy to apply, since it involves so many terms; but on the basis of this work Cochran (1952) concluded that the following simple relation between the signs of three terms ($s(hkl)$ stands for the sign of $hkl$) is *probably* true if the three structure amplitudes are large:

$$s(hkl) = s(h'k'l') \cdot s(h+h', \, k+k', \, l+l').$$

The same result was obtained by Zachariasen (1952) by a different method. It appears to be nearly always valid when all three reflections have unitary structure amplitudes of 0·25 or more. By putting together the verdicts of many relations of the above type, a web of sign relations is set up. For the structure of metaboric acid, $HBO_2$ (monoclinic, $P2_1/a$, 9 atoms in the asymmetric unit), which had not yielded to other methods, Zachariasen (1952), working in three dimensions from the start, chose three signs arbitrarily (the alternatives correspond to the use of alternative centres of symmetry for the origin), found 14 signs by Harker–Kasper inequality relations, and then by the above sign relation obtained the signs of all reflections having $U \geqslant 0\cdot25$, 138 in all; he then extended the scheme even to reflections with $U$'s down to 0·20 (but using stronger ones for $h'k'l'$ in the above relation), raising the number of signs to 198, out of a total of 1,000 observed reflections. The use of these signs led to a three-dimensional electron density distribution that showed the right number of atoms arranged in a reasonable way, and from this point the structure was refined success-fully by standard methods.

To extend the application of the Cochran–Zachariasen sign relation to more complex structures, in which the proportion of strong reflections is smaller, Cochran and Douglas (1955, 1957) have used an electronic digital computer to produce a number of alternative sets of signs, and to select the most probable ones on the basis of certain criteria. The most important criterion for correctness is that

$$\chi = \sum_{hkl} \sum_{h'k'l'} U_{hkl} \cdot U_{h'k'l'} \cdot U_{h+h',k+k',l+l'}$$

should be large and positive, which is in effect a way of rejecting sign combinations that give negative electron densities; the value of $\chi$ which the correct set of signs can be expected to give can be calculated, and this is obviously the criterion to use. For the rather complex structure of glutathione ($\gamma$-L-glutamyl-L-cysteinyl-glycine, $C_{10}H_{17}N_3O_6S$), which contains 20 atoms (excluding hydrogen atoms) in the asymmetric unit, Wright (1958) found that the Cochran–Douglas sign-determining method was the most successful of the various methods used in trying to solve the structure; it played an important part in leading to the final solution.

**Ultimate refinement, and tests for correctness and accuracy.**
Most of this chapter has been concerned with methods of solving
the essential structural problem: finding the approximate positions of
the atoms. Many investigations, however, have as their objective the
placing of the atoms with as much accuracy as possible, to measure
bond lengths or angles in the development of quantitative stereochemistry. This is most often done by the methods of refinement
used in the earlier stages—either by further stages of electron density
synthesis or by using the error synthesis to adjust atomic positions,
this being followed by further calculations of structure factors to see
if any phase angles must be revised. It is worth remembering that
when straight electron density syntheses are used, and an adjustment
of an atomic coordinate by $\Delta x$ is indicated by the new position of a
peak, the process of refinement is considerably speeded up by moving
the atom $2\Delta x$ for the next calculations of phase angles (Lipson and
Cochran, 1953, p. 280). When no further changes of phase angles occur,
it is assumed that the structure is the best that the experimental
measurements can give.

What degree of agreement between observed and calculated structure
amplitudes constitutes an assurance that the structure is correct, and
what is the likely degree of precision of the atomic coordinates which
are obtained? Neither of these questions can be answered definitely
and precisely, though much thought has been given to the problems
involved. In relation to the first question, it has become customary to
express the overall agreement as the mean discrepancy, the sum of the
differences between $F_{obs}$ and $F_{calc}$, divided by the sum of the $F_{obs}$ figures;
this is the 'residual'

$$R = \frac{\sum||F_{obs}|-|F_{calc}||}{\sum|F_{obs}|}.$$

It appears that when $R$ is about 0·20 there is little doubt that the
structure is correct; in some investigations in which hydrogen atoms
and anisotropic thermal motions are included in the calculations, figures
as low as 0·10 are obtained. These discrepancy figures, 10 to 20 per
cent., may seem high compared with those attained in some other
types of scientific work; but it should be remembered that the number
of reflections involved is usually large—it may be thousands in a
complex structure—and a general degree of agreement of 10 to 20 per
cent. for so many independent measurements is convincing. There are
several reasons why the discrepancies exist even in the best work: the

accuracy of measurement of intensities (especially if estimated visually) is not high, it is often difficult to correct for absorption and extinction, the scattering factor curves are known with only moderate precision, and, finally, the problems of anisotropic thermal motions and non-spherical electron distributions in bonded atoms are difficult to solve.

There is no definite value of $R$ that guarantees a structure to be correct. If there are heavy atoms in an organic structure, fairly good agreement can be obtained from the heavy atoms alone, and thus it is possible that even when the value of $R$ is low, some lighter atoms may be misplaced. Moreover, flat molecules and chain molecules give patterns in which a great deal of intensity is concentrated in a few reflections at small angles, and the calculated $F$'s of these can be correct even for structures that are wrong in detail. It is advisable to evaluate $R$ for successive shells of the reciprocal lattice; a fair $R$ figure for the outer shells is a better criterion of correctness than a good overall figure. Another problem is that of reflections within the outermost shell that are not detected, although their calculated $F$'s are appreciable: it is not known whether they are merely lost in the background scattering or whether they are genuinely absent. If they are omitted altogether ($F_{\text{calc}}$ and $F_{\text{obs}} = 0$), a much lower value of $R$ is obtained than if they are assumed to have $F_{\text{obs}} = 0$ but $F_{\text{calc}}$ appreciable. The most reasonable procedure seems to be to give them a figure for $F_{\text{obs}}$ equal to half the minimum that can be detected at the angle in question. The procedure adopted should always be stated.

In the earlier stages of structure analysis, it is useful to have in mind a figure for $R$ that gives some hope of a solution; experience has shown that structures having $R = 0 \cdot 5$ for a centrosymmetric or $0 \cdot 4$ for a non-centrosymmetric crystal often refine successfully. If they refine only to say $0 \cdot 3$, it may be that a minority of atoms are misplaced or that the structure is only partially correct in some other way. These figures are mentioned as rough guides, and should not be taken too literally; structures with higher values of $R$ may sometimes be roughly correct overall, while others with lower values might be incorrect in some details.

There has been much discussion of the probable limits of error of atomic coordinates in crystal structures, the upshot of which is the conclusion that earlier estimates of accuracy were too optimistic. Cruickshank (1949) showed that the relation between the standard deviation $\sigma(x)$ of a coordinate of an atom and the differences between observed and calculated structure factors $(F_{obs}-F_{calc})$ is (for a centrosymmetric structure)

$$\sigma(x) = \frac{2\pi\{\sum h^2(F_{obs}-F_{calc})^2\}^{\frac{1}{2}}}{aVC}$$

where $h$ is the usual $h$ index, $a$ the length of the unit cell edge, $V$ the volume of the unit cell, and $C$ the curvature at the centre of the atom $(\partial^2\rho/\partial x^2$, in which $\rho$ is electron density); the expression is summed for all the reflections used. For a non-centrosymmetric structure $\sigma(x)$ is doubled. For the other coordinates $y$ and $z$, corresponding expressions hold; the results may differ for $x$, $y$, and $z$. The standard deviation of the length of a bond between two atoms $\sigma(d_{12})$ is given by

$$\sigma^2(d_{12}) = \sigma^2(x_1)+\sigma^2(x_2)$$

if the atoms are in general positions not related by symmetry elements ($x$ here stands for the bond direction). Cruickshank (1950) gives a typical example of a structure in which all atoms have standard deviation 0·015 Å; bond length differences in this structure of less than 0·05 Å are not significant.

Another useful equation due to Cruickshank (1950) is the relation of the standard deviation of electron density $\sigma(\rho)$ and the discrepancies between observed and calculated structure factors:

$$\sigma(\rho) = \frac{1}{V}\{\sum (F_{obs}-F_{calc})^2\}^{\frac{1}{2}}.$$

This expression is useful for deciding, for instance, whether patches of negative electron density are within the limits of experimental error to be expected, or whether they must be taken seriously as indications that there is something wrong with the structure.

# XI

## CRYSTAL SIZE AND TEXTURE

HITHERTO, in this book, we have been concerned chiefly with sharp X-ray reflections which occur at the Bragg angle and over a very narrow angular range near it—the reflections given by crystals which are comparatively large ($> 10^{-5}$ cm in diameter) and have a uniform regular internal structure. (Not perhaps perfectly regular: most crystals have some dislocations or other imperfections, though not in sufficient proportion to affect the diffraction pattern seriously.) Specimens are, however, sometimes encountered which give broadened X-ray reflections: for instance, powder photographs may be obtained which show rather diffuse lines. This may mean that some crystals have slightly different unit cell dimensions from others, or that the unit cell dimensions vary in different regions of the same crystal, owing to variations of composition or to strains. In these circumstances certain crystals or parts of crystals give X-ray reflections at slightly different angles from others, and a broad line is the result. Alternatively, the broadening may mean that the crystals are extremely small. Just as an optical diffraction grating with comparatively few lines gives diffuse diffracted beams, so a crystal of very small dimensions gives reflections over a wider angular range than a large crystal. More complex broadening effects may be caused by structural irregularities on a very small scale and by the thermal movements of the atoms in crystals. In addition to the broadening of Bragg reflections, some diffraction patterns may show diffuse scattering in non-Bragg positions, which again may be due either to thermal movements or to structural irregularities. Finally, the study of diffraction effects at very small angles, very close to the primary X-ray beam, has revealed many interesting features which can be interpreted in terms of crystal size or the texture of specimens.

The interpretation of these phenomena is of obvious importance in relation to the physical properties of materials, and much work is being done from this viewpoint. In addition, there may be, for certain substances, some correlation between these diffraction effects and particular chemical properties. The rate of a chemical reaction may, for instance, depend on the size of the crystals of a solid reactant (small crystals reacting more rapidly than large ones); thus, if the size involved lies in the range below $10^{-5}$ cm it may be possible to correlate reactivity with the broadening of the Bragg reflections, or the small-angle scattering. The activity of solid catalysts is also likely to depend first of all on the size of the crystals: the adsorption which is believed to be a prerequisite for many catalytic reactions is more extensive the greater the surface area (which is a function of crystal size). Size, however, is not the only factor involved in catalytic activity. The 'active spots' which are believed to exist on catalyst surfaces may be associated with local strains, due perhaps to the presence of foreign atoms inserted in the main crystals. ('Promoters', the secondary substances often added to increase the activity of catalysts, may have the function of providing these foreign atoms which strain the crystals and thus give rise to active spots.)

The correlation of line-broadening with the chemical conditions of preparation of materials also falls within our scope. Consider, for instance, pigment materials; we are not concerned with the colour or other physical properties as such; but the colour of a powder may depend not only on the crystal structure of the particles, but also on their size; and the size may depend on the chemical conditions of preparation.

In all such circumstances the problem which presents itself is, in the first place, that of distinguishing between the different possible causes of line-broadening; and then, if a definite verdict on this point can be given, to attempt quantitative interpretation in terms of this factor, be it crystal size, or the extent of the variation of lattice dimensions, or the periodicity of structural irregularities or thermal movements.

**Relation between crystal size and breadth of X-ray reflections.** If an extremely narrow X-ray beam is diffracted by a large perfect crystal which is rotated, each diffracted beam (making an angle of $2\theta$ with the primary beam, where $\theta$ is the Bragg angle) is extremely narrow —it has a width of only a few seconds of arc on either side of the theoretical angle $2\theta$. Most crystals are imperfect in the sense that different regions of the crystal are not exactly parallel to each other; but this does not affect the angular range of the diffracted beam: the crystal may continue to give a diffracted beam when it is rotated through several minutes of arc, or even as much as half a degree, but the diffracted beam is not broadened by such imperfections, provided that the perfect sections of the crystal are larger than $10^{-5}$ cm; the imperfections of the crystal may be regarded as part of its rotation. (On

Weissenberg photographs the reflections are often short streaks owing to such imperfections.)

If such a crystal were ground to fragments, and a powder photograph were taken, using an extremely narrow X-ray beam and a very small specimen, the angular width of the arc would still be only a few seconds, provided that the crystal fragments were larger than $10^{-5}$ cm in diameter. In practice, somewhat divergent X-ray beams, and powder specimens of very appreciable width, are used (otherwise exposures

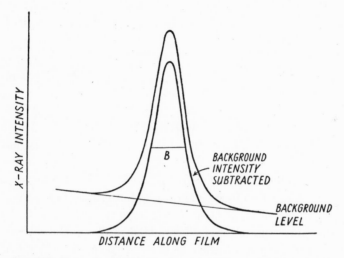

Fig. 233. Intensity distribution in an arc of a powder photograph.

would be inconveniently long), and it is these circumstances which are responsible for the widths of the arcs on typical powder photographs such as those in Plate IV. The arcs on the photograph of quartz, for instance, would be described as perfectly sharp; in other words, the breadth of the arcs is almost entirely due to camera conditions, not to the diffracting properties of the specimen.

A crystal smaller than about $10^{-5}$ cm in diameter gives a broadened diffracted beam. For quantitative treatment it is first necessary to define 'breadth'. A line on a powder photograph (Fig. 233) shows maximum intensity at the centre, and fades away on either side; a simple definition of breadth is the angular width between the points at which the intensity falls to half its maximum value. In an 'ideal' powder photograph of an extremely narrow specimen taken with a very narrow beam, the relation between this 'breadth at half height' $\beta$ and the size of the crystals would be

$$\beta \text{ (in radians)} = \frac{C\lambda}{t} \sec \theta,$$

where $t$ is the thickness of the crystal, $C$ is a constant, $\lambda$ the X-ray wavelength, and $\theta$ the Bragg angle (Scherrer, 1920; Seljakow, 1925; Bragg, 1933). The constant $C$ has the value of 0·9; strictly speaking, this is valid only when the particles are spherical, belong to the cubic system, and are uniform in size, but the shape and size distributions in a specimen are usually not known, and the best that can be done is to use the equation to give an approximate size; in relation to experimental errors and other uncertainties, no serious error is incurred in accepting a value of $C = 0\cdot9$.

An alternative definition of line breadth, first used by Laue (1926), is the area of the curve divided by its height—the integral breadth; if this definition is used, the constant $C$ in the Scherrer equation is rather larger; Stokes and Wilson (1942) give values from 1·0 to 1·3 for various reflecting planes of differently shaped crystals of cubic symmetry; in practice, when the shape is not known, a value of 1·15 should be used.

The pure diffraction broadening discussed in the last two paragraphs increases the breadths of lines on powder photographs when the crystals are very small. In order to deduce the size of the crystals it is necessary to find the pure diffraction broadening $\beta$, and for this purpose it is necessary to know the breadth of lines ($b$) given by crystals greater than $10^{-5}$ cm under the same camera conditions. This breadth $b$ is determined not only by the divergence of the X-ray beam and the size of the specimen, but also by the absorption. (See Chapter V.) Numerous attempts have been made to correct for such factors by calculation (for summary, see Cameron and Patterson, 1937); but the safest method is that of Jones (1938), who mixes the solid under investigation with another substance consisting of crystals larger than $10^{-5}$ cm. The diffraction arcs of both substances are affected in exactly the same way by the camera conditions and absorption in the specimen; consequently the breadths of the sharp lines of the reference substance give $b$, while those of the substance under investigation give $B$, the total breadth including diffraction broadening. Both these vary with $\theta$, and the procedure is therefore to measure on the microphotometer the intensity distribution in various lines of both substances at different Bragg angles (converting from photographic opacity to X-ray intensity by the use of a calibration wedge, as described in Chapter VII), and to plot the breadths $b$ of the sharp lines against $\theta$; by interpolation, the value of $b$ at the Bragg angle of each of the broadened lines is read off. To obtain the pure diffraction broadening $\beta$ from $B$ and $b$, Scherrer assumed that $\beta = B-b$. Strictly speaking, it depends on the intensity distribution in a line (Jones, 1938) and the ideal method of obtaining $\beta$ is by a Fourier analysis of the line shape (Stokes, 1948); in practice it is doubtful whether such elaboration is worth while, and it is usually sufficient to use correction curves given by Jones (1938) for the relation between $b/B$ and $\beta/B$ for different line-shapes, or to use Warren's (1941) relation $\beta^2 = B^2-b^2$ which gives very similar results (Klug and Alexander, 1954).

In the Scherrer formula $\beta$ is proportional to sec $\theta$. For other causes of line-broadening, the relation is different; therefore, in studying a particular substance, if $\beta$ is found to be proportional to sec $\theta$, it is probably justifiable to assume that the broadening is due to the small size of the crystals.

No great accuracy can be expected in work of this sort. A further source of doubt is in the effect of the wide range of crystal sizes present in most specimens; Jones states, as a general conclusion, that on this account the observed mean size will be greater than the true mean size, but that the difference is unlikely to be greater than 30 per cent. of the observed mean size.

The above discussion relates, strictly speaking, only to spherical crystals. For other shapes the breadths of different reflections depend on the dimensions of the crystals in different directions and on the indices. The breadths of different lines thus do not vary regularly with the Bragg angle. The subject will not be considered in detail; but, in a general way, it may be observed that the breadth of a line depends on the thickness of a crystal in a direction at right angles to the reflecting planes. Plate-like crystals, for instance, will give broader reflections from planes parallel to the plane of the plate than from those perpendicular to this plane. For other planes it is necessary to consider the volume average† of the thickness of the crystal in the direction at right angles to the reflecting planes. (Stokes and Wilson, 1942.) For further information see also Jones (1938), Patterson (1939), Klug and Alexander (1954), and Stokes (1955).

There are other possible causes of differential broadening, as we shall

† The 'volume average' is $\dfrac{\int T_{hkl}\, dV}{V}$ , where $V$ is the volume of the crystal and $T_{hkl}$ is the thickness of the crystal in the direction normal to the $hkl$ plane.

see later; and a distinction between the different possible causes is much more difficult than in the case of broadening which is some function of the Bragg angle only. But if there are external reasons for believing that small crystal size is the only likely cause for broadening in a particular specimen, then a general idea of the size and shape of the crystals may be gained in the way indicated in the last paragraph.

This section will be concluded by an emphasis on three points. First, that for powders the X-ray method gives the size of crystals, not particles (which may be aggregates of crystals). Second, that the range of sizes covered is the range below $10^{-5}$ cm, and that estimates of crystal size between $10^{-6}$ and $10^{-5}$ cm are very rough, since the line-broadening is slight. It is only below $10^{-6}$ cm that broadening is really sufficient for reliable measurements. For larger crystals the range above $10^{-4}$ cm (1 $\mu$) is usually dealt with by measuring and counting particles of crystals under the ordinary microscope. The range below $10^{-4}$ cm is now catered for by the electron microscope. The third point is that the line-broadening gives no information on the size distribution among the crystals responsible for the effect; it indicates only an average size. The electron microscope, when it can be used, gives much more detailed information—it shows the shapes of the crystals and the size distribution.

**Lattice distortions.** When a mixed crystal phase is formed the composition is likely to vary from one crystal to another, and unless a long time is allowed for the attainment of equilibrium, this difference of composition between crystals, or even different parts of the same crystal, is likely to persist. The lattice dimensions will vary with the composition, and therefore a powder photograph will show broadened lines. In distorted crystals also the lattice dimensions vary, with a similar effect on the powder photograph; this may happen in crystals of fixed composition as well as in mixed crystals. If the variation of lattice dimensions is uniform in all directions, the breadth of the X-ray reflections is proportional to $\tan \theta$. We have already seen that broadening due to small crystal size is proportional to $\sec \theta$; hence, if data are available for a sufficient angular range, it is possible to distinguish between these two possible causes of line-broadening. (Stokes, Pascoe, and Lipson, 1943; Lipson and Stokes, 1943; Smith and Stickley, 1943.). It is interesting to appreciate the difference between the two situations in terms of the reciprocal lattice. A reduction in the size of crystals†

---

† For non-spherical shapes the reciprocal points expand anisotropically, being greatest in the direction of the smallest real dimension; all the reciprocal points become the same shape and size.

causes all the points of the reciprocal lattice to expand to the same
extent (see Fig. 234 $a$); but a variation of lattice dimensions means a
variation of reciprocal lattice dimensions, with the result that the outer
points are drawn out more than the inner ones (Fig. 234 $b$). The
breadths of reflections are given by the relative times taken by different
reciprocal 'points' (they are really small volumes) to pass through the
surface of the sphere of reflection on rotation; it is thus evident that

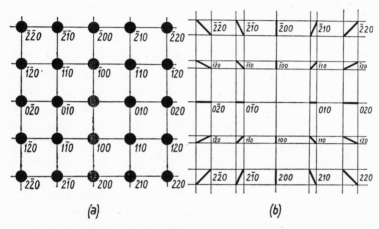

Fig. 234. $a$. One level of the reciprocal lattice of a very small crystal.
$b$. Effect of variation of reciprocal lattice dimensions.

the relations between breadth of reflection and $\theta$ are different in the
two cases. For discussions of the relation between strain-broadening
of different reflections and the elastic constants of the crystals, see
Klug and Alexander (1954), Stokes (1955), and Greenough (1955).

Another cause of the broadening of X-ray reflections is to be found
in the thermal motions in crystals. It has already been mentioned in
Chapter VII that, on account of the thermal motions, the reflecting
power is not concentrated entirely in the points of the reciprocal lattice,
but is to some extent spread along the lines joining the points. The
'points' are really small volumes having a three-dimensional star-shape.
On single-crystal photographs the result is the formation of extra spots
and streaks, much weaker than the normal 'Bragg' reflections, and only
appreciable in intensity in the case of certain substances and under
certain experimental conditions. (See Lonsdale, 1942.) On powder
photographs the effect would be to extend the 'foot' of the curve (Fig.
233) representing the distribution of intensity in an arc; this may make

the background level uncertain; but this effect is likely to be serious only in the case of crystals near their melting-points.

One more cause of broadening will be mentioned. This is the existence of structural irregularities in crystals. The nature of such irregularities will be illustrated by one of the simplest cases—that of the metal cobalt. This element may crystallize either with a hexagonal structure or a face-centred cubic structure. These structures are different types of close-packing of spheres, arising in the following way. If a single layer of spheres is arranged in close-packed formation (positions 1 in Fig. 235) and a second layer is put on top of the first, resting in the hollows

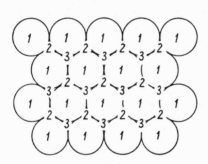

FIG. 235. Illustrating alternative close-packed structures.

marked 2, the third layer put over the first, and the fourth over the second, the arrangement is hexagonal close-packed. If the third layer, instead of being put over the first, is put in the alternative set of positions marked 3, and then this 1, 2, 3 succession is repeated, the arrangement is face-centred cubic (the layers being 111 planes). Some specimens of cobalt give X-ray photographs which indicate that these two possible arrangements occur indiscriminately throughout the crystals. The evidence is that while some X-ray reflections are sharp, others are broadened in different degrees. The phenomena will not be explained in detail, but it may be observed that the building plane of the above description (001 of the hexagonal form, 111 of the cubic form) is perfect, and gives a sharp reflection, but that planes inclined to it exhibit random faults, which give rise to reciprocal lattice points extended in particular directions and thus to X-ray reflections broadened in different degrees. (Edwards and Lipson, 1942; Wilson, 1942 a.) More complicated cases which have been studied are those of $AuCu_3$ (Jones and Sykes, 1938; Wilson, 1943), and $Cu_4FeNi_3$ (Daniel and Lipson, 1943). The distribution of the faults may give rise to extension of the reciprocal lattice points in particular directions and in different degrees, or to the existence of satellites round certain reciprocal points.

The streaks which occur in fibre photographs of chain polymers have a similar origin. In well-formed crystalline regions of the nylons, hydrogen-bonded sheets of molecules are packed together to give structures of triclinic or monoclinic symmetry (Bunn and Garner, 1947;

Holmes, Bunn, and Smith, 1955); but the diffraction patterns of some specimens show also continuous streaks along the layer lines, due to the displacement of the sheets along the chain direction, up and down in a random manner in successive sheets. Streaks on photographs of the fibrous mineral chrysolite (Warren and Bragg, 1930), spreading along the layer lines from certain reflections, are due to a much more radical and surprising departure from normal crystalline regularity; it appears that the lattice is bent into a cylindrical form (Whittaker, 1953).

It will be evident that when differential broadening is encountered in powder photographs, it may often be difficult to decide which is the most likely cause. If single-crystal photographs can be obtained, more detailed and more certain interpretation may be attempted. But, beyond the observation that thermal effects will obviously vary in intensity with temperature (Preston, 1939, 1941; Lonsdale, 1942), no general rules can be given; each case must be considered individually. Mathematical treatment is likely to be difficult, and even qualitative consideration far from straightforward; here, the optical diffraction methods introduced by Bragg are likely to be very useful (see Bragg and Lipson, 1943): patterns can be made exhibiting particular types of faults, and the optical diffraction effects compared with the X-ray diffraction effects of actual crystals. These methods have been used effectively by Taylor, Hinde, and Lipson (1951) in the study of the progressive ordering process that takes place when copper–gold alloys are annealed, by Willis (1957, 1958) in the study of the effects of dislocations on the diffraction patterns of crystals, and by Whittaker (1955) in the study of diffraction by cylindrical lattices.

**Small-angle scattering.** The scattering of X-rays at very small angles, very close to the primary beam, is used as an alternative X-ray method of measuring particle size, and also of investigating the structure of crystalline or partially crystalline substances which have very large periodicities. Special apparatus is required for this work; the standard powder cameras and goniometers measure spacings up to only perhaps 20 Å ($2\theta = 4°$) when $CuK\alpha$ radiation is used; to measure spacings up to 1,000 Å, it is necessary to record diffracted X-rays to within 0° 5' of the primary beam. Two types of camera have been used, one based on fine apertures and long distances (with evacuation of the X-ray path), the other on focusing by curved crystals. Spacings up to 1,400 Å have been recorded by the first method (Bolduan and Bear, 1949), but exposure times naturally tend to be very long, owing to the narrowness of the beam; focusing methods, since they use a divergent primary X-ray beam, permit much shorter exposure times, but have been used only for spacings up to about 250 Å.

An isolated small crystal scatters X-rays at small angles to give an intensity distribution that declines with increasing angle, the slope depending on the size; if the crystal is perfect, the distribution of intensity round the primary beam corresponds to the broadening of the large-scale Bragg reflections, and can be regarded as resulting from the diffuseness of the 000 reciprocal lattice point, which is the same as that of the other reciprocal lattice points (see Fig. 234 a). The small-angle scattering, however, would be just the same if the particle were an imperfect or a non-crystalline particle; in fact, the small-angle scattering is a measure of particle size, and does not depend on internal order; it is determined by the difference between the electron density inside the particle and that of its surroundings.

In solid specimens the particles or crystals are close together, and interference between X-rays scattered by neighbouring particles occurs: the transform of the individual particle is crossed by dark bands due to interparticle interference. However, the transform is least affected close to the primary beam, and a method devised by Guinier for calculating particle size from the slope of the intensity curve at the smallest angles (see Guinier and Fournet, 1955) has been used for solids; for particles of uniform size, the plot of logarithm of intensity against the square of the scattering angle (on the independent scattering theory) is a straight line, the slope of which gives the particle size. If the slope is $-\alpha$ when $CuK\alpha$ radiation is used, and the particles are assumed to be spheres of uniform electron density, the radius of the particles is given by $0 \cdot 834\sqrt{\alpha}$. In a few cases, the particle size obtained in this way has been found to agree with that obtained from the broadening of wide-angle reflections or from measurements of surface area by gas adsorption. For many specimens the Guinier plot tends to curve as the angle increases; the interpretation of its shape is ambiguous, for the effect of particle shape, size distribution, and interparticle interference may all be present. For examples of the use of small-angle scattering to estimate particle size, see Dragsdorf, 1956 (colloidal silica), Marculaitis, 1957 (pigments), Gunn, 1958 (catalysts used in petroleum refining), and Heyn, 1955 (fibres).

It should be remembered that the small-angle scattering gives particle size, not necessarily crystal size; if the particles are grains containing several perfect crystals, the small-angle particle size will be larger than the crystal size determined from the broadening of Bragg reflections; on the other hand, if the particle size from small-angle scattering is smaller than that indicated by the broadening of Bragg reflections, the latter is probably partly due to crystal imperfections. For a detailed treatment of small-angle scattering, see the book on the subject by Guinier and Fournet (1955); also Riley (1955), Klug and Alexander (1954), Beeman, Kaesberg, Anderegg, and Webb (1957).

Some of the most interesting small-angle scattering effects are those given by certain specimens of high-polymer fibres, such as Polythene, polyamides, and polyethylene terephthalate: short streaks astride the meridian are observed, the distance of which from the primary beam indicates, if the Bragg equation is used, a periodicity along the fibre axis varying from 80 to 200 Å in different specimens (Hess and Kiessig, 1953; Arnett, Meibohm, and Smith, 1950). This periodicity must be connected with the existence of alternating crystalline and non-crystalline (less dense) regions; but Guinier and Fournet (1955) have emphasized that a simple Bragg treatment may be misleading, and that the distribution of intensity should be explored. Still more intriguing is the appearance in some photographs of off-the-axis spots, suggesting some sort of three-dimensional regularity of arrangement of micelles. Moreover, the apparent (Bragg) spacings and the distance of the spots from the meridian change with temperature (Belbeoch and Guinier, 1958), indicating changes in the size and arrangement of the crystalline and non-crystalline regions.

**Interpretation of diffraction effects of non-crystalline substances.** It has been pointed out in Chapter V that there is no sharp dividing line between crystalline and 'amorphous' substances: with decrease of crystal size, X-ray diffraction patterns become more and more diffuse until, finally, any attempt to calculate crystal size by the method given earlier in this chapter gives a figure of only a few Ångström units—that is, about one unit cell; in these circumstances the word 'crystal', with its implication of pattern-repetition, is inappropriate. The alternative word 'amorphous' is not entirely satisfactory either: on account of the sizes of atoms and their preference for particular environments, the distribution of atomic centres cannot be entirely random. The word 'non-crystalline' is really preferable.

With increasing diffuseness of the diffraction pattern the possibilities of interpretation obviously become more restricted; but even in the extreme cases of glass-like substances and liquids it is possible to draw definite conclusions on the manner of association of the atoms, at any rate in the simpler cases. As in crystal analysis, there are two ways of proceeding. Particular arrangements of atoms may be postulated, and the intensity of diffraction at different angles calculated, for comparison with the actual diffraction pattern of the specimen. The opposite method is to convert the experimental diffraction pattern, by the Fourier series method, into a vector diagram. Provided that there is only one type of atom in the specimen, this diagram will represent the radial distribution of atoms round any atom in the specimen. In the more general case, where there is more than one type of atom, we may say that all the vectors in the specimen are superposed in all directions; it is then necessary to consider the interpretation of the vector diagram in terms of atomic arrangements.

In either case, the first step is to record the diffraction pattern of the substance; it must be a true record of the absolute intensity of diffraction of monochromatic X-rays over a wide angular range. 'White' radiation effects, superimposed on the monochromatic pattern, would complicate the situation; hence it is necessary to use strictly mono-chromatic X-rays reflected from a crystal (see Chapter V); and it is also advisable to evacuate the X-ray camera to avoid scattering by air. (Warren, Krutter, and Morningstar, 1936.) The photographic intensities are measured on the microphotometer, and converted to X-ray inten-sities in the usual way. It is also desirable to correct for 'Compton scattering'—the incoherent scattering of X-rays with concomitant change of wavelength. (See Warren, 1934; Wollan, 1932.)

In the method of trial the intensity $I$ of scattered radiation at any angle $\theta$ is given (for a solid containing two different types of atom) by the Debye equation

$$I = \sum_m \sum_n \frac{f_m f_n \sin S r_{mn}}{S r_{mn}},$$

where $f_m$ and $f_n$ are the scattering powers of atoms $m$ and $n$, $S = \dfrac{4\pi \sin \theta}{\lambda}$, and $r_{mn}$ is the distance from atom $m$ to atom $n$ (Debye, 1915).

In the Fourier series method the weighted radial distribution func-tion, which represents the number of atoms at a distance $r$ from any atom, weighted by the products of the diffracting powers, is given by the expression

$$\sum K_m 4\pi r^2 \rho_0 + \frac{2r}{\pi} \int_0^\infty iS \sin S r \, dS,$$

which is evaluated for a range of values of $r$. In the first term of this expression $K_m$ is the effective number of electrons in atom $m$, and $\rho_0$ the average number of electrons per unit volume; the summation is over a unit of composition. In the second term $i = \left(\dfrac{I}{Nf^2} - 1\right)$, $I$ being the absolute intensity (in electron units) at an angle $\theta$, $N$ the number of atoms in the sample, and $f$ their absolute diffracting power.

Warren (1937, 1940) calculates $iS$ from the experimental intensity curve and plots it as a function of $S$; he then carries out the integration

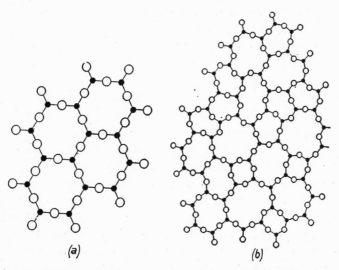

FIG. 236. Two-dimensional representation of the difference between a crystal (left) and a glass (right), according to Zachariasen (1932).

for about forty different values of $r$ ranging from 0 to 8 Å, either graphically or with a harmonic analyser.

For an example of tlíe results obtained in this way, see the paper by Warren, Krutter, and Morningstar (1936) on silica glass. It appears that the immediate surroundings of any one atom are much the same as in cristobalite (one of the crystalline forms of silica); this is the reason why the diffraction pattern of silica glass is like a very diffuse version of that of cristobalite. On the larger-scale aspects of glass structure, the X-ray data do not give definite information; they are equally consistent with Zachariasen's model (1932) of a continuous random network (Fig. 236 $b$) and with the ideas of Hägg (1935) and Preston (1942), who suggest that large discrete groups of atoms may be present—in other words, that the bond-scheme of Fig. 236 b is not maintained continuously throughout the specimen. See also Fournet (1957).

Similar conclusions may be drawn from the diffraction patterns of organic non-crystalline (glass-like or rubber-like) substances. When a substance can be obtained in either crystalline or non-crystalline form (for instance, rubber and polyethylene terephthalate), the diffraction pattern of the non-crystalline form is like a very diffuse version of the crystalline pattern, because the local surroundings of the atoms are similar in the two forms; but no definite information can be obtained on the longer-range configuration and arrangement of the chain molecules; Simard and Warren (1936) calculated the radial distribution function for unstretched rubber, and concluded that it is not possible to decide whether the chains are curled randomly or have roughly straight segments.

Those high polymers that crystallize do not succeed in crystallizing completely: the diffraction patterns show sharp crystalline reflections superimposed on diffuse 'amorphous' scattering. One of the most important applications of X-ray diffraction in this field is the determination of the proportions of crystalline and non-crystalline material in specimens; these proportions depend on the degree of regularity of the molecular structure (the more branched polythenes being less crystalline than the unbranched ones), and many of the properties (hardness, modulus of elasticity, melting-point) are closely correlated with the proportion of crystalline material. One method of estimating crystallinity, based on the crystal density calculated from unit cell dimensions, has already been mentioned (p. 200). Another is to resolve the diffraction pattern graphically into crystalline and non-crystalline diffraction components and to estimate the proportions of the two phases from the intensities; one procedure is to compare the intensity of amorphous scattering with that given by an entirely non-crystalline specimen (Goppel, 1949; Arlman, 1949); another is to use the ratio of crystalline to non-crystalline diffraction, after applying corrections depending on scattering angle (Matthews, Peiser, and Richards, 1949; Natta, Corradini, and Cesari, 1957).

X-ray diffraction methods have also been used in the study of the structures of liquids. The continual movements which occur in liquids do not affect the determination of the principal interatomic distances. For earlier work on the subject see Randall's book (1934). Among later papers, those of Harvey (1939) on ethanol and Bray and Gingrich (1943) on carbon tetrachloride are typical.

The interpretation of the diffraction effects of gases of simple molecular structure is simplified by the fact that the molecules are very far apart, and therefore it is necessary to consider only the distances between the atoms in one molecule. Much information on the structures of molecules has been gained in this way by Debye and others. The subject is well treated in a book by Pirenne (1946).

**Conclusion.** This book is concerned with optical and X-ray methods; but there are of course other methods of studying the structures of crystals and molecules. The diffraction of electrons and of neutrons depends on the same general principles as that of X-rays or visible light; but there are important theoretical differences, and the experimental arrangements are very different. It is not proposed to deal with either of these subjects here, but a few remarks will be made on their relation to the X-ray diffraction method.

Electron diffraction patterns, both of gases and crystals, are strongly similar to the X-ray diffraction patterns of the same substances. Much valuable information on the geometry of gas molecules has been gained by Pauling, Brockway, and others. (See Brockway, 1936.) But for crystals, electron diffraction patterns have not been used much for structure determination; the absorption is very high, so that except for exceedingly small crystals the diffraction effects are confined to the surface layer; moreover, the scattering of electrons is very much more efficient than that of X-rays, and for this reason gives rise to more complex phenomena. (See Bragg, 1933; Thomson and Cochrane, 1939; Pinsker, 1953.) However, for very thin films of high polymers, the electron diffraction patterns are strikingly similar to the X-ray patterns (Storks, 1938), and have been used effectively for structure determination (Natta, Bassi, and Corradini, 1956). Electron diffraction methods are also used for the identification of crystalline substances in very thin films, and for the study of crystal orientation in similar circumstances.

Neutron diffraction patterns differ from X-ray patterns in other ways. The neutron scattering powers of atoms bear no simple relation to atomic number; consequently, for a crystal composed of two or more different types of atoms, the relative intensities of the reflections are very different from those in the X-ray patterns; moreover, although the phase change on scattering is $180°$ for most atoms, it is $0°$ for a few, notably $^1H$. These differences have been put to good use in the determination of the positions of light atoms such as hydrogen, which are not easy to locate accurately by X-ray methods, and in distinguishing atoms of similar atomic number which have very similar diffracting

G g

powers for X-rays but very different diffracting powers for neutrons. Another special application is to the study of the structure of crystals containing magnetic atoms—for instance, in the determination of the arrangement of spin moment orientations. There are special experimental difficulties, due to the fact that available neutron beams are relatively weak, and must be monochromatized by reflection at a crystal surface; specimens for examination by neutron diffraction, whether powders or single crystals, must be centimetres in diameter, whereas for X-rays a fraction of a millimetre is large enough. The subject of neutron diffraction has been well treated in a review article by Bacon and Lonsdale (1953). (See also Ringo, 1957.)

# APPENDIX 1

## IMMERSION LIQUIDS AND THEIR STANDARDIZATION

By mixing pure liquids any refractive index between those of the pure constituents can be attained. If two liquids having widely different refractive indices are chosen, a considerable range can be covered by mixing them in different proportions. Liquids for mixing in this way should preferably have similar vapour pressures at room temperature, so that evaporation does not lead to appreciable change of refractive index. Sets of liquids suitable for the identification of minerals have been suggested by several writers (Larsen and Berman, 1934.) These are mostly very oily substances, which for inorganic chemical work on certain substances have the disadvantage that they are intolerant of water: crystals which are slightly damp, when immersed in such oily liquids, do not make optical contant with the liquids, so that genuine Becke line effects are not seen. It is an advantage to use liquids which can dissolve a small proportion of water; the change of refractive index caused by the dissolution of a surface film of water is usually negligible. The following liquids have been found suitable:

| | |
|---|---|
| 1·373–1·396 | Ethyl acetate and amyl acetate. |
| 1·396–1·490 | Amyl acetate and xylene. |
| 1·490–1·559 | Para-cymene and monobromobenzene. |
| 1·559–1·598 | Monobromobenzene and bromoform. |
| 1·598–1·658 | Bromoform and α-bromonaphthalene. |
| 1·658–1·740 | α-Bromonaphthalene and methylene iodide. |
| 1·74–1·78 | Solutions of sulphur in methylene iodide. |
| 1·78–1·88 | Solutions of sulphur, $SnI_4$, $AsI_3$, $SbI_3$, and iodoform in methylene iodide. (See Larsen and Berman, 1934.) |
| 1·85–2·10 | Solutions of arsenic trisulphide in methylene iodide. (See Bryant, 1932.) |

The most important range for inorganic chemicals is between 1·40 and 1·70. But there are some substances, such as certain oxides and sulphides, whose indices lie well above this range, or even well above 2·0. Media which are liquid at room temperature and have such high refractive indices are not available, but certain mixtures of substances which solidify to glasses may be used. A little of the medium is melted on a microscope slide, the substance under examination is dusted into the melt, a cover-glass is pressed on, and the slide is then allowed to cool. Substances which have been used in this way are mixtures of piperine with arsenic and antimony tri-iodides (for indices 1·7–2·1), mixtures of sulphur and selenium (2·0–2·7)—for details, see Larsen and Berman (1934)—and mixtures of the halides of thallium (Barth, 1929).

Crystals of many organic substances are soluble in the liquids given in the above list, and for these it is necessary to use aqueous solutions. Cadmium borotungstate is a suitable substance, solutions of which have refractive indices up to 1·70; potassium mercuric iodide is another, for indices up to 1·72. Owing to evaporation of the water, the refractive index of a solution may change; therefore, if stock solutions are used, their refractive indices should be checked frequently; or, alternatively, the refractive index of a crystal should be matched by adjusting the composition of a solution, which is then immediately checked on the refractometer. To lessen the evaporation of water, solutions of potassium mercuric iodide in mixtures of glycerol and water may be used. (Bryant, 1932.)

Stock solutions may be kept in 30-c.c. bottles with ground stoppers carrying dropping rods. For refractive indices up to 1·7 it is best to keep a set of liquids having refractive indices differing by 0·005; from 1·7 to 1·9, intervals of 0·01 are sufficient. The refractive indices of liquids are best measured by means of the Abbé refractometer.

### List of crystals suitable for checking refractive indices of immersion liquids

| Refractive index | Substance | Refractive index | Substance |
|---|---|---|---|
| 1·326 | NaF | 1·585† | NaNO$_3$ |
| 1·352 | KF | 1·616 | NaBrO$_3$ |
| 1·392 | LiF | 1·642 | NH$_4$Cl |
| 1·410 | KCN | 1·658† | CaCO$_3$ (calcite) |
| 1·434 | CaF$_2$ (fluorspar) | 1·667 | KI |
| 1·456 | K$_2$SO$_4$.Al$_2$(SO$_4$)$_3$.24H$_2$O | 1·703 | NH$_4$I |
| 1·482 | K$_2$SO$_4$.Fe$_2$(SO$_4$)$_3$.24H$_2$O | 1·711 | NH$_4$Br |
| 1·490 | KCl | 1·755 | As$_4$O$_6$ |
| 1·515 | NaClO$_3$ | 1·768† | Al$_2$O$_3$ (corundum) |
| 1·525† | NH$_4$H$_2$PO$_4$ | 1·774 | NaI |
| 1·544 | NaCl | 1·784 | Pb(NO$_3$)$_2$ |
| 1·559 | KBr | 1·83 | CaO |
| 1·572 | Ba(NO$_3$)$_2$ | 1·870 | SrO |
| | | 1·955 | LiI |
| | | 1·97† | HgCl |
| | | 1·98 | BaO |
| | | 2·07 | AgCl |

† These are ω values of uniaxial substances. All the other substances are cubic.

If no refractometer is available, the refractive indices of a set of liquids made by mixing known volumes of two pure liquids can be obtained in the following way. The refractive indices of the two pure liquids can be found in Lange's *Handbook of Chemistry* (1956). Assuming that the relation between volume-concentration and refractive index is linear, a regular series of mixtures, 0·005 apart in refractive index, is made up. The actual refractive indices, which will differ slightly from the expected values, are found by examining a known crystalline substance in two adjacent liquids, one above and one below, and estimating the relative differences between the refractive indices of the liquid and the crystal by the Becke line effect; since the two liquids differ by 0·005, the actual refractive indices are then known. This procedure is repeated for other crystals, and a curve is then drawn for the whole range of mixtures, the refractive indices of the untested liquids being read off from the curve. Cubic and uniaxial crystals are most suitable for this purpose. A list of suitable substances is shown opposite.

# APPENDIX 2

## THE SPACINGS OF CRYSTAL PLANES

**Rectangular unit cells.** In Fig. 237, $OA$, $OB$, and $OC$ are orthogonal axes. Consider any set of crystal planes; one plane passes through the origin, the next $(XYZ)$ makes intercepts of $a/h$, $b/k$, and $c/l$ on the axes. Drop

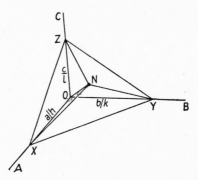

Fig. 237. The spacings of planes of orthogonal crystals.

a perpendicular $ON$ from the origin to the plane $XYZ$; we have to find the length of $ON$ $(= d)$ in terms of $a$, $b$, $c$, $h$, $k$, and $l$.

Now
$$d = \frac{a}{h}\cos\angle NOX = \frac{b}{k}\cos\angle NOY = \frac{c}{l}\cos\angle NOZ,$$
therefore
$$\cos\angle NOX = \frac{hd}{a}, \quad \cos\angle NOY = \frac{kd}{b}, \quad \text{and} \quad \cos\angle NOZ = \frac{ld}{c}.$$

The law of direction cosines states that
$$\cos^2\angle NOX + \cos^2\angle NOY + \cos^2\angle NOZ = 1,$$
therefore
$$\left(\frac{hd}{a}\right)^2 + \left(\frac{kd}{b}\right)^2 + \left(\frac{ld}{c}\right)^2 = 1,$$
whence
$$d^2 = 1 \Big/ \left(\frac{h^2}{a^2} + \frac{k^2}{b^2} + \frac{l^2}{c^2}\right)$$
and
$$d = 1 \Big/ \sqrt{\left(\frac{h^2}{a^2} + \frac{k^2}{b^2} + \frac{l^2}{c^2}\right)}.$$

For tetragonal crystals $(a = b)$ this expression reduces to
$$d = 1 \Big/ \sqrt{\left(\frac{h^2 + k^2}{a^2} + \frac{l^2}{c^2}\right)},$$

and for cubic crystals $(a = b = c)$ to

$$d = 1 \Big/ \sqrt{\left(\frac{h^2+k^2+l^2}{a^2}\right)} = a/\sqrt{(h^2+k^2+l^2)}.$$

**Hexagonal unit cells.** The $c$ axis is at right angles to $a$ and $b$ which are equal in length and are at 120° to each other. To use the above formula, it is required to find the intercepts made by any plane on orthogonal axes, two of which are chosen as $OC$ and $OB$ (Fig. 238), the third being $OQ$ in the plane $AOB$. The intercepts made by plane $hkl$ on $OB$ and $OC$ are $a/k$ and $c/l$ respectively. It is required to find the length $OW$ $(= r)$.

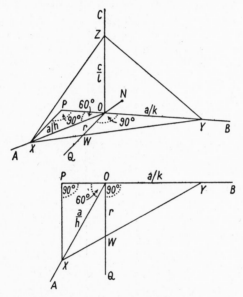

FIG. 238. The spacings of planes of hexagonal crystals. Above: general view of plane $XYZ$, indices $hkl$. Below: normal view of basal plane $(AOB)$ of this diagram.

Produce $YO$ to $P$, and join $XP$, where $\angle XPO = 90°$.
The right-angled triangles $YOW$ and $YPX$ are similar, hence

$$\frac{YO}{OW} = \frac{YP}{PX} = \frac{YO+OP}{PX}.$$

$$\therefore \quad \frac{a/k}{r} = \frac{a/k+(a/h)\cos 60°}{(a/h)\cos 30°}, \qquad \therefore \quad r = \frac{\dfrac{\sqrt{3}}{2}\dfrac{a}{hk}}{\dfrac{1}{k}+\dfrac{1}{2h}} = \frac{\sqrt{3}a}{2h+k}.$$

From the formula for direction cosines,

$$\left(\frac{d}{r}\right)^2 + \left(\frac{kd}{a}\right)^2 + \left(\frac{ld}{c}\right)^2 = 1,$$

therefore

$$d = 1 \bigg/ \sqrt{\left(\frac{1}{r^2} + \frac{k^2}{a^2} + \frac{l^2}{c^2}\right)} = 1 \bigg/ \sqrt{\left(\frac{(2h+k)^2}{3a^2} + \frac{k^2}{a^2} + \frac{l^2}{c^2}\right)}$$

$$= 1 \bigg/ \sqrt{\left(\frac{4h^2 + 4hk + 4k^2}{3a^2} + \frac{l^2}{c^2}\right)}$$

$$= 1 \bigg/ \sqrt{\left(\frac{4}{3} \frac{(h^2 + hk + k^2)}{a^2} + \frac{l^2}{c^2}\right)}.$$

For rhombohedral unit cells, it is best to transform indices to hexagonal indices, and to use the above formula for the spacings of planes.

For monoclinic and triclinic cells, the formulae for the spacings are very unwieldy. Graphical methods based on the conception of the reciprocal lattice are recommended (Chapter VI).

# APPENDIX 3

## CHARTS FOR INDEXING DIFFRACTION PATTERNS

**Tetragonal (including cubic) crystals.** Bjurstrom (1931) showed that if, on a rectangular framework $AMNC$ (Fig. 239 $a$), values of $h^2+k^2$ are

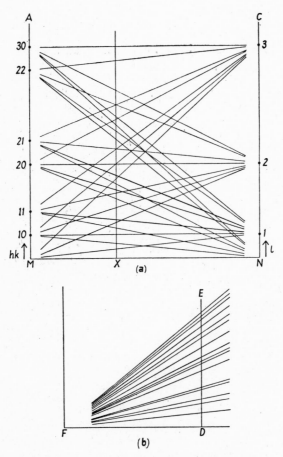

FIG. 239. Bjurstrom's chart. Tetragonal crystals.

plotted along $MA$ and values of $l^2$ along $NC$, and all the points on $MA$ are joined to all the points on $NC$ by straight lines, as in the diagram, then for a crystal whose axial ratio corresponds to position $X$ along $MN$, the ordinates of all the lines represent the relative values of $1/d^2$ for all values of $hkl$. The reason for this can be seen by writing the equation for the plane-placings in a tetragonal crystal thus:

$$\frac{1}{d^2} = \frac{h^2+k^2}{a^2}+\frac{l^2}{c^2} = \frac{h^2+k^2}{a^2}-\frac{l^2}{a^2}+\frac{l^2}{a^2}+\frac{l^2}{c^2} = (h^2+k^2-l^2)\frac{1}{a^2}+l^2\left(\frac{1}{a^2}+\frac{1}{c^2}\right).$$

If we make $(1/a^2+1/c^2)$ a constant (this actually means using different units of length for every different crystal), the above expression is, for given values of $h$, $k$, and $l$, of the form $y = K_1 x + K_2$, that is to say, the graph of $y$ against

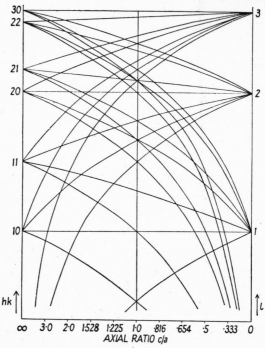

FIG. 240. Logarithmic form of Bjurstrom's chart. Tetragonal crystals.

$x$ is a straight line. In Bjurstrom's chart the constant $(1/a^2+1/c^2)$ is the length $MN$ of the base of the chart:

$$\frac{MX}{MN} = \frac{1/c^2}{1/a^2+1/c^2}, \qquad \frac{NX}{NM} = \frac{1/a^2}{1/a^2+1/c^2}, \quad \text{and} \quad \frac{XN}{XM} = \frac{c^2}{a^2}.$$

The value of $1/d^2$ for each arc on a powder photograph is calculated from the Bragg equation. Since, however, we do not know on what scale to plot these values, it is necessary to represent them with a wide range of scales; that is, to plot them, on transparent paper, along a line $DE$ as in Fig. 239 b, and join them all to a point $F$ on the perpendicular to $DE$. This 'fan' diagram is moved about on the chart, keeping $FD$ coincident with $MN$, until 'fan' lines cross chart lines consistently along a line parallel to $AM$ and $NC$; along this line the indices for each 'fan' line are given by the chart line crossing it. The axial ratio $c/a$ is given by $\sqrt{(XN/MX)}$, but it is better to calculate it from suitable pairs of spacings. In practice, this method is found to be very unsatisfactory; the two sets of lines are so confusing that it is difficult to find the match position. The difficulty can be removed by making the chart logarithmic along the direction $MA$. Thus, values of $\log(h^2+k^2)$ are plotted along $MA$, and values of $\log l^2$ along $NC$, and all these points are joined by logarithmic curves, giving a chart of the type shown in Fig. 240, which can be used in the same way as the Hull and Davey charts (Chapter VI). The construction of such a chart is naturally not quite so simple as that of the straight-line Bjurstrom chart, but, inasmuch as no calculations are required, it is very much simpler than that of a chart of the Hull and Davey type. As an example of the method of construction, consider the plotting of the 213 curve, which joins $\log 5$ (i.e. $\log(h^2+k^2)$) on one side to $\log 9$ (i.e. $\log l^2$) on the other. Nine other points, at intervals of $MN/10$, are enough for the construction of the curve. Since on the straight-line Bjurstrom chart the ordinates at these points would be 5·4, 5·8, 6·2, 6·6, 7·0, 7·4, 7·8, 8·2, and 8·6, we simply plot on the new type of chart $\log 5·4$, $\log 5·8$, and so on; this can be done directly on large-scale logarithmic graph paper; or on ordinary graph paper by reading off the values in a table of logarithms.

This type of chart has one undesirable feature; at the two sides (that is, for very small or very large values of $c/a$) some of the lines are nearly parallel to $MA$ and $NC$, and appear very crowded. It is better, therefore, to spread out the diagram in these regions by plotting against $\log c/a$ instead of against $\dfrac{1/c^2}{1/a^2+1/c^2}$. Plotting the curves is no more difficult than in the previous type of chart, if it is remembered that (to use the same example as before) $\log 5·4$, $\log 5·8$, and so on are plotted against values of $\log c/a$ given by $\dfrac{1/c^2}{1/a^2+1/c^2} = 1/10, 2/10$, and so on; straight lines at these values of $\log c/a$ are first drawn temporarily, and used as a scaffold for the plotting of the $\log 1/d^2$ curves. This, the best type of chart, is illustrated in principle in Fig. 72.

**Hexagonal and trigonal crystals.** A chart for these crystals can be constructed by plotting values of $\log(h^2+hk+k^2)$ along $MA$ and values of $\log l^2$ along $NC$, and joining them by logarithmic curves. The axial ratio $c/a$ can be obtained from the relation $\dfrac{MX}{MN} = \dfrac{1/c^2}{4/3a^2+1/c^2}$, but again it is better to calculate it from suitable pairs of spacings. A better form of chart is obtained by plotting against $\log c/a$; no calculations are needed if it is remembered that in the original Bjurstrom chart the graph of $1/d^2$ against $MX$ (defined above) is a straight line. Thus, for the 213 curve, $h^2+hk+k^2 = 7$, while $l^2 = 9$; on the Bjurstrom chart, the straight line for these indices joins the point at 7 along $MA$ with that at 9 along $NC$; for the logarithmic chart we plot $\log 7·2$, $\log 7·4$, $\log 7·6$, etc., at points along the $\log c/a$ axis where $\dfrac{1/c^2}{4/3a^2+1/c^2} = 1/10, 2/10, 3/10$, etc.

For rhombohedral crystals, which can always be referred to a large hexagonal cell containing more than one pattern-unit, this same chart may be used, the indices $h_H$ $k_H$ $l_H$ relating to the hexagonal cell being subsequently transformed to those relating to the rhombohedral cell—$h_R$ $k_R$ $l_R$—by the relations

$$3h_R = h_H - k_H + l_H,$$
$$3k_R = h_H + 2k_H + l_H,$$
$$3l_R = -2h_H - k_H + l_H.$$

Many reflections which would be given by a simple hexagonal crystal are necessarily absent for a rhombohedral crystal. Only those reflections $h_H$ $k_H$ $l_H$ for which $h_H - k_H + l_H$, $h_H + 2k_H + l_H$, and $-2h_H - k_H + l_H$ are all divisible by three occur when the true unit cell is rhombohedral. In view of this, a special chart from which the unwanted hexagonal lines are omitted may be constructed in the way already described.

**Zero layer on single-crystal rotation photographs.** The spacings $d$ of the $h0l$ planes of an orthorhombic crystal are given by $d = 1\bigg/\sqrt{\left(\dfrac{h^2}{a^2} + \dfrac{l^2}{c^2}\right)}$.

The spacings for all axial ratios $c/a$ can be represented on a chart which is similar to those already described but has values of $\log h^2$ on one side and $\log l^2$ on the other. The tetragonal chart could be used, curves other than $h0l$ being ignored; but the many unwanted curves are confusing, and it is therefore better to construct a special chart from which the unwanted lines are omitted. Since this chart is symmetrical about the centre line, it is necessary to construct only half of it. The use of this chart is illustrated in Fig. 78.

This chart may be used for single-crystal photographs of orthorhombic crystals rotated about any axis, or for tetragonal crystals rotated about $a$ or $c$ (in the latter case the cell base is square and the axial ratio 1). It may also be used for hexagonal crystals rotated about $a$ or $c$; in the latter case true hexagonal indices will not be given, but indices in reference to an orthorhombic cell having an axial ratio of $\sqrt{3}$. The orthorhombic indices $h_O$ $k_O$ are converted to hexagonal indices $h_H$ $k_H$ by the relations

$$h_H = \frac{h_O - k_O}{2}; \qquad k_H = k_O.$$

It may also be used for monoclinic crystals rotated about $a$ or $c$, since the projection of a monoclinic cell along either of these axes is rectangular.

All these charts should be drawn on a large scale; it is found that if a difference of $0.1$ in $\log 1/d^2$ is made 2 inches, all reflections including those at Bragg angles near $90°$ can be indexed, except in the case of very large unit cells. In using the charts, values of $-2 \log d$ are plotted on a strip which is moved about on the chart in the manner described in Chapter VI.

Copies of these charts on a large scale can be obtained from the Institute of Physics, 47 Belgrave Square, London.

# APPENDIX 4

## PROOF THAT RECIPROCAL POINTS FORM A LATTICE

CONSIDER a crystal with its $c$ axis ($OZ$ in Fig. 241) vertical. All reciprocal points corresponding with the vertical $hk0$ (real) lattice planes lie in the horizontal plane $x^*y^*$.

Consider now any set of real lattice planes having indices $hkl$. If one plane passes through the origin $O$, the next plane $RST$ makes an intercept of $c/l$ on the $OZ$ axis. Draw a perpendicular to this plane, meeting it at $N$ ($ON = d$, the spacing of the planes), and produce $ON$ to $P$, where $OP = \lambda/d$. $P$ is the reciprocal lattice point corresponding to the set of real lattice planes $hkl$.

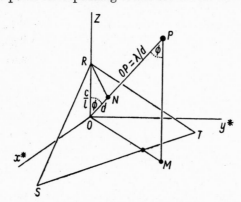

FIG. 241. Proof that reciprocal points form a lattice.

Now since the angle $RNO$ is $90°$, $ON\ (= d) = OR \cos \phi = (c/l)\cos \phi$;

$$\therefore \quad \cos \phi = dl/c.$$

Drop a perpendicular $PM$ on to the horizontal plane $x^*y^*$. We have to find the length of $PM$, the height of the reciprocal lattice point above the horizontal plane.

$PM = OP \cos \angle MPO$. Since $PM$ is parallel to $OZ$, $\angle MPO = \angle NOR = \phi$. Thus $PM = OP \cos \phi$. But $OP = \lambda/d$;

$$\therefore \quad PM = (\lambda/d)\cos \phi$$
$$= (\lambda/d)(dl/c) = \lambda l/c, \text{ which is constant for a given value of } l.$$

Thus all points having the same $l$ index lie at the same distance from the horizontal plane $x^*y^*$, and thus lie on a plane parallel to the plane $x^*y^*$; moreover, the distance of each such plane of points from the plane $x^*y^*$ is proportional to $l$. Therefore successive sets of points for the successive values of the index $l$ lie on a set of equidistant planes, spaced $\lambda/c$ apart.

Similarly, it can be shown that the reciprocal $hkl$ points lie on planes perpendicular to the $a$ axis (spaced $\lambda/a$ apart), and on planes perpendicular to the $b$ axis (spaced $\lambda/b$ apart). Thus the whole assemblage of points forms a lattice.

# APPENDIX 5

## TRANSFORMATION OF INDICES WHEN CHANGING CRYSTALLOGRAPHIC AXES

IT is often necessary, or at any rate advantageous, to change from one set of crystallographic axes to another. This involves changes in the indices of crystal planes and X-ray reflections, and it is necessary to establish the transformation formulae. Such problems are quite simple if it is remembered that the indices of a set of parallel crystal planes represent the numbers of planes crossed in travelling from one lattice point to the next, in each axial direction (Figs. 9 and 10, pp. 25 and 26), and that, correspondingly, the indices of X-ray reflections represent the differences of phase between waves diffracted by neighbouring lattice points in each axial direction (p. 141); successive planes in the first definition represent one wavelength phase-

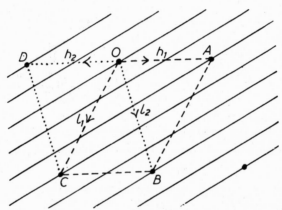

FIG. 242. Relations between indices of alternative cells. 203 for cell $OABC$ is $\bar{2}05$ for cell $ODCB$. $h_2 = -h_1$; $l_2 = h_1 + l_1$.

difference in the second definition. The principle in finding the formulae for index transformation is to travel from one lattice point to another by two different routes, first by way of the old axes and then by way of the new, counting planes (phase-differences) along each axial direction on the way; the totals, which must be equal, are then equated. It is simply a question of visualizing the two paths correctly by means of a diagram.

Consider first a two-dimensional example. It is desired to change axes $OA$ ($= a_1$) and $OC$ ($= c_1$) (Fig. 242) to $OD$ ($= a_2$) and $OB$ ($= c_2$); this would be necessary, for instance, in changing the description of a monoclinic crystal from $P2_1/n$ to $P2_1/c$. A set of planes indexed 203 for the first setting is illustrated ($h_1 = 2$, $l_1 = 3$): waves from $A$ are two wavelengths in front of waves from $O$, while waves from $C$ are three wavelengths in front of waves from $O$. Now turn to the second setting; for $h_2$, we must travel in the negative direction of $a$, crossing two planes per lattice point; in fact, waves from $D$ are two wavelengths *behind* waves from $O$; hence the new index $h_2$ is $\bar{2}$, and in general $h_2 = -h_1$. To obtain $l_2$, note that waves from $B$ are five wavelengths in front of waves from $O$ (five planes are crossed in going directly from $O$ to $B$), so that $l_2 = +5$; to derive this in terms of the old indices, take a journey from $O$ to $B$ by way of $OA$ and $AB$; two planes are crossed in going from $O$ to $A$ $(= +h_1)$, and three planes in going from $A$ to $B$ $(= +l_1)$; evidently $l_2 = h_1 + l_1$. Thus 203 for the first setting is $\bar{2}05$ for the second; the formulae for index transformation are $h_2 = -h_1$ and $l_2 = h_1 + l_1$.

For a three-dimensional example, consider the transformation of rhombohedral to hexagonal indices, which seems at first sight one of the most awkward problems of index transformation. The arrangement of lattice points in a rhombohedral crystal, seen along the threefold axis, is shown in Fig. 243 $a$. If the height of one lattice point above the next along the threefold axis is 1, there are other lattice points at heights $\frac{1}{3}$ and $\frac{2}{3}$ in the positions shown. The corresponding hexagonal cell and its relation to the rhombohedral cell is shown in Fig. 243 $b$. (Fig. 243 $a$ is a projection of this, looking straight down $OO'$.)

Suppose we have rhombohedral indices $h_R k_R l_R$ and wish to transform them to hexagonal indices $h_H k_H i_H l_H$. The $c$ axis of the hexagonal cell is $OO'$ (through the middle of the rhombohedron). Pass from $O$ to $O'$, first of all directly; the phase-difference between waves from $O'$ and those from $O$ is $l_H$. Now go from $O$ to $O'$ by way of rhombohedral axial directions—for instance, via $OD$, $DK$, and $KO'$. Waves from $D$ are $h_R$ wavelengths ahead of those from $O$, those from $K$ are $k_R$ wavelengths ahead of those from $D$, and those from $O'$ are $l_R$ wavelengths ahead of those from $K$. The total is $h_R + k_R + l_R$. Thus $l_H = h_R + k_R + l_R$.

For $h_H$, pass from $O$ to $A$, first of all directly: the phase-difference is $h_H$. Now go by way of $OD$ and $DA$. The phase-difference from $O$ to $D$ is $+h_R$; next, note that $D$ lies on the straight line $ADKB'$, and the journey from $D$ to $A$ is along the negative $b_R$ direction. Thus the phase-differences encountered in this journey are $h_R - k_R$. Thus $h_H = h_R - k_R$. Similarly, it is found that $k_H = k_R - l_R$ and $i_H = l_R - h_R$.

To check this by a specific example, consider the 431 rhombohedral reflection. To find the $l_H$ index in terms of rhombohedral indices, we must travel from $O$ to $O'$ by way of rhombohedral axes, that is, via $OD$, $DK$, and $KO'$; it is evident from Fig. 243 $b$ that from $O$ to $D$ we cross four planes $(h_R)$, from $D$ to $K$ three planes $(k_R)$, and from $K$ to $O'$ one plane $(l_R)$, so that in all eight planes are crossed $(h_R + k_R + l_R)$. For $h_H$, we have to go from $O$ to $A$; to get there by way of rhombohedral axial directions, the simplest course is via $OD$ and $DA$; from $O$ to $D$ four planes are crossed, while from $D$ to $A$ three planes are crossed, but these have to be subtracted because we are returning towards the original plane through $O$ (or, in other words, travelling along the negative $b_R$ direction); thus the number of planes crossed in going direct from $O$ to $A$ is $4-3 = 1$ plane $(h_R-k_R)$. The other relations may be checked in a similar way. The set of planes which has rhombohedral indices 431 has hexagonal indices $12\overline{3}8$.

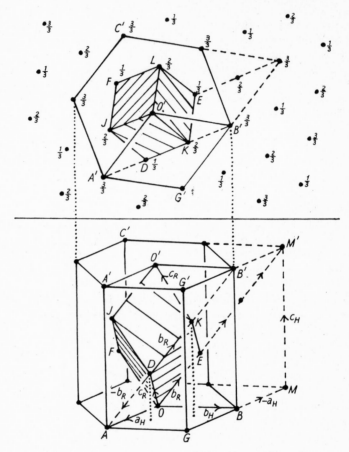

Fig. 243. Relations between rhombohedral and hexagonal indices. *ODKEO'LFJ*, rhombohedral cell; *OAGBO'A'G'B'*, hexagonal cell.

Consider now the reverse transformation, from hexagonal to rhombohedral indices. It is necessary to go from the origin to some point, first by way of rhombohedral axes and then by way of hexagonal axes. Such a point is $M'$; if we go there directly, the distance is $3b_R$, and thus the phase-difference between waves from $O$ and $M'$ is $3k_R$. Now go from $O$ to $M'$ by way of hexagonal axes—for instance, via $B$ and $M$. From $O$ to $B$ the phase-difference is $k_H$, from $B$ to $M$ it is $-h_H$ (since we are going in the negative $a_H$ direction), and from $M$ to $M'$ it is $l_H$; the total is $k_H-h_H+l_H$. Thus $3k_R = k_H-h_H+l_H$.

Similarly, it is found that $3h_R = h_H - i_H + l_H = 2h_H + k_H + l_H$, and

$$3l_R = i_H - k_H + l_H = -h_H - 2k_H + l_H.$$

To sum up, the relations between rhombohedral indices $h_R \, k_R \, l_R$ and hexagonal indices $h_H \, k_H \, i_H \, l_H$ are:

$$h_H = h_R - k_R \qquad\qquad 3h_R = h_H - i_H + l_H = 2h_H + k_H + l_H$$
$$k_H = k_R - l_R \qquad\qquad 3k_R = k_H - h_H + l_H = -h_H + k_H + l_H$$
$$i_H = l_R - h_R \qquad\qquad 3l_R = i_H - k_H + l_H = -h_H - 2k_H + l_H$$
$$l_H = h_R + k_R + l_R.$$

These relations are for the particular mutual orientation of the two cells chosen in Fig. 243 (the point $D$ having hexagonal coordinates $\frac{2}{3}\,\frac{1}{3}\,\frac{1}{3}$). For the alternative orientation in which the rhombohedral cell is rotated 60° so that point $D$ now has hexagonal coordinates $\frac{1}{3}\,\frac{2}{3}\,\frac{1}{3}$, the relations are:

$$h_H = l_R - k_R \qquad\qquad 3h_R = k_H - i_H + l_H = h_H + 2k_H + l_H$$
$$k_H = h_R - l_R \qquad\qquad 3k_R = i_H - h_H + l_H = -2h_H - k_H + l_H$$
$$i_H = k_R - h_R \qquad\qquad 3l_R = h_H - k_H + l_H$$
$$l_H = h_R + k_R + l_R.$$

All other problems of index transformation can be dealt with in the same way, provided that the geometrical relations between the two alternative cells are clearly visualized.

H h

# APPENDIX 6

## POINT-GROUPS

| Hermann–Mauguin† | Schoenflies |
|---|---|
| *Triclinic* | |
| $1$ | $C_1$ |
| $\bar{1}$ | $C_i, S_2$ |
| *Monoclinic* | |
| $2$ | $C_2$ |
| $m$ | $C_s, C_{1h}$ |
| $2/m$ | $C_{2h}$ |
| *Orthorhombic* | |
| $222$ | $D_2, V$ |
| $mm2\ (mm)$ | $C_{2v}$ |
| $mmm$ | $D_{2h}, V_h$ |
| *Tetragonal* | |
| $4$ | $C_4$ |
| $\bar{4}$ | $S_4$ |
| $4/m$ | $C_{4h}$ |
| $422\ (42)$ | $D_4$ |
| $4mm$ | $C_{4v}$ |
| $\bar{4}2m$ | $D_{2d}, V_d$ |
| $4/mmm$ | $D_{4h}$ |
| *Trigonal and Hexagonal* | |
| $3$ | $C_3$ |
| $\bar{3}$ | $C_{3i}, S_6$ |
| $32$ | $D_3$ |
| $3m$ | $C_{3v}$ |
| $\bar{3}m$ | $D_{3d}$ |
| $6$ | $C_6$ |
| $\bar{6}$ | $C_{3h}$ |
| $6/m$ | $C_{6h}$ |
| $622\ (62)$ | $D_6$ |
| $6mm$ | $C_{6v}$ |
| $\bar{6}m2\ (\bar{6}m)$ | $D_{3h}$ |
| $6/mmm$ | $D_{6h}$ |
| *Cubic* | |
| $23$ | $T$ |
| $m3$ | $T_h$ |
| $432\ (43)$ | $O$ |
| $\bar{4}3m$ | $T_d$ |
| $m3m$ | $O_h$ |

† The symbol given in *International Tables* (1952) is given first. Where it differs from that given in *Internationale Tabellen* (1935) (used in the 1st edition of this book), the latter follows in brackets.

# APPENDIX 7

## PLANE-GROUPS
## ('TWO-DIMENSIONAL SPACE-GROUPS')

| System | International Tables (1952) | Bragg and Lipson (1936)[†] |
|---|---|---|
| Oblique | $p1$ | $P1$ |
|  | $p2$ | $P2$ |
| Rectangular | $pm$ | $Pm$ |
|  | $pg$ | $Pb$ |
|  | $cm$ | $Cm$ |
|  | $pmm$ | $Pmm$ |
|  | $pmg$ | $Pbm$ |
|  | $pgg$ | $Pba$ |
|  | $cmm$ | $Cmm$ |
| Square | $p4$ | $P4$ |
|  | $p4m$ | $P4m$ |
|  | $p4g$ | $P4b$ |
| Hexagonal | $p3$ | $C3$ |
|  | $p3m1$ | $C3m$ |
|  | $p31m$ | $H6m$ |
|  | $p6$ | $C6$ |
|  | $p6m$ | $C6m$ |

† Commonly used from 1936 onwards, and in the 1st edition of this book.

## SPACE-GROUPS

| Point-group | Hermann–Mauguin symbols† | | Schoenflies symbols |
|---|---|---|---|
| *Triclinic* | | | |
| 1 | $P1$ | | $C_1^1$ |
| $\bar{1}$ | $P\bar{1}$ | | $C_i^1, S_2^1$ |
| *Monoclinic‡* | *1st setting (z-axis unique)* | *2nd setting (y-axis unique)* | |
| 2 | $P2$ | $P2$ | $C_2^1$ |
| | $P2_1$ | $P2_1$ | $C_2^2$ |
| | $B2. A2, I2$ | $C2. A2, I2$ | $C_2^3$ |
| *m* | $Pm$ | $Pm$ | $C_s^1$ |
| | $Pb. Pa, Pn$ | $Pc. Pa, Pn$ | $C_s^2$ |
| | $Bm. Am, Im$ | $Cm. Am, Im$ | $C_s^3$ |
| | $Bb. Aa, Ia$ | $Cc. Aa, Ia$ | $C_s^4$ |
| $2/m$ | $P2/m$ | $P2/m$ | $C_{2h}^1$ |
| | $P2_1/m$ | $P2_1/m$ | $C_{2h}^2$ |
| | $B2/m. A2/m, I2/m$ | $C2/m. A2/m, I2/m$ | $C_{2h}^3$ |
| | $P2/b. P2/a, P2/n$ | $P2/c. P2/a, P2/n$ | $C_{2h}^4$ |
| | $P2_1/b. P2_1/a, P2_1/n$ | $P2_1/c. P2_1/a, P2_1/n$ | $C_{2h}^5$ |
| | $B2/b. A2/a, I2/a$ | $C2/c. A2/a, I2/a$ | $C_{2h}^6$ |
| *Orthorhombic* | *Normal setting* | *Other settings* | |
| 222 | $P222$ | | $D_2^1, V^1$ |
| | $P222_1$ | $P2_122, P22_12$ | $D_2^2, V^2$ |
| | $P2_12_12$ | $P22_12_1, P2_122_1$ | $D_2^3, V^3$ |
| | $P2_12_12_1$ | | $D_2^4, V^4$ |
| | $C222_1$ | $A2_122, B22_12$ | $D_2^5, V^5$ |
| | $C222$ | $A222, B222$ | $D_2^6, V^6$ |
| | $F222$ | | $D_2^7, V^7$ |
| | $I222$ | | $D_2^8, V^8$ |
| | $I2_12_12_1$ | | $D_2^9, V^9$ |

† The Hermann–Mauguin symbols given first are those given in *International Tables* (1952). When these differ from the symbols given in *Internationale Tabellen* (1935) (used in the 1st edition of this book), the latter are given in brackets.

‡ The normal symbol is given first; then follow the symbols for alternative unit cells of the same size.

| Point-group | Hermann–Mauguin symbols | | Schoenflies symbols |
|---|---|---|---|
| | Normal | Other settings | |
| $mm2$ | $Pmm2\ (Pmm)$ | $P2mm,\ Pm2m$ | $C_{2v}^{1}$ |
| | $Pmc2_1\ (Pmc)$ | $P2_1ma,\ Pb2_1m,\ Pm2_1b,\ Pcm2_1,\ P2_1am$ | $C_{2v}^{2}$ |
| | $Pcc2\ (Pcc)$ | $P2aa,\ Pb2b,\ P2aa$ | $C_{2v}^{3}$ |
| | $Pma2\ (Pma)$ | $P2mb,\ Pc2m,\ Pm2a,\ Pbm2,\ P2cm$ | $C_{2v}^{4}$ |
| | $Pca2_1\ (Pca)$ | $P2_1ab,\ Pc2_1b,\ Pb2_1a,\ Pbc2_1,\ P2_1ca$ | $C_{2v}^{5}$ |
| | $Pnc2\ (Pnc)$ | $P2na,\ Pb2n,\ Pn2b,\ Pcn2,\ P2an$ | $C_{2v}^{6}$ |
| | $Pmn2_1\ (Pmn)$ | $P2_1mn,\ Pn2_1m,\ Pm2_1n,\ Pnm2_1,\ P2_1nm$ | $C_{2v}^{7}$ |
| | $Pba2\ (Pba)$ | $P2cb,\ Pc2a,\ Pba2,\ P2cb$ | $C_{2v}^{8}$ |
| | $Pna2_1\ (Pna)$ | $P2_1nb,\ Pc2_1n,\ Pn2_1a,\ Pbn2_1,\ P2_1cn$ | $C_{2v}^{9}$ |
| | $Pnn2\ (Pnn)$ | $P2nn,\ Pn2n$ | $C_{2v}^{10}$ |
| | $Cmm2\ (Cmm)$ | $A2mm,\ Bm2m$ | $C_{2v}^{11}$ |
| | $Cmc2_1\ (Cmc)$ | $A2_1ma,\ Bb2_1m,\ Bm2_1b,\ Ccm2_1,\ A2_1am$ | $C_{2v}^{12}$ |
| | $Ccc2\ (Ccc)$ | $A2aa,\ Bb2b$ | $C_{2v}^{13}$ |
| | $Amm2\ (Amm)$ | $B2mm,\ Cm2m,\ Am2m,\ Bmm2,\ C2mm$ | $C_{2v}^{14}$ |
| | $Abm2\ (Abm)$ | $B2cm,\ Cm2a,\ Ac2m,\ Bma2,\ C2mb$ | $C_{2v}^{15}$ |
| | $Ama2\ (Ama)$ | $B2mb,\ Cc2m,\ Am2a,\ Bbm2,\ C2cm$ | $C_{2v}^{16}$ |
| | $Aba2\ (Aba)$ | $B2cb,\ Cc2a,\ Ac2a,\ Bba2,\ C2cb$ | $C_{2v}^{17}$ |
| | $Fmm2\ (Fmm)$ | $F2mm,\ Fm2m$ | $C_{2v}^{18}$ |
| | $Fdd2\ (Fdd)$ | $F2dd,\ Fd2d$ | $C_{2v}^{19}$ |
| | $Imm2\ (Imm)$ | $I2mm,\ Im2m$ | $C_{2v}^{20}$ |
| | $Iba2\ (Iba)$ | $I2cb,\ Ic2a$ | $C_{2v}^{21}$ |
| | $Ima2\ (Ima)$ | $I2mb,\ Ic2m,\ Im2a,\ Ibm2,\ I2cm$ | $C_{2v}^{22}$ |
| $mmm$ | $Pmmm$ | | $D_{2h}^{1},\ V_h^{1}$ |
| | $Pnnn$ | | $D_{2h}^{2},\ V_h^{2}$ |
| | $Pccm$ | $Pmma,\ Pbmb$ | $D_{2h}^{3},\ V_h^{3}$ |
| | $Pban$ | $Pncb,\ Pcna$ | $D_{2h}^{4},\ V_h^{4}$ |
| | $Pmma$ | $Pbmm,\ Pmcm,\ Pmam,\ Pmmb,\ Pcmm$ | $D_{2h}^{5},\ V_h^{5}$ |
| | $Pnna$ | $Pbnn,\ Pncn,\ Pnan,\ Pnnb,\ Pcnn$ | $D_{2h}^{6},\ V_h^{6}$ |
| | $Pmna$ | $Pbmn,\ Pncm,\ Pman,\ Pnmb,\ Pcnm$ | $D_{2h}^{7},\ V_h^{7}$ |
| | $Pcca$ | $Pbaa,\ Pbcb,\ Pbab,\ Pccb$ | $D_{2h}^{8},\ V_h^{8}$ |
| | $Pbam$ | $Pmcb,\ Pcma$ | $D_{2h}^{9},\ V_h^{9}$ |
| | $Pccn$ | $Pnaa,\ Pbnb$ | $D_{2h}^{10},\ V_h^{10}$ |
| | $Pbcm$ | $Pmca,\ Pbma,\ Pcmb,\ Pcam,\ Pmab$ | $D_{2h}^{11},\ V_h^{11}$ |
| | $Pnnm$ | $Pmnn,\ Pnmn$ | $D_{2h}^{12},\ V_h^{12}$ |
| | $Pmmn$ | $Pnmm,\ Pmnm$ | $D_{2h}^{13},\ V_h^{13}$ |
| | $Pbcn$ | $Pnca,\ Pbna,\ Pcnb,\ Pcan,\ Pnab$ | $D_{2h}^{14},\ V_h^{14}$ |
| | $Pbca$ | $Pcab$ | $D_{2h}^{15},\ V_h^{15}$ |
| | $Pnma$ | $Pbnm,\ Pmcn,\ Pnam,\ Pmnb,\ Pcmn$ | $D_{2h}^{16},\ V_h^{16}$ |
| | $Cmcm$ | $Amma,\ Bbmm,\ Bmmb,\ Ccmm,\ Amam$ | $D_{2h}^{17},\ V_h^{17}$ |
| | $Cmca$ | $Abma,\ Bbcm,\ Bmab,\ Ccmb,\ Acam$ | $D_{2h}^{18},\ V_h^{18}$ |
| | $Cmmm$ | $Ammm,\ Bmmm$ | $D_{2h}^{19},\ V_h^{19}$ |
| | $Cccm$ | $Amaa,\ Bbmb$ | $D_{2h}^{20},\ V_h^{20}$ |
| | $Cmma$ | $Abmm,\ Bmcm,\ Bmam,\ Cmmb,\ Acmm$ | $D_{2h}^{21},\ V_h^{21}$ |
| | $Ccca$ | $Abaa,\ Bbcb,\ Bbab,\ Cccb,\ Acaa$ | $D_{2h}^{22},\ V_h^{22}$ |
| | $Fmmm$ | | $D_{2h}^{23},\ V_h^{23}$ |
| | $Fddd$ | | $D_{2h}^{24},\ V_h^{24}$ |
| | $Immm$ | | $D_{2h}^{25},\ V_h^{25}$ |

| Point-group | Hermann–Mauguin symbols | | Schoenflies symbols |
|---|---|---|---|
| | Normal | Other settings | |
| mmm (cont.) | $Ibam$ | $Imcb, Icma$ | $D_{2h}^{26}, V_h^{26}$ |
| | $Ibca$ | $Icab$ | $D_{2h}^{27}, V_h^{27}$ |
| | $Imma$ | $Ibmm, Imcm, Imam, Immb, Icmm$ | $D_{2h}^{28}, V_h^{28}$ |

| Point-group | Normal | Larger cell | Schoenflies symbols |
|---|---|---|---|
| **Tetragonal** | | | |
| 4 | $P4$ | $C4$ | $C_4^1$ |
| | $P4_1$ | $C4_1$ | $C_4^2$ |
| | $P4_2$ | $C4_2$ | $C_4^3$ |
| | $P4_3$ | $C4_3$ | $C_4^4$ |
| | $I4$ | $F4$ | $C_4^5$ |
| | $I4_1$ | $F4_1$ | $C_4^6$ |
| $\bar{4}$ | $P\bar{4}$ | $C\bar{4}$ | $S_4^1$ |
| | $I\bar{4}$ | $F\bar{4}$ | $S_4^2$ |
| 4/m | $P4/m$ | $C4/m$ | $C_{4h}^1$ |
| | $P4_2/m$ | $C4_2/m$ | $C_{4h}^2$ |
| | $P4/n$ | $C4/n$ | $C_{4h}^3$ |
| | $P4_2/n$ | $C4_2/n$ | $C_{4h}^4$ |
| | $I4/m$ | $F4/m$ | $C_{4h}^5$ |
| | $I4_1/a$ | $F4_1/a$ | $C_{4h}^6$ |
| 422 | $P422$ | $C422$ | $D_4^1$ |
| | $P42_12$ | $C422_1$ | $D_4^2$ |
| | $P4_122$ | $C4_122$ | $D_4^3$ |
| | $P4_12_12$ | $C4_122_1$ | $D_4^4$ |
| | $P4_222$ | $C4_222$ | $D_4^5$ |
| | $P4_22_12$ | $C4_222_1$ | $D_4^6$ |
| | $P4_322$ | $C4_322$ | $D_4^7$ |
| | $P4_32_12$ | $C4_322_1$ | $D_4^8$ |
| | $I422$ | $F422$ | $D_4^9$ |
| | $I4_122$ | $F4_122$ | $D_4^{10}$ |
| 4mm | $P4mm$ | $C4mm$ | $C_{4v}^1$ |
| | $P4bm$ | $C4mb$ | $C_{4v}^2$ |
| | $P4_2cm\ (P4cm)$ | $C4_2mc\ (C4mc)$ | $C_{4v}^3$ |
| | $P4_2nm\ (P4nm)$ | $C4_2mn\ (C4mn)$ | $C_{4v}^4$ |
| | $P4cc$ | $C4cc$ | $C_{4v}^5$ |
| | $P4nc$ | $C4cn$ | $C_{4v}^6$ |
| | $P4_2mc\ (P4mc)$ | $C4_2cm\ (C4cm)$ | $C_{4v}^7$ |
| | $P4_2bc\ (P4bc)$ | $C4_2cb\ (C4cb)$ | $C_{4v}^8$ |
| | $I4mm$ | $F4mm$ | $C_{4v}^9$ |
| | $I4cm$ | $F4mc$ | $C_{4v}^{10}$ |
| | $I4_1md\ (I4md)$ | $F4_1dm\ (I4dm)$ | $C_{4v}^{11}$ |
| | $I4_1cd\ (I4cd)$ | $F4_1dc\ (I4dc)$ | $C_{4v}^{12}$ |
| $\bar{4}2m$ | $P\bar{4}2m$ | $C\bar{4}2m$ | $D_{2d}^1, V_d^1$ |
| | $P\bar{4}2c$ | $C\bar{4}c2$ | $D_{2d}^2, V_d^2$ |
| | $P\bar{4}2_1m$ | $C\bar{4}m2_1$ | $D_{2d}^3, V_d^3$ |
| | $P\bar{4}2_1c$ | $C\bar{4}c2_1$ | $D_{2d}^4, V_d^4$ |

| Point-group | Hermann–Mauguin symbols | | Schoenflies symbols |
|---|---|---|---|
| | Normal | Larger cell | |
| $\bar{4}2m$ (cont.) | $P\bar{4}m2$ | $C\bar{4}2m$ | $D_{2d}^5, V_d^5$ |
| | $P\bar{4}c2$ | $C\bar{4}2c$ | $D_{2d}^6, V_d^6$ |
| | $P\bar{4}b2$ | $C\bar{4}2b$ | $D_{2d}^7, V_d^7$ |
| | $P\bar{4}n2$ | $C\bar{4}2n$ | $D_{2d}^8, V_d^8$ |
| | $I\bar{4}m2$ | $F\bar{4}2m$ | $D_{2d}^9, V_d^9$ |
| | $I\bar{4}c2$ | $F\bar{4}2c$ | $D_{2d}^{10}, V_d^{10}$ |
| | $I\bar{4}2m$ | $F\bar{4}m2$ | $D_{2d}^{11}, V_d^{11}$ |
| | $I\bar{4}2d$ | $F\bar{4}d2$ | $D_{2d}^{12}, V_d^{12}$ |
| $4/mmm$ | $P4/mmm$ | $C4/mmm$ | $D_{4h}^1$ |
| | $P4/mcc$ | $C4/mcc$ | $D_{4h}^2$ |
| | $P4/nbm$ | $C4/amb$ | $D_{4h}^3$ |
| | $P4/nnc$ | $C4/acn$ | $D_{4h}^4$ |
| | $P4/mbm$ | $C4/mmb$ | $D_{4h}^5$ |
| | $P4/mnc$ | $C4/mcn$ | $D_{4h}^6$ |
| | $P4/nmm$ | $C4/amm$ | $D_{4h}^7$ |
| | $P4/ncc$ | $C4/acc$ | $D_{4h}^8$ |
| | $P4_2/mmc\ (P4/mmc)$ | $C4_2/mcm\ (C4mcm)$ | $D_{4h}^9$ |
| | $P4_2/mcm\ (P4/mcm)$ | $C4_2/mmc\ (C4/mmc)$ | $D_{4h}^{10}$ |
| | $P4_2/nbc\ (P4/nbc)$ | $C4_2/acb$ | $D_{4h}^{11}$ |
| | $P4_2/nnm\ (P4/nnm)$ | $C4_2/amn$ | $D_{4h}^{12}$ |
| | $P4_2/mbc\ (P4/mbc)$ | $C4_2/mcb\ (C4/mcb)$ | $D_{4h}^{13}$ |
| | $P4_2/mnm\ (P4/mnm)$ | $C4_2/mmn\ (C4/mmn)$ | $D_{4h}^{14}$ |
| | $P4_2/nmc\ (P4/nmc)$ | $C4_2/acm$ | $D_{4h}^{15}$ |
| | $P4_2/ncm\ (P4/ncm)$ | $C4_2/amc$ | $D_{4h}^{16}$ |
| | $I4/mmm$ | $F4/mmm$ | $D_{4h}^{17}$ |
| | $I4/mcm$ | $F4/mmc$ | $D_{4h}^{18}$ |
| | $I4_1/amd\ (I4/amd)$ | $F4_1/ddm$ | $D_{4h}^{19}$ |
| | $I4_1/acd\ (I4/acd)$ | $F4_1/ddc$ | $D_{4h}^{20}$ |
| Trigonal and Hexagonal | | | |
| 3 | $P3\ (C3)$ | $(H3)$ | $C_3^1$ |
| | $P3_1\ (C3_1)$ | $(H3_1)$ | $C_3^2$ |
| | $P3_2\ (C3_2)$ | $(H3_2)$ | $C_3^3$ |
| | $R3$ | | $C_3^4$ |
| $\bar{3}$ | $P\bar{3}\ (C\bar{3})$ | $(H\bar{3})$ | $C_{3i}^1, S_6^1$ |
| | $R\bar{3}$ | | $C_{3i}^2, S_6^2$ |
| 32 | $P312\ (C312)$ | $(H32)$ | $D_3^1$ |
| | $P321\ (C32)$ | $(H312)$ | $D_3^2$ |
| | $P3_112\ (C3_112)$ | $(H3_12)$ | $D_3^3$ |
| | $P3_121\ (C3_12)$ | $(H3_112)$ | $D_3^4$ |
| | $P3_212\ (C3_212)$ | $(H3_22)$ | $D_3^5$ |
| | $P3_221\ (C3_22)$ | $(H3_212)$ | $D_3^6$ |
| | $R32$ | | $D_3^7$ |
| $3m$ | $P3m1\ (C3m)$ | $(H31m)$ | $C_{3v}^1$ |
| | $P31m\ (C31m)$ | $(H3m)$ | $C_{3v}^2$ |

| Point-group | Hermann–Mauguin symbols | | Schoenflies symbols |
|---|---|---|---|
| | Normal | Larger cell | |
| 3m (cont.) | $P3c1$ ($C3c$) | ($H31c$) | $C_{3v}^3$ |
| | $P31c$ ($C31c$) | ($H3c$) | $C_{3v}^4$ |
| | $R3m$ | | $C_{3v}^5$ |
| | $R3c$ | | $C_{3v}^6$ |
| $\bar{3}m$ | $P\bar{3}1m$ ($C\bar{3}1m$) | ($H\bar{3}m$) | $D_{3d}^1$ |
| | $P\bar{3}1c$ ($C\bar{3}1c$) | ($H\bar{3}c$) | $D_{3d}^2$ |
| | $P\bar{3}m1$ ($C\bar{3}m$) | ($H\bar{3}1m$) | $D_{3d}^3$ |
| | $P\bar{3}c1$ ($C\bar{3}c$) | ($H\bar{3}1c$) | $D_{3d}^4$ |
| | $R\bar{3}m$ | | $D_{3d}^5$ |
| | $R\bar{3}c$ | | $D_{3d}^6$ |
| 6 | $P6$ ($C6$) | ($H6$) | $C_6^1$ |
| | $P6_1$ ($C6_1$) | ($H6_1$) | $C_6^2$ |
| | $P6_5$ ($C6_5$) | ($H6_5$) | $C_6^3$ |
| | $P6_2$ ($C6_2$) | ($H6_2$) | $C_6^4$ |
| | $P6_4$ ($C6_4$) | ($H6_4$) | $C_6^5$ |
| | $P6_3$ ($C6_3$) | ($H6_3$) | $C_6^6$ |
| $\bar{6}$ | $P\bar{6}$ ($C\bar{6}$) | ($H\bar{6}$) | $C_{3h}^1$ |
| 6/m | $P6/m$ ($C6/m$) | ($H6/m$) | $C_{6h}^1$ |
| | $P6_3/m$ ($C6_3/m$) | ($H6_3/m$) | $C_{6h}^2$ |
| 622 | $P622$ ($C62$) | ($H62$) | $D_6^1$ |
| | $P6_122$ ($C6_12$) | ($H6_12$) | $D_6^2$ |
| | $P6_522$ ($C6_52$) | ($H6_52$) | $D_6^3$ |
| | $P6_222$ ($C6_22$) | ($H6_22$) | $D_6^4$ |
| | $P6_422$ ($C6_42$) | ($H6_42$) | $D_6^5$ |
| | $P6_322$ ($C6_32$) | ($H6_32$) | $D_6^6$ |
| 6mm | $P6mm$ ($C6mm$) | ($H6mm$) | $C_{6v}^1$ |
| | $P6cc$ ($C6cc$) | ($H6cc$) | $C_{6v}^2$ |
| | $P6_3cm$ ($C6_3cm$) | ($H6_3mc$) | $C_{6v}^3$ |
| | $P6_3mc$ ($C6_3mc$) | ($H6_3cm$) | $C_{6v}^4$ |
| $\bar{6}m2$ | $P\bar{6}m2$ ($C\bar{6}m$) | ($H\bar{6}2m$) | $D_{3h}^1$ |
| | $P\bar{6}c2$ ($C\bar{6}c$) | ($H\bar{6}2c$) | $D_{3h}^2$ |
| | $P\bar{6}2m$ ($C\bar{6}2m$) | ($H\bar{6}m$) | $D_{3h}^3$ |
| | $P\bar{6}2c$ ($C\bar{6}2c$) | ($H\bar{6}c$) | $D_{3h}^4$ |
| 6/mmm | $P6/mmm$ ($C6/mmm$) | ($H6/mmm$) | $D_{6h}^1$ |
| | $P6/mcc$ ($C6/mcc$) | ($H6/mcc$) | $D_{6h}^2$ |
| | $P6_3/mcm$ ($C6/mcm$) | ($H6/mmc$) | $D_{6h}^3$ |
| | $P6_3/mmc$ ($C6/mmc$) | ($H6/mcm$) | $D_{6h}^4$ |

| Point-group | Hermann–Mauguin symbol | Schoenflies symbol |
|---|---|---|
| Cubic 23 | $P23$ | $T^1$ |
| | $F23$ | $T^2$ |
| | $I23$ | $T^3$ |
| | $P2_13$ | $T^4$ |
| | $I2_13$ | $T^5$ |
| $m3$ | $Pm3$ | $T_h^1$ |
| | $Pn3$ | $T_h^2$ |
| | $Fm3$ | $T_h^3$ |
| | $Fd3$ | $T_h^4$ |
| | $Im3$ | $T_h^5$ |
| | $Pa3$ | $T_h^6$ |
| | $Ia3$ | $T_h^7$ |
| $432$ | $P432$ $(P43)$ | $O^1$ |
| | $P4_232$ $(P4_23)$ | $O^2$ |
| | $F432$ $(F43)$ | $O^3$ |
| | $F4_132$ $(F4_13)$ | $O^4$ |
| | $I432$ $(I43)$ | $O^5$ |
| | $P4_332$ $(P4_33)$ | $O^6$ |
| | $P4_132$ $(P4_13)$ | $O^7$ |
| | $I4_132$ $(I4_13)$ | $O^8$ |
| $\bar{4}3m$ | $P\bar{4}3m$ | $T_d^1$ |
| | $F\bar{4}3m$ | $T_d^2$ |
| | $I\bar{4}3m$ | $T_d^3$ |
| | $P\bar{4}3n$ | $T_d^4$ |
| | $F\bar{4}3c$ | $T_d^5$ |
| | $I\bar{4}3d$ | $T_d^6$ |
| $m3m$ | $Pm3m$ | $O_h^1$ |
| | $Pn3n$ | $O_h^2$ |
| | $Pm3n$ | $O_h^3$ |
| | $Pn3m$ | $O_h^4$ |
| | $Fm3m$ | $O_h^5$ |
| | $Fm3c$ | $O_h^6$ |
| | $Fd3m$ | $O_h^7$ |
| | $Fd3c$ | $O_h^8$ |
| | $Im3m$ | $O_h^9$ |
| | $Ia3d$ | $O_h^{10}$ |

# REFERENCES AND NAME INDEX

Abbott, N. B., and Elliott, A., 1955. *Proc. Roy. Soc.* **A234,** 247 . . 317
Abrahams, S. C. *See* Grenville-Wells, H. J.
Aka, E. Z. *See* Straumanis, M. E.
Albrecht, G., 1939. *Rev. Sci. Instrum.* **10,** 221 . . . . . 222
Alexander, L. E. *See* Klug, H. P.
Allison, S. K., 1932. *Phys. Rev.* **41,** 1 . . . . . . . 223
Ambrose, E. J., Elliott, A., and Temple, R. B., 1949. *Proc. Roy. Soc.*
   A199 . . . . . . . . . . . 183, 317
American Society for Testing Materials (ASTM) . . . . . 132
Amoros, J. L. *See* Torroja, J. M.
Anderegg, J. W. *See* Beeman, W. W.
Anderson, N. G., and Dawson, I. M., 1953. *Proc. Roy. Soc.* **A218,** 255 . 58
Andrew, E. R., and Eades, R. G., 1953. *Proc. Roy. Soc.* **A218,** 537 . 322
Arlman, J. J., 1949. *Appl. Sci. Res.* **A1,** 347 . . . . . 448
Arndt, U. W., 1955. *See* Peiser, Rooksby, and Wilson, 1955, chapter 7 . 119
Arnett, L. L., Meibohm, E. P. H., and Smith, A. F., 1950. *J. Pol. Sci.*
   **5,** 737 445
Arteméev, D. N., 1910. *Z. Krist.* **48,** 417 . . . . . . 21
Astbury, W. T., and Preston, R. D., 1934. *Nature* **133,** 460 . . . 112
—— and Sisson, W. A., 1935. *Proc. Roy. Soc.* **A150,** 533 . . . 191
—— and Street, A., 1931. *Phil. Trans.* **A230,** 75 . . . . . 188
—— and Woods, H. J., 1933. *Phil. Trans.* **A232,** 333 . . . 188
—— and Yardley, K., 1924. *Phil. Trans.* **A224,** 221 . . . 258, 273

Babinet . . . . . . . . . . . . 85
Bacon, G. E., and Lonsdale, K., 1953. *Rep. Progr. Phys.* **16,** 1 . . 450
Baker, G. D. *See* Parsons, J.
Bamford, C. H., Brown, L., Elliott, A., Hanby, W. E., and Trotter, I. F.,
   1952. *Nature* **169,** 357 . . . . . . . . . 425
—— Elliott, A., and Hanby, W. E., 1956. *Synthetic Polypeptides.* New
   York: Academic Press . . . . . . . . . 318
Banerjee, S. *See* Krishnan, K. S.
Barker, T. V., 1922. *Graphical and Tabular Methods in Crystallography.*
   London: Murby . . . . . . . . . . 30
—— 1930. *Systematic Crystallography.* London: Murby. . . 11, 55, 95
Barlow, W. . . . . . . . . . . . 267
Barth, T. F. W., 1929. *Amer. Min.* **14,** 358 . . . . . 451
—— and Posnjak, E., 1932. *Z. Krist.* **82,** 325 . . . . . 364
—— *See also* Donnay, J. D. H.; Posnjak, E.
Bassi, I. *See* Natta, G.
Beach, J. Y. *See* Brockway, L. O.
Bear, R. S. *See* Bolduan, O. E. A.
Becke, F. . . . . . . . . . 66, 67, 68, 72
Beeman, W. W., Kaesberg, P., Anderegg, J. W., and Webb, M. B., 1957.
   'Size of Particles and Lattice Defects', p. 321 in *Encyclopedia of
   Physics,* ed. Flügge. Vol. 32. Springer . . . . . 445
Beevers, C. A., 1952. *See* Pepinsky, 1952, p. 18 . . . . 419
—— and Hughes, W., 1941. *Proc. Roy. Soc.* **A177,** 251. . . 403
—— and Lipson, H., 1934. *Proc. Roy. Soc.* **A146,** 570 . . . 381

Beevers, C. A., and Lipson, H., 1936. *Proc. Phys. Soc.* **48**, 772 . . 394

—— —— 1938. *Proc. Phys. Soc.* **50**, 275 . . . . . 290

—— and Robertson, J. H., 1950. *Acta Cryst.* **3**, 164 . . . . 419

—— and Schwartz, C. M., 1935. *Z. Krist.* **91**, 157 . . . . 411

—— *See also* Robertson, J. H.

Beher, W. T. *See* Parsons, J.

Belbéoch, B., and Guinier, A., 1958. *C. R. Acad. Sci., Paris* **247**, 310 . 445

Benedict, T. S., 1955. *Acta Cryst.* **8**, 747 . . . . . . 210

Berek . . . . . . . . . . . . 85

Berman, H. *See* Larsen, E. S.

Bernal, J. D., 1926. *Proc. Roy. Soc.* **A113**, 117 . 159, 160, 161, 162, 173, 175

—— 1932. *Nature* **129**, 277 . . . . . . . . 274

—— and Carlisle, C. H., 1947. *J. Sci. Instrum.* **24**, 107 . . . . 79

—— and Crowfoot, D. M., 1933*a*. *Trans. Faraday Soc.* **29**, 1032 . . 316

—— —— 1933*b*. *Nature* **131**, 911 . . . . . . . 196

—— —— 1933*c*. *Ann. Rep. Chem. Soc.* **30**, 411 . . . . . 7

—— —— 1934*a*. *Nature* **133**, 794 . . . . . . . 149

—— —— 1934*b*. *Nature* **134**, 809 . . . . . . . 200

—— —— 1935. *J. Chem. Soc.* 93 . . . . . . . 268

—— Crowfoot, D. M., and Fankuchen, I., 1940. *Phil. Trans.* **A239**, 135 . 196

—— and Wooster, W. A., 1932. *Ann. Rep. Chem. Soc.* **28**, 262 . . 362

Bertrand . . . . . . . . . . . 80, 99

Bhagavantam, S., 1929. *Proc. Roy. Soc.* **A124**, 545 . . . 309

—— 1930. *Proc. Roy Soc.* **A126**, 143· . . . . . . 310

Biggs, B. S. *See* White, A. H.

Bijvoet, J. M., 1949. *Kon. Nederl. Akad. Wet.* B**52**, 313. . . . 400

—— 1952. *See* Pepinsky, 1952, p. 84 . . . . . . 406

—— *See also* Bokhoven, C.; Peerdeman, A. F.

Bishop, W. S. *See* White, A. H.

Bjurstrom, T., 1931. *Z. Phys.* **69**, 346 . . . . . . 457

Blow, D. M., 1958. *Proc. Roy. Soc.* **A247**, 302 . . . . 407

Boas, W. *See* Schmid, E.

Bodo, G. *See* Kendrew, J. C.

Bogue, L. H. *See* Brownmiller, L. T.

Bohlin, H., 1920. *Ann. Physik* **61**, 421 . . . . . 129

Bokhoven, C., Schoone, J. C., and Bijvoet, J. M., 1951. *Acta Cryst.* **4**,
275 . . . . . . . . . 384, 386, 406

Bolduan, O. E. A., and Bear, R. S., 1949. *J. Appl. Phys.* **20**, 983 . . 443

(van) Bommel, A. J. *See* Peerdeman, A. F.

Bond, W. L., 1955. *Acta Cryst.* **8**, 741 . . . . . . 210

Booth, A. D., 1945. *Trans. Faraday Soc.* **41**, 434 . . . . 396

—— 1947. *J. Appl. Phys.* **18**, 664 . . . . . . 294

—— 1948. *Fourier Technique in Organic Structure Analysis.* Cambridge
University Press . . . . . . . . . 294

Bosanquet, C. H. *See* Bragg, W. L.

Bouman, J., and de Jong, W. F., 1938. *Physica* **5**, 817 . . . 219

—— *See also* de Jong, W. F.

Bouwers, A., 1923. *Z. Phys.* **14**, 374 . . . . . . 208

Boyes-Watson, J., Davidson, E., and Perutz, M. F., 1947. *Proc. Roy.
Soc.* **A191**, 83 . . . . . . . . . 428

Bozorth, R. M., 1923. *J. Amer. Chem. Soc.* **45**, 2128 . . . 281

Bradley, A. J., 1935. *Proc. Phys. Soc.* **47**, 879 . . . 221, 222

Bradley, A. J., Bragg, W. L., and Sykes, C., 1940. *J. Iron Steel Inst.*
  **141,** 63 . . . . . . . . . . 134
—— and Jay, A. H., 1932. *Proc. Phys. Soc.* **44,** 563 . . . 128, 194
—— Lipson, H., and Petch, N. J., 1941. *J. Sci. Instrum.* **18,** 216 . 117, 133
—— and Rodgers, J. W., 1934. *Proc. Roy. Soc.* A144, 340 . . . 300
Bragg, W. H., 1914. *Phil. Mag.* **27,** 881 . . . . . 207
—— 1921. *Proc. Phys. Soc.* **33,** 304 . . . . . . 327
—— and Bragg, W. L., 1913. *Proc. Roy. Soc.* A88, 428 . . . 206
Bragg, W. L. . . . . . . . . . . 124, 155
—— 1913. *Proc. Camb. Phil. Soc.* **17,** 43 . . . . . 121
—— 1914. *Proc. Roy. Soc.* A89, 468 . . . . . . 241
—— 1924*a*. *Proc. Roy. Soc.* A105, 16 . . . . . 60, 241, 340
—— 1924*b*. *Proc. Roy. Soc.* A105, 370; A106, 346 . . . 306, 340
—— 1929*a*. *Proc. Roy. Soc.* A123, 537 . . . . . 373
—— 1929*b*. *Z. Krist.* **70,** 475, 489 . . . . . 381, 382, 397
—— 1930. *Z. Krist.* **74,** 237 . . . . . . . 302
—— 1933. *The Crystalline State.* London: Bell . . 260, 397, 438, 449
—— 1937. *Atomic Structure of Minerals.* Cornell University Press . . 270
—— 1939. *Nature* **143,** 678 . . . . . . 6, 398
—— 1942. *Nature* **149,** 470 . . . . . . . 6
—— 1944. *Nature* **154,** 69 . . . . . . . 294
—— Howells, E. R., and Perutz, M. F., 1952. *Acta Cryst.* **5,** 136 . . 428
—— James, R. W., and Bosanquet, C. H., 1921. *Phil. Mag.* **42,** 1 . 218, 224
—— —— —— 1922. *Phil. Mag.* **44,** 433 . . . . . 224
—— and Lipson, H., 1936. *Z. Krist.* **95,** 323 . . . 287, 467
—— —— 1943. *J. Sci. Instrum.* **20,** 110 . . . . . 443
—— and Perutz, M. F., 1954. *Proc. Roy. Soc.* A225, 315 . . . 428
—— and West, J., 1926. *Proc. Roy. Soc.* A111, 691 . . . 278
—— —— 1929. *Z. Krist.* **69,** 118 . . . . 221, 222, 224
—— —— 1930. *Phil. Mag.* **10,** 823 . . . . . . 398
—— *See also* Bradley, A. J.; Bragg, W. H.; Warren, B. E.
Brandenberger, E. *See* Waldmann, H.
Brandes, H., and Volmer, 1931. *Z. phys. Chem.* A155, 466 . . 23
Branson, H. R. *See* Pauling, L.
Bravais, A. . . . . . . . . . . . 238
Bray, E. E., and Gingrich, N. S., 1943. *J. Chem. Phys.* **11,** 351 . . 448
Brentano, J. C. M., 1925. *Proc. Phys. Soc.* **37,** 184 . . . . 117
—— 1937. *Proc. Phys. Soc.* **49,** 61 . . . . . . 117
Brill, R., 1950. *Acta Cryst.* **3,** 333 . . . . . . 327
Brindley, G. W., 1945. *Phil. Mag.* **36,** 347 . . . . . 135
—— 1955. *See* Peiser, Rooksby, and Wilson, 1955, chapter 4 . . 112, 129
—— and Ridley, P., 1938. *Proc. Phys. Soc.* **50,** 737 . . . 221
—— —— 1939. *Proc. Phys. Soc.* **51,** 73 . . . . . 221
—— *See also* James, R. W.
Brockway, L. O., 1936. *Rev. Mod. Phys.* **8,** 231 . . . . 449
—— Beach, J. Y., and Pauling, L., 1935. *J. Amer. Chem. Soc.* **57,** 2693 . 241
—— *See also* Pauling, L.
Brown, C. J., and Corbridge, D. E. C., 1948. *Nature* **162,** 72 . . 316
—— —— 1954. *Acta Cryst.* **7,** 11 . . . . . . 316
—— and Cox, E. G., 1940. *J. Chem. Soc.* 1 . . . . . 418
—— *See also* Daubeny, R. de P.
Brown, L., and Trotter, I. F., 1956. *Trans. Faraday Soc.* **52,** 537 . . 426

Brown, L. *See also* Bamford, C. H.

Brownmiller, L. T., and Bogue, L. H., 1930. *Amer. J. Sci.* **20**, 241 . 133

Bryant, W. M. D., 1932. *J. Amer. Chem. Soc.* **54**, 3758 . . 105, 451, 452

—— 1941. *J. Amer. Chem. Soc.* **63**, 511 . . . . . 88, 105

—— 1943. *J. Amer. Chem. Soc.* **65**, 96 . . . . . 87, 105

Buckley, H. E., 1930. *Z. Krist.* **75**, 15. . . . . . . 38

Buerger, M. J., 1934. *Z. Krist.* **88**, 356 . . . . . . 181

—— 1935. *Z. Krist.* **91**, 255 . . . . . . . . 181

—— 1936. *Z. Krist.* **94**, 87. . . . . . . . . 179

—— 1937. *Z. Krist.* **97**, 433 . . . . . . . . 194

—— 1940. *Proc. Nat. Acad. Sci., Wash.* **26**, 637 . . . . 219

—— 1942. *X-ray Crystallography.* New York: Wiley . . 149, 181, 191

—— 1944. *The Photography of the Reciprocal Lattice.* ASXRED Monograph
No. 1. Cambridge, Mass.: The American Society for X-ray and Electron
Diffraction . . . . . . . . . . . 182

—— 1946. *J. Appl. Phys.* **17**, 579 . . . . . . . 418

—— 1951. *Acta Cryst.* **4**, 531 . . . . . . . . 398

Bunn, C. W., 1933. *Proc. Roy. Soc.* **A141**, 567 . . . 22, 62

—— 1939. *Trans. Faraday Soc.* **35**, 482 . . . . 202, 283, 396

—— 1941. *J. Sci. Instrum.* **18**, 70 . . . . . 135, 197, 365

—— 1942a. *Proc. Roy. Soc.* **A180**, 40 . . . . . 285, 290, 355

—— 1942b. *Proc. Roy. Soc.* **A180**, 67 . . . . . . 302, 355

—— 1942c. *Proc. Roy. Soc.* **A180**, 82 . . . . . . 200, 355

—— 1947. *J. Chem. Soc.* 297 . . . . . . . . 426

—— 1948. *Nature* **161**, 929 . . . . . . . . 366

—— 1953. Chapter 10 of *Fibres from Synthetic Polymers*, ed. R. Hill.
Elsevier . . . . . . . . . . . 63, 94

—— 1955. *See* Peiser, Rooksby, and Wilson, 1955, chapter 14 . . 147

—— 1957. Chapter 7 of *Polythene*, ed. Renfrew and Morgan. London:
Iliffe . . . . . . . . . . . 106, 200

—— Clark, L. M., and Clifford, I. L., 1935. *Proc. Roy. Soc.* **A151**, 141. 134, 309

—— and Daubeny, R. de P., 1954. *Trans. Faraday Soc.* **50**, 1173 . . 313

—— and Emmett, H., 1949. *Disc. Faraday Soc.* **5**, 119 . . . 19

—— and Garner, E. V., 1942. *J. Chem. Soc.* 654 . . . . 203, 356

—— —— 1947. *Proc. Roy. Soc.* **A189**, 39 . . . . 315, 442

—— and Holmes, D. R., 1958. *Disc. Faraday Soc.* **25**, 95 . . 303, 426

—— Peiser, H. S., and Turner-Jones, A., 1944. *J. Sci. Instrum.* **21**, 10 . 177

—— *See also* Crowfoot, D. M.; Daubeny, R. de P.; Holmes, D. R.; Turner-
Jones, A.

Burbank, R. D., 1952. *Rev. Sci. Instrum.* **23**, 321 . . . . 219


Cameron, G. H., and Patterson, A. L., 1937. *Symposium on Radiography
and X-ray Diffraction.* Amer. Soc. for Testing Materials . . 438

Carlisle, C. H., and Crowfoot, D. M., 1945. *Proc. Roy. Soc.* **A184**, 64 . 384, 400

—— *See also* Bernal, J. D.

Carpenter, G. B., 1952. *Acta Cryst.* **5**, 132 . . . . . 337

—— 1955. *Acta Cryst.* **8**, 852 . . . . . . . . 337

Cauchois, Y., and Hulubei, H., 1947. *Longueurs d'onde des émissions X et
des discontinuités d'absorption X.* Paris: Hermann et Cie . . 131

Cesari, M. *See* Natta, G.

Chakravorty, N. C. *See* Krishnan, K. S.

Cruickshank, D. W. J., 1957. *Acta Cryst.* **10**, 504　　.　　.　　.　　. 394
—— *See also* Cox, E. G.

Dana, E. S., 1932. *Textbook of Mineralogy*, 4th edn. revised by W. E. Ford.
　　New York: Wiley　.　　.　　.　　.　　.　　.　　.　　.　　. 60
Daniel, V., and Lipson, H., 1943. *Proc. Roy. Soc.* **A181**, 368　.　　.　　. 442
Darwin, C. G., 1922. *Phil. Mag.* **43**, 808　.　　.　　.　　.　　.　　. 218
Dauben, C. H., and Templeton, D. H., 1955. *Acta Cryst.* **8**, 841　　263, 380, 408
Daubeny, R. de P., Bunn, C. W., and Brown, C. J., 1954. *Proc. Roy. Soc.*
　　**A226**, 531　.　　.　　.　　.　　.　　.　　.　　.　　.　　. 193
—— *See also* Bunn, C. W.
Davey, W. P., 1934. *A Study of Crystal Structure and its Applications.*
　　New York: McGraw-Hill　.　　.　　.　　.　　.　　.　　.　　. 261
—— *See also* Hull, A. W.
Davidson, E. *See* Boyes-Watson, J.
Dawson, I. M., and Vand, V., 1951. *Proc. Roy. Soc.* **A206**, 555　.　　. 19
—— *See also* Anderson, N. G.
Dawton, R. H. V. M., 1937. *J. Sci. Instrum.* **14**, 198　.　　.　　.　　. 208
—— *See also* Robertson, J. M.
Debye, P. .　　.　　.　　.　　.　　.　　.　　.　　.　　.　　.　　. 449
—— 1915. *Ann. Physik* **46**, 809　.　　.　　.　　.　　.　　.　　. 446
—— and Scherrer, P., 1916. *Phys. Z.* **17**, 277　.　　.　　.　　.　　. 113
de la Mare, P. B. D. *See* Klyne, W.
Delaunay, B., 1933. *Z. Krist.* **84**, 132　.　　.　　.　　.　　.　　. 147, 185
Deming, W. E. *See* Hendricks, S. B.
Denbigh, K. G., 1940. *Trans. Faraday Soc.* **36**, 936　.　　.　　. 312, 313
Desch, C. H. *See* Lea, F. M.
Dickinson, R. G., 1923. *J. Amer. Chem. Soc.* **45**, 958　.　　.　　.　　. 245
—— and Goodhue, E. A., 1921. *J. Amer. Chem. Soc.* **43**, 2045　.　　. 242
—— and Raymond, A. L., 1923. *J. Amer. Chem. Soc.* **45**, 22　.　　.　　. 306
Dinsmore, R. P. *See* Gehman, S. D.
Dintzis, H. M. *See* Kendrew, J. C.
Donnay, J. D. H., 1939. *Amer. Min.* **24**, 184　.　　.　　.　　.　　. 306
—— 1943. *Amer. Min.* **28**, 313　.　　.　　.　　.　　.　　.　　. 48, 50
—— and Harker, D., 1937. *Amer. Min.* **22**, 446　.　　.　　.　　. 306
—— and Nowacki, W., 1954. *Crystal Data.* The Geological Society of
　　America　.　　.　　.　　.　　.　　.　　.　　.　　.　　.　　. 195
—— *See also* Morse, H. W.
Douglas, A. S. *See* Cochran, W.
Dragsdorf, R. D., 1956. *J. Appl. Phys.* **27**, 620　.　　.　　.　　.　　. 444
Dubinina, V. N. *See* Mikheev, V. I.
Dunitz, J. D., 1949. *Acta Cryst.* **2**, 1　.　　.　　.　　.　　.　　.　　. 285
Dürer, A. .　　.　　.　　.　　.　　.　　.　　.　　.　　.　　.　　. 11

Edmunds, I. G., Lipson, H., and Steeple, H. 1955. *See* Peiser, Rooksby,
　　and Wilson, 1955, chapter 15　.　　.　　.　　.　　.　　.　　. 194
Edwards, D. A., 1931. *Z. Krist.* **80**, 154　.　　.　　.　　.　　.　　. 150
Edwards, O. S., and Lipson, H. 1941. *J. Sci. Instrum.* **7**, 389 .　　.　　. 112
—— —— 1942. *Proc. Roy. Soc.* **A180**, 268　.　　.　　.　　.　　. 442
Elliott, A., and Malcolm, B. R., 1959. *Proc. Roy. Soc.* **A249**, 30　.　　. 427
—— *See also* Abbott, N. B.; Ambrose, E. J.; Bamford, C. H.
Emmett, H. *See* Bunn, C. W.

Erickson, C. L. *See* Fuller, C. S.

Eucken, A., 1939. *Z. Elektrochem.* **45**, 126 . . . . . . 322

Evans, R. C., 1939. *Crystal Chemistry.* Cambridge University Press . 203

—— Hirsch, P. B., and Kellar, J. N., 1948. *Acta Cryst.* **1**, 124 . . 112

—— and Peiser, H. S., 1942. *Proc. Phys. Soc.* **54**, 457 . . . . 294

Ewald, P. P., 1921. *Z. Krist.* **56**, 129 . . . . . . 154


Fankuchen, I., 1937. *Nature* **139**, 193 . . . . . . 112

—— *See also* Bernal, J. D.

Farquhar, M. C. M., and Lipson, H., 1946. *Proc. Phys. Soc.* **58**, 200 . 194

Faust, R. C., 1955. *Proc. Phys. Soc.* B**68**, 1081 . . . . . 66

Fedorov, E. S. . . . . . . . . . . 11, 267

Field, J. E. *See* Gehman, S. D.

Firth, E. M. *See* James, R. W.

Fischer . . . . . . . . . . 400, 401

Fournet, G., 1957. 'Structure of Liquids and Amorphous Substances', p. 238 in *Encyclopedia of Physics*, ed. S. Flügge. Vol. 32. Springer . . . . . . . . . . 448

—— *See also* Guinier, A.

Fowler, R. H., 1935. *Proc. Roy. Soc.* A**151**, 1 . . . . . 322

Fowweather, F., and Hargreaves, A., 1950. *Acta Cryst.* **3**, 81 . . . 265

Franklin, R. E., and Gosling, R. G., 1953. *Nature* **171**, 737 . . . 425

Fresnel . . . . . . . . . . . 66

Freudenberg, K., 1932–4. *Stereochemie.* Leipzig: Deuticke . . . 302

Frevel, L. K., 1935. *Rev. Sci. Instrum.* **6**, 214 . . . . . 117

—— *See also* Hanawalt, J. D.

Friedel, G., 1913. *C. R. Acad. Sci., Paris* **157**, 1533 . . . . 259

—— and Friedel, E. (and others), 1931. *Z. Krist.* **79**, 1 . . . . 362

Frosch, C. J. *See* Fuller, C. S.

Fuller, C. S., 1940. *Chem. Rev.* **26**, 143 . . . 188, 202, 283

—— and Erickson, C. L., 1937. *J. Amer. Chem. Soc.* **59**, 344 . . . 190

—— and Frosch, C. J., 1939*a*. *J. Phys. Chem.* **43**, 323 . . . . 190

—— —— 1939*b*. *J. Amer. Chem. Soc.* **61**, 2575 . . . . . 190

—— Frosch, C. J., and Pape, N. R., 1940. *J. Amer. Chem. Soc.* **62**, 1905 188, 283

Furnas, T. C., and Harker, D., 1955. *J. Appl. Phys.* **26**, 449 . . . 210


Garner, E. V. *See* Bunn, C. W.

Gaubert, P., 1906. *C. R. Acad. Sci., Paris* **143**, 936 . . . . 22

—— 1908. *C. R. Acad. Sci., Paris* **146**, 829 . . . . . 94

—— 1916. *C. R. Acad. Sci., Paris* **162**, 554 . . . . . 94

—— 1927. *C. R. Acad. Sci., Paris* **184**, 1565 . . . . . 94

Gehman, S. D., and Dinsmore, R. P., 1938. *Proc. Rubber Technology Conference*, 961 . . . . . . . . . 356

—— and Field, J. E., 1939. *J. Appl. Phys.* **10**, 564 . . . . 191

Gille, F., and Spangenberg, K., 1927. *Z. Krist.* **65**, 207 . . . 13

Gingrich, N. S. *See* Bray, E. E.

Goldschmidt, H. J. . . . . . . . . . 117

Goodhue, E. A. *See* Dickinson, R. G.

Goodwin, T. H., and Hardy, R., 1938*a*. *Proc. Roy. Soc.* A**164**, 369 . . 396

—— —— 1938*b*. *Phil. Mag.* **25**, 1096 . . . . . . 396

—— *See also* Cox, E. G.

Goppel, J. M., 1949. *Appl. Sci. Res.* A**1**, 3 . . . . . . 448

Gosling, R. G. *See* Franklin, R. E.
Green, D. W., Ingram, V. M., and Perutz, M. F., 1954. *Proc. Roy. Soc.*
    A225, 287 . . . . . . . . . 383, 428
Greenough, G. B., 1955. *See* Peiser, Rooksby, and Wilson, 1955, chapter 30. 441
Greenwood, G., 1924. *Phil. Mag.* 48, 654 . . . . . . 270
Grenville-Wells, H. J., 1955. *Acta Cryst.* 8, 512 . . . . 219
—— and Abrahams, S. C., 1952. *Rev. Sci. Instrum.* 23, 328 . . . 219
—— and Lonsdale, K., 1954. *Nature* 173, 1145 . . . . . 263
Groth, P., 1906–19. *Chemische Krystallographie.* Leipzig: Engelmann
    20, 55, 233, 311
Guha, B. C. *See* Krishnan, K. S.
Guinier, A., 1937. *C. R. Acad. Sci., Paris* 204, 1115 . . . . 112
—— and Fournet, G., 1955. *Small-Angle Scattering of X-rays.* New York:
    Wiley . . . . . . . . . 444, 445
—— *See also* Belbéoch, B.
Gunn, E. L., 1958. *J. Phys. Chem.* 62, 928 . . . . . . 444

Hägg, G., 1931. *Z. phys. Chem.* B12, 33 . . . . . . 197
—— 1933. *Z. Krist.* 86, 246 . . . . . . . . 133
—— 1935a. *J. Chem. Phys.* 3, 42 . . . . . . . 447
—— 1935b. *Z. phys. Chem.* B29, 95 . . . . . . . 365
—— and Phragmen, G., 1933. *Z. Krist.* 86, 306 . . . . . 194
—— and Regnström, G., 1944. *Ark. Kemi, Min., Geol.* 18A, Paper No. 5 . 129
—— and Söderholm, G., 1935. *Z. phys. Chem.* B29, 88 . . . . 365
—— and Sucksdorff, L., 1933. *Z. phys. Chem.* B22, 444 . . . 365
Hanawalt, J. D., Rinn, H. W., and Frevel, L. K., 1938. *Ind. Eng. Chem.*
    (*Anal.*) 10, 457 . . . . . . . . . 132
Hanby, W. E. *See* Bamford, C. H.
Hanson, A. W., and Lipson, H., 1952. *Acta Cryst.* 5, 145 . . . 299
—— Lipson, H., and Taylor, C. A., 1953. *Proc. Roy. Soc.* A218, 371 . 424
—— Taylor, C. A., and Lipson, H., 1951. *Nature* 168, 160 . . . 398
Harcourt, A., 1942. *Amer. Min.* 27, 63 . . . . . . 132
Hardy, R. *See* Goodwin, T. H.
Hargreaves, A., 1946. *Nature* 158, 620 . . . . . . 407
—— 1955. *Acta Cryst.* 8, 12 . . . . . . . . 265
—— 1957. *Acta Cryst.* 10, 191, 196 . . . . . . . 380
—— *See also* Chaudhuri, B.; Fowweather, F.
Harker, D., 1936. *J. Chem. Phys.* 4, 381 . . . . . . 415
—— 1956. *Acta Cryst.* 9, 1 . . . . . . . . 386
—— and Kasper, J. S., 1948. *Acta Cryst.* 1, 70 . . . . . 429
—— *See also* Donnay, J. D. H.; Furnas, T. C.; Kasper, J. S.
Hartree, D. R., 1928. *Proc. Camb. Phil. Soc.* 24, 89, 111 . . . 216
—— *See also* James, R. W.
Hartshorne, N. H., and Stuart, A., 1960. *Crystals and the Polarising*
    *Microscope.* 3rd edn. London: Arnold . . . . 64, 89, 105
—— and Swift, P. McL., 1956. *J. Roy. Mic. Soc.* 75, 129 . . . 79
Harvey, G. G., 1939. *J. Chem. Phys.* 7, 878 . . . . . . 448
Heide, H. G., 1951. *Acta Cryst.* 4, 29 . . . . . . . 219
Helmholtz, L., 1936. *J. Chem. Phys.* 4, 316 . . . . . . 221
Helwig, G. V., 1932. *Z. Krist.* 83, 485 . . . . . . 301
Hendershot, O. P., 1937a. *Rev. Sci. Instrum.* 8, 324 . . . . 222
—— 1937b. *Rev. Sci. Instrum.* 8, 436 . . . . . . . 187

Klyne, W. (ed.), 1954. *Progress in Stereochemistry*, Vol. I. London:
Butterworth . . . . . . . . 302, 303
—— and de la Mare, P. B. D. (ed.), 1958. *Progress in Stereochemistry*,
Vol. II. London: Butterworth . . . . . 302, 303
Knaggs, I. E., 1935. *Proc. Roy. Soc.* A150, 576 . . . . . 399
Knol, K. S. *See* Coster, D.
Kordes, E., 1935a. *Z. Krist.* 91, 193 . . . . . . . 365
—— 1935b. *Z. Krist.* 92, 139 . . . . . . . . 364
Kossel, W., 1927. *Nachr. Ges. Wiss. Göttingen* 135. . . . 23, 306
Kowarski, L., 1935. *J. Chim. phys.* 32, 303, 395, 469 . . . . 19
Kratky, O., and Krebs, G., 1936. *Z. Krist.* 95, 253 . . . . 187
—— and Kuriyama, S., 1931. *Z. phys. Chem.* B11, 363 . . . 188
Krebs, G. *See* Kratky, O.
Krimm, S., 1954. *J. Chem. Phys.* 22, 567 . . . . . . 317
—— Liang, C. Y., and Sutherland, G. B. B. M., 1956. *J. Chem. Phys.*
25, 549 . . . . . . . . . . 317
—— *See also* Liang, C. Y.
Krishnan, K. S., and Banerjee, S., 1935. *Phil. Trans.* A234, 265; *Curr. Sci.*
3, 548 . . . . . . . . . . 319
—— Chakravorty, N. C., and Banerjee, S., 1934. *Phil. Trans.* A232, 103 . 319
—— Guha, B. C., and Banerjee, S., 1933. *Phil. Trans.* A231, 235 . 319, 320
Krutter, H. *See* Warren, B. E.
Kuriyama, S. *See* Kratky, O.

Lange, J. J. de, Robertson, J. M., and Woodward, I., 1939. *Proc. Roy.*
*Soc.* A171, 398 . . . . . . . . . . 272
—— *See also* Jong, W. F. de.
Lange, N. A., 1956. *Handbook of Chemistry.* Sandusky, Ohio: Handbook
Publishing . . . . . . . . 97, 102, 452
Larsen, E. S., and Berman, H., 1934. *Microscopic Determination of the*
*Non-opaque Minerals.* Washington: U.S. Geol. Survey Bulletin 848,
2nd edn. . . . . . . . . 89, 97, 102, 309, 451
Laue, M. von . . . . . . . . . . 6, 260, 261
—— 1926. *Z. Krist.* 64, 115 . . . . . . . . 438
Laves, F., 1930. *Z. Krist.* 73, 202 . . . . . . . 365
—— *See also* Nicolaides, N.
Lea, F. M., and Desch, C. H., 1935. *The Chemistry of Cement and Concrete.*
London: Arnold . . . . . . . . . 134
Le Fèvre, C. G., and Le Fèvre, R. J. W., 1954. *J. Chem. Soc.* 1577. . 313
—— —— 1955. *Chem. and Ind.* 506, 1121 . . . . . 312, 313
—— —— 1958. *Proc. Chem. Soc.* 283 . . . . . . 313
Liang, C. Y., and Krimm, S., 1956. *J. Chem. Phys.* 23, 563 . . . 317
—— *See also* Krimm, S.
Lindemann, F. A. . . . . . . . . . . 115
Lindsey, J. *See* Hodgkin, D. C.
Lipson, H., 1943. *J. Inst. Metals* 69, 1 . . . . . . 134
—— 1949. *Acta Cryst.* 2, 43 . . . . . . . . 147
—— and Cochran, W., 1953. *The Determination of Crystal Structures.*
London: Bell . . . . . . 374, 379, 380, 392, 396,
415, 418, 419, 432
—— Nelson, J. B., and Riley, D. P., 1945. *J. Sci. Instrum.* 22, 184 . 112
—— and Riley, D. P., 1943. *Nature* 151, 250, 502 . . . . 131

Pauling, L., 1940. *The Nature of the Chemical Bond.* 2nd edn. Cornell
    University Press . . . . . . . . . 302, 340
—— and Brockway, L. O., 1934. *J. Chem. Phys.* **2**, 867 . . . 243
—— —— 1937. *J. Amer. Chem. Soc.* **59**, 1223 . . . . . 245
—— Corey, R. B., and Branson, H. R., 1951. *Proc. Nat. Acad. Sci., Wash.*
    **37**, 205 . . . . . . . . . . . 425
Peerdeman, A. F., van Bommel, A. J., and Bijvoet, J. M., 1951. *Kon. Nederl.*
    *Akad. Wet.* B**54**, 16 . . . . . . . . . 404
Peiser, H. S., Rooksby, H. P., and Wilson, A. J. C., 1955. *X-ray Diffraction*
    *by Polycrystalline Materials.* London: The Institute of Physics
                                                        108, 112, 117
—— *See also* Bunn, C. W.; Evans, R. C.; Matthews, J. L.
Pepinsky, R., 1952. *Computing Methods and the Phase Problem in X-ray*
    *Crystal Analysis.* Publ. by Pennsylvania State College, Pa., U.S.A.
                                                        294, 396
—— 1956. *Record Chem. Progr.* **17**, 145 . . . . 222, 263, 380,
                                                        415, 421
—— and Okaya, Y., 1956. *Proc. Nat. Acad. Sci., Wash.* **42**, 286 . . 421
—— —— 1957. *Phys. Rev.* **108**, 1231 . . . . . . 421
—— *See also* Okaya, Y.
Percival, E. G. V. *See* Herbert, R. W.
Perutz, M. F., 1939. *Nature* **143**, 731 . . . . . . . 316
—— 1953. *Acta Cryst.* **6**, 859 . . . . . . . 316
—— 1954. *Proc. Roy. Soc.* A**225**, 264 . . . . . . 428
—— 1956. *Acta Cryst.* **9**, 867 . . . . . . . 387, 415
—— *See also* Boyes-Watson, J.; Bragg, W. L.; Green, D. W.
Petch, N. J. *See* Bradley, A. J.
Peterson, S. W., 1955. *Nature* **176**, 395 . . . . . 263, 404
Phillips, D. C. *See* Howells, E. R.
Phillips, F. C., 1933. *Min. Mag.* **23**, 458 . . . . . . 106
Phragmen, G. *See* Hägg, G.
Pickett, L. W., 1933. *Proc. Roy. Soc.* A**142**, 333 . . . . . 344
—— *See also* Clark, G. L.
Pickup, L. *See* Owen, E. A.
Pickworth, J. *See* Hodgkin, D. C.
Pinnock, P. R., and Taylor, C. A., 1955. *Acta Cryst.* **8**, 687 . . . 428
Pinsker, Z. G., 1953. *Electron Diffraction.* Trans. J. A. Spink and E. Feigl.
    London: Butterworth . . . . . . . . . 449
Piper, S. H., 1937. *J. Soc. Chem. Ind.* **56**, 61T . . . . . 197
Pirenne, M. H., 1946. *The Diffraction of X-rays and Electrons by Free*
    *Molecules.* Cambridge University Press . . . . . . 449
Planck, M. . . . . . . . . . . . 109
Polanyi, M., 1921. *Naturwiss.* **9**, 337 . . . . . . . 188
Porter, M. W., and Spiller, R. C., 1939. *Nature* **144**, 298 . . . 56
—— —— 1951, 1956. *The Barker Index of Crystals.* Vols. I and II.
    Cambridge: W. Heffer & Sons . . . . . . 11, 56, 95
Posnjak, E., and Barth, T. F. W., 1931. *Phys. Rev.* **38**, 2234 . . . 361
—— *See also* Barth, T. F. W.; Wyckoff, R. W. G.
Powell, H. M. *See* Huse, G.
Prasad, M. *See* Robertson, J. M.
Preston, E., 1942. *J. Soc. Glass Tech.* **26**, 82 . . . . . 447
Preston, G. D., 1939. *Proc. Roy. Soc.* A**172**, 116 . . . . . 443

Robertson, J. M., and Woodward, I., 1937. *Proc. Roy. Soc.* A**162**, 568 . . . 272, 381, 382

—— —— 1940. *J. Chem. Soc.* 36 . . . . . . . 375, 377

—— *See also* Lange, J. J. de.

Robinson, B. W., 1933. *J. Sci. Instrum.* **10**, 233 . . . . . 208

Rodgers, J. W. *See* Bradley, A. J.

Rogers, A. F., and Kerr, P. F., 1942. *Optical Mineralogy.* New York:
    McGraw-Hill . . . . . . . . . . 105

Rogers, D., 1950. *Acta Cryst.* **3**, 455 . . . . . . 266

—— 1953. *Nature* **171**, 929 . . . . . . . . 91

—— *See also* Howells, E. R.

Rogers-Low, B. W. *See* Crowfoot, D. M.

Rooksby, H. P., 1941. *J. Sci. Instrum.* **18**, 84 . . . . . 136

—— 1942. *J. Roy. Soc. Arts* **90**, 673 . . . . . . 115

—— *See also* Peiser, H. S.; Randall, J. T.

Rosenhain, W., 1935. *Introduction to Physical Metallurgy.* London: Constable 96

Rosenheim, O., and King, H., 1932. *Chem. and Ind.* **51**, 464 . . . 275

Royer, L., 1926. *C. R. Acad. Sci., Paris* **182**, 326 . . . . . 62

—— 1933. *C. R. Acad. Sci., Paris* **196**, 282 . . . . . 62

—— 1934. *C. R. Acad. Sci., Paris* **198**, 185, 585 . . . . . 22


Sandeman, I., 1955. *Proc. Roy. Soc.* A**232**, 105 . . . . . 317

—— *See also* Keller, A.

Saunders, D. W., 1956. *Trans. Faraday Soc.* **52**, 1414, 1425 . . . 315

—— 1957. *Trans. Faraday Soc.* **53**, 860 . . . . . . 315

Sauter, E., 1937. *Z. phys. Chem.* B**36**, 405 . . . . . . 188

Sayre, D., 1952. *Acta Cryst.* **5**, 60 . . . . . . . 430

Scherrer, P., 1920. *See* Zsigmondy's book *Kolloidchemie*, 3rd edn., p. 387 . 438

Schmid, E., and Boas, W., 1935. *Kristallplasticität.* Berlin: Springer . 193

Schomaker, V. *See* Stevenson, D. P.

Schönflies, A. . . . . . . . . 267, 466–73

Schoone, J. C. *See* Bokhoven, C.

Schwartz, C. M. *See* Beevers, C. A.

Seemann, H., 1919. *Ann. Physik* **59**, 455 . . . . . . 129

Seljakow, N., 1925. *Z. Phys.* **31**, 439 . . . . . . . 438

Shaw, W. F. B. *See* Cox, E. G.

Shearer, H. M. M. *See* Robertson, J. M.

Shoemaker, C. B. *See* Hodgkin, D. C.

Siegbahn, M., 1943. *Nature* **151**, 502 . . . . . . 131

Sim, G. A. *See* Robertson, J. M.

Simard, G. L., and Warren, B. E., 1936. *J. Amer. Chem. Soc.* **58**, 507 . 448

Sinclair, H. *See* Taylor, A.

Sisson, W. A. *See* Astbury, W. T.

Smith, A. F. *See* Arnett, L. L.

Smith, C. S., and Stickley, E. E., 1943. *Phys. Rev.* **64**, 191 . . . 440

Smith, D. J. *See* Holmes, D. R.

Smith, F. *See* Herbert, R. W.

Smith, J. A. S. *See* Cox, E. G.

Smits, D. W. *See* Wiebenga, E. H.

Smyth, C. P. *See* Turkevitch, A.

Snell . . . . . . . . . . . . 64

Söderholm, G. *See* Hägg, G.

Soller . . . . . . . . . . . 118

Truter, M. R., 1954. *Acta Cryst.* **7**, 73 . . . . . . . 337
Tulinsky, A., and White, J. G., 1958. *Acta Cryst.* **11**, 7 . . . . 366
Turkevitch, A., and Smyth, C. P., 1940. *J. Amer. Chem. Soc.* **62**, 2468 . 322
Turner-Jones, A., and Bunn, C. W., 1944. *J. Sci. Instrum.* **21**, 10 . . 188
—— *See also* Bunn, C. W.; Crowfoot, D. M.
Tutton, A. E. H., 1922. *Crystallography and Practical Crystal Measurement.*
    London: Macmillan . . . . . . . . 30, 64

Vand, V., 1949. *Nature* **163**, 169 . . . . . . . . 294
—— 1950. *J. Sci. Instrum.* **27**, 257 . . . . . . . 294
—— 1955. *J. Appl. Phys.* **26**, 1191 . . . . . . . 224
—— *See also* Cochran, W.; Dawson, I. M.
Van 't Hoff . . . . . . . . . . . 404
Vegard, L., 1916. *Phil. Mag.* **32**, 65 . . . . . . . 226
Verwey, E. J. W., 1935. *Z. Krist.* **91**, 65 . . . . . 365
Viervoll, H., and Ögrim, G., 1949. *Acta Cryst.* **2**, 277 . . . 217
Volmer, M., 1923. *Z. phys. Chem.* **102**, 267 . . . . . 19
—— *See also* Brandes, H.
de Vries, A., 1958. *Nature* **181**, 1193 . . . . . . . 404

Wahlstrom, E. E., 1955. *Petrographic Mineralogy.* Chapman & Hall . 64
Waldmann, H., and Brandenberger, E., 1932. *Z. Krist.* **82**, 77 . . 309
Waller, I. *See* James, R. W.
Wallerant, F., 1907. *Bull. Soc. Fr. Min.* **30**, 43 . . . . 94
Wang, S. N., 1939. *J. Chem. Phys.* 1939, **7**, 1012 . . . . . 312
Warren, B. E., 1934. *Phys. Rev.* **45**, 657 . . . . . 446
—— 1937. *J. Appl. Phys.* **8**, 645 . . . . . . . 447
—— 1940. *Chem. Rev.* **26**, 237 . . . . . . . 447
—— 1941. *J. Appl. Phys.* **12**, 375 . . . . . . . 439
—— 1945. *J. Appl. Phys.* **16**, 614 . . . . . . . 128
—— and Bragg, W. L., 1930. *Z. Krist.* **76**, 201 . . . 188, 443
—— Krutter, H., and Morningstar, O., 1936. *J. Amer. Ceram. Soc.* **19**, 202
                                          446, 447
—— *See also* Simard, G. L.
Waser, J., 1951. *Rev. Sci. Instrum.* **22**, 563, 567 . . . . 219
Watson, D. G. *See* Robertson, J. M.
Watson, J. D., and Crick, F. H. C., 1953. *Nature* **171**, 737 . . 425
Webb, M. B. *See* Beeman, W. W.
Weissenberg, K., 1924. *Z. Phys.* **23**, 229 . . . . . 178
Wells, A. F., 1938. *Proc. Roy. Soc.* A**167**, 169 . . . . 399
West, J. *See* Bragg, W. L.
Wheatley, P. J., 1955. *Acta Cryst.* **8**, 224 . . . . 245
White, A. H., Biggs, B. S., and Morgan, S. O., 1940. *J. Amer. Chem.*
    *Soc.* **62**, 16 . . . . . . . . . 322, 361
—— and Bishop, W. S., 1940. *J. Amer. Chem. Soc.* **62**, 8 . . 322, 361
White, J. G. *See* Hodgkin, D. C.; Robertson, J. M.; Tulinsky, A.
Whittaker, E. J. W., 1953*a*. *Acta Cryst.* **6**, 218 . . . 219
—— 1953*b*. *Acta Cryst.* **6**, 747 . . . . . . . 443
—— 1955. *Acta Cryst.* **8**, 265 . . . . . . . 443
Wiebenga, E. H., 1947. *Rec. trav. chim. Pays-Bas* **66**, 746 . . 209
—— and Smits, D. W., 1950. *Acta Cryst.* **3**, 265 . . . . 209

Wilchinsky, Z. W., 1947. *J. Appl. Phys.* **18,** 260 . . . . . 128
Wilkins, M. H. F., Stokes, A. R., and Wilson, H. R., 1953. *Nature* **171,** 737. 425
Willis, B. T. M., 1957. *Proc. Roy. Soc.* **A239,** 184 . . . . . 443
—— 1958. *Proc. Roy. Soc.* **A248,** 183 . . . . . . 443
Willis, H. A. *See* Miller, R. G. J.
Wilson, A. J. C., 1940. *Proc. Camb. Phil. Soc.* **36,** 485 . . . . 194
—— 1942a. *Proc. Roy. Soc.* **A180,** 277 . . . . . 442
—— 1942b. *Nature* **150,** 152 . . . . . . 225, 264
—— 1943. *Proc. Roy. Soc.* **A181,** 360 . . . . . . 442
—— 1949a. *Acta Cryst.* **2,** 318 . . . . . . 264, 429
—— 1949b. *Rev. Sci. Instrum.* **20,** 831 . . . . . . 129
—— 1950. *Acta Cryst.* **3,** 258 . . . . . . . 266
—— and Lipson, H., 1941. *Proc. Phys. Soc.* **53,** 245 . . . . 194
—— *See also* Lipson, H.; Peiser, H. S.; Stokes, A. R.
Wilson, H. R. *See* Wilkins, M. H. F.
Winchell, A. N., 1931. *The Microscopic Characters of Artificial Minerals.*
  New York: Wiley . . . . . 85, 97, 102, 309, 311
—— 1951. *Elements of Optical Mineralogy. Part III, Determinative Tables.*
  2nd edn. New York: Wiley . . . . . . 64, 97, 102
—— 1954. *Optical Properties of Organic Compounds.* 2nd edn. Academic
  Press . . . . . . . . . . 102, 309, 314
Wollan, E. O., 1932. *Rev. Mod. Phys.* **4,** 233 . . . . . 446
Wood, R. G., and Ayliffe, S. H., 1935. *J. Sci. Instrum.* **12,** 194 . . 79
—— —— 1936. *Phil. Mag.* **21,** 321 . . . . . . 83
Woods, H. J. *See* Astbury, W. T.
Woodward, I. *See* Lange, J. J. de; Robertson, J. M.
Woolfson, M. M. *See* Lipson, H.
Wooster, N., 1932. *Sci. Progr.* **26,** 462 . . . . . . 61
Wooster, W. A., 1931. *Z. Krist.* **80,** 495 . . . . . 308
—— 1936. *Z. Krist.* **94,** 375 . . . . . . 399
—— 1938. *A Textbook on Crystal Physics.* Cambridge University Press
  64, 92, 309, 321, 322
—— 1957. *Experimental Crystal Physics.* Oxford: Clarendon Press  319, 322
—— and Martin, A. J. P., 1936. *Proc. Roy. Soc.* **A155,** 150 . . 206
—— —— 1940. *J. Sci. Instrum.* **17,** 83 . . . . 179, 207
—— *See also* Bernal, J. D.; Henry, N. F. M.
Wright, W. B., 1958. *Acta Cryst.* **11,** 632 . . . . . 431
Wrinch, D. M., 1939. *Phil. Mag.* **27,** 98 . . . . . 419
Wyckoff, H. *See* Kendrew, J. C.
Wyckoff, R. W. G., 1930. *Z. Krist.* **75,** 529 . . . . 206, 333
—— 1931. *The Structure of Crystals.* New York: Chemical Catalog Co.  261, 301
—— 1932. *Z. Krist.* **81,** 102 . . . . . . 225, 333
—— 1948. *Acta Cryst.* **1,** 292 . . . . . . . 19
—— and Corey, R. B., 1934. *Z. Krist.* **89,** 102 . . . 225, 333
—— *See also* Corey, R. B.

Yardley, K. (Lonsdale, K.) *See* Astbury, W. T.

Zachariasen, W. H., 1929. *Z. Krist.* **71,** 501, 517 . . . 242, 309, 311
—— 1932. *J. Amer. Chem. Soc.* **54,** 3841 . . . . . 447
—— 1933. *J. Chem. Phys.* **1,** 634, 640 . . . . . 338
—— 1952. *Acta Cryst.* **5,** 68 . . . . . . 430, 431
Zeigler, G. E., 1931. *Phys. Rev.* **38,** 1040 . . . . 334, 337

# SUBJECT INDEX

K k

PRINTED IN GREAT BRITAIN
AT THE UNIVERSITY PRESS, OXFORD
BY VIVIAN RIDLER
PRINTER TO THE UNIVERSITY